# EUROPE

# EUROPE
## A REGIONAL GEOGRAPHY

Margaret Reid Shackleton

SEVENTH EDITION, REVISED AND ENLARGED

REVISED UNDER THE DIRECTION OF
### W. GORDON EAST

*With chapters on the United Kingdom and
the Republic of Ireland by*
### F. J. MONKHOUSE

FREDERICK A. PRAEGER, *Publishers*
NEW YORK • WASHINGTON

BOOKS THAT MATTER

Published in the United States of America in 1969
by Frederick A. Praeger, Inc., Publishers
111 Fourth Avenue, New York, N.Y. 10003

The original edition of this book was published in Great Britain and in
the United States of America in 1934 by Longmans, Green & Co., Ltd.;
subsequent editions were published in 1936, 1939, 1950, 1954, 1958,
and 1964.

Seventh Edition © Longmans, Green & Co., Ltd., 1964

Seventh Edition, Revised and Enlarged © 1969
by Longmans, Green & Co., Ltd.

Library of Congress Catalog Card Number: 68–58194


Printed in the United States of America

# PREFACE TO THIS EDITION*

THIRTY-FIVE years have elapsed since this well conceived and well wrought text first appeared for the benefit of students of geography and others, and nearly twenty years since Margaret Shackleton revised it for the fourth edition. It is a tribute to the soundness of her grasp of the regional geography of Europe and of her method of treatment that, revised by other hands, this book is still of service to the increasing numbers who seek or need to learn. 'A knowledge of structure', the author wrote in the preface to her fourth edition, 'is even more necessary to the geographer than a knowledge of anatomy to the artist.' And in thus putting emphasis on the relatively stable physical background the author curtailed the space which she allotted to ever-changing political, economic, and social conditions. Since the scale and pace of such changes have so much increased, it became evident that some of the original writing, despite attentive revisions, had become 'dated'. Further, it has become more and more evident that textbooks should, in respect of human geography, look forward rather than backward and should take note of the closer bonds that now often link one country to other countries.

Professor W. Gordon East shouldered the heavy task of organising, supervising, and carrying out a thorough revision of this book, with the help of a team of his own choosing. The economic summaries have been rewritten and lengthened. New maps and diagrams supplement those of the earlier editions, and some of the older ones have been revised. Fresh photographs have been conveniently grouped in the sections which they illustrate. The References and Appendixes have been brought up to date and also extended. No chapter has escaped changes, and some have been literally or virtually rewritten: yet much of the original text, and the particular character of Margaret Shackleton's book, are preserved. Chapter 2 (climate) has been rewritten, and chapters 3 (Vegetation and Soils), and 4 (Languages, Nationalities and States) are largely new. In Section I (Southern Europe) and Section II (Western Europe), considerable new writing occurs, especially in

* Adapted from Dr F. G. Mann's Preface to the 1964 edition.

Chapter 6 (Italy) and in Chapter 13 (The Benelux Group) respectively. Section III (Northern Europe) contains many improvements, particularly the newly written Chapter 18 on Denmark. Certainly a large share of the new writing occurs in Section 4 (Central Europe), where chapters 20–22, dealing with Germany, now give a more balanced view of the human geography, with due consideration of the *de facto* division of Germany into two states. The radical changes now in progress in South-Central Europe (Section V) are discussed in the light of recent first-hand knowledge. Similarly, the treatment accorded to Eastern Europe (Section VI) reveals the revolutionary changes which continue in the Soviet Union in its efforts to challenge and outstrip the United States in economic production. In short, this Seventh Edition has acquired a 'forward look' and more attention is now paid to Europe's remarkable economic stance—a stance developed and maintained despite the loss of empire and the challenge of the two mighty states in the shelter of whose defensive strength its countries, west and east of the Iron Curtain, successfully survive.

The following contributors have revised (and where necessary rewritten) the portions of the book indicated:

W. GORDON EAST   Section VI (Eastern Europe) chapters 34–40, also the Introduction and Chapter 4, and general revision of the whole work.

ALLAN J. CATCHPOLE   Chapter 2.

DONALD S. WALKER   Section I (Southern Europe), chapters 5–8.

JOHN F. DAVIS   Section II (Western Europe), chapters 9, 12 and 13, also Chapter 26, the Postscript and the Appendixes.

BRIAN T. BUNTING   Section III (Northern Europe), chapters 14–18, also Chapter 1, Chapter 3, and Chapter 25.

PETER G. HALL   Section IV (Central Europe), chapters 19–22, 24 and 27.

H. C. K. HENDERSON   Chapter 23.

F. E. I. HAMILTON   Section V (South-Central Europe), chapters 28–33.

For the Seventh Edition, Revised and Enlarged, which was prepared especially for use in the United States, F. J. Monkhouse, of the University of Southampton, wrote the entirely new chapters 10 (The United Kingdom) and 11 (The Republic of Ireland).

The index has been prepared by Mrs Sylvia Saunders.

Fresh photographs for this edition have been gratefully received from Mr Walker and Dr Hamilton, and also from various persons noted in the text.

I am indebted to the above writers not only for the excellence of their contributions, but also for the steady speed with which they worked: this factor ensured that the completion of the various sections of the work almost synchronised and that, with the very helpful co-operation of the publishers and the printers, this Edition has appeared very rapidly after the initial undertaking of the revision.

## PREFACE TO THE FIRST EDITION

THIS book is intended primarily for university students, but the needs of the more general reader have also been kept in mind. The treatment is fundamentally physical, for the author believes that a knowledge of structure is even more necessary to the geographer than a knowledge of anatomy to the artist, and that the physiognomy and form of the earth's surface are incomprehensible without a knowledge of the solid bones of structure beneath. But since this is a geographical and not a geological work, an attempt is made not only to correlate structure with relief, but also relief with climate and all three with vegetation, and so to indicate the main aspects of the whole natural environment in each region. It is not assumed, however, that men are compelled to act in any particular way by their natural environment, but that the various opportunities offered to them by nature can be dealt with in various ways, according to the stage and type of culture which has been attained, the word 'culture' here being used in the anthropological sense.

As regards the arrangement of the material, a compromise has been made in the regional section between a division based solely on natural regions, and one based solely on political divisions. In a continent such as Europe with a long historical past one cannot ignore the differences between the various countries which are due in turn to differences of historical or historico-economic development. One country may differ greatly even from its neighbour, not only in language but in the stage of social and economic evolution, so that regions closely similar in physical aspects may yet differ markedly in their human activities and in the use made of their resources. Contrast, for instance, Germany and Poland, Finland and Russia, Spain and Italy. If, however, each of the many countries were to be treated as an isolated unit, one would be apt to lose sight of the broad patterns of structure, relief, and climate which dominate the continent. Accordingly, for the purpose of this book, Europe has been divided into a number of large regions, based primarily on similarities of climate and structure, but also partly on historico-economic affinities. The old-established countries of Europe have also been treated individually in separate chapters.

I should like to take this opportunity of expressing my very sincere thanks to those authorities, both in Cambridge and elsewhere, who have given me invaluable assistance in the preparation of this book. Professor O. T. Jones, F.R.S., read the chapter on Structure and Relief and made many helpful suggestions in regard to its contents, and Mr J. A. Steers, M.A., did the same for the chapter on the Alpine Region. Dr C. E. P. Brooks read the chapter on Climate and also very kindly had the isotherm maps of Europe drawn for me from the latest material available at the Meteorological Office. Professor E. J. Salisbury, F.R.S., read the chapter on Vegetation, Mr R. Aitken the chapter on Iberia, Miss I. J. Curnow, Ph.D., the chapter on Greece, and Mr A. Stevens, M. A., the sections on Fennoscandia and South-Central Europe. I have pleasure also in thanking Professor J. H. Clapham for helpful suggestions in regard to the economic history of Western Europe, and Dr L. Dudley Stamp for general help and advice. My deep gratitude is due also to Professor F. Debenham for the kind permission he so readily gave me to use the Library and Map Room of the Geography Department of the University of Cambridge.

The photographs reproduced in the book have been supplied for the most part by the various Embassies, Legations, and their Travel Agencies, and in most cases were specially procured for me from the countries concerned. Permission to reproduce the photographs from the *Journal of Ecology* was given by the Editor, Professor A. G. Tansley, F.R.S., and is very gratefully acknowledged. The Spanish photographs were most kindly lent by Professor Hernandez Pacheco of the University of Madrid.

Finally, I wish to express my deep indebtedness to Mr W. G. East, M.A., and to Miss Alice Garnett, B.A., for undertaking the arduous task of reading the proofs.

MARGARET R. SHACKLETON
*Cambridge, 1934*                                     (*Mrs. F. G. Mann*)

# CONTENTS

## PART I

## General Survey

## PART II

## Regional Geography

### Section I—Southern Europe

### Section II—Western Europe

# PHOTOGRAPHS

xii

*Facing page*

*Facing page*

# TABLES FOR CONVERSION TO METRIC MEASUREMENTS

| Inches | Centimetres | Feet | Metres | Miles | Kilometres |
|---|---|---|---|---|---|
| 1 | 2·540 | 1 | 0·304 | 1 | 1·609 |
| 2 | 5·080 | 2 | 0·609 | 2 | 3·219 |
| 3 | 7·620 | 3 | 0·914 | 3 | 4·828 |
| 4 | 10·160 | 4 | 1·218 | 4 | 6·437 |
| 5 | 12·700 | 5 | 1·524 | 5 | 8·047 |
| 6 | 15·240 | 6 | 1·828 | 6 | 9·656 |
| 7 | 17·780 | 7 | 2·132 | 7 | 11·265 |
| 8 | 20·320 | 8 | 2·439 | 8 | 12·875 |
| 9 | 22·860 | 9 | 2·743 | 9 | 14·484 |
| 10 | 25·400 | 10 | 3·048 | 10 | 16·093 |
| 20 | 50·800 | 20 | 6·096 | 20 | 32·187 |
| 30 | 76·200 | 30 | 9·144 | 30 | 48·280 |
| 40 | 101·600 | 40 | 12·192 | 40 | 64·374 |
| 50 | 127·000 | 50 | 15·240 | 50 | 80·467 |
| 60 | 152·400 | 60 | 18·288 | 60 | 96·561 |
| 70 | 177·800 | 70 | 21·336 | 70 | 112·654 |
| 80 | 203·200 | 80 | 24·384 | 80 | 128·748 |
| 90 | 228·600 | 90 | 27·432 | 90 | 144·841 |
| 100 | 254·000 | 100 | 30·480 | 100 | 160·934 |

| Square miles | Km$^2$ | Acres | Hectares | Population Density Per sq. mile | Per km$^2$ |
|---|---|---|---|---|---|
| 1 | 2·590 | 1 | 0·405 | 1 | 0·386 |
| 2 | 5·180 | 2 | 0·809 | 2 | 0·662 |
| 3 | 7·770 | 3 | 1·214 | 3 | 1·158 |
| 4 | 10·360 | 4 | 1·619 | 4 | 1·544 |
| 5 | 12·950 | 5 | 2·023 | 5 | 1·930 |
| 6 | 15·540 | 6 | 2·428 | 6 | 2·316 |
| 7 | 18·130 | 7 | 2·833 | 7 | 2·702 |
| 8 | 20·720 | 8 | 3·237 | 8 | 3·088 |
| 9 | 23·310 | 9 | 3·642 | 9 | 3·474 |
| 10 | 25·900 | 10 | 4·047 | 10 | 3·861 |
| 20 | 51·800 | 20 | 8·094 | 20 | 7·722 |
| 30 | 77·700 | 30 | 12·140 | 30 | 11·583 |
| 40 | 103·600 | 40 | 16·187 | 40 | 15·444 |
| 50 | 129·499 | 50 | 20·234 | 50 | 19·305 |
| 60 | 155·399 | 60 | 24·281 | 60 | 23·166 |
| 70 | 181·299 | 70 | 28·328 | 70 | 27·027 |
| 80 | 207·199 | 80 | 32·375 | 80 | 30·888 |
| 90 | 233·099 | 90 | 36·422 | 90 | 34·749 |
| 100 | 258·999 | 100 | 40·469 | 100 | 38·610 |

# NOTE

The reading of this book involves the continual use of an atlas, or better, of a variety of atlases, for each of these has its virtues and' shortcomings. The following may be recommended and the latest edition should be sought:

*Bartholomew's Advanced Atlas of Modern Geography*, Edinburgh: John Bartholomew and Son.

*Britannica World Atlas International*, New York: Frederick A. Praeger.

*Diercke Weltatlas*, Braunschweig: Georg Westermann Verlag.

*McGraw-Hill International Atlas*, New York: McGraw-Hill Book Company.

*National Geographic Atlas of the World*, Washington, D.C.: National Geographic Society.

*The Times Atlas of the World*, Comprehensive Edition, Boston: Houghton Mifflin Company.

Other atlases are published by Funk & Wagnalls (*Reader's Digest Great World Atlas*), Golden Press (*Odyssey World Atlas*), Hammond Incorporated, Oxford University Press, and Rand McNally & Co.

# PART I

# GENERAL SURVEY

## INTRODUCTION

GEOGRAPHICALLY speaking, Europe may be looked upon as the most favourable continent for mankind. It contains a greater proportion of land suited to agriculture than any other continent, and, unlike the others, has practically no desert. Its mineral wealth is considerable and varied, and it is especially rich in coal and iron. Its mountain chains, though high, are not impassable barriers, and moreover, the continent is deeply penetrated by arms of the ocean such as the Baltic, Mediterranean, and Black Seas, so that in proportion to its area it has the longest sea-coast of any continent, and therefore the greatest opportunities for ocean transport, the most economical form of bulk conveyance. Although Europe on the north extends well within the Arctic Circle, yet the winters are remarkably warm for these high latitudes, especially in the north-west, so that settlement and cultivation have here been carried nearer the Pole than anywhere else in the world. The great diversity of environment, especially west of the USSR, gave opportunities for the accumulation of different types of experience and for the active exchange of goods and ideas. Insufficient work has been done in the field of socio-geography to enable the positive conclusions to be drawn on the relation between environment and civilisation, but the early development of civilisation in Europe, its present thickly populated surface, and the spread of Europeans and European ideas over the whole world, all seem to reflect the favourable nature of the environment for man.

Many people consider that Europe reached the height of its prosperity and prestige in the early years of the present century, and it is certain that the two great wars seriously, if temporarily, impoverished the continent. Moreover, with the settlement of Europeans overseas and the acquisition of European knowledge by other peoples, the relative importance of our continent seems bound to diminish. It may, however, be claimed that although other peoples have copied European civilisation there is remarkably little evidence that they have improved upon it. In regard to material progress, any challenge to Europe has come almost entirely

1

from peoples of European origin now domiciled in other continents, while on the spiritual side no non-European peoples have rivalled our triple heritage of the Greek spirit of free enquiry, the Roman respect for law and justice, and the Christian ideal of love towards God and man.

Any threat to Europe's position as the world's leading continent may be said to come from within rather than from without. The extreme political subdivision of Europe west of the river Dniester, which may be tentatively correlated with its great physical diversity, was rather an asset than a liability in earlier days, and was an important factor in saving Europe on several occasions from control by a crushing despotism. Under modern conditions, however, this political fragmentation is obviously one of Europe's chief

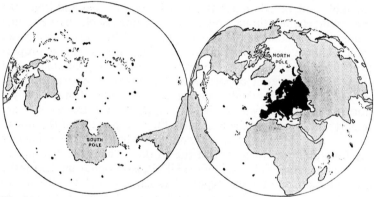

Fig. 1. LAND AND WATER HEMISPHERES, SHOWING THE FAVOURABLE
POSITION OF EUROPE

sources of weakness, but it is perhaps itself a result of Europe's amazing richness in ideas and the astonishing vitality of its people, for even small nations can point with pride to glorious achievements unsurpassed elsewhere in the world, and so strive to retain their individual identities. Thus, success itself is proving an obstacle to that adaptation to changing conditions which is so vital to any organism.

*Position.* – The most northerly point of the mainland of Europe is Cape Nordkyn in Norway, 71° 8′ N., and the most southerly is Cape Tarifa in Spain, 36° N. The islands give the continent only a slightly greater extension, the North Cape on the island of Magerö being 71° 15′ N., and the southern coast of Crete about 35° N. Europe has thus a smaller extension in latitude than the other continents with the exception of Australasia.

In relation to the disposition of the main expanses of land and water in the world, Europe is fortunate in being placed in the middle of the land hemisphere (see Fig. 1), and therefore is centrally situated in the inhabited half of the globe, whereas its antipodes, in the islands of the South Pacific, are situated far from the main centres of human life. Paradoxically, however, Europe combines the advantages of this mid-land position with easy access to other parts of the globe by sea.

*Size and Population.* Europe is almost the smallest of the continents, with a total area of 3·8 million square miles. Only Australasia is smaller, while Asia is nearly five times as large.

Europe's population approaches 600 millions which is near one-fifth of the world's total. Europe supports a higher density of population than any other continent. Comparable figures per square mile are as follows: Europe 158; Asia 104; South and Central America 27; North America 23; Africa 23; and Australia only 2·5.

*Boundaries.* On the north, west, and south, Europe is bounded by the sea, which forms an unmistakable frontier even where narrow, but on the east it merges into the Asiatic mainland, and here its limits are artificial. The eastern boundary was, indeed, extended successively towards the north-east as the knowledge of the area increased, but it has never been considered very satisfactory. The Ural Mountains, stretching from north to south, appear to make a convenient boundary when seen on a small-scale map, but actually they are not very high, are easily crossed in many places, and form a relatively slight physical barrier. They have never formed a political frontier, nor do they serve to divide political or administrative divisions of the USSR. Between the Urals and the Caspian Sea stretch arid lowlands some 300 miles wide in which there is no physical obstacle and which have repeatedly proved a zone of easy movement for invaders from Asia. In physical geography the eastern limit of Europe may be found here along the Emba river. To the north it lies along the eastern foot of the Urals. Between the Black and Caspian seas the physical limit of Europe is usually related to the Manych depression and the eastern shore of the Sea of Azov. In political terms, however, the landward limits of Europe should be carried farther south across the Caucasus Mountains to the Soviet boundaries with Turkey and Iran. These eastern limits of Europe mark also those of Eastern Europe which is, in effect, European USSR. But since it is broadly agreed among geographers that the Soviet Union should not be divided sharply into its European and Asian parts for treatment in geography texts, an attempt is made (in Chapter 40) to survey this country as a whole.

CHAPTER 1

# STRUCTURE AND RELIEF

EUROPE is almost equally divided into two great physical regions, an eastern and a western. Even from a small-scale atlas-map it is possible to perceive the contrast between the low relief of the extensive plains of eastern Europe and the rapid alternation of mountain and valley, hill, plain, and plateau in the rest of the continent, especially in the south and north-west. This contrast is primarily based on differences of structure, since Europe east of the Carpathians has a uniformity of structure in comparison with the complexity of that in the rest of the continent. This contrast is based on differences of geological history, since most of eastern Europe has been a region of great structural stability through vast eras of geological time, whereas western Europe has experienced great earth-storms which have raised up four great mountain systems at different times.

**Eastern Europe.** This region, founded on the Balto-Russian Shield, or Fennosarmatia, is overlain by strata which range in age from Cambrian to Tertiary and have remained almost undisturbed since the strata were laid down beneath the shallow seas. The margins of the Russian Platform sloped south and east towards a geosyncline – for example that of the Donets basin with its great thickness of Carboniferous material – while the Urals were uplifted from a shallower feature at the end of the period. Some faulting of the Shield took place and sufficient warping to give rise to gentle swellings and depressions. These slight undulations in turn allowed the work of erosion to denude the more recent deposits from the broad upswellings, thereby exposing wide surfaces of the Mesozoic and Palæozoic[1] strata and partially filling up the depressions as at Perm and Moscow, so that by early Oligocene times a low plain of denudation was produced which extended across the formations.

The whole area later underwent a slight positive movement or bodily uplift *en masse*, which resulted in the present moderate height and in a rejuvenation of the river system – that is to say, the erosive power of the rivers was increased as a consequence of the increased elevation. The general relief of the plain remained, only slightly diversified, with local structures and Quaternary forms; occasional

[1] See Appendix I, page 635, for Table of Geological Sequences.

4

developments of escarpments in Orel and Kursk and in north-west
Ukraine, and of hills composed of morainic material deposited in
mid- and late-Pleistocene times, as near Smolensk and in the Oka
valley, on the edge of former ice-sheets. Even so, the change of
level is so gradual that the effect of sameness remains. The river
valleys form the major breaks in the continuity of the plain, since
their courses are often rather deeply incised, and the regions over
600 ft high being in parts dissected by gullies. At lower levels the

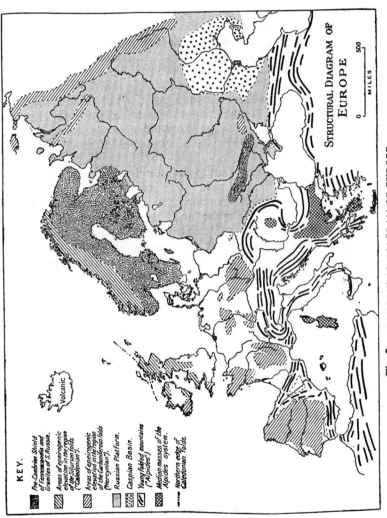

Fig. 2. STRUCTURAL DIAGRAM OF EUROPE

valleys are not obvious until the brink is almost reached, and they cannot be said to form marked breaks in the landscape. The crustal stability of this large area is unique in Europe and contrasts strikingly with the complicated geological history of the rest of the continent. Even here, however, there are one or two exceptions. Folded strata are met with in the Donets plateau in southern Russia and, in the valleys of the Bug and Dnieper, denudation has revealed the ancient gneisses and granites which form the Ukrainian, or Podolian-Azov, massif: the Archæan floor to the platform (Fig. 2).

**The Folded Mountains of Europe.** These belong to four main cycles of folding, the earliest of which took place in pre-Cambrian times, forming the craton of Ur-Europe. Next came the Caledonian folding in late Silurian and early Devonian times to add Palæo-Europe to the north-west of the Shield. This was followed by the Armorican, in Permo-Carboniferous times, which formed Meso-Europe to the south (centre) and east and finally by the Alpine orogeny, the uplift of Neo-Europe – sometimes known as the Alpides, but more often simply as 'young folded mountains' of mid-Cretaceous and Oligocene age.

Although there is some overlapping, for the most part the great mountain chains of Europe were raised successively farther south, so that the youngest mountains border the Mediterranean, those of medium age are in mid-Europe, and the older ranges of Palæo-Europe are in the north. All except the young folded mountains have been eroded down to their very stumps, and owing to subsequent depression and to transgression by the sea have been partly covered by great thicknesses of younger material. Their reappearance above sea-level has occurred generally at a later geological period, and may be connected with the great earth disturbance which raised up the young folded mountains in Tertiary times.

Generally speaking, only fragments of the older mountain systems are visible on the surface, while the young folded mountains form long unbroken mountain chains and are generally of higher relief. As the young folded mountains, or European Alpides, are the most recent, and have the appearance at the present day once possessed by the older mountain systems of Europe, a short account of their mode of origin will help towards an understanding of the nature of the older ranges.

These young folded mountains comprise the chains bordering the Mediterranean Sea in Andalusia, in Italy (Apennines), and in the Balkan peninsula (Dinarics), also the Pyrenees and the great arcs of the Alps and Carpathians, the Balkan Mountains of Bulgaria, the Crimean and the Caucasus Mountains. They continue eastwards into Asia to the Himalayas and beyond, and the mountains of Turkey and the Rif also belong to the same great system.

Before the young folded mountains were raised there existed a Triassic Sea, occupying what geologists call the 'Tethys' geosyncline, far wider than the present Mediterranean – for instance overlapping most of Iberia – and lying between and partly upon the old continents of 'Ur-Africa' and 'Ur-Europe', and encircling the earth. The two proto-continents may be looked upon as consisting of solid resistant masses of old compacted rocks, but the floor of the sea between them was covered with marine sediments which were relatively much less dense and more flexible. For some reason, the old continents began to move towards one another, and as a result shallow seas invaded central and west Europe and then, in mid-Cretaceous times, the geosyncline became smaller and the sediments of the sea between them were buckled to form the central part of the new mountains. These at first were probably simple, but, as the pressure increased, the folding became more intense in the late Cretaceous period and ultimately successive folds were piled upon one another. They may be described as earth-waves breaking upon the resistant shore of the old continent of Europe. The resulting mountains are therefore of extreme complexity; the folds are of the type described as recumbent, in which the lower limbs are completely inverted so as to lie horizontally under the upper limbs. In many cases the folds were torn off from their roots and were thrust forward to the north, and there piled up on top of other folds. Recumbent folds of this type are known as *nappes* in French and *Decken* in German, but there appears to be no English equivalent. The process of their formation can best be illustrated by actual sections (see Fig. 3).

These *nappes* were first recognised in the Swiss Alps and have since been identified in the Betic Cordillera of Andalusia, the Apennines, the Carpathians, and in the young folded mountains of the Balkan peninsula. As each *nappe* consists of layers of stratified rock of different types and ages, erosion produces a rapid alternation of outcrop, though long, narrow bands of one type of material run generally in the direction of the length of the chain. In some areas denudation has taken place to such a depth as to expose lower *nappes*, which are revealed in what are called 'windows'; in other areas whole *nappes* have been completely removed. The elucidation of the structure of these young folded mountains is therefore a matter of great difficulty, and two distinct phases may be discerned – Lithogenesis (accumulation, intrusion, compression) and Orogenesis (elevation, deformation, crumpling) – followed by erosion. Geographers, studying the earth primarily as the home of man, may be content to know the broad outlines of the geological hypotheses

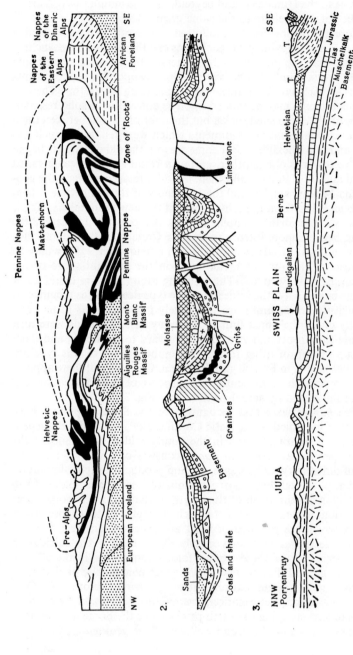

Fig. 3.   SECTIONS ACROSS THE ALPS SHOWING: (1) THE NAPPES; (2) AN EARLY OROGENIC STAGE; (3) THE SWISS
FORELAND AND JURA FOLDS

referred to above, and to turn to a study of the position and height of these mountains and to the actual material of which they are composed.

The sediments which were folded to form these young mountains were accumulated in two oceanic basins of moderate depth (c. 10,000 ft), separated by a ridge, and consisted of limestones derived from algae and coral (see Chapter 25). The more deep-seated layers, which were subjected to enormous pressure, have generally undergone metamorphism and have become crystalline. Where denudation has advanced sufficiently far these crystalline metamorphic rocks have been exposed, but most of the chains of the Alpides include a considerable proportion of limestones of various ages, ranging from Triassic to early Tertiary, and of andesitic lavas, especially in the southern Alps. As the folds rose from beneath the sea, shallow-water deposits were laid down, on the outer sides of the ranges, and these consist usually of clastic deposits (marls, sandstone, and clays) known as Flysch. In the western Alps denudation has advanced so far that the original surface beneath all the *nappes*, the crystalline basement of the Pennine trough, has been exposed in certain areas, whereas in the Apennines there is a large development of rocks of Flysch type and of Cretaceous limestones. In the Alpides as a whole, however, so much material has been removed by denudation that the mountains would have been reduced to low ranges at the present day if a further upward movement *en masse* had not occurred. Such a movement is termed 'epeirogenic' in contrast to the 'orogenic' or folding movement. It probably took place towards the close of the Tertiary and the beginning of the Quaternary era.

The mountains raised by the Alpine movement show a marked tendency in both Europe and Asia to extend in long arcs round interior basins. It is supposed by some that these arcs were formerly more continuous with each other, but have become separated through a sinking of intervening areas. For instance, the Alps and Carpathians are now separated by the depression traversed by the Danube – the Vienna basin, while other older massifs – of Pannonia, Tyrrenhia, and of Walachia and another now underlying the Po basin – all sank, while the Alps were separated from the Pyrenees by the Rhône *Graben*. As the direct evidence largely lies beneath the sea or beneath great depths of later sediments, reconstruction is a matter of conjecture, though close petrological study of the rocks and of the direction of thrust of the *nappes* is clearing up some of the difficulties and invalidating some of the earlier hypotheses. Thus it is no longer held that the mountains of the Rif in North Africa were once connected with those of the Sierra Nevada by intervening mountains which have disappeared. Different theories of the connexion between the young folded ranges are given in diagrammatic form (see Fig. 4). There are rival theories also to account for the position and direction of the fold ranges, though it is agreed that the spread of the Alps and Carpathians northwards was limited by the solid resistant masses of old rocks which formed the stumps of the Hercynian system. There are various explanations, moreover, of the areas between the folded ranges which were apparently not affected by the Tertiary folds, such as the great depressions of the Hungarian (Pannonian) basin and of the western Mediterranean, or the old mountain masses of the Rhodope in the Balkans. Perhaps Kober's theory of the unfolded 'Median Mass' or *Zwischengebirge* is the most convincing (see Fig. 4). In the case of the Alps this unfolded Median Mass does not exist owing to the intensity of the

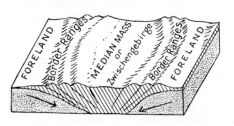

(*after Kober*)

Fig. 4. BLOCK DIAGRAM SHOWING A 'MEDIAN MASS' (ZWISCHENGEBIRGE) BETWEEN FOLDED RANGES

earth movements. Possibly the present width of the Mediterranean is due to a recent northward drift of Europe away from Africa. But it is agreed that the regions included within the great arcs of folding are part of the young folded mountain system, though they themselves were not subject to folding in Tertiary times.

As far as elevation is concerned the highest mountains of Europe are to be found in the young folded mountains. Thus Mt Blanc (15,782 ft), in France, is the highest peak and the Alps have the greatest average height.[1] The great chains of the young folded mountains have naturally a great influence on the lines of communication in Europe, without, however, being the insuperable barriers which they might appear at first sight. The manner in which they closely border some parts of the Mediterranean and Adriatic seas makes communication inland a difficult matter and concentrates attention on the few gaps which exist between the ranges. Of these gaps two are of outstanding importance: first, that formed by the Rhône–Saône valley with the port of Marseilles and the route-centre of Lyons; and second, that formed by the Dardanelles, Sea of Marmara, and Bosporus (Istanbul). Besides these there are two other important routes which also lead from the southern seas to the northern plains. The first connects the head of the Adriatic with the middle Danube (Pannonian) plain via Trieste

[1] This is exceeded by Mt Elbruz (18,467 ft) in the Caucasus Mountains, but these are conventionally included in Asia.

or via Rijeka, the latter alternative to Zagreb, being more difficult. The second is a long and tortuous route from the Ægean (Salonika) to the same plain via Skoplje and the valley of the River Vardar. The Alps themselves, by their height and length, offer a great obstacle to transport, but they possess a large number of passes, which, if not easy for road construction, at least are not insuperably difficult. Also these high but narrow chains have been crossed by tunnels, which, though of great length in several cases, are not uneconomic in a rich and civilised continent.

North of the young folded mountain zone are fragments of other folded ranges of much earlier geological date which probably were formed in much the same way as the Alpides, and were once equally continuous and extensive (see Fig. 5).

Immediately to the north of the young folded zone lie the relics of the Hercynian mountain system which was raised up in Namurian times in the late Carboniferous period. It extended from what is now western Iberia (Galicia and the Meseta) and southern Ireland through much of France, central Germany, Bohemia, Poland (Silesia), and beyond to Dobrogea and Stavropol, presumably forming festoons or arcs similar to those of the Alpides. The main mountain building took place in three phases; the early Bretonian phase in the south of the geosyncline, which created the Rhenish slate mountains; the Sudetic folding forming the main Variscan mountains, and a later Asturian phase at the end of the Carboniferous period. In the deep parts of the parent geosyncline in the intervening quiet periods, limestones formed, while swamps on the borders provided the basis for coal formation. A prolonged period of denudation reduced the mountains to

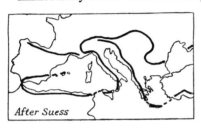

After Kober

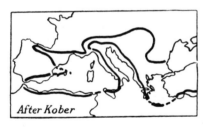

After Suess

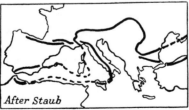

After Staub

Fig. 5. SUGGESTED RELATIONSHIPS BETWEEN THE YOUNG FOLDED MOUNTAINS OF EUROPE

peneplains, and by a gradual transgression of the then continent by the sea, the peneplained roots of the old mountains were covered by thick deposits of limestones and sandstones of the Permian, Triassic, Jurassic, and Cretaceous periods. The old land masses were most fully submerged in Cretaceous times, the greatest transgression being in Cennomanian times, when the high land masses of north-west Britain and the Ardennes were flooded, and very few remnants of the Hercynian system stood above the sea during that period to connect with the land mass to the west. At the end of Cretaceous times there was a recovery, and in mid-Tertiary times there were large areas of low peneplain whose surface was in places covered by lagoons, in which were formed brown coal deposits.

A further recovery of land then took place which was associated with the earth disturbances involved in the building up of the Alpides to the south. The earth-storm was generally unable to cause much folding of the resistant stumps of the Hercynian mountains, but they were exposed to severe pressure, to such an extent that numerous great fractures were developed, both in the old rock and in the younger overlying sediments. Sometimes, also, there was slight warping, but generally any disturbances to which they have been subjected were due to uplifts of segments of the old chains as blocks or horsts, accompanied by a general positive movement of the land. The best examples are the Rhine *Graben*, Vosges and Black Forest; and on a larger scale, the Central Sierras of Spain and the Tagus Trough, together with the block uplift of the Meseta. As certain segments of the old chains rose higher than others, denudation began to strip off the Secondary and Tertiary sediments from the uplifted portions, and to lay bare the old peneplain surfaces of the Hercynian stumps. Owing to the slowness of denudation in these older and more resistant rocks, the former peneplains are still recognisable, and smoothed forms are the rule. In the depressions between these horsts or blocks the younger, often lacustrine or terrigenous sediments were preserved, usually slightly tilted in conformity with the movement of the Hercynian floor. Erosion, working on comparatively thin strata of different resistances, had led to a great development of scarplands and mesa-like forms, which are a feature of the more low-lying parts of the basins within Hercynian zone. Consequently there is a great variety of relief in the region affected by the Hercynian system, horsts of old crystalline and metamorphic rocks alternating with plains and low plateaus of clays, sandstones, and limestones – more commonly referred to as synclinal basins.

The Hercynian zone of west-central Europe disappears in the west under the waters of the Bay of Biscay, in the north under the deposits of the Paris basin, and under the recent sediments of the

Germano-Polish lowland – the Münster, Saxony, Thuringian, and Silesian basins, many consisting of the debris of older sediments eroded into low scarplands.

The north-western part of Europe represents the relics of two still older mountain systems. The Caledonian system is now represented by two main segments, one occupying the north-western part of the British Isles and the other forming the highland backbone of Scandinavia (Norway and Sweden) as well as being found at shallow depth under Britain and north Belgium as the London–Brabant platform. Formerly these must have been connected across the North Sea and continued into the Arctic in Svalbard (Spitzbergen). It is not necessary here to trace their long and complicated geological history, which may be treated briefly together with that of the Archæan floor on which they stand. This Archæan floor emerges from beneath the unfolded sediments of the Russian platform on the border between Russia and Finland, and on the south from beneath the Baltic where it is thinly mantled by glacial deposits. It is composed of crystalline rocks such as gneiss, granite, and crystalline schists, and evidently represents the roots of at least four vast and primeval mountain systems. Traces of unfolded Cambrian and Silurian sediments indicate that strata similar to those of the Russian platform once covered Finland and the greater part of Sweden. On the western borders of Sweden, however, and over the greater part of Norway, Silurian and earlier rocks were folded by the Caledonian movements. It is possible that the greater part of Scandinavia and Finland has been above sea-level since Devonian times, but the present elevation is due to an epeirogenic uplift, probably in the middle or late Tertiary era, which tilted up the western side of Scandinavia to form the present lofty mountains. These, like the horsts of the Hercynian system, are in reality a dissected uplifted peneplain, but the tilting was more uniform than in the Hercynian region. The Highlands of Scotland had a somewhat similar history. Old folded mountain chains were eroded to a peneplain which was later spasmodically uplifted so that the rivers were repeatedly rejuvenated and the work of erosion hastened, resulting in the formation of deep valleys. A third segment of the Caledonides may possibly be identified in the Timan Mountains.

Much of the hill-land of central Europe shows erosion surfaces developed in relation to the gradual withdrawal of the Cennomanian Sea after it had achieved its maximum extent; the oldest forming the flat or bevelled skylines of many of the older uplands of western Europe – in Wales at 2,000 ft or more and similarly in the Central Plateau, the Ardennes, Harz, and Thüringerwald; often capped by tor-like remnants. The height of these summit surfaces varies, and may reach 5,000 ft in areas of greater block uplift in later times, as in Norway and Iberia. At lower levels 1,200–2,000 ft, more limited erosion surfaces are developed as middle and lower peneplains and as valley-side benches, much dissected by the rejuvenation of drainage lines in response to the falling sea levels. These are well developed in the southern Pennines, on Dartmoor, in Condroz, the Eifel–Hunsrück and elsewhere.

A pause in the retreat of the sea gave a chance for widespread Pliocene planation at 600–700 ft in the chalk hills of south-east England; much higher in uplifted Norway, lower in Russia, while, due to the downwarping of the southern North Sea, the base of the Pliocene lies at 6,500 ft under Amsterdam.

**Quaternary and Recent Events.** The northern part of Europe, particularly the highlands of Scandinavia and Scotland, preserves abundant evidence of one of the most recent episodes in the geological history of Europe, namely, the Great Ice Age of the Quaternary era. The cause of the successive glaciations and intervening interglacial warm periods of this Pleistocene period is controversial, but there is no doubt that great caps of ice, similar to those now covering Greenland and Antarctica, developed over Scandinavia and pushed their way out across the North Sea and Baltic into the bordering lands of Russia, north Germany, Poland, and the eastern coast of the British Isles. Similar but smaller ice-sheets developed in north-west Britain and on other mountainous regions, particularly the Alps, with varying regional dominance and power in the successive cold periods (Fig. 6).

The effect of these Pleistocene glaciations on the geography of Europe has been immense. The erosion in the core areas of Norway and Sweden has denuded the land of loose material and has deranged drainage patterns and created waterfalls. Great quantities of rock and soil were moved and redeposited on the lowlands to the south, filling the Pliocene river of the southern Baltic, flowing to the North Sea basin; and forming the lowlands of Denmark, northern Germany, the basis of the Netherlands, and the hills and plains of Poland, whilst a similar process took place on a smaller scale in the British Isles. Deposits vary in age, stoniness, and thickness, but form a usually fertile material for soil, especially those derived from limey materials. In the Alps the ice made a profound impression on the ranges, transforming their mild curves to the sharp peaks and 'horns' that we look upon as typically Alpine (see Chapter 25).

The successive cold periods in Europe have been termed *Günz*, (most clearly evident in the Alps from its meltwater deposits); the *Mindel* and the *Riss*, which were very intense in the Alps and also strong and far-reaching in northern Europe when the ice stretched from Scandinavia into Britain, Holland (Cleve), and then into the Carpathians in the east. In Russia its boundary was more lobate following the valleys. The final phase, the *Würm* or *Weichsel*, was not so extensive, but its deposits are the most fresh. Its outwash plains and *Löss* bulk large in the geography of the North European Lowland and in southern Scandinavia.

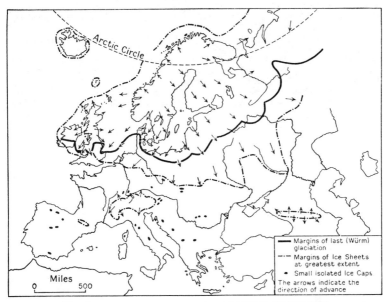

Fig. 6. THE QUATERNARY GLACIATION OF EUROPE

Since the end of the Pleistocene, minor oscillations of sea level have occurred in numerous areas which show that the European continent is far from stable. The presence of active volcanoes in southern Europe and the frequency of earthquakes in certain regions indicate zones of specially marked instability.

The landforms of any particular area of Europe show the combined influences of the structure on the one hand and of the type and phase of erosion on the other. In northern Europe periglacial smoothing of slopes in recent times produced a monotonous landscape. Deposits of 'head' or soliflual material are also common in oceanic Europe.

REFERENCES

The most up-to-date study of the geology of Europe is R. Brinkmann, *Geological Evolution of Europe*, Stuttgart, F. Enke Verlag, 1960. General principles of European structure and evolution are presented in L. Kober, *Der Bau der*

*Erde*, Berlin, Borntraeger, 1928; P. Birot, *Morphologie Structurale*, Paris, Orbis, Presses Universitaires, 1958, especially Tome 2; and Chapters 3–4 and 12–15 of L. C. King, *Morphology of the Earth*, Edinburgh, Oliver and Boyd, 1962.

The main sources on Quaternary events are J. K. Charlesworth, *The Quaternary Ice Age*, Vol. 2, London, Arnold, 1957; and F. E. Zeuner, *The Pleistocene Period*, Parts II, III, VI, IX, London, Hutchinson, 1959.

On Russia three works may be consulted, S. Von Bubnoff, *Fennosarmatia*, Berlin, Borntraeger, 1952; D. V. Nalivkin, *Geology of the U.S.S.R.*, Monographs on Earth Sciences, 8, Oxford, Pergamon, 1960; and N. S. Schatski and A. P. Markovsky (ed.), *Structure Géologique de l'U.R.S.S.*, Moscow, Centre National de la Recherche Scientifique, Paris, 1959, especially fascicule 1, *Géomorphologie*, and fascicule 6, *Quaternaire*.

For the historical geology, L. J. Wills, *Palaeographical Atlas of the British Isles and Parts of Europe*, London, Blackie, 1951, is a useful cross-reference and may be studied along with A. K. Wells and J. F. Kirkaldy, *Outline of Historical Geology*, London, Murby, 1959. L. U. de Sitter, *Structural Geology*, Part 3, London, McGraw-Hill, 1956 is also useful.

A recent summary of post-glacial happenings is H. E. Wright, 'The Late-Glacial Chronology of Europe', *American Journal of Science*, 255, 1957, 447–460.

### CHAPTER 2

# CLIMATE

THE distribution of climates in Europe is very complex.  This is to be expected in view of the moderately large size of the continent and its great diversity of relief.   Low annual rainfall averaging just over 16 in (406 mm) is recorded on some Dutch islands and less than 20 in (508 mm) is a common total in much of eastern Scandinavia, Russia, and Spain (see Fig. 7).   By contrast, over 100 in (2,540 mm)

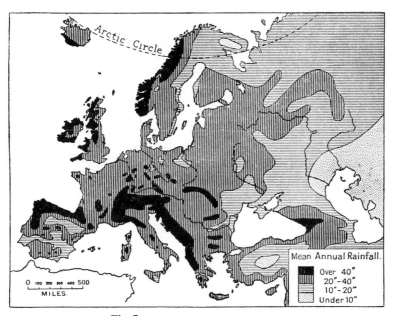

Fig. 7.   RAINFALL MAP OF EUROPE

per year on particularly exposed summits and over 60 in (1,524 mm) on uplands in Spain, Italy, Great Britain, and Scandinavia, for example, indicate the excessive wetness of many less fortunate localities.   Similar wide variations of temperature, humidity, and sunshine data in Europe increase the difficulty of describing its climates.   However, many of these local variations are caused by

17

relief features and when they are ignored a fairly simple pattern of climate emerges which reflects general atmospheric and continental influences.   Large-scale relief effects, such as those caused by the Alps, cannot be neglected since these dominate atmospheric influences over wide areas.

Two features emerging from a broad view of the climates of Europe are its general uniformity over large areas and the infrequency of sharp boundaries between different areas.   Both of these features may be attributed to the frequency with which maritime influences penetrate into the continent.   The general uniformity of the climates is caused by the modifying influences of the maritime air masses, while the intensity of frontal activity which accompanies them discourages the development of sharp climatic boundaries. In fact the familiar threefold climatic division of Europe depends upon the occasional exclusion of the maritime influence from parts of the continent.   Continental climates prevail in the east where the Siberian anticyclone dominates the circulation in winter, the Mediterranean area is dominated by the subtropical anticyclone in summer, and the maritime area in the west is open to low-pressure influences at all times.   Sharp boundaries between these areas occur only in conjunction with mountain ranges.   The Alps correspond roughly with the northern limit of the sub-tropical anticyclone in summer and assist in the creation of a sharp northern boundary to the Mediterranean area.   The Scandinavian mountains form a sharp boundary between the maritime and continental areas since in winter they frequently limit further westward extension of cold Siberian air.   In central Europe there are only gradual climatic transitions.

The following account of seasonal changes in the nature of air-mass activity is intended to emphasise the significance of this threefold division of the continent.   Later some climatic features of each of the three parts will be outlined.

**Seasons.**   In mid-summer the pattern of the general atmospheric circulation over Europe is fairly simple and its main features are shown in Fig. 8.   All elements of the circulation are displaced polewards from their average position and the interior of the continent is dominated by a low-pressure system caused by intense heating.   The polar front and the belt of most frequent depressions is displaced slightly northward off the Scottish and Scandinavian coasts.   However, maritime air masses and depressions are attracted deeply into the Eurasian interior by the thermal low.   Along the southern margin an eastward extension of the Azores subtropical anticyclone dominates the Mediterranean area.   Here maritime air masses and depressions are rare but not entirely absent.

In addition the circulation is relatively weak in summer because the contrast in temperature between the equator and poles is at a

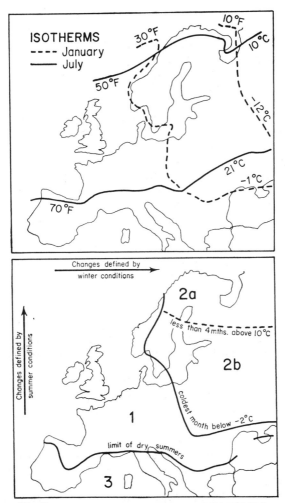

Fig. 8.   DISTRIBUTION OF CLIMATES IN EUROPE

1. Maritime, 2a. cold continental, 2b. warm continental, 3. Mediterranean The January and July isotherms indicate the seasonal changes in the distribution of climatic types.   These changes are seen to be the basis for the definition of each type in the lower diagram.

minimum.   This also reduces the contrast between tropical and polar air masses so that the polar front and depressions developing along it are relatively weak.

These generalisations refer only to average summer conditions and large deviations from these are common. Occasionally anticyclones extend northwards and dominate the whole of the continent, while at other times they withdraw and expose the Mediterranean to maritime influences.

Summer climatic features resulting from this circulation pattern can be summarised in terms of air-mass effects. North of the Mediterranean area, maritime air masses predominate, and while these are generally moist and equable they vary considerably according to stability, temperature, and associated weather. Polar maritime (Pm) air is most common and is frequently associated with the cold sectors of depressions. It is characterised by coolness, low absolute humidity, and instability. This last arises from the heating of the surface layers during the movement into warmer latitudes. The instability causes frequent showers along coastal margins but the total moisture content is low and the rainfall decreases inland. Sunny intervals are common with Pm air particularly in the interior. By contrast tropical maritime air (Tm) arriving at Europe is warm, stable and heavily charged with moisture. It is quite common in summer and is mainly associated with the warm sectors of depressions. The resultant weather is often overcast in western areas with prolonged drizzle and hill fog. The greater heat of the interior reduces the relative humidity and stability of this air, so dispersing much of the layer cloud. Therefore durations of sunshine are greater in the interior than in western districts. Often intense heating in central Europe makes Tm air unstable. Since it is heavily charged with moisture the associated thunderstorms produce copious rainfall which reinforces a summer maximum of rainfall in the interior. Occasionally Tm air is associated with northward extensions of the Azores anticyclone and it produces warm, sunny weather in all areas. Unfortunately this rarely happens in July or August.

Continental air masses are relatively uncommon in summer because the prevailing circulation discourages their westward extension into Europe. This is untrue in the south where tropical continental (Tc) air is dominant in July and August, producing warm, dry conditions over the Mediterranean area. Intensely hot dry weather is caused here by occasional incursions of Tc air from the Sahara. Similar movements of Tc air into north Europe produce tropical heat waves but these rarely penetrate north-westwards over Britain.

The transitional features of autumn will only be examined briefly. In September the equatorwards migration of the pressure system begins and this proceeds gradually until mid-winter. More frequent incursions of maritime air and attendant depressions into the Mediterranean area are expected in September. However, early autumn is still fairly settled because small anticyclones quite frequently become detached from the Azores high and move eastwards at this time. In October and November the frequency of westerlies and intensity of depressions rises rapidly to the winter level. The ocean still retains much of the summer warmth at this time and so a late autumn rainfall maximum is observed in much of western Europe. Fogs are common in November when the moist air is chilled over the continent but frosts are rare. In November the cold Siberian anticyclone is developing and the first waves of cold Polar continental (Pc) air are likely to be felt in western Europe. Fogs are particularly common in these cold spells.

True winter conditions are fully established in December, January, and February when the circulation system is displaced equatorwards and the cold continental anticyclone is developed (see Fig. 9). The polar front is now in the latitude of western Europe which, as a result, is located along the line of most frequent depressions. Airmass contrasts are very great at this time and so depressions are intense. A fairly constant succession of depressions passes eastward over western Europe to be eventually deflected either northwards over Scandinavia or southwards over the Mediterranean Sea by the continental high-pressure system. Between these tracks maritime influences rarely penetrate and the centre of the continent is exposed to cold, dry, easterly airstreams. Occasionally the Siberian anticyclone extends westwards or the polar anticyclone extends southwards over western Europe. When this happens, bifurcation of the westerlies takes place sooner, depressions are deflected off Scandinavia or across southern France into the Gulf of Lions and Britain is invaded by cold Pc air streams. This anticyclonic 'blocking activity' is fortunately less common in mid-winter than in spring but a notable occasion of its development was January and February 1963.

Air masses are more strongly contrasted in winter than in summer. Pm air is particularly common in winter because of the intensity of the polar anticyclone. The source regions of Pm air are very cold in winter, therefore relative warming during the southward passage is much greater than in summer and the air arrives over Europe in a highly unstable condition. This is true especially of those air masses which follow a direct southward journey from the Arctic. Such northerly air streams bring very cold weather together with heavy snow showers along exposed coasts. The total moisture content is low, however, and cold, dry conditions are experienced inland. Pm air arriving less directly after a considerable journey over the North Atlantic is more common than the direct variety and, although milder, is still responsible for cold weather with frequent precipitation. The latter comes in the form of snow mainly over uplands.

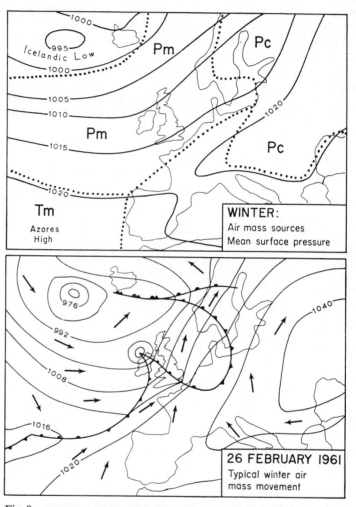

Fig. 9.　WINTER: PRESSURE SYSTEMS AND AIR MASSES OF EUROPE

There is a strong pressure gradient between the cold anticyclone over eastern Europe and the low-pressure cell near Iceland. Maritime air is unable to penetrate deeply into the Continent.

The heavy precipitation from Pm air is largely responsible for the winter rainfall maximum along the western margin of Europe.

Relatively mild temperatures are associated with Tm air and these lead to the remarkable warmth of western Europe in winter. This air is stable over Europe because cooling of the surface layers is intense during the poleward journey. Consequently very damp conditions with frequent mist or fog in urban areas are associated with Tm air. Pc air dominates eastern Europe and Siberia in winter. Although intensely cold and stable this air is dry in its source region and because of this the unpleasantness of the associated weather is slightly reduced. Only when this air extends westwards over adjacent seas, absorbing moisture in the process, does it become damp. Therefore central and eastern Europe has least rainfall in winter but there are slight falls of snow which cover the ground for long periods. The Alps effectively protect the Mediterranean area from incursions of Pc air in winter, except where they are broken by gaps. Where these exist, intensely cold northerly winds occasionally penetrate into the Mediterranean, for example, the Mistral of the Rhône valley and the Carcassonne gap, the Maestral of Genoa, the Bora of northern Dalmatia and the Vadarak of northern Greece. Cold fronts occur at the leading edge of these winds and depressions occasionally develop from these fronts.

In March, April, and May there is a gradual return to summer conditions although this is slightly retarded by the relative coldness of the sea and upper air at this time. The warming of both of these lags behind that of the land. This together with the high frequency of anticyclonic blocking action in spring encourages the development of cold spells reminiscent of winter conditions. In May the westerlies are at their rarest and the maritime influences at a minimum. By early June the Siberian anticyclone has completely dissolved and is replaced by the first appearance of the continental low. This is not fully developed until July and so, lacking an intense maritime influence, June often produces some of the pleasantest weather in western Europe. The subtropical high is not yet fully extended over the Mediterranean area which still experiences restricted maritime influences and incursions of depressions.

A useful climatic division of Europe follows directly from these seasonal changes in the relative importance of the maritime and continental influences. In its simplest form this is a threefold division depending on the predominance of maritime conditions throughout the year, or in winter or summer alone. It is difficult to allocate boundaries to each of the subdivisions since obvious relief barriers are often lacking. Fortunately the criteria adopted by Köppen in his general classification of the world's climates provide a satisfactory subdivision of Europe from the point of view of these dynamic influences. Thus in Fig. 8 a coldest month mean temperature of less than —2° C (28·4° F) includes that part where continental influences are expected to predominate in winter. Subdivision of this area into cold and warm continental types is valid in view of the

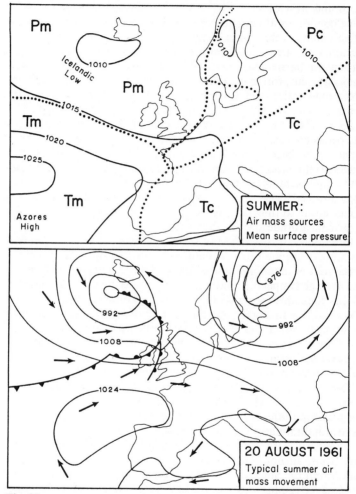

Fig. 10.   SUMMER: PRESSURE SYSTEMS AND AIR MASSES OF EUROPE

Pressure gradients are relatively weak and maritime air penetrates deeply into the Continent.

much warmer summer temperatures in the south. Significantly the adopted division based on a minimum of four summer months with a mean temperature of over 10° C (50° F) corresponds roughly to the boundary between deciduous and coniferous forests. Summer rainfall conditions are used to define the Mediterranean area experiencing predominantly subtropical anticyclone influences in summer.

**Maritime Europe.** A large part of western Europe north of the Alps and west of Poland and Sweden experiences prevailing maritime conditions at all times of the year. While the general location of this area is determined by the atmospheric circulation, in detail it occupies an area favourable to the penetration of the westerlies. Mountain barriers facing westwards are either lacking or, where they do occur, form the inner border of the area, as in Scandinavia. Deep indentations along the coastline also assist this eastward penetration.

Temperature and rainfall features in this area are a reflection of the persistent eastward succession of maritime influences and depressions. This succession is rarely interrupted by anticyclones or continental influences and while the daily weather is generally unsettled and unpleasant the climate lacks extremes and is favourable for agriculture. There is a fairly general increase in extremes towards the east due to the decrease in the maritime influences.

At low altitudes mild temperatures are observed throughout this area. This is due to the relative coolness of the sea in summer and its warmth in winter. The latter is particularly outstanding. A small part of the Norwegian coast is over 40° F (22° C) warmer than the average temperature for its latitude in January and in a large part of the area this 'positive temperature anomaly' amounts to over 20° F (11° C) in January. The net result is that mean annual temperature ranges are low in this maritime belt. Ranges of less than 15° F (8° C) along the west coast of Ireland, rising to 20° F (11° C) in eastern England and over 25° F (14° C) in eastern France and Germany are typical.

Rainfall is sufficient for general agricultural needs throughout the maritime area. This is partly because the low summer temperatures reduce evaporation considerably, so leaving a fairly large percentage of the total rainfall for agricultural use. Total annual rainfall varies considerably here. Heaviest amounts are in the uplands, particularly those in north-western districts facing the first impact of the maritime air. Some of the largest rainfall totals in Europe, amounting to over 120 in (3,048 mm) occur on high summits in Britain and Scandinavia. Rain-shadow effects are well developed to the lee of the uplands and the associated rapid changes in vegetation and agricultural landscape are characteristic of the area. This close relation between rainfall and relief, together with its occurrence in a winter or autumn maximum, can be attributed to general air-mass effects. Most of the rainfall is brought by Pm or Tm air. The former is unstable and so a certain amount of convective rainfall is associated with it in summer. Nevertheless rainfall from both of these air masses is generally caused by forced uplift either at fronts or in upland areas. Annual sunshine totals and cloud amounts also vary considerably according to local relief. General increases in sunshine totals occur towards the south of course but there is only a slight increase towards the interior of the continent. Sunshine totals in Denmark amount to roughly 120 per cent and those in Russia amount to roughly 130 per cent of values at equivalent latitudes in Britain. The increase in the amount of sunshine towards the east is much more rapid in summer than in winter.

**Continental Europe.** Maximum continental conditions are only experienced in central Siberia and depressions occasionally penetrate into European USSR even in mid-winter. Nevertheless, over a large part of eastern Europe, continental conditions predominate in winter and this is the unique feature of the climate of this area. In summer depressions penetrate deeply into the USSR, often from a north-western quarter, and there are no sharp climatic boundaries across the continent.

Very low winter temperatures are typical of the area. Mean January temperatures decrease fairly quickly eastwards from 28° F (−2° C) at Vienna, to 21° F (−6° C) at Kiev and 14° F (−10° C) at Moscow. In sympathy with these changes mean annual temperature ranges rise towards the east from over 30° F (17° C) in central Europe to over 50° F (28° C) in European USSR. The increase in summer temperatures towards the east is comparatively slight.

Rainfall is relatively low in the continental area, partly because of its distance from the sea. An annual total of less than 25 in (635 mm) occurs over much of north Germany and Poland, while in substantial areas, particularly in the extreme east, less than 20 in (508 mm) are recorded. The general summer maximum of rainfall is attributable to the intensity of the maritime influences at that time. Surface heating of originally stable Tm air masses reduces their stability and releases heavy convective showers. Winter precipitation is low and it comes mainly in the form of snow showers which, although light over lowlands, cover the surface for over three months.

**Mediterranean Europe.** This area is particularly distinguishable from the remainder of Europe by its characteristic landscape features. Partly this is due to non-climatic factors including peculiarities of the relief, coastal features, structure, and historical development. Nevertheless opportunities for a distinct climatic boundary along the northern edge of the Mediterranean basin are emphasized by a number of factors. Close juxtaposition of the coastline and Alpine barrier with the limits of the subtropical anticyclone effectively exclude cold continental conditions from the area in winter. Also at this time the sea acts as an eastward extension of the Atlantic Ocean and it is a natural routeway for depressions. In summer Tc conditions dominate the area and these are only slightly modified by the presence of the sea. On-shore winds are locally cool and relatively moist but the high stability usually prevents rainfall within them and their effects are often excluded from the interiors of the peninsulas.

The summer dry period, which characterises the Mediterranean climate, is not absolutely dry but is defined with reference to the seasonal distribution of rainfall. In all parts of the basin some rainfall is expected in summer but this is particularly rare in the south. Less than 15 per cent of the total annual rainfall is received in summer everywhere, excluding north-eastern Spain, the north-eastern half of Italy and most of southern France. In these areas less than 25 per cent of the annual total is received in summer. Much of this summer rainfall is derived from thunderstorms which develop over the hot land surfaces. During the remainder of the year rainfall is generally associated with the maritime situations typical of northern Europe. Winters are generally mild but snow lasts for a considerable duration on the higher summits.

The Mediterranean area is the warmest part of Europe throughout the year. This is to be expected in view of its location on the equatorward side of the continent and, in fact, Mediterranean temperatures in both July and January are only slightly above their latitudinal means. The mildness of winter temperatures is also attributable to the ease with which maritime influences penetrate eastwards through the area. This is reflected in the distribution of January temperatures (see Fig. 8) since the general north to south trend of European winter isotherms is replaced here by an east to west trend. Marked temperature variations within the region are associated with the diversity of relief, land and sea distribution, and distance from the Atlantic. Generally conditions are more extreme in the interiors of the peninsulas. The mean annual temperature range at Madrid is 37° F (21° C) while that at Barcelona is only 28° F (16° C). Annual temperature ranges in the west are usually lower than those in the more continental east but this small effect is often obscured by other factors.

Much of the attraction of the area for the tourist industry arises from the clarity of its weather. Sunshine totals are high and cloud amounts are low, particularly in the south. The mean annual duration of sunshine over much of the Mediterranean basin is roughly 160 per cent of the equivalent value in England.

## MARITIME EUROPE

| No. | Station | Lat. N | Long. | Height in feet | Days with | |
|---|---|---|---|---|---|---|
| | | | | | Rain | Snow |
| 1 | Corunna | 43° 23′ | 8° 23′ W | 82 | 125 | 0 |
| 2 | Bordeaux | 44° 50′ | 0° 36′ W | 157 | 160 | 0 |
| 3 | Paris | 48° 18′ | 2° 7′ E | 164 | 162 | 14 |
| 4 | Scilly | 49° 56′ | 6° 18′ W | 131 | 207 | 3 |
| 5 | Kew | 51° 28′ | 0° 19′ W | 18 | 167 | 13 |
| 6 | Bergen | 60° 23′ | 5° 21′ E | 72 | 206 | 38 |

### MEAN TEMPERATURE – DEGREES C

| No. | Jan. | Feb. | Mar. | Apr. | May | June | July | Aug. | Sep. | Oct. | Nov. | Dec. | Year |
|---|---|---|---|---|---|---|---|---|---|---|---|---|---|
| 1 | 9·2 | 9·7 | 10·4 | 11·8 | 14·1 | 16·4 | 17·8 | 18·1 | 17·1 | 14·4 | 11·8 | 10·4 | 13·4 |
| 2 | 5·9 | 7·5 | 8·7 | 11·2 | 14·1 | 17·8 | 19·9 | 19·7 | 17·7 | 13·7 | 8·8 | 5·8 | 12·6 |
| 3 | 2·6 | 4·1 | 6·3 | 9·6 | 13·4 | 16·4 | 18·2 | 17·5 | 14·7 | 10·0 | 5·8 | 3·4 | 10·2 |
| 4 | 7·6 | 7·4 | 7·8 | 9·2 | 11·4 | 14·0 | 15·8 | 16·0 | 14·8 | 12·1 | 9·9 | 8·6 | 11·2 |
| 5 | 3·8 | 4·5 | 5·8 | 8·5 | 11·9 | 15·1 | 17·1 | 16·4 | 13·9 | 9·9 | 6·7 | 4·6 | 9·8 |
| 6 | 1·2 | 1·3 | 2·2 | 5·7 | 9·4 | 12·9 | 14·4 | 13·7 | 11·1 | 7·4 | 4·0 | 2·0 | 7·1 |

Conversion: degrees Centigrade to degrees Fahrenheit: multiply by 9, divide by 5, and add 32.

### AVERAGE RAINFALL – MILLIMETRES

| No. | Jan. | Feb. | Mar. | Apr. | May | June | July | Aug. | Sep. | Oct. | Nov. | Dec. | Year |
|---|---|---|---|---|---|---|---|---|---|---|---|---|---|
| 1 | 81 | 79 | 81 | 64 | 56 | 36 | 23 | 30 | 56 | 89 | 106 | 112 | 813 |
| 2 | 71 | 104 | 84 | 74 | 66 | 66 | 56 | 53 | 38 | 81 | 127 | 79 | 899 |
| 3 | 38 | 36 | 41 | 43 | 48 | 53 | 56 | 53 | 48 | 58 | 48 | 51 | 574 |
| 4 | 76 | 66 | 61 | 48 | 43 | 43 | 56 | 66 | 61 | 94 | 84 | 112 | 810 |
| 5 | 46 | 38 | 43 | 38 | 43 | 53 | 56 | 56 | 48 | 69 | 56 | 58 | 605 |
| 6 | 229 | 168 | 157 | 109 | 119 | 104 | 145 | 198 | 234 | 236 | 216 | 226 | 2,141 |

Conversion: Millimetres to inches (approx.): multiply by 0.04.

## CONTINENTAL EUROPE

| No. | Station | Lat. N | Long. | Height in feet | Days with | |
|---|---|---|---|---|---|---|
| | | | | | Rain | Snow |
| 1 | Stockholm | 59° 21′ | 18° 3′ E | 146 | 168 | 58 |
| 2 | Warsaw | 52° 13′ | 21° 1′ E | 436 | 160 | 57 |
| 3 | Archangel | 64° 35′ | 40° 36′ E | 22 | 174 | 99 |
| 4 | Leningrad | 59° 56′ | 30° 16′ E | 16 | 173 | 72 |
| 5 | Moscow | 55° 46′ | 37° 40′ E | 512 | 169 | 82 |
| 6 | Kazan | 55° 47′ | 49° 8′ E | 266 | 121 | 54 |
| 7 | Kiev | 50° 27′ | 30° 30′ E | 600 | 153 | 56 |
| 8 | Astrakhan | 46° 21′ | 48° 2′ E | −45 | 56 | 31 |

### MEAN TEMPERATURES – DEGREES C

| No. | Jan. | Feb. | Mar. | Apr. | May | June | July | Aug. | Sep. | Oct. | Nov. | Dec. | Year |
|---|---|---|---|---|---|---|---|---|---|---|---|---|---|
| 1 | − 2·9 | − 3·1 | −1·3 | 3·4 | 8·7 | 14·1 | 16·6 | 15·2 | 11·4 | 6·3 | 1·6 | − 1·8 | 5·7 |
| 2 | − 3·1 | − 1·9 | 1·8 | 7·9 | 14·0 | 17·2 | 18·7 | 17·5 | 13·4 | 8·0 | 2·2 | 1·2 | 7·9 |
| 3 | −13·5 | −12·8 | −7·3 | −1·2 | 5·0 | 11·9 | 15·7 | 13·5 | 8·0 | 1·2 | −5·7 | −11·3 | 0·3 |
| 4 | − 7·8 | − 8·0 | −4·2 | 2·4 | 9·1 | 14·7 | 17·4 | 15·6 | 10·6 | 4·7 | −1·0 | − 5·8 | 4·0 |
| 5 | −10·4 | − 9·9 | −4·9 | 3·3 | 12·1 | 16·3 | 18·9 | 16·6 | 10·9 | 4·7 | −2·4 | − 7·1 | 3·9 |
| 6 | −13·6 | −11·5 | −6·2 | 3·5 | 13·0 | 17·4 | 19·9 | 17·4 | 11·0 | 3·4 | −4·3 | −10·3 | 3·3 |
| 7 | − 6·0 | − 4·7 | −0·5 | 6·9 | 14·7 | 17·4 | 19·3 | 18·2 | 13·4 | 7·3 | 0·7 | − 3·5 | 6·9 |
| 8 | − 7·1 | − 5·4 | 0·4 | 8·8 | 17·5 | 22·5 | 24·5 | 23·2 | 17·0 | 9·7 | 2·2 | − 3·0 | 9·2 |

AVERAGE RAINFALL – MILLIMETRES

| No. | Jan. | Feb. | Mar. | Apr. | May | June | July | Aug. | Sept. | Oct. | Nov. | Dec. | Year |
|---|---|---|---|---|---|---|---|---|---|---|---|---|---|
| 1 | 36 | 30 | 36 | 36 | 38 | 43 | 66 | 76 | 48 | 46 | 46 | 48 | 549 |
| 2 | 30 | 28 | 33 | 38 | 48 | 66 | 76 | 74 | 48 | 41 | 38 | 38 | 561 |
| 3 | 23 | 18 | 20 | 18 | 30 | 46 | 61 | 56 | 41 | 30 | 30 | 23 | 428 |
| 4 | 25 | 23 | 23 | 25 | 41 | 51 | 63 | 71 | 53 | 46 | 36 | 30 | 490 |
| 5 | 33 | 30 | 36 | 36 | 46 | 66 | 81 | 79 | 56 | 53 | 43 | 41 | 599 |
| 6 | 23 | 18 | 20 | 23 | 36 | 61 | 56 | 53 | 43 | 38 | 33 | 25 | 429 |
| 7 | 36 | 30 | 43 | 43 | 51 | 74 | 81 | 56 | 46 | 48 | 41 | 41 | 589 |
| 8 | 13 | 10 | 10 | 18 | 18 | 20 | 13 | 13 | 13 | 13 | 13 | 15 | 167 |

## MEDITERRANEAN EUROPE

| No. | Station | Lat. N | Long. | Height in feet | Days with Rain | Days with Snow |
|---|---|---|---|---|---|---|
| 1 | Gibraltar | 36° 6′ | 5° 21′ W | 53 | 84 | 0 |
| 2 | Madrid | 40° 24′ | 3° 41′ W | 2,149 | 95 | 4 |
| 3 | Barcelona | 41° 23′ | 2° 8′ E | 136 | 70 | 3 |
| 4 | Marseilles | 43° 18′ | 5° 23′ E | 246 | 101 | 2 |
| 5 | Rome | 41° 54′ | 12° 29′ E | 207 | 102 | 2 |
| 6 | Naples | 40° 52′ | 14° 15′ E | 489 | 112 | 1 |
| 7 | Athens | 37° 58′ | 23° 43′ E | 351 | 99 | 6 |

MEAN TEMPERATURE – DEGREES C

| No. | Jan. | Feb. | Mar. | Apr. | May | June | July | Aug. | Sept. | Oct. | Nov. | Dec. | Year |
|---|---|---|---|---|---|---|---|---|---|---|---|---|---|
| 1 | 12·7 | 13·3 | 14·1 | 15·9 | 18·2 | 20·8 | 23·0 | 23·8 | 22·2 | 18·7 | 15·8 | 13·4 | 17·6 |
| 2 | 4·6 | 6·5 | 8·7 | 12·1 | 16·1 | 20·9 | 25·1 | 24·8 | 19·6 | 13·4 | 8·5 | 5·0 | 13·8 |
| 3 | 9·7 | 9·3 | 10·7 | 13·3 | 16·7 | 20·4 | 23·4 | 23·7 | 20·8 | 16·8 | 12·2 | 9·2 | 15·4 |
| 4 | 8·1 | 7·9 | 9·9 | 12·7 | 16·2 | 19·7 | 22·1 | 21·4 | 19·1 | 14·8 | 10·7 | 7·6 | 14·1 |
| 5 | 8·3 | 8·2 | 10·5 | 13·7 | 18·0 | 21·6 | 24·5 | 24·2 | 20·9 | 16·5 | 11·5 | 8·0 | 15·4 |
| 6 | 10·6 | 9·1 | 10·7 | 13·6 | 17·7 | 21·2 | 24·0 | 24·0 | 21·4 | 17·3 | 12·6 | 9·5 | 15·6 |
| 7 | 10·7 | 9·7 | 11·2 | 14·8 | 19·0 | 23·4 | 26·6 | 26·4 | 23·0 | 18·9 | 14·1 | 11·2 | 17·3 |

AVERAGE RAINFALL – MILLIMETRES

| No. | Jan. | Feb. | Mar. | Apr. | May | June | July | Aug. | Sept. | Oct. | Nov. | Dec. | Year |
|---|---|---|---|---|---|---|---|---|---|---|---|---|---|
| 1 | 129 | 107 | 122 | 69 | 43 | 13 | 0 | 3 | 36 | 84 | 160 | 140 | 901 |
| 2 | 33 | 33 | 41 | 41 | 43 | 33 | 10 | 13 | 38 | 46 | 51 | 41 | 422 |
| 3 | 36 | 38 | 46 | 48 | 43 | 38 | 25 | 33 | 76 | 79 | 46 | 36 | 544 |
| 4 | 43 | 36 | 48 | 56 | 43 | 28 | 18 | 20 | 58 | 97 | 71 | 53 | 574 |
| 5 | 81 | 68 | 74 | 66 | 56 | 41 | 18 | 25 | 63 | 127 | 109 | 99 | 831 |
| 6 | 94 | 74 | 71 | 64 | 51 | 36 | 15 | 28 | 74 | 117 | 114 | 112 | 848 |
| 7 | 51 | 43 | 30 | 21 | 20 | 18 | 8 | 13 | 15 | 41 | 66 | 66 | 394 |

## REFERENCES

F. K. Hare, *The Restless Atmosphere*, London, Hutchinson, 1953, Chapters 13 and 14 describe seasonal changes in the distribution of air masses and the associated types of weather in Europe; W. G. Kendrew, *The Climates of the Continents*, Oxford, Oxford University Press, 4th ed., 1953, Chapters 26 and 27; W. Köppen and R. Geiger, *Die Klimate der Erde*, Berlin, 1932; G. T. Trewartha, *The Earth's Problem Climates*, Wisconsin and London, Methuen, 1961, Chapters 14, 15, and 16 deal with more detailed aspects of Europe's climates and it contains a large bibliography of papers concerning this topic.

### CHAPTER 3

# VEGETATION AND SOILS

THE natural vegetation of Europe has been so much interfered with by man that few traces remain of the unmodified covering except in the higher and more unfavourable latitudes and altitudes. Even uncultivated areas have often been affected to such an extent by man's activities (e.g. by fire and animal grazing) that the vegetation may have altered greatly. However, the plant associations have undergone many changes since Pleistocene times in response to many biotic and climatic happenings and vicissitudes. Were man's inter-ference to cease, it is unlikely that the original vegetation would re-establish itself in exactly the same form. Nevertheless, the 'natural', 'characteristic', or 'climax' vegetation, as it is variously called, is essentially a result of climatic and soil conditions, and, indeed, culti-vated vegetation also is influenced by these factors. In turn, the broad zones of soil are themselves dependent on climate, though minor variations of soil owe much to the underlying rocks, or to deposits of alluvium or lead, and of glacial till and other unconsoli-dated materials. Likewise some soils of Europe owe much to the activity of man: the polder and plaggen of north-west Europe, the vitisols of central and southern Europe and the long-cultivated post-podzols of the North European Plain.

Five main belts of vegetation may be distinguished in Europe (see Fig. 11): the tundra, the coniferous forest, the mixed forest in which deciduous trees predominated, the Mediterranean evergreen xerophytic, and the steppe grasslands of the south-east. In addition a small area of desert shrub occurs in the south-east, and patches of Alpine grassland are found on the higher mountains throughout the continent, though bare rock dominates in many areas of glacial erosion.

**The Tundra Zone.** This cold, treeless belt, sometimes known as the Arctic Steppe, lies mainly within the Arctic Circle in a narrow zone bordering the Barents Sea, but it sends tongues southwards in the Ural Mountains and those of Scandinavia, variously known as the Kjöllen Mountains or as the Scandes.

As the soil is frozen for the greater part of the year and the subsoil is permanently frozen (permafrost), only shallow rooted plants can grow, and this precludes the growth of trees, with the exception of dwarf polar willows and of birches in some places. The latter grow only a few inches high and cling closely to the ground so that they are barely recognisable as trees. The vegetation, although entirely low-growing, varies considerably from place to place, mainly according to the state of drainage and to slight variations in regolith or exposure. Lichens, including the well-known 'reindeer moss', cover the localised drier, sandy sections; the more common badly drained areas develop a peat-bog flora where sphagnum and other mosses are the dominant vegetation. The most favoured areas develop summer meadows, but on the other hand many of the rock

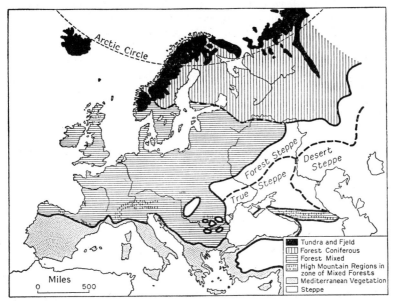

Fig. 11. VEGETATION ZONES OF EUROPE

stretches are almost devoid of vegetation. The northern berry-bearing bushes, such as cloudberry, blueberry, and cranberry, occur only in very favoured places. Agriculturally the region is almost useless, though reindeer husbandry is practised, and vegetable crops are grown in the short summer, with its day-long illumination.

There is no sharp boundary between the tundra and the taïga, or coniferous forest, which succeeds it. A few isolated willows and birches begin to appear, then stunted conifers hung with bearded lichens, until eventually whole woods can be seen.

At the southern edge of the tundra are many dead trees, or trees whose tops have died off, due to keen frosts and increasing hydro-morphism and peat formation.

The tundra soils are formed mainly from glacial deposits of a gravelly nature, or from wind-blown silt, and mainly under conditions of high humidity, for although the precipitation is low it is far greater than the evaporation, and the frozen subsoil is impermeable.   The soils show signs of gleying, or are of the peat-bog type, for decomposition of organic residues is slow.   Both types are characteristically very acid and their temperature is much lower than that of the air.

**The Taïga or Coniferous Forest Zone.**   The name taïga is of Siberian origin, meaning forest, but has come to be widely used to denote the Northern Coniferous Forests, as distinct from coniferous forests of other climatic regions.   The zone extends southwards from the tundra to about 58° N in Norway and Sweden, to about 60° N in Finland, but trends still farther southwards to 56° N in the Tatar Republic.   The highlands of Scandinavia interpose a long tongue of tundra-like vegetation into this belt.   Owing to the short growing season, the relatively low summer temperatures, and the acid soils of this forested region, agriculture is very difficult, only a few clearings have been made, and the forest remains the chief European reserve of timber.   Spruce (*Picea excelsa*), on moist soils and in peaty areas, and Scots pine (*Pinus sylvestris*), on dry soils and rocky heaths, predominate, though *excelsa* is not common in western Norway.   Siberian species, for example larch (*Larix siberica*), Siberian spruce (*Picea sibirica*), and fir (*Abies sibirica*) occur in Russia.   The silver birch (*Betula alba*), is found throughout the belt, whilst alder (*Alnus glutinosa*) and rowan (*Pyrus aucuparia*) appear to some extent.

In spite of the vast extent of the taïga, the tenure of the coniferous forest trees is not so secure as appears at first sight.   Peat bogs, dominated by sphagnum, termed *high moor*, are a marked feature of the landscape and cover thousands of acres as continuous strips at the northern coastlands of the Gulf of Bothnia and those of the White Sea, and they appear to be spreading at the expense of the forest.   They are favoured by the abundance of waterlogged areas, but in these cool, humid, northern latitudes they can actually invade areas which were previously dryish.   The surface of the soil under forest is covered by a thick layer of plant debris or *mor humus* which is hygrophilic, keeping the mineral soil beneath from drying out. It encourages moss growth which absorbs rain or snowmelt and spreads to form a carpet, thickening and preventing aeration of the soil, gradually killing the trees, in the same way as the Canadian *muskeg* is formed.   Grassy *low-moor*, varying in lime content and acidity according to the drainage waters, but usually acid or neutral, also occurs in depressions.   If the coniferous trees are destroyed by fire or by felling operations their place is often taken by birch or alder. There is also considerable competition among the conifers themselves; for instance, the spruce in Norway has spread widely at the expense of the Scots pine and is still advancing, the reason being that the spruce seeds every three or four years, whereas the pine seeds only about every six or seven years. Also conifers grow more rapidly in the southern parts of the belt, and to less height and girth in the north.

As regards agriculture, only the hardier cereals and roots, such as six-row barley, black oats, and potatoes, can be cultivated, and these with difficulty. Fruit trees are generally absent, but berry-bearing bushes are numerous. Hay grows well in the long days of the northern summer, but is difficult to dry.

The soils of the coniferous forest zone are termed *podzolised*, or ashen soils. Actually the colour of the surface mineral horizon underlying the *mor* varies from whitish-grey to greyish-brown. The soils show three well-marked diagnostic horizons; the A horizon is the grey one, and is podzolised by percolating solutions derived from snowmelt and rain and containing organic acids of a complex nature formed during the decomposition of plant residues. Podzols form most readily on sandy materials of low lime content. Bases are removed from silicate minerals and the metallic hydroxides formed are then moved in solution from the A horizon by a process known as *cheluviation* to be redeposited as sesquioxides of iron and aluminium in a middle layer or B horizon, which may often show a hard, compacted stratum or 'pan', in its upper part; a reddish sandy loam or B2 underneath, and thirdly a less-altered C horizon – the presumed parent material. Incidentally the pan is conducive to water-logging and thus to the probable development of *gley-podzolic* or *peaty-podzolic* soils. In the southern part of the taïga, *sod-podzolic* or 'turfey' podzolic soils occur. Associated with older tills of the third or the first part of the fourth glaciation and other non-sandy materials, they are akin to *leached brown earths*, called variously *parabraunerde* or *grey-brown podzolic soils* in western Europe. In the Baltic republics true brown earths occur on till of the fourth glaciation, and rendzinic soils occur on various limestones. The turfey podzolic soils achieve full dominance in the Russian part of the zone of mixed forests, along with true brown earths.

**The Zone of Mixed Forest.** This once covered the greater part of temperate Europe; broad-leaved, deciduous trees predominated, but conifers were found to some extent on the sandier podzolised soils and in the mountainous districts. In Great Britain there are only two native coniferous trees, the Scots pine and the yew (*Taxus* *baccata*), and only the pine formed forests of any extent. Unlike the coniferous forest, the mixed forest belt has mainly been cleared for agriculture, and generally only the acid brown and podzolic soils, or steep mountain slopes, are now forest-covered, often by controlled reafforestation. One result of man's interference with nature in this belt has been to reduce the proportion of deciduous trees in favour of the conifers, for two reasons. Since the deciduous trees grew mainly on the nutrient-rich brown earths they have been largely cut down to make way for ploughland, while reafforestation schemes have concentrated on the quick-growing and less exacting conifers which give a speedier and economic return.

The soils of this zone vary from podzols on sands, where coniferous trees predominate, and which are a zonal form in eastern Europe and Russia but have formed quite rapidly on the deforestation and degradation of base-poor acid brown earths in western Europe; to the characteristic *brown forest soils* of western and central Europe, which are less acid and have a higher base content and mull humus. Such soils may be subdivided according to their lime and iron contents, or by reference to their colour or geographic position. Distinctive soils are also formed on basalt; also upon calcareous rocks, where *rendzinic* soils develop; dark in colour at the surface with stable humus of a black colour, and light, perhaps almost white colours, in the C horizon. Variants of these rendzinas are many – they form on hard Jurassic and Cretaceous limestones in north-east Spain; on softer limestones in central Europe, especially in Poland; in an Alpine form in the Dolomites, while in Britain 'calcimorphic brown earths' are found in the dry valleys and rendzinas on chalk scarps. In the Mediterranean region rendzinas are replaced on limestone by *terra rossa*, or perhaps rendzinas develop with time into *terra rossa*.

As a result of the wide extension in latitude, from about 44° N to 61° N, and the gradual change from the oceanic climate of the west to the continental climate of the east, this zone gives opportunity for a great variety of natural vegetation, soils, and cultivated crops. The chief cereal is wheat in the central and southern parts of the belt, with two-row barley and white oats, also very widely grown. Rye tends to be the most important bread cereal in the eastern part of the zone, especially in Poland and in Russia. Maize is of some significance along the south-central margin. Root crops are generally grown, including sugar-beet and potatoes. Cultivated grasses, including clover, are widely grown, and in the wetter north-west meadows cover a large area, much of which may at one time have been occupied by other types of vegetation. A large number of fruit trees are grown, such as the apple, pear, and plum, and small fruits also flourish. The vine is widely cultivated south of about 48° N reaching its northernmost extent in the Rhine valley just south of Bonn. The milder south-western portion of the belt (Aquitaine–Basque country) shows a particularly rich variety of crops, including maize and many leguminous crops and the vines of Gironde.

Intruding into this zone are outlying patches of the grassland-steppe belt in the plains of Hungary and Walachia, while the higher parts of the Alps, Pyrenees, and Carpathians rise above the forests into the altitudinal zone of Alpine vegetation. It is also possible to separate out a south-western zone of fully deciduous character, essentially consisting of lowland France and lowland Britain and Ireland as well as eastern Denmark and Skåne. Other variants are the western Netherlands, the Fens, and the Po valley as alluvial plains of high fertility.

**The Mediterranean Zone.** The natural vegetation of the Mediterranean lands consists of plants which can either withstand or evade the summer drought. The characteristic Mediterranean trees, for instance, have small leaves, low stature, and other devices for checking loss of moisture, but each tree needs a considerable area of root space to supply it with sufficient water in the dry season, and the characteristic Mediterranean evergreen forest grows in open formation. It easily degenerates into scrub, known under various names, such as *maquis* in Corsica, *macchia* in Italy, and *garrigue* in southern France. Actually *maquis* describes the moister areas with a short dry season, having cork oak and siliceous or limonitic *terra fusca* soils of a brownish colour; *garrigue* applies to calcareous areas, often with ferric *terra rossa* soils and longer dry periods in summer. Few tree species have been successful in their adaptation to the unfavourable Mediterranean climatic regime. Such are the olive, holm oak (*Quercus ilex*), cork oak (*Q. suber*), and various conifers, such as *Pinus maritima*, the Aleppo pine (*P. halepensis*), and the stone pine (*P. pinea*). On the mountains having considerable rain, and where the summer drought is less marked, deciduous trees occur, especially the sweet chestnut (*Castanea sativa*), and on the higher slopes various conifers, but the latter have been largely cleared. Once the vegetation cover was removed from the mountains the torrential rain swept away the soil cover, which is not easily renewed in this climate, and provided deep valley infillings. Hence the predominance of bare rock in mountainous districts and of flats of stony alluvium in the valleys.

Various heaths and aromatic herbs such as lavender, myrtle, rosemary, and thyme also manage to survive the drought, and these shrubs, like the trees, also have devices to prevent loss of moisture. Grass withers in early summer and seldom grows in close formation except in the swampy deltas and coastlands. However, lowland grazing is available for stock in winter, and mountain pasture in summer, giving rise to transhumance over long distances, now motorised or rail-borne. The cultivated grasses, of which certain primitive strains of barley, wheat, and red oats may be native, similarly evade the drought by ripening in May, June, or early July, according to latitude and altitude. Bulbs evade it by lying dormant in summer and flowering in winter and spring. Yet the main means of crop and orchard production is by irrigation, while market garden 'primeur' crops are produced for northern markets in the winter period.

Owing to the scarcity of grass the rearing of cattle is unimportant but the aromatic herbage provides food for sheep and goats, though it has little value and often gives the flesh a peculiar taste. The sheep and goats, in nibbling the leaves of young trees, are among the many enemies of the re-establishment of the Mediterranean wood-lands. Owing to the absence of cattle there is a general absence of dairy produce, although sheep's and goat's milk is used to some extent, the oil of the olive and other vegetable oils replacing animal fats.

The cultivated Mediterranean fruits are generally not natives of the basin, nor, as a rule, are they perfectly suited to the climate. The orange is native to the summer-rain lands of southern China, is not naturally adapted to summer drought, and therefore needs irrigation. The closely allied lemon is confined to the southern margins of Europe, commercial production being largely restricted to Sicily, for it is even more sensitive to cold than the orange, and also generally needs irrigation. Even the vine is often irrigated in the Mediterranean zone, and except in regions of rather heavy rainfall is usually grown in hollows where it can take advantage of all the moisture available. It is, of course, widely grown outside the region of Mediterranean climate. Peaches and apricots also are not indigenous; in fact, the only two indubitably native fruits appear to be the olive (originating in Syria) and the pomegranate (Granada-apple, lit. trans.). The olive forms a useful guide to the limits of the Mediterranean climate on the north, but the mountains inside the region are too cold for it (see Fig. 12). The three traditional food staples, however, throughout the Mediterranean zone are white bread, wine, and olive oil.

The distinctiveness of the soils of this zone is recognised by French writers, though they are somewhat similar to those of the southern parts of the mixed forest zone. Yet, where the underlying rock is calcareous, a bright red soil known as *terra rossa* often occurs, as in Apulia, on the sides of the lower Rhône valley, and elsewhere. It varies greatly in thickness, and its thin surface layers of plant debris and leached material have often been eroded. It is a clay-rich heavy soil, retentive of moisture and fertile, and, though greatly weathered, is not devoid of lime or nutrients though lacking in organic matter. The soil provides a remarkable colour contrast with the pure white limestone which forms a substrate, though it is probably not the parent rock. This rock frequently outcrops above the pockets of *terra rossa* in the valleys and runoff from it is often rapid and remarkably erosive. In wetter areas brown soils occur, either limey *terra fusca* on marls or impure limestone or non-calcic *meridional brown*

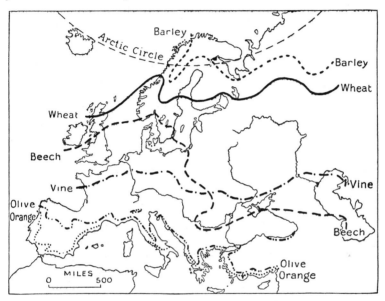

Fig. 12. NORTHERN LIMITS OF CERTAIN PLANTS AND TREES IN EUROPE
Note, however, isolated regions of olive culture in northern Italy and on the southern shore of the Black Sea.

*earths* on sandy materials. In the drier parts of the Mediterranean zone *calcic reddish brown soils* occur, even *saline soils* form, in wet depressions, which periodically dry out as, for example, in the Ebro and Murcian lowlands.

**The Grassland or Steppe Zone.** This belt stretches in a south-west to north-east direction and lies mainly in the USSR, though beginning at Bucharest. Actually this zone contains three subsections which reflect slight but significant differences of climate. Along the northern and western margins of the zone there is a transitional belt between the true grasslands and the mixed forest zone which may be termed the *wooded steppe*; along the southern and eastern margins there is a transitional belt towards the desert which may be termed the *semi-desert steppe*; the main belt consists of a region where tall grasses and other herbaceous vegetation flourish, but where trees do not grow except along watercourses or in places where water is supplied artificially. The great west–east extent of the zone also entails some longitudinal climatic diversity.

Generally speaking, trees do not grow in the steppes because conditions of physiological drought prevail during both the arid months of late summer and in the freezing months of winter. Grasses, as well as many flowering plants and bulbs, can lie dormant during these inclement periods and rush into rapid growth during the spring and early summer when snowmelt and rain are available.

*The Wooded Steppe* has a curious history. It is probable that this area was covered by herbaceous vegetation consisting of steppe grasses and flowering plants during the climatic optimum of 'Atlantic' times, but that it was invaded by deciduous trees in later phases of proto-historic time. The predominating trees were oaks, maples, and limes of various kinds, together with the common ash, with a second storey of smaller trees and shrubs, such as the cherry, blackthorn, hazel, dog-rose, etc. These formed thick and extensive woods, though there appear to have been considerable patches in which steppe vegetation prevailed. The grasslands of the middle Danubian basin and most of the grasslands of Rumania belong to the wooded steppe, which, however, attains its greatest extent in European USSR (see Fig. 11). The clearing of the woods took place gradually, possibly in early historic times in the middle Danubian basin, and as late as the seventeenth century in Russia; it has been carried so far that nowadays few trees remain, except round some of the villages, though reafforestation has taken place on a small scale in Hungary, while a few patches of natural woodland remain in Walachia. The wooded steppe now resembles the true steppe in appearance, both having been brought under cultivation, the main difference being that trees, including fruit trees, can be grown successfully without irrigation in the wooded steppe provided that sufficient care is given in the early stages. The soil of the wooded steppe strongly resembles that of the true steppe, but is technically known as 'degraded' *chernozem*, either leached or podzolised, as well as having *grey forest soils*, with a thick humus-rich A horizon and a peculiar nutty-structured B horizon, somewhat similar to the prairie earths of North America and to their intergrades with the grey-brown podzolic soils.

*The True Steppe or Prairie.* In this zone the precipitation is lower and the evaporation higher than in the wooded steppe, so that the total amount of moisture available is smaller and the droughty periods are longer. The characteristic vegetation consists of steppe grasses (species of *Stipa, Andropogon, Chrysopogon*, etc.), together with brightly coloured flowering plants in great variety, among which the members of the compositae, legume, crucifer, umbellifer, and labiate families are conspicuous. Tubers and bulbs, such as a yellow dwarf iris (*Iris pumila*) and the white Star of Bethlehem (*Ornithogalum tenuifolium*), also occur. The natural vegetation of the steppe springs into life after the snow has melted, usually during April, and presents a brilliant carpet of colour until about June, when the plants begin to wither and dry up. For the rest of the summer and during the autumn the steppe takes on the appearance of a semi-desert, while in winter the whole region has a mantle of snow, varying in thickness from a thin powdering to a substantial covering.

The chief crops in the widely cultivated steppe zone, as in the wooded steppe, are cereals, especially winter wheat as far east as Rostov, and spring wheat and winter wheat as far east as the Volga, but only spring wheat further eastwards; together with barley in the south-west; oats to the north-east and rye in the north, with maize and millet in the warmer portions. Sunflowers (for oil), sugar beet, hemp, and tobacco are of considerable importance in localised areas. Crops other than annuals are difficult to grow. For instance, although the summers are long and warm enough for the vine in the south-western part of the zone, the stumps (*ceps*) have to be protected in winter under mounds of earth. The chief fruit is the melon, while vegetables include cucumber, pumpkin, gherkin, paprika, and onions. Crop yields range more widely (through drought) in the true steppe than in the wooded steppe further north.

Before being brought under cultivation the steppe was the domain of cattle-keeping horsemen, and the steppes are eminently suited to livestock, though little natural pasture remains. Mixed dairy and beef rearing is usual, with dairying important near the industrial areas of the eastern Ukraine. Pig rearing is also widespread. The only uncultivated parts of the steppe are those patches which are either too saline or too sandy, or too cut by gullying for cultivated crops; these had, and still have, a somewhat different vegetation from the true steppe.

The characteristic soil of the true steppe consists of 'blackearth' or *chernozem*.[1] This soil, which was first studied in Russia by Dokuchayev, is a deep friable loam. It is only slightly leached, with a lime-accumulating loamy B horizon at a depth of about one metre, underlying a deep, humus-rich (*c.* 10 per cent), dark surface

[1] Pronounced 'chernozyem'.

horizon of neutral or base-saturated character. It therefore contrasts strongly with the acidic podzolic soils of the coniferous and mixed forest zones. The high percentage of humus results from the decaying steppe vegetation over a considerable period of time, and the humus is a stable form, combined with lime. Various subtypes of chernozem are recognised by the varying amount and depth of humic material, and the depth of leaching of free lime. The *southern chernozem* have surface soils which are hardly leached and subsoils may contain gypsum. Generally, because of its reserves of humus, good structure and nutrient supply at shallow depth, the chernozem is highly fertile and easy to work, though it tends to become sticky when wet and powdery when dry. There are *compact* clayrich forms also. In the northern parts, in the wooded steppe, the chernozem shows signs of leaching or even of podzolisation and is distinguishable from the chernozem by its shallow grey A horizon, and an illuvial calcic horizon at great depth – more than 6 ft.

*The Artemisia Steppe.* This zone occurs to the south of the chernozemic zone round the northern coastlands of the Black, Azov, and Caspian Seas, where the annual precipitation decreases to less than 12 in. Formerly called uncultivated steppe, this is still largely grazing land, but with much extensive agriculture established in recent times. The region is named *desert steppe* in Fig. 11, and is roughly coterminous with the zone of *chestnut* and *solonetsic* soils. Rainfall deficiency is marked, and winter cold is intense in the south-east. Most of it carries seasonal grazing, though the grasses and other herbaceous plants do not form a continuous covering as in the true steppe, but tend to grow in tufts, with patches of bare earth between them. Towards the south-east in the lower reaches of the Volga and Ural rivers large areas are almost completely devoid of vegetation, and throughout the zone a good deal of the surface is impregnated with salts of various kinds where only a few salt-loving plants can survive. The many sand-dunes also have a scanty but specialised flora. The characteristic soils are known as *Chestnut*, but their colour is greyish brown, resembling the bark of the Spanish chestnut tree and not the colour of horse-chestnuts, which the name perhaps suggests to American readers. They are unleached, lime-accumulating soils, and the humus content is moderately high, so that they are relatively fertile under irrigation, though the possibilities of the latter are limited. On the northern *dark chestnut* soils agriculture is feasible without irrigation, but the *lighter chestnut* soils of low humus content and some salinity are but little used for crops. A final bioclimatic area in Europe is the subtropical moist area of the eastern Black Sea – the Sochi–Batumi littoral. Here a former deciduous vegetation has been largely replaced by subtropical crops

– yielding, for example, tea and tung oil, and is marked by *red/yellow podzolic* soils.

## REFERENCES

A work of synthesis of the vegetation of Europe is still awaited. Students may consult J. Schmithüsen, *Allgemeine Vegetationsgeographie*, Berlin, Gruyter, 1959, especially the map, page 171. M. I. Newbigin, *Plant and Animal Geography*, London, Methuen, latest reprint 1960, discusses many concepts in plant geography, though on a floristic and taxonomic basis rather than referring to the vegetation and ecology. L. Aario, *Biologische Geographie*, Braunschweig, Westermann, 1958, is a useful elementary summary, see pp. 32–46 and 65–78. A more advanced text is J. Braun-Blanquet, *Plant Sociology*, London, McGraw-Hill, 1932, parts v and vi.

Two full studies of the forests of northern Europe are E. Hulten, *Atlas över Växternas Utbredning i Norden*, Stockholm, GLA Forläg, 1950; and H. Sjörs, *Nordisk Växtgeografi*, Stockholm, GLA Forläg, 1956. Also on forest clearing, H. C. Darby, 'The Clearing of the Woodland in Europe', in *Man's Role in Changing the Face of the Earth*, Chicago, 1955, ed. W. L. Thomas, pp. 183–216.

The soils of Europe are studied in W. L. Kubiena, *Soils of Europe, Diagnosis and Systematics*, London, Murby, 1953; R. Tavernier, 'La Carte des Sols de l'Europe', *Pédologie*, x, 2, Gand, 1960, 324–47; and in Ph. Duchaufour, *Précis de Pédologie*, Paris, Masson, 1960. A fine study of the soils of temperate Europe, with coloured profiles, is E. Mückenhausen, *Entstehung, Eigenschaft und Systematik der Böden der Bundesrepublik Deutschland*, Frankfurt a.M., DLG Verlag, 1962.

On the physical basis of agriculture in Europe, the two most relevant works are J. Papadakis, *Agricultural Geography of the World*, Buenos Aires, 1952; and J. C. J. Mohrmann and J. Kessler, *Water Deficiencies in European Agriculture*, Wageningen, International Institute for Land Reclamation and Improvement, 1959.

On the cultural and economic aspects of agriculture, see P. M. Lamartine Yates, *Food, Land and Manpower in Western Europe*, London, Macmillan, 1960; and B. Oury, *L'Agriculture au Seuil du Marché Commun*, Paris, Presses Universitaires, 1959. The maps in *Agricultural Regions of the E.E.C.*, published by the OEEC, Paris, 1960, are also aids to the understanding of the agricultural scene.

### CHAPTER 4

# LANGUAGES, NATIONALITIES
# AND STATES

THE human geography of Europe reveals mosaic patterns and numerous complexities which are the outcome of its prolonged history. Europe stands among the Old World continents which first provided a home to man: its earliest known human occupants lived precariously and in extremely small numbers, in the cold lands south of the ice sheets of the Pleistocene period from times as remote as about 500,000 years ago. These were men of breeds which became extinct, and the real precursors of the European peoples of today, our biological ancestors, were immigrants during times relatively recent which began with the retreat northwards of the Fenno-Scandian ice-sheets and the amelioration of Europe's regional climates. As woodlands spread northwards from southern Europe, thus providing habitats for a varied fauna, men too immigrated from north Africa, to be followed during later millennia by many others, above all from the east. *Homo sapiens* proved himself very mobile and the successive streams of mankind, who moved into Europe and eventually established themselves there in sedentary settlements, can be only broadly envisaged in the light of archaeological research. It is possible to distinguish the advances in culture which were effected at different times in the different parts of the Continent; it is as yet impossible to disentangle the 'races' which intermingled in Europe to form the ancestors of its present peoples.

**Races and Ethnic Types.** A word or two may first be said to clarify the popular confusion which may still exist about the terms 'race' and 'ethnic type'. 'Race' refers to biological groups of mankind which desirably we would wish to distinguish. The idea of a 'pure race' or 'pure races' from which European peoples have derived finds no support in scientific studies, for what seems most evidently true is that men in Europe, as elsewhere, all belonging to one subspecies (*Homo sapiens*), have continually intermingled. It is possible that the study of human blood groups, which began in the 1920s, may throw a much clearer light on the antecedents and relationships of European peoples, yet it must be admitted that such scientific knowledge would probably have no obvious bearing on the remarkable differences among the European peoples today which are ascribable to more evident and understandable differentials – of language, nationality, history, geography, and culture. Similarly, the study of 'ethnic types', to which some anthropologists have given much attention, has little relevance to the peculiar social divisions which now characterise the Continent.

Studies of 'ethnic types', which are concerned solely with the physical characteristics of individuals, make it possible to establish specific types on the basis of certain average features, such as skull shape, stature, and of skin, hair, and eye colour. Nothing can be claimed as to the relationship of such types to particular languages and nationalities; nor indeed can anything be firmly concluded as to the relationship of specific ethnic types to specific races which may have existed in the past. It is of interest, if only for descriptive purposes, to know the distinguishable features of the Nordic, Alpine, and Mediterranean ethnic types, but these types are based on averages which individuals necessarily only in some degree represent. The people of all the major nation states of Europe include a great variety of physical types. For instance, the people of France include a sprinkling of fair, longheaded individuals in the north, a large body of broadheads in the middle, and a sprinkling of rather dark-skinned longheads in the south. The Germans show just as much variety, while the Italians, far from belonging entirely to the Mediterranean type, as might be imagined, are largely broadheaded, although their coloration varies from very brunette in the south to a considerable amount of blondness in the north. Conversely no political grouping possesses a monopoly of any particular physical type, although it is well known that the belief, however mistakenly held by a group of people, that they are of homogeneous race, has often fostered their sense of cohesion, or in other words, their national spirit. Similarly, it may be recalled that so-called 'ethnographic maps' have often been used in support of political claims, although they have usually shown merely language distributions.

It will have been gathered from the above that ethnic types do not correspond with national, linguistic, or political groupings. The evidence of blood group investigations reveals a similar lack of identity between blood groups and cultural or political distributions. On passing from east to west in Europe there is seen to be a gradual change in the proportion of people belonging to the four main blood groups. This grouping does not correspond with any frontiers; for instance, there is a closer resemblance in the blood group relationships of the peoples of south-eastern Germany and of the Danubian lands (Czechs, Hungarians, etc.) than between those of south-eastern and north-western Germany.

**Languages and Language Patterns.** Beyond doubt linguistic differences sharply divide the peoples of Europe, even though most of their languages belong to one family, the Indo-European. Despite the fact that at particular stages in the past men appear to have migrated freely and intermingled, sedentary communities long lived in some aloofness from each other, their settled areas being separated by stretches of forest, marsh, or mountain, in days when the means of transport were rudimentary, slow and dangerous. Thus many distinct tongues differentiated from the Indo-European speech which is believed to have become virtually uniform throughout the Continent after the influx of people of Bronze Age culture from the eastern steppes in the second millennium B.C.

The Indo-European language family is represented in Europe by seven distinct groups – the Celtic, Germanic, Romance, Slav, Baltic, Hellenic, and Thraco-Illyrian. The Celtic language survives among a small number of people in western Europe, and deliberate efforts are made to preserve it in the Republic of Ireland and in Wales. The Germanic group includes, besides German, English, the Scandinavian languages, and Netherlandish (Dutch and Flemish); the Romance includes above all French, Italian, Spanish, Portuguese, and Rumanian, and since all are derived from Latin, they remain as a legacy of ancient Rome. The Slav languages are spoken over a large part of the Continent since within this group fall Russian, the closely allied Ukrainian, Polish, Czech, Slovak, Serbo-Croat, Bulgarian, and a few others. The Baltic group of archaic Indo-European languages is represented today by Lithuanian and Latvian, while the Hellenic survives in modern Greek, and the Thraco-Illyrian in Albania. Languages other than Indo-European are spoken by many different people, numerically small, and mainly in eastern Europe. Thus Ural-Altaic languages are spoken in Finland (Finnish), Hungary (Magyar), and in European USSR, where Estonian, Mordvinian, Komi, Udmurt, Mari, Vogul, Ostyak, and Nentsy are distinguished as national languages within this group. Lastly it may be noted that a Semitic language (Maltese) established itself in the Maltese islands, and that the very ancient Basque language persists in north-east Spain.

The emergence and present distribution of the languages of Europe is evidently the outcome of historical processes long operative under specific environmental conditions. That Europe has become so polyglot has no less evident social importance, since language imposes a severe obstacle to common understanding and, moreover, became a symbol of national sentiment. Fig. 13 indicates how Europe's language patterns are relatively simple in the west, north, and south, but become increasingly complex in east-central Europe as also in European USSR, especially astride and beyond

the Volga river.    The pattern of language, as also of nationality, in
what has been called the Shatter Zone of east-central Europe is,
however, somewhat less complex as a result of the refugee movements which began towards the end of World War II.    Even in

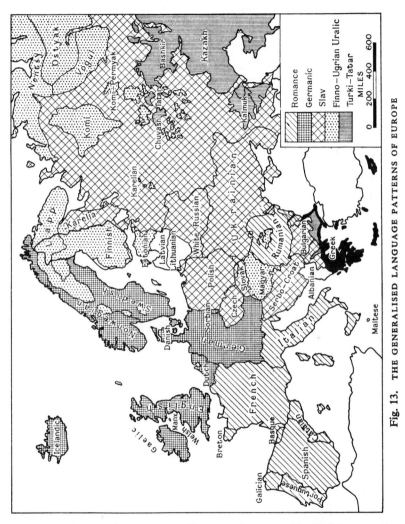

Fig. 13.   THE GENERALISED LANGUAGE PATTERNS OF EUROPE

western Europe in some small countries, notably Belgium and
Switzerland, language groupings, although not complex, are sharply
defined, and in the former country are politically significant in
reflecting basic differences of view.

Europe is thus much divided on ground of language, yet its division is made even deeper by the comparable divisions caused both by nationality and by political organisation, each of which call for brief discussion.

**Nationality and Nationalism.** At the present day the greater part of Europe is organised politically on a national basis, in contrast to that which persisted widely there until times as recent as sixty years ago. When World War I started in 1914 many of the distinguishable nations of Europe were organised over a wide area within imperial states which were essentially multi-national in character. These were the Russian, Austro-Hungarian, German, and Ottoman (Turkish) empires, while to most Irishmen the United Kingdom no less appeared to be an imperialist organisation. The idea that nationality should find expression politically in independent statehood is a relatively modern and revolutionary idea which originated in Europe and has spread widely throughout the world.

The connotations of nationality are so complex and variable that mere definition of this term is a difficult matter. Many nationalities, well enough recognised, lived together within the Roman Empire without consciously seeking special status on ground of nationality, and such wider loyalties, as to the Russian tsars and to the Habsburg emperors of Austro-Hungary, long made possible the survival of civilised and extensive multi-national states. The development of national spirit and of the strong belief that a national group should live politically apart are concepts and political forces of nineteenth-century Europe, which were long resisted and held in check as dangerously disruptive of the existing order.

Nationalism proved so strong a force that it overcame all opposition. It springs from the idea that a nation group possesses coherence and solidarity as a result of generations of living together within a homeland, speaking the same language (or languages), and sharing similar modes of life and traditions. This feeling of group-consciousness is not wholly new; national consciousness seems to have emerged in England and France, for example, during the Hundred Years' War when English was becoming the language of the ruling classes in England in place of French. Before that time the old Roman idea of the unity of the civilised world and the dream of reviving the old Roman Empire in the new guise of the Holy Roman Empire were still cherished for many centuries, especially by the Church, which wished to see a peaceful Europe in which all men should be citizens of Christendom: a noble ideal, but one which was doomed to failure in the presence of many semi-barbaric groups and in the absence of any adequate system of communication and transport. The germ of the national spirit may be traced in many countries in the late Middle Ages: it may be regarded as a development from patriotism, which is merely the love of country and the will to defend it.  The germ of the national spirit may be discerned in Dante's aspirations for a united Italy, but the sword was all powerful and the imperial or dynastic idea usually prevailed.  The new twist to the idea of nationality, which gave rise to nationalism, came in the nineteenth century with the notion that those who wanted to join together in a national group had a definite right to do so, a democratic idea to be connected with the spread of the French revolutionary doctrine that men had rights as well as duties.  At the end of the Napoleonic Wars in 1815, only seven of the present-day states of Europe, namely the United Kingdom, France, Spain, Portugal, Denmark, Switzerland, and multi-national Russia (now the USSR) had something like their present limits, and the remainder, numbering twenty-eight (including four microstates), existing today, were either non-existent then or very different in extent.  Belgium and Holland in 1839 were the first of the new states to achieve their present outlines, Italy became united in 1861, the German Empire in 1871, Greece, Serbia, and Rumania won their independence from the Turks during the nineteenth century, Sweden and Norway separated in 1905, and the remaining newcomers to the political map of Europe mainly appeared after 1918.

**The Political Division of Europe.**  It should not be assumed that all the states of Europe are single-nation states or that their areas are coterminous with those occupied by distinct nationalities.  Nor is the political pattern so simple that any one state has only one language, and one spoken only there.  While the trend, well marked by the political settlement after World War I, has been increasingly to recognise the political claims of well-organised and articulate national groups, there are many cases where the simple formula of one nation one state does not apply.  On the one hand, the USSR has contrived, while recognising national groups and according to them specific status and rights, to organise them within one large-scale and federal multi-national Union.  On the other, many states perforce include nationalities other than the one which is numerically dominant; striking illustrations are provided by the United Kingdom, Czechoslovakia, Yugoslavia, Rumania, and Italy.  Similarly, although states tend to have one dominant and widely spoken language, they tend also to contain communities speaking other tongues.  Thus Italy contains the German-speaking people of South Tirol and Rumania the Magyar communities within Transylvania; France has German-speaking Alsatians, Italian-speaking Corsicans, Bretons speaking their Celtic tongue, and even small numbers speaking Basque.  In European USSR, besides the widely spoken Russian,

many other languages are spoken and used in publications, including
newspapers. Some languages are used outside their principal habitats. In the Republic of Ireland the use of English persists, although
the Celtic Erse language is preserved as one of two official languages;
German is not only the national language of the two German states
(the German Federal Republic and the German Democratic Republic) which emerged after World War II, but also the principal language of Switzerland which has four official languages. Similarly,
the official language of Luxembourg, another independent state, is
French.

Europe is more politically divided than any other continent: it
concentrates about a quarter of all the independent states of the
world, despite the fact that it occupies only a twelfth of its inhabited
area. The precise total of such states may be put at thirty-five: this
figure includes Turkey, Cyprus, Malta, and West Berlin, and the four
microstates – the Vatican City, Liechtenstein, Monaco, and San
Marino. Although this distributional pattern falls for special study
to political geography, it cannot be ignored by the student of
regional geography. He must perforce take account not only of the
capabilities of each part of Europe as regards productivity, but also
of the many political influences at work in modifying the type of
production, by artificial encouragement or restriction, and in altering
the natural currents of exchange. It was during the interwar years,
1919–39, that political factors had so strong an influence in restricting
freedom of trade between states, each in control of its own economic
affairs.

Europe thus presented, and still does if to a less extent, a sharp
contrast to the United States of America which is comparable to it
in size, populated mainly by the descendants of European nationals,
yet integrated into one state and one market. The United States
had the advantage of starting with all the experience of Europe, and
especially of the most advanced part of Europe, behind it, with
settlers of one dominating speech and tradition. Around this nucleus
the later newcomers of various nationalities gathered, merged and,
being scattered throughout the length and breadth of the country,
seldom formed solid blocks. Moreover, the United States developed
at a time when improvements in the methods of communication and
transport made large administrative units easy to organise. Europe,
on the other hand, had to learn from its own experience, starting
with the disadvantage of a multitude of small groups with different
customs and languages, and each attempt towards unity was interrupted by the incursions of fresh invaders, and frustrated or hindered
throughout by the difficulties of communication before the era of
railways and telegraphs. The frequent presence of mountains,

forest, and swamp enhanced the difficulties of communication and helped to isolate groups, so that communities living only 25 miles apart could develop almost unknown to each other, and many languages evolved and persisted. It is not surprising then that Europe inherited a legacy of separatism and antagonism between its political groups; nor is it surprising that its nations have resisted unification by force such as was attempted by Napoleon, Kaiser Wilhelm II, and Hitler. Even so, there has been recognition since World War II ended that political separatism is not only a hindrance in view of the increasing inter-dependence of economic life but also dangerous from the standpoint of national security.

**Trends towards Unification.**[1] These have manifested themselves alike in western and eastern Europe, reflecting that deep division between, on the one hand, west and south European countries which have joined together with the United States the better to ensure their defence, and on the other, the communist countries of Europe other than Yugoslavia and Albania, which are similarly organised alongside the Soviet Union. Thus the fear of continued Soviet expansion westwards lies behind the creation of the North Atlantic Treaty Organisation in 1949, in which ten (and later thirteen) European states joined with the United States and Canada in a grand alliance for common defence in the hope that at a later stage an Atlantic Community might develop. Similarly the USSR, by the Warsaw Pact of 1955, associated with itself for defence seven communist countries beyond its European frontier. Between these two power blocs lie a number of states which are either clearly neutral in status or at least unaligned: Sweden, Switzerland, Austria, Ireland, Yugoslavia, and Spain. Similarly, in economic affairs advances have been made towards the formation of large associations of states, in order to organise more efficiently and profitably modern industry and trade. Among these may be noted the Organisation for European Co-operation and Development which includes eighteen countries of western Europe, including neutral states. The most dramatic development in western Europe has been the emergence of the European Economic Community which was constituted in 1958, following the earlier successful association of the same six countries in the European Coal and Steel Community (in 1952). EEC is creating a large internal market comprising the territories of France, the German Federal Republic, Belgium, the Netherlands, Luxembourg, and Italy, and may perhaps foreshadow the creation of a federal multi-national state comparable in population and economic resources with the United States. The European Free Trade Association (EFTA), popularly known as the Outer Seven, was designed to

[1] See Postscript, and Appendix J, p. 636.

promote trade, and does not imply any movement towards political integration. In eastern Europe the most striking association of states for economic purposes is the Council for Mutual Economic Aid (Comecon) which, set up in 1949, has provided the means by which the satellite countries of the USSR – Poland, Czechoslovakia, Eastern Germany, Hungary, Rumania, and Bulgaria – can integrate their economic plans, as indeed they did those for the 1959–65 Plan period.

Thus Europe remains 'an astoundingly riven structure'; too much history has been enacted there to permit the development easily and rapidly of that broad sense of community on which ultimate union may be built. Certainly new ideas challenge the usefulness of the self-contained sovereign state and foster increasingly wide associations for specific purposes, even though the Continent remains sharply divided into its 'western' and 'communist' sectors. It follows that a regional geography of Europe must still take careful note of its political compartments. Hence in this book, against the physical background of the region within which they lie, the various countries will be separately discussed.

## REFERENCES

A small and competent introduction is J. S. Huxley and A. C. Haddon, *We Europeans*, London, Jonathan Cape, 1935. G. M. Morant's *The Races of Central Europe: A Footnote to History*, London, Allen & Unwin; New York, W. W. Norton, 1940, makes special reference to blood groups. C. S. Coon's *The Races of Europe*, New York, The Macmillan Co., 1939, is the modern successor to W. L. Ripley's *Races of Europe*, London, 1899. H. J. Fleure's *The Peoples of Europe*, Oxford, is brief and useful.

On the languages of Europe, see L. Dominian, *The Frontiers of Nationality and Language in Europe*, New York, Henry Holt, 1917; H. Munro Chadwick, *The Nationalities of Europe*, Cambridge University Press, 1945, and A. Meillet, *Les Langues dans l'Europe Nouvelle*, 2nd ed. revised, Paris, Payot, 1928.

On the political geography of Europe, see I. Bowman, *The New World: Problems in Political Geography*, 4th ed. 1928 for the territorial settlement made after World War I, and W. G. East and A. E. Moodie (Eds.), *The Changing World: Studies in Political Geography*, 1956, which in Chapters 1–8 and 14–18 discusses the problems of Europe and the USSR after World War II: both published New York, The World Book Co.; London, Harrap.

G. W. Hoffman (Ed.), *A Geography of Europe*, 2nd ed., New York, The Ronald Press, and London, Methuen, 1961 may be consulted on the historical background (Chapter 2) and on Europe's place in the world (Chapter 10).

On the historical geography, see W. G. East, *An Historical Geography of Europe*, London, Methuen and New York, Dutton, 4th ed. revised, 1962.

# PART II

# REGIONAL GEOGRAPHY

## *SECTION I – SOUTHERN EUROPE*

### CHAPTER 5

## GENERAL INTRODUCTION TO SOUTHERN EUROPE

SOUTHERN Europe, as here conceived, consists essentially of the lands bordering the northern side of the Mediterranean Sea, with the exception of Asia Minor. Its long history and its paramount contribution to western civilisation increase the fascination of the Mediterranean as an area in which to study the interaction of the natural endowment and human effort. The climate and its vegetational accompaniment provide a strong unifying element within the basin which tends to evoke a common agricultural response and a common way of life, but within this unity there is an infinite diversity – between the coast and the interior, between island and mainland, and between the plain and the highland. In the south, desert conditions present a challenge and sharpen the ancient conflict between the interests of the pastoralist and those of the settled cultivator. In the north, particularly in northern Iberia and northern Italy, where the rainfall is highest in summer and the temperatures reflect the influence of the Atlantic and of continental Europe respectively, the climate varies so widely from the Mediterranean 'norm' as to present a geographical environment which is Mediterranean only by association.

Another feature which is common to the northern Mediterranean coastlands is their high proportion of hilly and mountainous land. To the north the almost continuous mountain obstacle, although of considerable climatic significance, has proved less of an effective protection against invasion than a serious obstacle to legitimate movement, which until recently has been concentrated in a small number of gaps and easy passes. In the peninsulas themselves the extreme fragmentation of relief has interposed wild and extensive mountain blocks between very limited areas of fertile lowland. In ancient times the landward isolation of these

more fortunate tracts may well have provided a favourable environment for the development of civilisation in the form of the city state,
whose founders arrived by sea and preserved a seaward outlook, but
the absence of major centres has hindered modern political and social
evolution and, indeed, in the case of Iberia and, much later, of Italy,
political unity was imposed from an extra-Mediterranean base.
Within these modern states the fragmentation of relief and the isolation it imposes are still an obstacle to unity and a constant encouragement to separatist, or at least regional, sentiment.   The
only period in history when the whole of the northern Mediterranean
coastlands were under one political administration was that of the
Roman Empire when a network of roads and well-protected seaways
triumphed over the fragmentation of the whole basin; the *Pax
Romana* provided a blessed pause in the area's turbulent story during
which the contributions to civilisation of Greek, Hebrew, and Roman
could be assimilated, consolidated, and eventually dispersed by
means of Rome's extra-Mediterranean conquests, to leaven the barbarian world.   Although the political unity of the Empire was
shattered for ever, the roots of Mediterranean civilisation survived
to sprout anew in an ecclesiastical form and later as the major
inspiration of the revival of learning.   Much more damaging than
the Germanic invasions to the unity of the Basin was the loss of the
southern and eastern shores to the Arabs and later the Turks, which
introduced a new and lasting cultural and religious cleavage within
the area.   Europe itself was not immune; much of Iberia was occupied for over six hundred years and the Arabs ruled Sicily for over
a century.   In these two areas, under the tolerant despotism of local
rulers, the civilisations of East and West were able to make contact
for a brief period, with profound results for the cultural and scientific
advance of Europe.

Some students of the scene are impressed by the succession of
brilliant civilisations which have flourished in the Mediterranean
only to be forcibly overthrown or to fall relentlessly into decay; the
graph of progress consists, as it were, of a series of peaks each falling
back to a barely inclined base level.   In this they see an essential
fragility in the character of the Mediterranean civilisation which,
although it finds expression in the city, is based on agriculture.
Whether or not we fully accept this view, there is undoubtedly an
element of instability in the Mediterranean geographical environment, which has militated against steady and sustained progress,
particularly in the field of agriculture.   The evergreen-oak woodlands of the European coastlands and islands were easily cleared
and converted into arable land or pasture; unfortunately the land
which yielded so easily soon began to be exhausted.   In time a

disastrous sequence set in: deforestation, soil erosion, flooding, and finally the destruction of the drainage in the productive plains below and the development of malarial marsh. The process was accelerated by the steep terrain, the erodibility of the exposed rock surfaces, the torrential rainfall and the pressure of population. At an early date settlement was forced to abandon the coastal plains (Agro Pontino, Maremma, the coastlands of Greece and of Ionian Italy) and population tended to be unnaturally concentrated in the hill-lands above, which themselves were harried by erosion. In fact, in spite of the ingenuity with which the peasant in many areas has adapted his methods to the physical conditions, the Mediterranean lands, for two millennia, have been suffering from a wasting disease whose effect has been to ruin both upland and plain alike. Fortunately, for the first time in history, the governments of the areas concerned now possess the means to face the major problem, one of water control – control to prevent flooding, for irrigation, for power, and for domestic and industrial purposes. In this respect the essential unit is the catchment basin; without control in the uplands, reclamation of the plains, which plays such an important part in the agricultural colonisation schemes of Italy, Spain, and Greece, is inevitably threatened.

Although these inherent difficulties in the Mediterranean environment manifested themselves so early in the history of the area, their stultifying effects are perhaps more clearly apparent from the sixteenth century onwards when, compared with western Europe, the Mediterranean entered on a period of economic stagnation and political eclipse. While the transoceanic discoveries were turning the Mediterranean into a backwater and shifting the commercial centre of gravity of Europe to the north and west, the Turks had occupied Greece and the Balkans, and their auxiliaries on the Barbary coast were terrorising the shores of Mediterranean Europe and were the cause of a further shift of population away from the coastlands to defensive and often inconvenient sites inland.

In the nineteenth century security was restored to the Mediterranean for the first time in fifteen hundred years, Greece and Italy emerged as nation states and, with the opening of the Suez canal, the former backwater became a busy highway. But these developments served only to throw into relief the stagnation of all but a few favoured regions of the countries of southern Europe. Their economies remained in chains to backward forms of agriculture and were weighed down by the burden of overpopulation. While the north of Europe was being transformed by industry, the countries of southern Europe, lacking water power, coal, raw materials, and techniques, and handicapped by the poverty of the home market,

## 54 EUROPE

found themselves once more at a marked disadvantage. In these circumstances it is not surprising that hundreds of thousands of despairing Italians, Spaniards, Portuguese, and Greeks seized the opportunities offered by emigration to the New World.

Although within each state the standard of living varies widely from region to region, as well as from class to class, taken as a whole the southern European countries are still a long way from catching up their northern neighbours. Since the end of the second world war, however, they have made extraordinary progress. Vast sums have been invested in reafforestation, marsh reclamation, colonisation schemes, and the fundamental rehabilitation of the land. The water resources are being thoroughly controlled for power and irrigation and Italy at least must now be recognised as a major industrial nation. The shortage of coal is no longer the handicap it once was since it can be cheaply imported from the United States and elsewhere. Even more important, oil is easily available from the Near East, North Africa, and the USSR, and the southern European ports compete with those of the Atlantic and North Sea as suppliers of oil to the European industrial interior. The prospects for cheap energy are enhanced by the proximity of the vast deposits of gas now being exploited in North Africa. With the general rise in European living standards, the Mediterranean coasts, once the preserve of the rich, are becoming the playground of the masses, to the great benefit of the balance of payments of the countries receiving them. Emigration still provides a powerful stream (directed as much to Europe as to the traditional receiving countries overseas), but it tends to be a movement prompted less by despair than by enterprise.

This is not to suggest that Mediterranean Europe is on its way to recovering its former pre-eminence in Europe; rather it is a plea for the rejection of the view that its economy and society are static, a view of the area which has persisted too long.

### REFERENCES

A recent illustrated study is D. S. Walker, *The Mediterranean Lands*, London, Methuen, 1962; M. I. Newbigin, *Southern Europe*, 3rd ed. revised by R. J. Harrison Church, London, Methuen, 1949, is a standard work in English. The same author's *Mediterranean Lands*, London, Methuen, 1924, deals mainly with the historical geography of the region in ancient times. E. C. Semple, *The Geography of the Mediterranean Region: its Relation to Ancient History*, New York, Holt, 1931, embodies historico-geographical researches. A. Philippson, *Das Mittelmeergebiet*, Leipzig, 1904, 4th ed., 1922, is a standard German work, Chapter 1 of which gives references on structure. W. G. East, *An Historical Geography of Europe*, 4th ed. revised, London, Methuen, 1962, describes the human geography of Europe at successive periods from the Roman Empire onwards and may profitably be consulted for western and central Europe. See also N. J. G. Pounds, *Europe and the Mediterranean*, New York, McGraw-Hill, 1953; J, M. Houston, *The Western Mediterranean World*.

### CHAPTER 6

# ITALY

THE Italian peninsula may be looked upon as the most Mediterranean in character of all the three southern peninsulas. Mediterranean influences permeate the region more fully than in the South-eastern peninsula or even in the Iberian peninsula, largely owing to its long and narrow shape. In climate, especially, it is more Mediterranean than the other two peninsulas. In the South-eastern peninsula only on the Dinaric coast does the Mediterranean climate extend as far north as in Italy, and the reason for this northward extension is essentially the same in both cases, i.e. the coastal character. Peninsular Italy is so long and narrow and so open to sea winds that it may be looked upon as climatically *all* coastal. It is too narrow to develop a marked pressure system of its own, but comes under the influence of pressure variations over the Tyrrhenian and Adriatic Seas, so that, whereas Niš in the interior of the South-eastern peninsula has a continental climate, Florence in the same latitude in the interior of peninsular Italy has a Mediterranean one.

Although the Mediterranean type of climate extends as far north as Genoa (44½° N), yet nearly a third of Italy lies outside the region of Mediterranean climate, both the North Italian Plain and the Italian Alps falling within the climatic region of central Europe, with cold winters and the absence of a dry season. Northern Italy, however, is not so remote from other types of Mediterranean influence as the interior of the South-eastern and Iberian peninsulas, since the plain of the Po opens widely to the Adriatic, and there is also a relatively easy outlet to the Mediterranean over the narrow Ligurian Alps. The names of Venice and Genoa call to mind the long history of the Mediterranean trading routes and their landward continuations over the North Italian Plain and the Alps. Moreover, Mediterranean culture and the Latin language spread over the great plain of northern Italy in classical times more thoroughly than the Greek language and culture were ever able to spread over the difficult mountainous interior of the South-eastern peninsula, and, what is more important, Mediterranean culture and a language based on Latin have managed to retain their hold in spite of repeated invasions from across the Alps.

**Relief and Structure.**    Italy falls into three main structural regions (see Fig. 14): (*a*) the folded Alpine zone which is dealt with in the section on the Alps (see Chapter 25), (*b*) the North Italian Plain or Plain of the Po, an area of young undisturbed sediments, (*c*) the folded Apennine zone, which comprises almost the whole of the

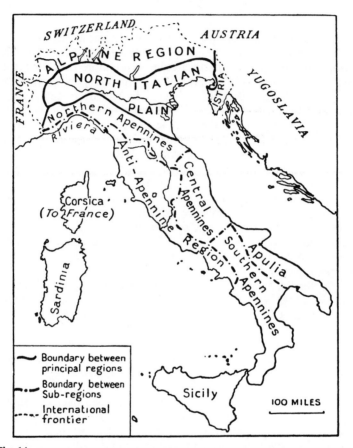

Fig. 14.  ITALY SHOWING THE MORE IMPORTANT NATURAL REGIONS

Italian peninsula, Sicily, and the adjacent islands.    The exact tectonic affinities of Sardinia are not very clear, but the island may be treated as part of a 'median mass' (see p. 10), together with the similar island of Corsica, which is politically French.    Among the minor structural elements are the little disturbed limestone platforms of the Murge and Gargano and the small area immediately behind Trieste which falls within the Dinaric system.

Although the Apennines are a comparatively simple mountain system, yet they have had a fairly long and complicated geological history.   At least two main periods of folding are distinguishable.

*(after O. Maull)*

Fig. 15.   STRUCTURAL DIAGRAM OF ITALY

The first occurred in early Tertiary times (late Eocene and early Oligocene) and involved principally the Mesozoic limestones of

'Tethys.' This was followed not only by pronounced denudation, but also by a retrogressive movement which caused the mass to sink below the sea in mid-Tertiary times (early and middle Miocene), during which period sands, marls, and clays were deposited. A second period of folding in late Miocene times, which involved these sands, marls, and clays, often known as Flysch, was followed by a second sinking, and at the end of the Tertiary period the northern and central Apennines were deeply penetrated by arms of the sea, while the southern Apennines were represented by an archipelago of small islands only. The subsequent re-elevation, which took place at the end of the Tertiary period, was epeirogenic in character. (See Chapter 1.) There was a general upward movement *en masse* which brought to light the clays, sands, marls, and conglomerates which had been deposited in the shallow seas and straits between and around the main folds. These Pliocene sediments are found as high as 3,900 ft in Aspromonte (Calabria) but they have suffered only minor warping; they cover much of Tuscany and form a continuous strip of dissected hill country from Monferrato to Basilicata which is very different in character from the folded Apennines proper. The post-Pliocene uplift was accompanied by widespread faulting and this was associated with severe vulcanism, especially on the side bordering the Tyrrhenian Sea, which is about three times as deep as the Adriatic (*c.* 9,000 ft, as against *c.* 3,000 ft maximum depth), and where consequently earth stresses are particularly great. Vesuvius, the only active volcano of the European mainland, lies on the Tyrrhenian side, and there are large tracts of land on either side of the river Tiber which are built up of volcanic material. The Lipari Islands, in the south-east of the Tyrrhenian Sea, include the small island of Vulcano which gave its name as a generic title for this type of mountain. Mt Etna and Monte Vulture are the only evidence of recent vulcanism lying on the eastern side of the Apennine folds. The numerous earthquakes of southern Italy, for example at Messina in 1908 and at Avezzano in 1915, demonstrate that earth movements are not yet at an end in the Apennine system.

The backbone of the peninsula contains the severely folded rocks of the early and mid-Tertiary foldings, and these stand out as the main ridges of the peninsula, largely owing to the presence of much resistant limestone. In the northern Apennines, however, the main chains are largely composed of Flysch and similar rocks, which weather more easily than the limestones and form lower and more dissected chains. Few parts of the Apennines show a really Alpine or high-mountain character, though the preponderance of limestones, combined with severe erosion, helps to give a wild appearance.

There was relatively little Quaternary glaciation, the best example of the resultant Alpine forms being in the mass of the Gran Sasso d'Italia (9,560 ft). Geologists have recently recognised *nappes* in the Apennines but they have little geographical significance.

The main Apennine chains swing in a wide curve from the Gulf of Genoa across the peninsula towards the Adriatic, enclosing between themselves and the Tyrrhenian Sea the hilly area known as the Anti-Apennine region, which includes within it, the volcanic zone of Latium and Campania. In Tuscany, the region consists mainly of lightly folded Tertiary sandstones and clays but incorporates fragments of older rocks, mainly Permian limestones, in the Catena Metallifera Toscana, Montagnola, and the Spezia and Argentario peninsulas. On the other flank of the Apennines the land falls to the sea through a belt of Miocene and Pliocene sediments which have been deeply incised by a number of short consequent rivers to form a complicated foothill zone; this is sometimes referred to as the Adriatic Sub-Apennines. The main Apennine chains cross over once again to the western side, leaving on the east in Apulia a limestone platform, which was not involved in the Apennine folding, but was raised *en masse* with the second, or later Tertiary, upward movement. On the south the chains run up against the crystalline masses which fill up almost the whole of Calabria. A similar, but smaller, crystalline mass forms the north-east corner of Sicily, but disappears westwards under the Apennine folds which border the northern coast of that island. In Sicily, young volcanic deposits are found exceptionally on the outer, here the southern, side of the arc. The rest of southern Sicily is taken up by young Tertiary material similar to that on the eastern slope of the eastern Apennines in peninsular Italy.

The Apennine chains are fairly easily penetrated by means of depressions, which were formerly occupied by arms of the sea or by lakes. Fig. 16 shows the main features of the present complex river system in the central and Anti-Apennines, with its remarkable series of longitudinal valleys. The Pliocene lake-basins have been considerably dissected, but nearly all the longitudinal valleys were occupied by lakes in geologically recent times, mainly because the Anti-Apennine region rose rather more quickly than the main chains and blocked the westward drainage of the Apennine streams, and also because volcanic material sometimes dammed up the passage of the river water. These longitudinal valleys afford easy communication among high and rugged mountain country, which would otherwise be difficult to penetrate.

Sardinia also contains several areas of young volcanic material, notably from Monte Ferru northwards. The crystalline fragments found in the Tuscan archipelago, in Elba for example, are widely regarded as remnants of a foundered 'median mass', but some authorities are impressed with their similarity with the interior crystalline blocks of the western Alps.

North of the Apennines lies the geosyncline of the North Italian

Fig. 16.   CENTRAL ITALY: MORPHOLOGICAL DIAGRAM

Plain.   It is evident that in late Tertiary times the shallow Adriatic Sea extended far west of its present limits, but a slight elevation, coupled with tremendous deposits of waste material from the bordering mountains, brought the present plain into being.   Most of the material composing the plain is derived from the Alps rather than the Apennines owing to the greater height of the former range; in consequence, there is generally a slight slope southwards as well as eastwards, so that the River Po flows nearer the southern than the northern border for the greater part of its course through the plain. Even this tranquil zone of plain shows some evidences of disturbances in two tiny groups of Tertiary volcanic hills, the Monti Berici and Monti Euganei.

**Climate.** The fundamental climatic divide in Italy lies along the northern Apennines; northwards the climate is basically a warmer variant of the central European type, while southwards it is essentially Mediterranean. In summer, when the Tropical Continental airmass tends to be dominant, there is a marked uniformity of temperature throughout the country (July means: Naples 75° F (24° C), Milan 75° F) and the significant variations from it are introduced less by latitude than by altitude and to a minor extent by proximity to the sea. Everywhere at low levels there is a long, warm growing period suitable for a wide variety of crops including maize, rice, and the more delicate temperate fruits. Whether in fact they are grown depends largely on the availability of water either directly from the atmosphere or from irrigation. In this respect the Northern Plain and the Alps are more fortunate since they enjoy a well distributed rainfall throughout the summer half-year and are well supplied with irrigation water. In origin the northern rainfall is partly convectional, particularly in the late summer, and partly cyclonic since the area is frequently invaded by Polar Maritime air. Mediterranean Italy, on the other hand, lies to the south of the main depression tracks and experiences a summer drought which is increasingly prolonged towards the south. Its effect is somewhat reduced in mountainous areas where evaporation is less, but at lower altitudes the vegetation is markedly xerophytic (evergreen oak, cork oak, Aleppo pine, stone pine) and, unless irrigation is available, the growing period for field crops is confined to winter and spring.

Whereas in summer the contrast between northern and southern Italy is mainly one of precipitation, in winter it is mainly one of temperature. The Northern Plain is somewhat cut off by relief from the mild western Mediterranean influences and is frequently visited by cool, humid Atlantic air or by drier, colder Polar Continental air. In calm anticyclonic periods cold air drains from the Alps causing temperature inversion so that raw, foggy weather is frequently experienced on the plain. When a pronounced pressure gradient builds up at the head of the Adriatic, an occurrence sometimes associated with barrier depressions, the area is visited by a cold blustering wind, the *bora*, which because of its descent is dry and is accompanied by clear skies.  Cool air-streams from the same quarter sometimes penetrate to the west of the peninsula itself (the *tramontana*).  Sheltered zones to the lee of the Alps, especially near the larger lakes, are notably milder than the plain (January means: Salò 39° F, 4° C, Piacenza 32° F, 0° C) and the influence of the Adriatic is shown in the winter temperature means along its shores (January mean: Venice 37° F, 2·8° C).  Winters in Mediterranean Italy are mild but this trait should not be exaggerated.  There are frequent incursions of cold continental air which are most severely felt on the Adriatic coast, and commercial citrus cultivation is risky north of Campania.  Winters in the high Apennines are severe and snow usually caps the summits till May.  The Ligurian Riviera, open to marine influences and sheltered from the north, is an especially favoured area (January mean: Genoa 47° F, 8° C).

In the winter half-year Mediterranean Italy shares in the precipitation which the north enjoys throughout the year.  In the South the régime shows a simple winter peak which is partly attributable to depressions of Atlantic origin passing on a southerly course. The southerly wind at the front of such depressions sometimes imports Saharan air into southern Italy especially in spring; this is the *scirocco*.  It is moistened by its passage over the sea and the atmosphere is warm, dust-laden, and enervating.  Where the southerly air-stream is forced to descend, for example on to the north coast of Sicily, a very rapid rise in temperature may occur with desiccating results on delicate crops at a critical period.  Further north most of the depressions are generated within the Mediterranean area along the divergence of modified Tropical Continental air and Polar Maritime air, i.e. along the Mediterranean front.  Here incursions of cold, humid air entering the Mediterranean through the Carcassonne and Rhône corridors meet warmer air over the Ligurian and Tyrrhenian seas to form depressions in which the cold front at the rear is particularly well developed.  The development of depressions is further encouraged by the barrier effect of the Alps acting on cold fronts swinging in from the north-west.  In consequence lee depressions frequently develop over the Ligurian Sea and the Po valley, particularly in autumn which is the peak rainfall period for the north and centre of the peninsula and most of the Northern Plain.  Lee depressions are also responsible for the *maestral*, a cold violent wind from the northern quarter experienced on the Ligurian coastlands.  Everywhere in Italy there is a clear correlation between precipitation and the height and orientation of relief, and in the Mediterranean zone in particular the precipitation tends to occur in the form of sharp destructive showers punctuated by long sunny periods when much of the benefit of the rainfall is lost by evaporation. A further handicap of the South is the unreliability of the rainfall from year to year.

MEAN MONTHLY AND ANNUAL RAINFALL IN INCHES AND MILLIMETRES

| Station | Alt. | Jan. | Feb. | Mar. | Apr. | May | June | July | Aug. | Sep. | Oct. | Nov. | Dec. | Total |
|---|---|---|---|---|---|---|---|---|---|---|---|---|---|---|
| Milan | 397 ft | 2·4 | 2·1 | 2·8 | 3·2 | 2·8 | 2·7 | 1·9 | 2·2 | 2·6 | 3·0 | 3·6 | 2·8 | 32·1 |
| | 121 m | 62 | 54 | 72 | 82 | 70 | 68 | 47 | 57 | 66 | 75 | 90 | 71 | 814 |
| Venice | 10 ft | 2·3 | 1·5 | 2·9 | 3·0 | 2·8 | 2·9 | 1·4 | 1·9 | 2·8 | 2·6 | 3·0 | 2·1 | 28·3 |
| | 3 m | 58 | 39 | 74 | 77 | 72 | 73 | 37 | 48 | 71 | 66 | 75 | 54 | 744 |
| Genoa | 69 ft | 4·3 | 4·1 | 4·0 | 3·2 | 2·4 | 1·7 | 1·4 | 2·4 | 2·5 | 5·3 | 8·1 | 4·4 | 43·8 |
| | 21 m | 109 | 105 | 101 | 82 | 61 | 42 | 35 | 62 | 63 | 135 | 206 | 112 | 1113 |
| Florence | 164 ft | 2·4 | 2·7 | 2·6 | 2·9 | 2·4 | 1·9 | 0·9 | 1·5 | 2·1 | 3·8 | 4·2 | 2·8 | 30·3 |
| | 50 m | 61 | 68 | 65 | 74 | 62 | 49 | 23 | 38 | 54 | 96 | 107 | 72 | 769 |
| Rome | 167 ft | 2·9 | 3·4 | 3·1 | 2·4 | 2·2 | 1·5 | 0·2 | 0·9 | 2·6 | 4·8 | 4·8 | 3·6 | 32·4 |
| | 51 m | 74 | 87 | 79 | 62 | 57 | 38 | 6 | 23 | 66 | 123 | 121 | 92 | 828 |
| Naples | 489 ft | 3·4 | 3·0 | 3·0 | 2·2 | 1·5 | 1·3 | 0·5 | 0·6 | 2·2 | 4·0 | 5·3 | 4·1 | 31·2 |
| | 149 m | 87 | 77 | 76 | 55 | 37 | 33 | 14 | 16 | 56 | 102 | 135 | 105 | 793 |
| Bari | 37 ft | 1·5 | 1·6 | 2·0 | 1·4 | 1·5 | 1·3 | 0·8 | 1·0 | 1·6 | 4·4 | 4·3 | 2·7 | 23·6 |
| | 12 m | 39 | 39 | 50 | 35 | 38 | 32 | 19 | 24 | 40 | 111 | 110 | 67 | 604 |
| Palermo | 233 ft | 5·6 | 5·1 | 3·5 | 2·6 | 1·3 | 0·6 | 0·2 | 1·1 | 2·1 | 4·8 | 3·9 | 7·1 | 37·9 |
| | 71 m | 141 | 129 | 89 | 65 | 32 | 16 | 6 | 29 | 54 | 123 | 99 | 179 | 962 |
| Cagliari | 240 ft | 2·1 | 2·3 | 2·0 | 1·7 | 1·5 | 0·2 | 0·1 | 0·4 | 1·3 | 2·1 | 2·2 | 2·9 | 18·9 |
| | 73 m | 54 | 59 | 50 | 43 | 39 | 5 | 3 | 10 | 32 | 53 | 57 | 74 | 479 |

MEAN MONTHLY AND ANNUAL TEMPERATURES IN DEGREES CENTIGRADE, WITH FAHRENHEIT EQUIVALENTS TO THE NEAREST DEGREE

| Station | Alt. | Jan. | Feb. | Mar. | Apr. | May | June | July | Aug. | Sep. | Oct. | Nov. | Dec. | Mean |
|---|---|---|---|---|---|---|---|---|---|---|---|---|---|---|
| Milan | 397 ft | 35 | 39 | 48 | 56 | 63 | 72 | 77 | 75 | 69 | 57 | 47 | 37 | 56 |
| | 121 m | 1·9 | 3·8 | 8·6 | 13·2 | 17·3 | 22·2 | 24·8 | 23·9 | 20·3 | 13·7 | 8·5 | 3·0 | 13·4 |
| Venice | 10 ft | 39 | 39 | 47 | 55 | 63 | 70 | 74 | 74 | 69 | 59 | 51 | 41 | 57 |
| | 3 m | 3·8 | 4·1 | 8·2 | 12·6 | 17·1 | 21·2 | 23·6 | 23·3 | 20·4 | 15·1 | 10·5 | 5·0 | 13·7 |
| Genoa | 69 ft | 47 | 48 | 53 | 58 | 64 | 72 | 76 | 77 | 73 | 65 | 56 | 49 | 61 |
| | 21 m | 8·4 | 8·7 | 11·5 | 14·5 | 17·8 | 21·9 | 24·6 | 25·0 | 22·8 | 18·1 | 13·3 | 9·5 | 16·3 |
| Florence | 164 ft | 42 | 42 | 50 | 56 | 63 | 72 | 77 | 76 | 70 | 60 | 52 | 43 | 59 |
| | 50 m | 5·6 | 5·8 | 9·9 | 13·3 | 17·4 | 22·1 | 25·0 | 24·5 | 21·2 | 15·8 | 11·2 | 6·0 | 14·8 |
| Rome | 167 ft | 45 | 46 | 53 | 58 | 65 | 73 | 78 | 78 | 72 | 64 | 56 | 48 | 62 |
| | 51 m | 7·4 | 8·0 | 11·5 | 14·4 | 18·4 | 22·9 | 25·7 | 25·5 | 22·4 | 17·7 | 13·4 | 8·9 | 16·4 |
| Naples | 489 ft | 48 | 48 | 53 | 58 | 65 | 72 | 77 | 77 | 72 | 66 | 58 | 51 | 62 |
| | 149 m | 8·7 | 8·7 | 11·4 | 14·3 | 18·1 | 22·3 | 24·8 | 24·8 | 22·3 | 19·1 | 14·5 | 10·3 | 16·6 |
| Bari | 37 ft | 47 | 47 | 51 | 57 | 64 | 72 | 76 | 76 | 71 | 65 | 59 | 50 | 61 |
| | 12 m | 8·4 | 8·5 | 10·8 | 13·9 | 17·5 | 21·9 | 24·5 | 24·3 | 21·7 | 18·2 | 14·8 | 10·2 | 16·2 |
| Palermo | 233 ft | 51 | 51 | 55 | 61 | 66 | 73 | 78 | 77 | 74 | 68 | 62 | 55 | 64 |
| | 71 m | 10·3 | 10·4 | 13·0 | 16·2 | 18·7 | 23·0 | 25·3 | 25·1 | 23·2 | 19·9 | 16·8 | 12·6 | 17·9 |
| Cagliari | 240 ft | 51 | 50 | 55 | 59 | 65 | 73 | 78 | 78 | 74 | 67 | 60 | 53 | 64 |
| | 73 m | 9·9 | 10·3 | 12·9 | 15·3 | 18·6 | 22·8 | 25·8 | 25·7 | 23·3 | 19·5 | 15·6 | 11·8 | 17·6 |

# CONTINENTAL ITALY

**The Transition Zone between the Northern Plain and the Alps.** A number of morainic amphitheatres lie at the exits of the great Alpine valleys. Behind these terminal moraines lie depressions often filled by the great Italian lakes, and elsewhere presenting a

ground moraine landscape. The rivers have cut through the
morainic walls in rather deep valleys with a considerable gradient;
consequently water power can be developed here, for example at
Paderno d'Adda. These morainic hills do not merge into each other
as on the northern side of the Alps, and between them the rock
material varies from bastions of solid rock to coarse detritus of many
kinds brought down by mountain torrents. On the Apennine side
there are no morainic hills and the transition between the plain and
the mountain takes place rather more quickly.

Where the soils and aspect are favourable in this encircling zone
of hill country it is occupied by small mixed farms producing maize,
fodder, fruit, vines, and livestock, but there are also numerous
patches of woodland and sterile heath, the latter traditionally used
for sheep grazing. The wines of the Veronese enjoy a considerable
reputation.

The Alpine valleys, especially between Lake Maggiore and Lake
Garda, though properly belonging to the Alpine zone, may be
treated here, since they prolong the lowland zone into the mountains,
and have some of the features of the Mediterranean climate. The
mountains give sufficient shelter against cold winter winds to allow
the olive to grow, a tree which is almost entirely absent from the
North Italian Plain owing to the winter cold. But the mean
January temperatures, even in this sheltered zone, are rather low.
The rainfall is heavy and the distribution is non-Mediterranean,
there being no dry season or month, and the summer six months
(March–August) having a heavier rainfall than the winter. The
months of maximum rainfall are usually May or June, with a pronounced secondary maximum in October. The climate may be
called pseudo-Mediterranean. A number of tourist centres have
grown up round the lakes.

**The Plain.** The plain itself is 250 miles long from the foothills of
Piedmont (It., Piemonte) to the mouths of the Po, about 50 miles
wide in Lombardy (It., Lombardia), and about 120 miles wide in
the longitude of the Po delta (see Fig. 17). The plain of Venetia
(It., Venezia Euganea) prolongs it in the north-east for another
80 miles, with a width of about 30 miles, until the karstic hills of
Istria are reached.

The plain is generally very flat except for the rounded Tertiary hills
of Montferrat (It., Montferrato) in Piedmont, which could more
properly be included in the Apennine system, and the little volcanic
Monti Berici and Monti Euganei in the province of Venetia. It is
also low-lying, and a rise of 300 ft in the level of the sea would
restore almost the whole area to its former state as an extension of
the Adriatic.

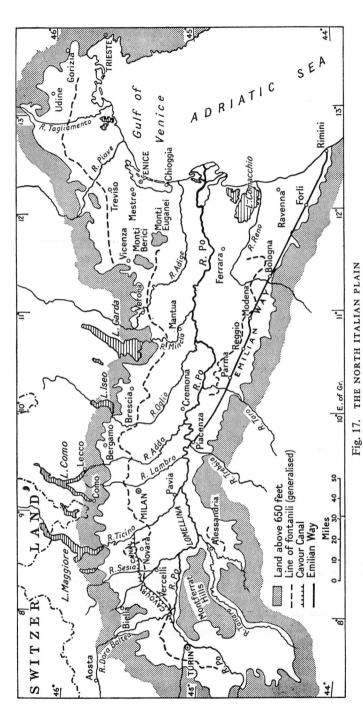

Fig. 17. THE NORTH ITALIAN PLAIN

**NOTE:** (*a*) the attenuation of the plain at its north-eastern and south-western extremities, (*b*) the lines of springs (*fontanili*), and (*c*) the absence of towns on the banks of the river Po below Piacenza.

The plain may be divided into two main zones, namely, the unirrigated and the irrigated. From the Alps towards the River Po the alluvial material of which the plain is composed becomes progressively finer, but usually so gradually that the conventional division into an outer zone of gravels and a central zone of fine silt is somewhat artificial, and a division based on capacity for irrigation is more valuable. There is, indeed, usually a marked contrast between the central part of the plain which is irrigated, and the zone to the north which is unable to obtain irrigation water, but the irrigation zone extends northwards in places into the zone of coarser material. It may seem strange at first sight that a plain which has a considerable rainfall, well distributed throughout the year, should need irrigation. Summer temperatures are high, however, usually over 70° F (21° C) for three months, and while it is true that some crops, such as mulberries, wheat, and hemp, usually grow perfectly well without irrigation, it is essential to such crops as rice, and it greatly increases the yield of others, particularly the forage crops.

The boundary between the arid and the irrigated zones corresponds roughly with a line of springs, which occur where the water-table cuts the north-to-south slope of the plain. In western Lombardia these springs occur in a band about 6 miles wide in the latitude just north of Milan. These springs, known as *fontanili*, increase in importance from east to west, and they play an important rôle in the irrigation of the plain, though the greater part of the water is derived from the rivers coming down from the Alps. In the north of the 'dry' zone these rivers are incised too far below the level of the plain for their water to be diverted economically, but the southern part of the 'dry' zone has generally been brought into the irrigation system, the most northerly canals, for example, the Canale Villoresi in Lombardia, running north of the *fontanili*. A similar line of springs occurs on the Apennine side of the plain.

*The Dry Zone bordering the Alpine Foothills.* This zone of permeable, rather infertile fluvio-glacial gravels stretches from Piemonte to the Yugoslav frontier and is generally narrow although in Venezia Euganea and Venezia Giulia it reaches a width of over 20 miles. Topographically it forms a long, low terrace which slopes gently southwards and is interrupted from time to time by the incised flood-plains of the more important Alpine rivers. The permeability of the gravels and the depth of the water-table on the interfluves are unfavourable to irrigation and, except in a few heathy areas which are too dry for cultivation, mixed farming, including milk and meat production, predominates. There is, however, a marked emphasis on the production of maize, wheat, and vines, and the cultivation of tree crops, including pears, apples, peaches, plums, and cherries, is also widespread. As in many areas of ancient settlement in Italy the tree crops are planted in lines among the field crops. The narrow floodplains of the Alpine rivers which cross the zone are better supplied with surface water and support a more intensive and more varied agriculture in which fodder crops have an important place.

*The Irrigated Zone.* The most easily exploited water resources on the plain are those provided by *fontanili* since they are regular in flow and the streams issuing from them are not deeply incised. The irrigation system utilising these sources dates mainly from the Middle Ages, as do several more ambitious projects, for example the precursor of the Naviglio Grande linking the Ticino and the Adda. The largest canals, whose purpose is to distribute the waters of the Alpine rivers over the interfluves as well as the floodplains, were built from the mid-nineteenth century onwards. Such is the Cavour canal whose waters irrigate some 400,000 acres between the Dora Baltea and the Ticino including some of the most productive ricefields and water-meadows in Italy.

The North Italian Plain presents the largest area under irrigation in Europe, and the greater part of Italy's 5 million acres of irrigated land are to be found there, but as in all such irrigation areas, the imposing network of canals which appears on the map resolves itself on the spot to inconspicuous ditches bordering a field. In spite of its extreme flatness, the plain does not present a monotonous aspect. Although there are usually no hedges, each field is bordered and traversed by lines of trees of various kinds, such as elms and fruit trees, with an occasional Lombardy poplar, so that the cultivated foreground seems to dissolve into a pleasant woodland. The small fields are occupied by strips of crops of different form and colour, such as rice, maize, flax, clover, wheat, lucerne, with patches of bare brown soil, occasionally glinting with irrigation water if the season be early enough. In the distance a village is usually to be seen, its harmonious groups of buildings half-hidden in its setting of trees.

In certain areas one crop or one activity becomes dominant: for example in the Lomellina, bordering the Po between the Sesia and the Ticino, where the majority of Italy's rice is grown, or in southern Lombardia which forms part of a zone stretching from Pavia to Modena where milk production is the outstanding activity. The animals, mainly Friesians, are stall fed and are rarely seen in the fields which are reserved for the intensive cultivation of fodder crops, mainly lucerne, clover, and hay. Abundant water, heavy manuring and a long growing season provide as many as seven cuttings annually. The demand for fluid milk in the large industrial cities furnishes an expanding market but the majority of the output is manufactured into butter or such famous cheeses as Parmesan and Gorgonzola. Vines are grown to some extent almost everywhere but particularly in the Mantua area (It., Mantova).

Although most of it is irrigated in summer, downstream from Piacenza and along the lowest sectors of the tributary valleys of the Po there lies a fenny zone where drainage and flood control are the fundamental problems. Without massive dykes and powerful pumps most of this area, whose drainage has been achieved tract by tract over the last hundred years, would revert to marsh. Behind a fringe of sandspits (*lidi*) much of the Po delta remains a dreary waste of swamp and lagoon and the struggle to extend the cultivable area is rendered more difficult by the tendency of the area to subside. As a rule reclamation is effected by poldering but in the lower Reno zone the silt content of the rivers is very high and the level of the land can be raised by diverting the flood waters into restricted areas. The 'new lands' of northern Emilia and southern Venezia have been laid out as a monotonous network of rectangular fields. From the first this was mainly the domain of the large landowner who could afford the expenses of drainage and of machinery. Sugar-beet, hemp, cereals, and vines are the main crops. Rice growing tends to decline as the drainage of an area improves. Rural overpopulation and underemployment have been the cause of social unrest in this zone and many estates have been obliged to yield part of their land under the postwar agrarian reform legislation. The Po delta is the only area in the North in receipt of aid otherwise reserved for the depressed areas of the South.

Between the foothills of the Apennines and the fens along the Po lies a roughly triangular area built up of the sediments washed down by the erratic, silt-laden rivers of the Emilian Apennines. The deposits have been naturally graded and the transition from the coarser sediments to the finer alluvium may be regarded as coinciding roughly with the Emilian Way. North of that ancient road much of the land is irrigated but the available water supplies in this part of Emilia are less regular and less abundant than those of Lombardia. The *fontanili* are less generous and the Apennine rivers tend to wilt in summer and flood disastrously in winter. Even so this is a rich and varied area of ancient settlement. In general the economy is based on cereals, sugar beet, vines, fodder crops, and animal rearing but tomatoes, onions, and fruit (mainly apples, pears, and stone fruits), are also important. As soon as the more difficult terrain of the Apennine foothills is reached the land is deprived of irrigation water and the variety of the plain gives way to a more impoverished agriculture based mainly on wheat, vines, and dry tree crops.

The pleasant, rolling hills of Montferrat (It., Montferrato) which belong geologically to the Sub-Apennine zone are set too high to benefit from the main sources of irrigation water. They are best known for their wines, especially the Spumante of Asti.

*Urban Development.* The cities of the North Italian Plain are notable not only for their antiquity but also for the continuity of their existence since their foundation. Most of them first achieved the status of cities as a result of the Roman colonisation of the plain in the second and first centuries B.C., but of these many occupied the sites of pre-Roman settlements. Bologna, for example, was an important centre even before the Etruscans exploited its position and Milan was a Celtic settlement long before it finally came under Roman domination. Venice and Alessandria are exceptional in that they were founded after the collapse of the Empire in the West, the former as a refuge settlement when the Huns swept on to the plain, and the latter in the Middle Ages.

Although in a level plain of this kind the distribution of settlement is apt to be somewhat sporadic most of the towns on it fall within one of the following groups.

(*a*) Settlements where routes down the Alpine valleys meet those along the edge of the plain. Such are Turin (1,019,000), Como (82,000), Bergamo (113,000), Brescia (174,000), and Verona (221,000), all of them of considerable strategic importance in their day but now mainly dependent on their commerce and industry especially since the development of hydro-electric power in the Alps over the last half-century.

(*b*) Settlements along the Via Emilia where it is met by roads leading down from the Apennine passes. Rimini (98,000), Forli (91,000), Bologna (441,000), Modena (139,000), Reggio Emilia (116,000), Parma (140,000), and Piacenza (87,000) fall into this category. All of these cities, some of which have been capitals in the past, are very dependent on the rich agriculture of the plain but most of them are also considerable centres of industry. Bologna which is the focus of four trans-Apennine roads, including the *Strada del Sole* motorway and the Futa pass route, as well as of two railways through the Apennines, is easily the most important town in the group. Agricultural processing and engineering predominate among its numerous industrial activities.

(*c*) Settlements at the junction of the dry and the irrigated zones which at one time was also the upper limit of the marshy area and in consequence a natural line of communication from east to west. Novara (86,000), Milan (1,580,000), Padua (198,000), and Treviso (75,000) are representative.

(*d*) Settlements along the Adriatic shore among which Venice

(It., Venezia: 336,000), Chioggia (52,000), and Ravenna (115,000) are the most notable. The existence of these towns has always been threatened by deltaic accumulation and the drift of coastal material by currents and waves. Adria and Ravenna, both important Roman ports, are now well inland although the latter has revived of late with the development of its new harbour installations on the coast and it is now one of Italy's foremost petrochemical centres.

(e) Settlements on the Po. Only two important towns are in this group, Piacenza and Turin, although Cremona is very near the river. The formerly marshy terrain, the tendency of the Po to flood and its unsuitability for serious navigation have discouraged urban development. Piacenza's importance derived originally from its bridge which carried the Via Emilia north-westwards towards Milan.

Milan (It., Milano), the largest town on the plain and second only to Rome in the country, may be looked upon as the commercial, financial, and industrial capital of Italy. There seems to be no particular geographical reason why the city stands exactly where it does but it is well situated in regard to routes both along the plain and through the Alps. Two most important trans-Alpine railway lines, the St Gotthard and the Simplon, focus on Milan as well as the roads over the Lukmanier, Splügen, Maloja, and S. Bernardino which carry a considerable amount of tourist traffic in summer. The city has a great variety of industries among which agricultural processing, textiles, clothing, motor vehicles, electrical engineering, and consumer goods, rubber and chemicals are outstanding. An oil pipeline from Genoa feeds the refinery at Rho, just outside the city. Milan is also the cultural and business centre of a cluster of towns whose industries cover a wide range, for example steel at Sesto S. Giovanni and Lecco, motor vehicles at Varese and Gallarate, cotton textiles at Busto Arsizio and Legnano, silk at Como, sewing machines at Pavia, and chemicals at Bovisa.

The immediate advantages of the site of Turin (It., Torino) are more obvious. It stands at the junction of the Po and the Dora Riparia whose double-headed valley leads up to the Mt Genèvre pass on the south and the Mt Cenis pass on the north. The latter route is used by the important Paris–Rome line via Genoa although the tunnel itself passes under the Col de Fréjus. Turin may expect to benefit from the road tunnel recently completed beneath the great St Bernard pass towards the head of the Dora Baltea. For several centuries Turin was a capital city but its economic life is now dominated by industry and in particular by the firm of Fiat whose many interests include motor vehicles (currently about 75 per cent of Italy's output), railway equipment, aircraft, marine engines, chemicals, and electrical goods.

It will have become apparent that the North Italian Plain, particularly those parts of it adjoining the Alps in Lombardia and Piemonte, is overwhelmingly the most active manufacturing zone in Italy and it is daily attracting large numbers of workers from the South and other parts of the country. Until 1945 it depended almost exclusively on hydro-electricity for its power but this had to be supplemented substantially by other sources of energy especially by natural gas, which was first discovered under the plain in large quantities in 1946, and by oil, much of which is piped from Genoa. The ease of distribution of these sources of energy has tended to reinforce the dispersed pattern of industry earlier encouraged by hydro-electricity so that many towns whose existence once depended mainly on agriculture and commerce have now assumed an industrial rôle.

Textile manufacturing is the oldest mass-production industry of the area and is scattered among a large number of centres at the foot of the Alps and on the higher plain. The woollen industry, with its roots deep in the past, is now especially notable at Biella and Vicenza as well as in a number of small towns in Bergamo province. Cotton spinning and weaving are wider spread but are particularly notable in the satellite towns to the north of Milan, for example Legnano, Gallarate, and Busto Arsizio. Silk and artificial silk manufacture are found at Treviso and Turin as well as at the better known centre of Como, while hemp and flax processing are well represented at Pavia and other towns in southern Lombardia.

Although the metal-using industries of Lombardia and Piemonte now rely heavily on the new Cornigliano plant near Genoa, there are a number of steel centres on the plain itself, in particular at Turin, Sesto S. Giovanni (just outside Milan), Bergamo, and Brescia, relying largely on scrap and electric furnaces. They support an impressive variety of engineering activities whose products range from heavy electrical equipment and marine diesels at Turin and Milan to typewriters at Ivrea and precision instruments at Bologna. The vehicle industry, one of the most rapidly expanding sectors, is dominated by Turin and Milan but Brescia, Varese, and Modena have a share in it. The same areas are also outstanding in the manufacture of cycles and motor cycles; this industry is also carried on at Padua, Bassano, and Bologna.

In the chemical industry Milan, Trecate, Ravenna, and Porto Marghera are extremely important for their petrochemicals, and a large number of plants from Turin to Trieste produce acids, soda, and fertilisers. Almost every town of any size has its agricultural processing industries as well as a selection of light industries such as the manufacture of furniture, clothing, paper, and electrical accessories.

Most of the international traffic of the plain moves through the Alpine passes but sea-borne trade, particularly in imported fuels and raw materials is also very important.   In this connexion Venice is less favoured than Genoa which is nearer the heavily industrialised section of the plain and unlike its ancient rival is spared the navigational problems commonly associated with an alluvial coast (cf. Calcutta, Shanghai).   The historic part of Venice, built on piles driven into the mud-flats of the lagoon, is now mainly a museum city living on tourism and its associated handicraft industries.   Mestre and Porto Marghera on the mainland opposite constitute the modern industrial zone of Venice with important oil-refining, chemical, and non-ferrous metal-smelting plants.

Overshadowed by the steep edge of the lower Karst plateau of Yugoslavia, Trieste (273,000) occupies a rocky peninsula between two navigable bays across which protective moles have been built. The port was originally developed as the main salt water outlet of Austria–Hungary but with the collapse of that empire in 1918 it was annexed to Italy.   Trieste's communications with its natural hinterland are inevitably somewhat tortuous but the difficulties of maintaining its transit trade were increased by the economic nationalism of the interwar period, and in particular by the clash of interests with Yugoslavia in this disputed marchland.   In 1945 Italy was obliged to cede a large part of Venezia Giulia to Yugoslavia, including Fiume (Rijeka), a natural competitor of Trieste.   For some years the attempt was made to establish the Free Territory of Trieste (cf. Danzig) but without success and in 1954 the city itself, which is overwhelmingly Italian-speaking, was awarded to Italy under an agreement with the Yugoslavs who were apportioned the larger but less populous area around the city to the south where the population was mainly Slav-speaking.   In view of the precariousness of the port's transit trade the Italians since the 1920s have built up Trieste into a considerable industrial complex with steel, shipbuilding, oil refining, and chemicals among its more important activities.   Monfalcone, at the edge of the alluvial coast further north, is also a shipbuilding centre of note.


## THE APENNINE PENINSULA

It cannot be said that any very satisfactory division into geographical regions presents itself, for the rapid alternation of high and low relief results in a veritable mosaic of contrasting landforms and climates.   A primary division into central and southern Italy can be justified to some extent on climatic and other grounds and will be adopted for the sake of convenience in treatment.

**Central Italy. 1. The Apennines.** *The Mountains of Liguria and the Northern Apennines.* Taken together these mountains separate the North Italian Plain from the Ligurian coast and the small fertile basins of north-central Italy. They have never been a serious barrier to communications and the numerous passes across them tend to be long rather than difficult.

In the Mountains of Liguria the Cadibona pass (1,505 ft), which serves to connect the busy port of Savona with its hinterland in the Turin area, is generally considered to mark the division between the Ligurian Alps and the Ligurian Apennines. Almost everywhere these mountains fall steeply to the sea so that the construction of roads and railways along the coast has been expensive and has demanded engineering of a high order. The difficulties are increased by the succession of short torrents one or two of which have built small alluvial plains. Elsewhere the only relatively flat land is found in the longitudinal valleys of the Lavagna and Vara on the Riviera di Levante. East of Genoa, which relies mainly on the roads and railways through the Giovi pass (1,548 ft) for its communications with the North Italian Plain, the Ligurian Apennines widen and in places reach over 5,500 ft so that the majority of the traffic in this sector is directed towards Genoa or to a less degree towards La Spezia via the Cisa pass.

Agriculturally Liguria is of little importance; the steep terrain limits the cultivable area and necessitates terracing but advantage is taken of the mildness of the winters on the Riviera, particularly the drier and less exposed Riviera di Ponente, for the cultivation of early vegetables and flowers. Olives, vines, and citrus fruits are also produced. The climate and the accessibility of the coast from the richer areas of Italy and north-west Europe have also encouraged a flourishing tourist trade at a host of resorts among which San Remo, Alassio, and Rapallo are perhaps the best known.

Outside the North Italian Plain for which it may be considered the principal outlet, Liguria is the most heavily industrialised region of Italy. The principal concentration is at Genoa (It., Genova; 775,000) which also handles more tonnage and more passengers than any other Italian port. A rocky enclosed bay provided the original harbour site and it is still used for the larger passenger liners, notably those sailing to America, but the demand for more quay space has necessitated the construction of a dock area behind protective moles to the west of the city. Genoa's hinterland is mainly in industrialised Piemonte and Lombardia but it also shares in the Swiss trade and will do so increasingly now that the oil pipeline to Milan has been continued into western Switzerland. Apart from foodstuffs, most of Genoa's imports consist of raw materials and fuels, especially oil, coal, and ores, and a high proportion of these is used locally in the heavy industries suited to a coastal site. At Corni-gliano, just to the west of Genoa, about half of Italy's steel is pro-duced in a recently completed full-cycle plant; other industries in the area include shipbuilding, marine engineering, railway equipment, motor vehicles, chemicals, and food processing. Savona (71,000) is a Genoa in miniature; it has shipbuilding, oil refining, and chemical industries and is the terminal of the oil pipeline to the petrochemical centre of Trecate. La Spezia (121,000) at the head of its sheltered gulf, is less favourably placed to serve the North Italian Plain and is principally an arsenal and naval base.

The Northern or Tusco-Emilian Apennines stretch roughly from the River Taro to the River Metauro. The core of the range con-sists of folded sandstones, clays, and marls with occasional bands of serpentine and, although the mountains exceed 6,000 ft in places (Mt Cimone 7,094 ft), there are few spectacular peaks, and com-munications are handicapped less by altitude than by the unstable clays which are subject to landslides and severe gullying. In places badland topography has developed. The southern flank of the range falls sharply to a number of longitudinal intermontane basins, for example those of the upper Serchio, Sieve, and Arno, while the northern flank slopes more gently to the Po plain across a highly dissected belt of erodible Pliocene sands and clays. There is a wide choice of road passes but the most important are the Poretta and the Futa leading from Bologna to Pistoia and Florence respectively. The *Strada del Sole* and two main line railways cross the Apennines in the same sector. The construction of the Bologna–Prato line involves a tunnel $11\frac{1}{2}$ miles in length, the second longest in Europe.

In the higher, less accessible tracts of the Northern Apennines oak, chestnut, and beech woodlands survive and there has been a considerable amount of reafforestation, particularly of conifers, but wide areas of deforested pasture land remain. Lower down the land use is dominated by cereals, vines, and tree crops, often at some risk to the soil cover. On the whole the range is of little agricultural importance and the population is tending to drain away to the towns of the plain.

*The Central Apennines.* Roughly along a line joining Ancona and Perugia the Apennine belt widens and its lithological character begins to change. In most of Umbria the rocks are still similar to those of the Northern Apennines with sandstones forming the higher, generally rounded features of relief, but limestones also make their appearance and by the time Abruzzi is reached they dominate the landscape. Even further south, as far as the crystalline blocks of Calabria, the principal massifs are calcareous in character although they often emerge as islands from a dissected hill country developed on clays and other less resistant sediments. In Abruzzi itself the principal features of relief are provided by a number of steep-sided mountain masses whose barren surfaces have long since lost most of their forest cover although painstaking efforts are being made to restore it. In general the summits, which sweep up from extensive karstic plateaus, are rounded or whale-backed but in places they are high enough to take on the sharper forms bequeathed by glaciation. This is most obviously the case in the Gran Sasso range where the peak of Corno Grande (8,558 ft), snow-capped for most of the year, towers above the Campo Imperatore, a high plateau pitted with sink holes and strewn with glacial debris.

The orientation of the limestone massifs and the intermontane basins which penetrate them is generally north-west to south-east so that movement across the Apennines in this sector is extremely tortuous and has to make use of the short, usually gorge-like transverse sectors of such rivers as the Pescara–Aterno and the Nera–Velino which drain the interior basins. Movement along the 'grain' of the range, on the other hand, is comparatively easy. The contribution of subterranean erosion seems to have been more important in the formation of the smaller, higher basins while the larger ones are usually considered to be mainly of tectonic origin. In fact, the whole area is still seismically unstable. Lacustrine deposits of Pliocene and more recent date occupy the floors of the depressions and provide the best agricultural land. In the past incomplete drainage was the main obstacle to the exploitation of the basins and it was only in 1876 that Lake Fucino, which occupied much of the Avezzano depression, was finally drained off to the Liri. In Abruzzi proper, the most obvious basins are those of Aquila, Sulmona, and Avezzano; the Terni–Narni basin and the Rieti basin are fundamentally similar but administratively they fall within Umbria and Lazio respectively. All these depressions support a mixed Mediterranean cultivation in which tree crops and vines intermingle with cereals and fodder crops but the lower basins have the advantage of a wider range of produce including sugar-beet, a crop of some importance in the Rieti area. The wide surfaces of the mountain massifs are traditionally the receiving areas for transhumant flocks from the coastal lowlands but they are more significant as the source of water reserves released steadily from the limestone to the great benefit of many of the rivers of central Italy including the lower Tiber.

The Central Apennines are an area from which population is drifting away. Most of the towns have some small-scale manufactures, usually of consumer goods such as confectionery and shoes, but the only major industrial centre is Terni where the hydro-electric power of the Velino river encouraged the establishment of electrochemical and electrometallurgical industries. The tourist attractions of the area, which include a number of winter sports resorts, are becoming increasingly important in the economy of the region.

*The Eastern Slope of the Apennines (The Sub-Apennines).* The land between the high Apennines and the Adriatic descends by a series of not very well defined terraces, and is a region of very complicated dissection developed in almost undisturbed young Tertiary clays, shales, and sands.

The topography is mainly the result of river work, the consequent streams being separated from each other by parallel residual ridges, though these are cut up in turn by innumerable minor valleys. In spite of a tendency for the clays to slip, it is a fertile, well-cultivated region with about 70 per cent of the surface under the plough, with wheat, sugar-beet, and maize as the chief crops. The vine is widely cultivated, but there are few trees except near the coast where mulberries and olives are grown; it appears that the compact clays are unfavourable to tree growth, as they crack and dry out badly in the droughty summer. Although this region is thickly populated there are few large centres. This is due to a variety of reasons. The concordant coast, bordered by low cliffs or deltaic formations, is harbourless, except for the port of Ancona (*c.* 100,000), where a limestone promontory occurs and gives rise to a bay. Secondly, owing to the large number of independent rivers there is an absence of nodal points. Thirdly, it is not the 'custom of the country' to live in large agricultural towns, as in the similar lands in the interior of Sicily, but in small ridge-top towns and villages, and in scattered farmhouses.

**Central Italy.   2. The Anti-Apennine Region.**   To the west of the Apennines proper between La Spezia in the north and Gaeta in the south lies a region which may be considered the foreland of the Apennines and which is generally referred to as the Anti-Apennines. Its curving eastern margin is marked by the depressions of the Val di Chiana, the longitudinal middle course of the Tiber and by the Sacco and Liri valleys, but from the point of view of human geography the hill country of Umbria may also be included. Although in places it reaches heights comparable with the Apennines themselves, it is generally lower and more productive, and includes some of the most densely populated areas in Italy.

Structurally the Anti-Apennine region consists of a number of higher fragments, formerly separated by arms of the sea but now joined together by depressions which are filled with upper Tertiary and Quaternary sediments as well as more recent alluvium. These depressions contain considerable deposits of brown coal which is used to generate thermal electricity. Many of the higher relief features, for example the Apuan Alps in the north and the Lepini and Aurunci Mountains in the south, are of limestone but in central Lazio the landscape reflects the consequences of late Tertiary and Quaternary volcanic activity. In general the Anti-Apennines are a region of pleasant hills and undulating plateaus studded with basins and laced with alluvial valleys some of which have only been recently drained (e.g. the Val di Chiana). The same is true of the alluvial coastal plains most of which are edged with sandspits festooned between rocky headlands.

*The Arno Basins.* The former lake basins (of which Lake Trasimeno is a shrunken remnant) along the Val d'Arno and the Val di Chiana are highly cultivated, densely populated, and afford valuable routes, but they are surpassed by the lower basins, particularly that associated with Florence (It. Firenze; 438,000) and Pistoia (82,000). This was still marshy as late as the Roman colonisation, and the early centres of population were sited on high ground round the margins. The floors of these basins are of great fertility now, and so are many of the neighbouring hills, for example the Chianti Hills which gave their name to the celebrated wine.

Largely because of the drainage difficulties experienced throughout so much of the Arno basin no city within it came into prominence until medieval times when the development of textile manufacturing, banking and trade with the Levant provided the economic basis for an urbanised civilisation of great refinement. Pisa (91,000), once the main port of the area, fell a prey to Florentine jealousy and Arno silt towards the end of the Middle Ages and its maritime functions have long since been taken over by Leghorn (It. Livorno; 160,000), which also counts shipbuilding, engineering, and oil refining among its activities. In Florence the tourist trade and its associated handicraft industries are the main economic occupation of the city but in the vicinity there are also factories processing food and producing engineering and electrical goods, furniture and precision instruments. Florence is also a major communications centre focusing the routes through the Apennines from Bologna, along the lower Val d'Arno from the coast and across the Tuscan plateau from Rome. The main line to Rome and the *Strada del Sole*, now nearing completion, makes use of the Val di Chiana, but this route was avoided until the railway age because of its poor drainage. Pistoia, controlling the original railway through this section of the Apennines, has electrical industries and Prato is notable for its wool textiles.

*The Apuan Alps.* North of the Arno estuary and separated from the Apennines by the Serchio basin stretch the Apuan Alps.  Reaching heights of over 6,000 ft these form one of the really high and mountainous parts of the Anti-Apennine zone.  The Triassic limestones of which they are composed have been eroded, in part by ice, into steep and rugged forms which recall the true Alps.  In places the limestone has been altered into the famous marbles which are worked at Massa and Carrara.  The heavy precipitation is favourable to forests, and sweet chestnuts cover a sizable area.

*The Hill Country of Tuscany.*  Between the Arno and the trachytic cone of Monte Amiata (5,687 ft) lies a hilly region which occasionally rises high enough to be classed as mountainous.  Most of it is developed on Tertiary clays, marls, and sands which lend themselves to severe gullying and the formation of badland, notably near Volterra and in the vicinity of Siena.  The older basement, mainly Permian in age, is revealed through the Tertiary sediments in the Colline Metallifere and in Montagnola, and also appears on the coast in the Argentario peninsula.  In these areas and elsewhere igneous intrusions have been responsible for a variety of minerals including copper, tin, silver, zinc, mercury, and pyrites, but only the last two are now of any significance.

The Tuscan hill country includes wide areas which are of little agricultural value, for example the marls and clays of the Crete Senesi, but most of the area produces wheat, vines, olives, and other tree crops, the latter arranged in lines among the field crops as is the custom in many areas of ancient settlement in the Mediterranean. Siena (62,000), once the rival of Florence and the only town of any size, is mainly a tourist centre.

*The Umbrian Hill Country.*  The hill country of Umbria belongs structurally to the Apennines, as it lies to the east of the Val di Chiana–middle Tiber trough but, in virtue of its many fertile basins, ease of communications, and historic towns, it belongs culturally to the Anti-Apennines and has much in common with the Arno region of Tuscany.  The landscape consists of rather flattened hill ridges, mainly of sandstone, which reach heights of over 3,000 ft and which are threaded by interconnecting basins of great fertility and drained chiefly to the upper Tiber and its tributary the Nera.  The towns of the area, which depend mainly on agriculture, the manufacturing of light consumer goods, and tourism, include Perugia (109,000), Spoleto, Foligno, and Assisi.  The only considerable industrial centre, Terni, has received attention above.

*The Volcanic Region of Latium* (*It., Lazio*).  This area consists essentially of a dissected plateau of volcanic ash above which rise up a number of lofty cones of Tertiary and Quaternary age. Lakes Bolsena, Bracciano, Albano, and de Vico are particularly good examples of crater lakes. The volcanic plateau is divided into two parts by the lower Tiber which traverses a broad saddle between the Sabatini Hills and the Alban Hills and has cut down into the Tertiary sediments. This saddle, including the flood plain of the lower Tiber, forms the Campagna Romana. The formerly marshy area on the Tiber delta and on the coastlands on either side of it has been reclaimed since the 1920s and produces large quantitities of fruit, wine, and vegetables for the capital, as well as milk and meat from animals fed on irrigated fodder crops. The slightly higher, hilly area immediately round Rome is much less valuable agriculturally and is still mainly devoted to extensive wheat production and sheep grazing, the traditional pursuits of the Campagna. In contrast, the Alban hills are an extremely productive vine-growing area.

The coastal plains of Lazio, like the Maremma of Tuscany, have suffered until recently from poor drainage caused by the erratic and often torrential discharge of the silt-laden rivers of the hinterland. The Pontine Marshes, where the problem was complicated by the karstic springs of the Lepini Hills and by the barrier of sandspits along the coast, were finally drained and resettled in the 1930s. The Maremma, formerly a desolate and sparsely populated region, the domain of latifundia producing little more than sheep and extensive wheat, has been reclaimed and colonised in the last decade by the Ente Maremma, one of several regional agencies set up to implement the land reform.

The city of Rome (It., Roma; 2,160,000) grew up on seven little residual hills of volcanic material on the left bank of the Tiber, but the fact that the river here breaks through the hilly Apennine foreland was one of the principal factors in the evolution of the city. Rome was essentially a route centre. The river was navigable up to this point and an island in the river facilitated bridge building. The 'cult of communications' was fostered by the chief priest who was also the chief bridge-builder, 'Pontifex Maximus'. Rome was in the best position of any town in Italy to gain control of the whole peninsula in early times since it stands on the largest river with the most extensive drainage area, and is centrally placed in regard to the length of the peninsula.

With the decline of the Empire, and particularly after the Gothic wars, Rome shrank within its ruins and many of its public buildings were converted into feudal fortresses. For centuries it remained significant as the centre of Christendom but it was only after it had become the capital of a united Italy in 1870 that it began to expand rapidly. The choice of Rome was almost inevitable, partly because of its enormous prestige, and partly because it was the only city generally acceptable as the capital by both northerners and southerners.

As in the days of the Empire, Rome is once more the main communications centre of the peninsula; a good system of roads, most of them bearing their ancient titles (Via Flaminia, Via Aurelia, Via Appia, etc.), radiates from the city, and two main railway lines along the west of the peninsula, one along the coast from Genoa to Naples and the other, taking the 'inner' route, from Florence to Naples, are obliged to merge at Rome. The *Strada del Sole*, for which the inner route was chosen, will soon greatly reinforce Rome's system of communications. Rome's airport, conveniently placed on the routes to the Middle and Far East and to East Africa, is the busiest in the Mediterranean area. For nearly a century administration has been Rome's main function just as, for a much longer period and in a wider and different sphere, it has been that of the tiny enclave of the Vatican City on the Tiber's right bank. As a place of pilgrimage and with unique attractions in other respects, Rome relies heavily on the tourist trade, but as an industrial centre, apart from the servicing and transport industries, it is still of minor importance. Since the war, however, a number of light industries have been established in the environs, for example, electrical goods assembly and pharmaceutical manufactures. Despite its poor industrial showing the city is attracting large numbers of people drifting in from the countryside and its population, in fact if not officially, has probably doubled since 1939.

**Southern Italy.** Between the geographical environments of northern and central Italy there is a fairly abrupt change along the line of the Northern Apennines; between central and southern Italy the transition is much more gradual. Indeed, the two areas interpenetrate one another and have many characteristics in common. In the *Mezzogiorno*, as in the centre, difficult hill and mountain country covers most of the surface, and the limestone blocks, the volcanic cones and plateaus, and the treacherous clays encountered first in Abruzzi and Lazio have their counterpart further south; but the limestones now are starker and more arid, the volcanic areas younger, more impressive and more menacing, and the clay hills more extensive and more ravaged by erosion. The coastal plains too are different only in degree; flooding, marsh formation, and malaria in the past discouraged the occupation of the coastal lowlands as effectively in Tuscany and Lazio as in Apulia and Basilicata (Lucania). Certainly some new landscapes appear, for example the waterless platforms of Apulia and the high crystalline moorlands of Calabria, but on the whole most of the 'typical' features of the southern environment have already made their début further north.

1   The Strada del Sole between Florence and Bologna

2   Dispersed settlement on land recently reclaimed and re-colonised under the land reform near Metaponto on the Ionian coast of Italy.  Community centre and agricultural processing factory in foreground.

3  Intensive cultivation, based largely on vines and dried tree crops, on the small farms of the Murge dei Trulli, Apulia.  Note the bee-hive trulli (one-roomed houses of dry stone with conical roofs) and the stone walling.

4  Mount Etna

ITALY

The difference is that in the South these features are writ large. While the lowlands enjoy winters mild enough for the orange, they also have to endure a longer and intense summer drought so that the contrast between the irrigated and the dry land becomes correspondingly sharper; on the one hand, there are vast areas of 'run-down' land, once the preserve of large land owners (*latifondisti*) and still largely devoted to wheat, olives, and sheep; on the other, there are numerous small pockets of fruit, vegetables, and industrial crops intensively cultivated under irrigation. Similarly in other economic spheres, the dominance of agriculture and the absence of industry are more marked in the south, the plight of the landless labourer and the sharecropper less enviable, and the concentration of the rural population in large agricultural centres (rather than isolated farmsteads) more marked. Furthermore, centuries of maladministration have encouraged, among a large section of the population, a conservative, almost fatalistic, attitude of mind in which suspicion and distrust of the motives of authority are almost inbred.

Since 1950 a determined attack has been mounted on the underlying causes of poverty in the South. The work is financed and co-ordinated by a government agency, the *Cassa del Mezzogiorno*, under whose auspices the fundamental rehabilitation of the land – soil conservation, forestry, flood control, drainage etc. – is being achieved. Many areas, particularly along the coast, have been reclaimed and resettled, and the large estates have been reduced in size under the land reform to provide farms for formerly landless peasants. Vast sums have been spent on drainage, deep ploughing, terracing and irrigation, and on the construction of roads, wells, aqueducts, farmsteads, and agricultural servicing stations. At the same time an attempt is being made to inculcate better methods and a more progressive, commercialised attitude towards farming. Realising the impossibility of solving the Southern Problem by means of agriculture alone, the government is offering incentives to encourage industry in the South. The established industrial centres, notably the two ports of Naples and Bari, have increased the range of their manufacturing activities and new trading estates have been set up elsewhere in areas formerly devoid of industry. The pressure of population, which is a fundamental element in the economic situation of the South, is being eased somewhat by the opportunities offered to the southern emigrant in the rapidly expanding industries of northern Italy, Switzerland, and the Federal Republic of Germany. In fact, apart from the flight from the land common to all parts of Italy, the flood of southerners to the northern cities is the most radical shift in population which Italy has experienced since the great exodus overseas before the first world war.

**1. The Campanian Lowlands.** In south Italy the Apennines cross over once more to the west coast, leaving a broad foreland in the east but allowing the development of only limited areas of lowland in the west, notably the lower Sele plain, the lower Volturno plain, and the Neapolitan plain. These Campanian lowlands are encumbered by the active volcanic areas of Vesuvius and the Campi Flegrei (to the west of Naples) but they are none the less one of the most productive agricultural zones of Italy with the advantages of volcanic soils, either *in situ* or redeposited as alluvium, a mild winter and a long growing period, an abundant if seasonal rainfall, and water supplies for irrigation either from wells or from rivers fed in part from such natural karstic reservoirs as the Matese group. Until recently poor drainage hindered the exploitation of the lower tracts of the Sele and Volturno plains but the remainder of the lowlands, particularly the area between Aversa and Nocera, is of remarkable fertility. A wide range of crops includes maize, wheat, sugar-beet, hemp, fodder, vegetables, tomatoes, stone fruits, olives, and nuts. Much of the produce, especially early vegetables and processed tomatoes, is exported. On the hilly margins of the lowlands tree crops share increasingly in the land use. Unfortunately the fertility of the Campanian lowlands, especially of the area of ancient settlement skirting Vesuvius, is offset by the excessive density of population, much of which is concentrated in towns whose functions are almost exclusively agricultural.

Naples (It., Napoli; 1,179,000), formerly the capital of the Kingdom of the Two Sicilies and still the focus of much of the business and cultural activity of southern Italy, is the third largest city of the country. Its dock installations, sheltered by moles built across the bay, are capable of accommodating very large ships and the port shares with Genoa the bulk of Italy's maritime passenger traffic, particularly to America, and is a good second to the Ligurian city in tonnage handled. Most of the imports are raw materials and fuels which are used mainly in the industries of Naples and its satellite towns grouped around the bay. Naples itself has jute and cotton mills, an oil refinery, engineering works, and food processing and chemical plants while Bagnoli depends on its iron and steel industry and Castellammare on its shipyards. Under the post-war drive to industrialise the South the range of industries represented in Campania has been widened, for example synthetic fibres at Caserta, and pharmaceutical goods and typewriter assembly at Naples. With good communications and such unrivalled attractions to offer as Vesuvius and the volcanic oddities of the Campi Flegrei, the antiquities of Pompeii, Herculaneum and Paestum, and the coasts of Capri, Sorrento, and Amalfi, Campania has for long been an important tourist area.

**2. The Southern Apennines** differ somewhat from those of central Italy in showing few parallel chains, but many isolated blocks. This is consequent upon less intensive folding, but more numerous dislocations. In the Calabrian Apennines even the Eocene strata are unfolded, though they represent *par excellence* the folded rock of the northern Apennines. The numerous depressions are filled with Pliocene and later material, and the one affording a route via Benevento, between the Neapolitan district and the east coast, is the most important. On the whole, the southern Apennines are lower than those of the centre, but Serra Dolcedorme reaches 7,374 ft. The crystalline plateau masses of Sila and Aspromonte take up almost the whole of the Calabrian peninsula. They were probably once covered with both Mesozoic and Tertiary material, but this has been denuded from the summits of the plateaus, though it is still found high up on the sides with consequent high extension of cultivation. The granite, gneiss, and mica schists, of which these masses are composed, carry many trees, such as sweet chestnuts, oaks, beech, and pine.

The high crystalline plateaus, reaching heights of 6,000 ft and more, have a heavy if somewhat unreliable precipitation and lie under snow for two or three months each year. This has provided the opportunity for the development of hydro-electric power on the Sila plateau. Although a few agricultural colonies have been established recently, the Calabrian plateaus are still sparsely populated; their extensive woodlands and moorlands afford a strong contrast to the bare steep sides of the massifs and to the semi-tropical vegetation of the coastlands. There is seldom a true coastal plain, but marine terraces at various heights give some fairly flat surfaces near the coast, though they are often seamed by gullies and gorges. The largest single tract of arable land lies in the Crati valley whose upper course occupies a rift. The regimes of the Calabrian rivers are even more erratic than those of the rest of peninsular Italy and many water-courses (known as *fiumare*, cf. *wadis*) are completely dry in summer. The lower slopes of the massifs are occupied by dry tree crops (olives, vines, figs, and almonds) while lower still, where irrigation water is available, a number of discontinuous strips produce citrus fruits. An attempt is being made to increase the irrigable area, particularly in the lower Crati plain which once supported the rich Greek colony of Sybaris, but large areas are still dominated by extensive wheat production. This is notably the case in Marchesato, a tract of uplifted Tertiary sediments between Crotone and the Sila where the land reform authorities have been active since 1950.

There are cotton mills at Cosenza (78,000) and a fertiliser works at Crotone using Sila power but on the whole industry is poorly represented in Calabria. The ferries which connect Villa S. Giovanni and Reggio Calabria (150,000) with Messina are equipped to carry motor vehicles and trains as well as passengers. The straits are also spanned by a power cable held clear of passing shipping by lofty pylons.

**3. The Apulian Foreland.** Apulia (It., Puglia) consists mainly of a platform of unfolded or lightly folded Mesozoic limestones, and until geologically recent times it was separated from the Apennines by an arm of the sea. These late Tertiary and recent marine sediments form a hilly corridor between the Gulf of Taranto and the Tavoliere di Puglia, where they spread out widely into a broad plain. On the whole they give rise to rather useless country, since they consist of sandy and gravelly material in the coastal plains bordering the Gulf of Taranto, and of highly dissected hills subject to landslips in the corridor, and since reckless deforestation has ruined whatever value this dry area once possessed, it is not surprising that population density is very low. The Tavoliere, however, is in process of reclamation. This 'chess-board' (about 60 miles long by 30 miles wide) is floored by Pliocene clays with a covering of sands and gravels, and in consequence is apt to dry out in summer and to become water-logged in winter; it was therefore devoted mainly to winter pasture for sheep which were taken in the summer to the mountains of Abruzzi and Molise. As the rivers dry up or are reduced to a mere trickle in summer, drinking water is scarce, so the region is not an easy area to live in; nevertheless, a good deal has been reclaimed and devoted to wheat cultivation, and the great Apulian aqueduct and its ramifications now supply part of the Tavoliere.

The Apulian aqueduct is one of the great engineering works of Europe. Work was begun in 1906, but the whole scheme was not completed until 1939. It involves the diversion of water from the westward-flowing River Sele by means of three tunnels, each about $9\frac{1}{2}$ miles long, through one of the Apennine ridges. The main aqueduct, which runs through Apulia parallel to, and about 15 to 20 miles inland from, the Adriatic coast is over 150 miles long and there are about 1,500 miles of subsidiary channels. At least two million people in one of the driest provinces of Italy are supplied with water by this means.

In spite of its lack of rivers, and until recently of good drinking water, the larger of the Apulian limestone plateaus, the Murge, is almost entirely cultivated. The coastal strip on either side of Bari has always been closely settled, but the colonisation of the thin and patchy covering of *terra rossa* further inland has been the work of the last hundred years. Dominated for centuries by the feudal sheep-grazing interests, it has been reclaimed piecemeal by an enterprising and tenacious peasantry whose livelihood depends on the cultivation of dry tree crops, especially vines, olives, and almonds. Apulia stands first in the country for the production of these three crops and is also noteworthy for its tobacco, particularly in the Lecce area. Except in that part of the Murge to the south-east of Bari where peculiar bee-hive-shaped stone farmhouses are common (*Murgia dei Trulli*), Apulia, like so many southern regions, has a very large proportion of its rural population grouped in large villages and towns. Foggia (117,000), to take a rather extreme example, was until recently almost entirely agricultural in function and many of its inhabitants are agricultural workers. Bari (311,000), on the other hand, is very different in character. It is the main commercial centre and port of Apulia and its rapidly expanding industries, notably in the field of food processing, chemicals, steel, and rubber, are second only to Naples in the south of Italy. Brindisi (70,000) and Taranto (191,000) too are benefiting from the drive to industrialise the south. The former has re-established its ancient link with the Balkans in the form of a car ferry service to Igoumenitsa and Patras and has been chosen as the site of a new petrochemical enterprise. At Taranto, formerly dependent on its rôle as a naval base, a new steel works, which it is hoped will become the core of an industrial complex, is nearing completion.

4. **Sicily.** Beyond the Straits of Messina, less than two miles across at their narrowest point, the Apennines sweep on westwards along the northern coast of Sicily. Lithologically they are far from homogeneous. In the east the Peloritani mountains are composed of gneiss and other crystalline rocks like the 'toe' of Calabria; further west in the Nebrodi mountains Tertiary sandstones and clays, similar to those of the northern Apennines, produce some very difficult terrain while in the Madonie mountains and in the hinterland of Palermo limestones provide the higher elements in the relief and incidentally act as useful natural reservoirs for the streams issuing from their flanks. The Sicilian Apennines themselves are of little agricultural value but along the coast are a number of narrow fertile lowlands where the intensive cultivation of citrus fruits helps to support a dense population. The plain of Palermo and the coastal strips in which Termini, Cefalu and Milazzo are situated are outstanding in this respect. Palermo itself (587,000), lying to the west of its sheltered gulf, is the main port and the capital of the autonomous region of Sicily. Despite its large population, it has few industries besides food processing and ship repairing.

Most of the south and centre of the island is composed of upper Tertiary clays and sands which have been eroded into a monotonous sea of rolling hills. Occasionally resistant limestone outcrops occur which assume the stature of mountains less from their height than from their ruggedness and isolation. The rivers in winter wander erratically across their bluff-bounded floodplains but they degenerate into a series of pools in the torrid summer. For the most part the empty countryside is treeless and hedgeless, a vast undulating expanse of green, sprouting wheat in spring and a parched wilderness of stubble in summer. Tree crops and vegetables are grown round the large hill-top villages in which the rural population is concentrated, but there is little scope for irrigation or diversification. Although there are more small proprietors than is generally realised, this is one of the traditional strongholds of the large estate (*latifondo*), an institution which has been receiving the attention of the land reform authorities since 1952. The *latifondo* relied mainly on the production of extensive wheat alternating with lentils or beans when the ground was not left fallow. Sheep are important in the economy and vines and olives are grown where the soil permits. Given the extremely difficult geographical conditions it is not easy to prescribe a more rewarding system of agriculture; in richer countries similar land would be abandoned altogether. In the Monti Erei, where limestones produce a more tabular landscape conditions are no better, but in the Monti Iblei, also predominantly limestone, sizeable areas are covered with basaltic lava and ash which encourage a wide development of tree crops.

The huge mass of Etna, 10,705 ft high and over 20 miles across, is separated from the central plateaus and the Apennines by a C-shaped tectonic depression. Most of the volcano's surface is a black wilderness of ash and lava, but on its lower slopes, where the weathered rock particles have been washed into pockets among the tortured lava streams, the soil is very fertile, producing vines, citrus fruits, and vegetables with the aid of irrigation. Catania (361,000) is the port and commercial centre for this productive and heavily populated region. The plain of Catania, like so many Mediterranean lowlands, suffers from the erratic behaviour of its rivers. In consequence the margins are more closely settled than the plain itself which is only now being systematically reclaimed under a comprehensive plan.

The landscape of the island to the west of Corleone is characterised by barren, isolated masses of limestone which emerge from an undulating expanse of less resistant sediments, mostly clays and soft sandstones. In this arid corner of Sicily the main speciality is viticulture, particularly along the coasts near Castellamare, Trapani, and Marsala; the latter gives its name to the famous, fortified red wine.

The economy of Sicily is, of course, overwhelmingly agricultural, but tunny fishing is locally of some importance at Trapani and there are a number of small sulphur mines in the centre of the island, especially near Caltanissetta (62,000). Much of the output is used to process imported phosphates at Porto Empedocle. Another useful mineral, only recently exploited, is the potash of the San Cataldo area. Sicily is also the country's main source of home-produced petroleum; the annual output, almost entirely from the Gela and Ragusa fields, is modest (under 2 million tons) but it has encouraged the establishment of petrochemical industries at Gela itself and along the gulf of Augusta. The capacity of these plants is far in excess of Sicilian production which is heavily supplemented by imports. The Augusta area has already developed into the most important industrial complex in the island. Tourism, a field in which Sicily has so much to offer, not least its climate and its Greek antiquities, is developing rapidly.

Despite the drive to rehabilitate its agriculture and develop its industry and tourism, Sicily remains one of the poorest regions of Italy, with a strong tradition of emigration. In the past the United States was the main goal of the emigrant but the exodus now is directed mainly to northern Italy, the Federal German Republic, Switzerland, and France.

**The Italian Tyrrhenian Islands.** Among these, apart from Sardinia, only the Lipari islands and the Tuscan archipelago are of any note. In the latter group Elba is of some importance for its iron ore, which is smelted on the mainland at Piombino, and for its growing tourist trade. The Lipari islands are of interest for their volcanoes, among them Vulcano itself, and Stromboli whose name has been borrowed to describe the continuous but relatively harmless form of volcanic activity typical of the mountain.

Sardinia, with almost exactly the same area as Sicily, has less than one-third of its population (1,143,000 compared with 4,711,000). The explanation of this striking difference is no doubt complex but one relevant item is certainly the impermeable character of so much of Sardinia's surface. Much of the island is composed of crystalline rocks on which water stagnates to provide a breeding place for the malarial mosquito. Furthermore, the rapid and erratic run-off from the impermeable surfaces has encouraged marsh development in the lowlands with the same evil consequences. Since 1947 a determined drive has been successful in controlling, if not eliminating, malaria – quite the most important event in the island's recent history.

Structurally Sardinia is a huge crystalline block fractured in the south to produce the Campidano lowlands.  The larger, northern

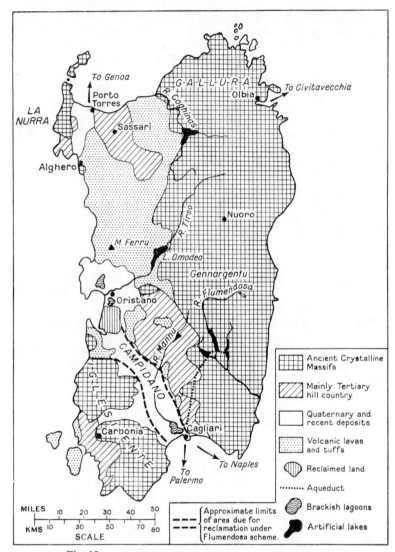

Fig. 18.  SIMPLIFIED GEOLOGICAL MAP OF SARDINIA

massif is covered in the west by Tertiary sediments and volcanic ash and lava, but roughly east of a line joining Cagliari and the mouth of the Coghinas river the ancient crystalline rocks – granites and gneisses in the north and schists further south – are exposed to form a high, rugged plateau rising to 6,016 ft in Gennargentu. Cork oak woodland, *maquis*, and rough pasture dominate the land use pattern except around the infrequent villages near which wheat and tree crops are grown. Nuoro (23,000) is the only town of significance in a huge zone whose economy is basically pastoral. The east coast is steep and inhospitable except in the north where Olbia, the packet port for Civitavecchia, stands on one of several rias. Even in the west of the massif where it is covered by Tertiary sedimentary and volcanic rocks, the population is sparse and the land is mainly given over to the extensive wheat production and to sheep grazing. In a few districts tree crops are of some importance, notably in the Sassari area which specialises in olives. Iglesiente, the detached block to the south of the Campidano rift, is no more productive than its northern counterpart, but it is of some significance for its minerals, especially lead, zinc, and coal. The last is mined at Carbonia and, being poor in quality, is used to produce thermal electricity.

The area with the greatest promise agriculturally is the Campidano. The northern end near Terralba, once a malarial marsh, was reclaimed and colonised between the wars, an achievement only made possible by the damming and control of the Tirso river for power and irrigation. Most of the rest of the Campidano, which is floored by Quaternary sediments, is still largely exploited for wheat and sheep grazing, but a project is well advanced which will enable much of it to be irrigated. The necessary water will be brought by tunnels from artificial lakes on the Flumendosa and its tributaries. The dams have already been built. Cagliari (181,000), situated on a hilly promontory which is flanked by sandspits and saline lagoons (now converted into salt pans), is the main commercial centre of the island with sea and air connexions to the mainland and Sicily. It has benefited from the boom in public works in the island since 1950; its biggest industry is the production of cement.

**Economic Summary.** With an area of 116,000 square miles, Italy in 1961 had a resident population of 50,460,000, an increase of 9·4 per cent over the 1951 figure. Despite the high proportion of hilly and mountainous terrain, nearly half the total area is classed as arable and nearly one tenth is under tree crops. The country is normally 80 per cent self-supporting in wheat and is capable of supplying most of the home demand for maize, rice, sugar-beet, wine, olive oil, vegetables, fruit, milk, and meat, although the consumption of animal foodstuffs is low by American standards. The principal agricultural products which Italy is obliged to import are the animal and vegetable fibres, mainly wool, jute, and cotton, tropical foodstuffs and beverages, notably coffee, cocoa, and vegetable oils, and rubber.    Fish is also imported in quantity – a reflection of the poverty of the Mediterranean in this respect.    The

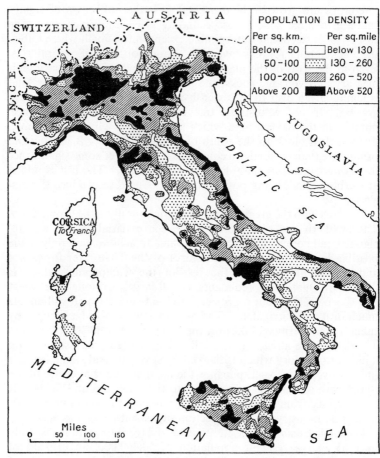

*(after E. Almagia)*

Fig. 19.    THE DISTRIBUTION OF POPULATION IN ITALY
NOTE: The present boundaries are shown.

impressive contribution of the northern plain to the total agricultural output will have already become apparent.

Since 1950 production in most sectors of agriculture has risen but the share of agriculture in the gross national product and in the total exports shows a continued decline as might be expected in a country in the throes of a rapid industrial expansion. Until the early 1950s the capacity of Italian industry remained obstinately low and the pressure of population manifested itself clearly in the form of unemployment, underemployment, low living standards, and social unrest. With the object of easing the situation in the countryside the government embarked on a vast programme of public works which not only provided immediate work for thousands of unemployed but also sought to carry out a fundamental rehabilitation of those areas which were suffering from the accumulated effects of centuries of neglect. Inevitably the effort has been concentrated in the South and the two main islands, but the Po delta and parts of Abruzzi, Lazio, and Tuscany are also benefiting, notably the Maremma. The programme, which is financed and coordinated by a government agency known as the *Cassa del Mezzogiorno* (The Southern Fund) includes reafforestation, soil conservation, and flood control, particularly in the uplands; the reclamation and settlement of wastelands, especially the formerly marshy plains along the Tyrrhenian and Ionian coasts and in Sicily and Sardinia; the extension of the irrigated area and the encouragement of agricultural diversification; the extension of the road system and the provision of water supplies, houses, schools, and other necessary amenities; the establishment of agricultural centres whose function is to furnish marketing facilities, technical advice, fertilisers, breeding stock, and machinery on loan. The implementation of the land reform is an integral part of the work of the *Cassa*; since 1952 about 1,680,000 acres have been surrendered, against compensation, by the larger landowners for the creation of thousands of small farms varying in size from 2 to 15 acres.

Italy exhibits a wide variety of farm types from large, highly capitalised units down to tiny subsistence holdings. Similarly there is a great variety in the forms of tenure; many of the more efficient farms are owned by private companies but peasant proprietorship is well represented. In central Italy many holdings are worked on a share-tenancy basis (*mezzadria*) while further south share-cropping is widely practised. Much remains to be done if Italian agriculture is to be put on a sound, competitive basis; far too many farms, particularly in the hilly areas and in the south generally, are too small and too ill-equipped to provide more than a meagre existence, and rural overpopulation in varying degrees is found almost everywhere. In the country as a whole, agricultural overpopulation has been put as high as 2 million. For many emigration has been the only escape from what appeared a hopeless situation. The direction of the emigrant stream has changed frequently over the last seventy years. Before 1915 and for a time after 1919 the United States, Argentina, Brazil, and France were the principal goals; after the second world war Venezuela and the British Dominions were popular outlets and in the last decade there has been a steadily mounting flood towards the expanding industrial areas of the Federal Republic of Germany, Switzerland, France, and not least the north of Italy itself.

The flight from the land and the rapid expansion of Italian industry emerge clearly from a comparison of the 1951 and the 1961 census figures. In 1951 the total engaged in agriculture was 8 million and in the manufacturing industries 6·4 million while ten years later the corresponding figures were 5·9 and 8·2 million. As a proportion of the active population this represents a decline from 41 per cent to 29 per cent in the case of agriculture and a rise from 32 per cent to 41 per cent in the case of industry. Although between the wars there was a notable expansion of industry, thanks very largely to the rapid and thorough development of the hydro-electric power resources of the Alps, Italy's progress in this field was halting and uneven. The home market was very limited and in the prevailing atmosphere of economic nationalism exports markets were difficult to win. Italy was markedly handicapped by a shortage of minerals and fuels – a hard fact which made nonsense of autarchy. Since the war, and particularly since 1953, Italy's position has changed radically for the better. She has seized the improved opportunities for export and at the same time the home market has expanded steadily. The lack of home-produced raw materials is no longer the handicap it once was since two major items, coal and oil, can now be imported fairly cheaply. Above all, the reserve of labour formerly tied up unrewardingly in agriculture is now being released to man the expanding industries.

As regards home-produced raw materials the outstanding developments since the war have been the discovery and exploitation of deposits of natural gas in the northern plain, and of oil in Sicily. Production is not likely to expand spectacularly but the discoveries came at an opportune moment and have stimulated a rapid expansion of the petrochemical industry. A state company (*Ente Nazionale Idrocarburi*) has a monopoly of natural gas production and is an active competitor in the oil business. Oil production has stood at about 2 million tons for some years but that of natural gas has risen steadily to exceed 7,000 million cubic metres in 1962, the equivalent of about 15 million tons of coal. With one of the largest refinery capacities in Europe, Italy is overwhelmingly dependent on imports, a sizeable proportion of which have been coming from the USSR in recent years. Apart from the plants near Milan, Trecate, Cortemaggiore, and Rome, the refineries are located on the coasts, notably at Genoa, Venice, Ravenna, La Spezia, Leghorn, Naples, Bari, and Augusta. Italy's coal production is of little significance; something under a million tons of low-grade coal are mined annually in south-west Sardinia and about 1,500,000 tons (1962) of brown coal in Tuscany, mainly in the upper Arno valley; in both cases the output is used mainly to produce thermal electricity. The other main source of energy is, of course, hydro-electricity, which reached an output of 42,000 million kWh in 1961, roughly twice the thermal production. The best sites have already been exploited and the share of hydro-electricity in the total energy consumption is declining steadily in favour of oil.

In addition to the mineral fuels mentioned above Italy possesses a wide variety of mineral raw materials, but with a few exceptions the deposits are small and incapable of any significant expansion. Limestone and clay are found in plenty in most regions and marble, particularly that from the Apuan Alps, is exported. Bauxite (322,000 tons in 1961) is also worked, mainly in the central Apennines, but Italy's reserves in this commodity were greatly reduced when Istria was ceded to Yugoslavia in 1945. This same area was also Italy's main source of mercury but fortunately she has other deposits in Tuscany which are capable of supplying her needs. The other minerals in which Italy is a sizeable producer are, with output in tons in 1961, lead (76,000) and zinc (240,000), both mainly from south-west Sardinia, sulphur (130,000), in which Italy once enjoyed a virtual monopoly, and pyrites, much of it from Tuscany. Other resources of interest to the chemical industry are salt from pans and from mines in Tuscany and elsewhere, and potash from the San Cataldo region of Sicily. Italy's production of iron ore (1,200,000 tons) is quite adequate for her growing needs; Elba is the biggest single source but small quantities are mined in western Sardinia and in the Val d'Aosta.

A more important sector of Italian industry, which has shown a marked expansion, is steel: in 1961 output had reached nearly 7 million tons, roughly three times the prewar figure. This achievement is largely attributable to the modernisation of the plants at Bagnoli and Piombino and the establishment of a large new works at Cornigliano. All these enterprises operate on water-borne fuel and ore, mostly American coal and West African ores. The Taranto plant which is nearing completion will expand production by 3 million tons. Except for the Aosta works, most of the older steel plants inland rely heavily on electric furnaces using scrap or pig produced elsewhere, and in consequence the main locational factors tended to be the market and the availability of electric power.

In the heavy engineering sector there has been a notable expansion in the capacity of Italy's shipyards, particularly at Genoa, which has the advantage of locally produced steel, and at Trieste. This industry has benefited from the need to replace the mercantile marine most of which was destroyed in the war and which now stands at over 5 million tons. Italy's yards, like those of Britain, were suffering in 1963 from the general fall in demand, both domestic and foreign. Other types of heavy engineering, especially in the electrical field, have made steadier and more sustained progress; Milan and Turin are overwhelmingly the most important centres. Light engineering, a sphere in which Italy has enjoyed a high reputation for some time, has expanded spectacularly since the war. Italy is a good fourth among the vehicle producers of Europe and has excelled in the manufacture of light cars, motor cycles, and motor scooters; a large part of the production, in which Milan and Turin are again pre-eminent, is exported. Electrical consumer goods, machine tools, typewriters, and calculating machines are other products in which Italy is a lively competitor in world markets.

In common with all industrialised countries the chemical industry of Italy has enjoyed a notable expansion over the last decade. With considerable resources of salt, sulphur, pyrites, potash, borax, and zinc Italy is in a stronger position as regards raw materials for this enterprise than she is for most others. She has also the advantage of considerable resources of hydro-electric power for the electro-chemical sector and of natural gas for petrochemicals, although the spectacular expansion in this field has been achieved only with the aid of very large imports of oil. Although one firm dominates all but the petrochemical side of the industry, and the North, as in most manufactures, has more than a fair share of the output, there are a large number of plants up and down the country, quite a few of them in areas such as Tuscany, Apulia and Sicily, which are poorly represented in other industrial activities. This is explained partly by the disposition of raw materials, partly by the dispersed character of the market for such commodities as cement and fertilisers, and partly by the influence of government planning.

After the mechanical industries and construction work, textile manufacturing is the biggest employer of labour (592,000). Italy is a major producer of cotton, rayon, wool, silk, and nylon yarn and fabrics and commands a considerable share in the world export market in these commodities, although in textiles as a whole the expansion has been modest when compared with that of vehicles and chemicals – a situation mirrored in many other European countries. The share of the northern plain, and in particular its Alpine margins, in this activity has already been emphasised. The same area is also pre-eminent in the clothing industry although on a workshop basis this manufacture is represented in almost every town.

With so much of the country's food produced at home the alimentary industries are inevitably of great importance. They include milling, malting, brewing, the manufacture of pasta, cheese, confectionery, and preserved meats, as well as the processing of wine, olive oil, vegetables, and fruit. As might be expected every agricultural region of any significance shares in this industry whose products figure substantially among Italy's exports, but the contributions of Campania and the Po valley are particularly large.

Two activities which tend to pass unnoticed are the construction industry and the tourist industry; in 1961 the former employed over 900,000 workers and the latter over 400,000. Even more important numerically are those employed in commercial pursuits – the wholesale and retail trades, banks, insurance, etc. – and in the servicing industries, particularly transport. All told these occupations in 1961 engaged well over one-third of the non-agricultural labour force.

The dominance of the North in the distribution of Italian industry and the absence of conurbations such as are found on the coalfields of Germany and Britain need not be further elaborated, but at least three other characteristics of Italian industry deserve passing mention. The first is the importance of a small group of very large concerns, each dominant in its particular field; this is best illustrated in the cases of rubber, cars, chemicals, and typewriters. The second is the large number of workpeople still employed in small units, particularly in tailoring, pottery, metalware, glass, leatherware, and furniture, all of them trades in which the tradition of craftsmanship survives. Thirdly, the state is in a position to influence the policy and distribution of many sectors of industry not only through the nationalised concerns proper (e.g. railways and electricity) but also through its financial holdings in many famous enterprises engaged in the production of steel, petrochemicals, ships, and engineering goods.

*Trade.* Italy must now be recognised not only as a major industrial nation but also as a major trading nation. Over the last decade the value of her trade has expanded very substantially and at the same time there has been a shift in emphasis in the items of which it is composed. Among the exports, manufactures, notably textiles, clothing, machinery, chemicals, and oil products, account for an increasing proportion of the total while farm and forest products show very little expansion. As regards imports, agricultural produce, particularly wheat, animal products and coffee, make up nearly one-third of the total (1961). In the mineral group oil is overwhelmingly the most important item, followed at a distance by coal. Somewhat surprisingly manufactures have made up about half the imports in recent years, a fact explained in part by the increasing complexity of the Italian economy. Italy's principal trading partners are the United States, the Federal Republic of Germany, France, the United Kingdom, Switzerland, Austria, and the oil-producing countries of the Middle East. A newcomer to the list is the USSR on which Italy depends for much of her oil. The balance of payments relies heavily on invisible items; these include emigrant remittances (a very substantial total with so many workers temporarily abroad) and the earnings from tourism and from various services, for example construction work, in which the Italians have earned a considerable reputation.

A continued expansion in world trade is fundamental to Italy's economic and social progress and in consequence she has become an active member of most organisations aimed at liberalising trade and reducing tariff barriers. Inevitably Italy is a member of the European Economic Community but with so many vital trading connexions outside that area it is in her interests to promote an outward-looking Community rather than an exclusive, introspective one.

## REFERENCES

The most readily available books in English which deal in any detail with the geography of Italy are D. S. Walker, *A Geography of Italy*, London, Methuen, 1967; M. I. Newbigin, *Southern Europe*, revised by R. J. Harrison Church, London, Methuen, 1949; and *The Mediterranean Lands*, revised ed., London, Methuen, 1962. The following should also be consulted: R. E. Dickinson, *The Population Problem in Southern Italy*, New York, Syracuse University Press, 1955; C. L. Dozier, 'Establishing a Framework for Development in Sardinia; the Campidano', *Geog. Review*, 47, 1957; L. Unger 'Rural settlement in Campania', *Geog. Review*, 43, 1953.

There is a rich literature in Italian but two books which cover the whole country deserve special mention, namely, R. Almagià, *L'Italia* (two vols.), Turin, Unione Tipografica, 1960, which is strong on the human and agrarian aspects; and F. Milone, *L'Italia nell'economia delle sue regioni*, Turin, Einaudi, 1958. Many of the publications of the Touring Club Italiano are rich in geographical material, in particular Vol. I, *L'Italia Fisica*, Vol. II, *La Flora*, and Vol. VII, *Il Paesaggio*, of the series *Conosci l'Italia*. The Touring Club is also associated with the land utilisation map of Italy on a scale of 1:200,000 which is being published under the auspices of the Consiglio Nazionale delle Ricerche, Rome. The work is under the direction of Prof. C. Colamonico, and Prof. F. Milone is one of several distinguished collaborators who have produced memoirs on the maps. So far only maps of Sicily and the Peninsula have been issued. Milone's book, *Sicilia: La Natura e L'Uomo*, Rome, Boringhieri, 1961, is the most recent survey of that island.

Among many French contributions to the geographical literature of Italy the following in particular deserve to be consulted: P. Birot and J. Dresch, *La Méditerranée et Le Moyen Orient*, Vol. I, Paris, Presses Universitaires de France, 1953; G. Chaine, 'Problèmes agricoles sur les bords septentrionaux du Bassin

Méditerranéen', *Annales de Géographie*, 68, 1959; A. M. Seronde, 'Les régions sous-développées de l'Italie, *Annales de Géographie*, 65, 1956; M. Le Lannou, *Pâtres et Paysans de la Sardaigne*, Tours, Arrault, 1941.

On Malta the most recent survey is B. S. Young, 'The Maltese Islands: Economic Problems and Prospects for Industrial Developments', *Geog. Review*, 53, 1963.

### CHAPTER 7

# THE IBERIAN PENINSULA

THE Iberian peninsula is the largest and most compact of the three southern peninsulas, and in contrast to the others it has the greater part of its area occupied by plateau. Consequently, in spite of being washed by the Atlantic Ocean as well as the Mediterranean Sea, it is more continental than the Italian peninsula or than Greece and hardly less continental than the interior of the South-eastern peninsula. The old saying that 'Africa begins at the Pyrenees' sums up the plateau character, the aridity, the great treeless spaces, which are common to large sections of both regions, and the long sojourn of the Moors in Spain emphasised the likenesses between the Iberian peninsula and the lands on the southern side of the Mediterranean. The saying, however, is misleading, since the comparison is only with North Africa, and it is equally true that 'Europe ends at the Atlas'.

**Relief and Structure.** The greater part of the peninsula is occupied by a mountain-ribbed plateau, averaging about 2,200 ft in height, known as the Meseta (='table'), which slopes gradually westward to the Portuguese lowlands from the Iberian Mountains which form the main water-parting of the peninsula. The plateau is bordered on the north by the lofty Cantabrian Mountains and on its southern edge by the lower Sierra Morena. It is also ribbed by two lines of high sierras running from east-north-east to west-south-west, the northern line being known under various names, from the Sierra de Guadarrama in the east to the Serra da Estrela in Portugal, but may conveniently be termed the Central Sierras. The southern line, which is less imposing, is known in its two highest ranges as the Sierra de Guadalupe and the Montes de Toledo. The Central Sierras divide the plateau into two main basins, which are surrounded on all sides, with the exception of certain gaps in the west, by higher and more rugged country. The surrounding mountain ramparts fall abruptly on their outer sides either directly to the coast or to narrow coastal lowlands, as on the north and south-east, or to great depressions as on the east and south in the Ebro basin and Andalusian basin respectively. On the farther side of each of these depressions rise mighty mountain ranges, namely, the Pyrenees to the north of the Ebro basin, and the Betic Cordillera to the south of the Andalusian depression. Coastal plains are generally absent, although the swampy threshold of the Andalusian or Guadalquivir depression borders the ocean, and there are lowlands midway along the Portuguese coast. There is also a conspicuous absence of deep bays and coastal indentations, except in the north-western corner of the peninsula, and in consequence good harbours are rare.

The structure of Iberia is a complicated one. Its geological history shows a long succession of mountain building extending from pre-Cambrian to Tertiary times, with intervening periods of peneplanation and sinking, but generally speaking, the land mass grew by accretions eastward or south-eastward.

The north-western part of the peninsula, comprising Galicia and northern Portugal, shows the roots of a Pre-Cambrian folded system similar to that of the Baltic shield and consisting mainly of granites, gneiss, slates, quartzites, and crystalline schists. The greater part of the Central Sierras also shows these old rocks on the surface (see Fig. 20). There are traces of a folded zone of Caledonian age, but these are very scanty and completely overshadowed by folded rocks of the next great period of earth disturbance, namely, the Hercynian, which took place at the close of Carboniferous times. According to R. Staub, the Hercynian folds make a great S-shaped bend on the eastern edge of the Archæan block, with a pronounced change of direction at the eastern end of the present Sierra de Guadarrama. Large segments of this old double arc are concealed under the Tertiary deposits of the Central Meseta, so that certainty in the matter is difficult to obtain, and though Staub's hypothesis is very attractive, it is not accepted by many Spanish geologists nor by Stille.

From the close of the Palæozoic onwards the region experienced a tranquil period during which even the great Hercynian mountains were worn down to their roots. Seas and lakes covered much of the old surfaces, and in these, Mesozoic and Tertiary materials were deposited, though the north-western corner of the peninsula has apparently been above water since pre-Cambrian times.

In spite of the early paroxysms mentioned above, the main lines of the present-day relief are due almost entirely to the mountain-building epoch which began at the close of Mesozoic times. At this period earth movements buckled the floor of the old 'Mediterranean' Sea or 'Tethys' into the true Alpine folds of the Betic Cordillera, which stretch from Cadiz to Cape de la Nao, and they also buckled up large parts of the more consolidated rocks of the 'European' foreland to the north. The Pyrenees, the Basque Mountains, and the Cantabrian Mountains were formed at this time, though parts of these areas had already undergone folding

in Hercynian times. The Iberian Mountains and Catalonian
Mountains are also attributed to the Tertiary era, and even the
Central Sierras, the Toledo Mountains, and the Sierra Morena
were in part a response to these later thrusts.

Naturally the amount of folding or deformation that took place

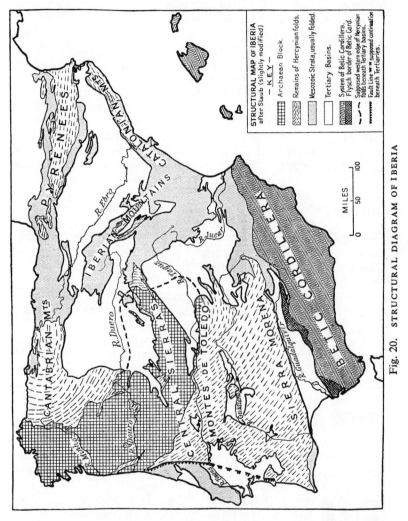

Fig. 20.   STRUCTURAL DIAGRAM OF IBERIA

depended on the plasticity of the material involved, and as the ranges
of the Meseta were re-formed out of tough old material, faulting
rather than folding was responsible for the elevation of the Central

Sierras, the Montes de Toledo, and the Sierra Morena. On the other hand, the Pyrenees, the Iberian Mountains, and the Catalonian Mountains included much Mesozoic material previously unfolded, though both systems incorporated portions of the old massif. Apart from the Pyrenees, none of these chains shows the *nappes* or *Decken* typical of the true Alpine folds, and even in the Pyrenees these are not well developed, so that fundamentally the mass of Iberia belongs to Hercynian Europe and is allied structurally to the central massif of France, the Bohemian massif, etc. This contrasts with the Betic Cordillera where full development of *nappes* has taken place, and which may therefore be compared with the Alps and the Apennines as belonging to the Alpides, the young folded mountain zone of Eurasia.

Equally important is the fact that, at the end of Tertiary times, the whole of the old land mass underwent epeirogenic, or vertical, elevation. This movement of re-elevation was responsible for many of the most characteristic minor features of the landscape at the present day. For instance, the rejuvenation of the river systems consequent upon the epeirogenic movement led to the incising of the river valleys, and to the development of the innumerable gorges which are such a hindrance to communications. The interior saline lakes were also drained off and give the present plateau basins of Old Castile–Leon and of New Castile, with their great stretches of level land. Moreover, the re-elevation was carried to such heights that gradients from the coast to the interior are everywhere severe, except along the central part of the Portuguese coast.

The Portuguese lowlands escaped great uplift owing to the development of a great north–south fault, which is traceable from the mouth of the Douro river almost as far as Cape St Vincent.

**Climate and Vegetation.** The position of the Iberian peninsula between the Mediterranean and the Atlantic might be expected to promote a more equable and more humid climate than is experienced in its Italian counterpart. That this is not the case is attributable to the behaviour of the relevant air masses and their associated divergences, to the size and compactness of the peninsula and to the nature of its relief. In winter Iberia comes under the influence of Polar Maritime and Tropical Maritime air; the depressions which have their origin along the divergence of these two masses (i.e. the Polar Front) result in precipitation over the entire peninsula but its distribution is markedly in favour of the north and west coasts. The relative dryness of so much of the centre and east of the peninsula at this season is partially explained by the interior position of these areas in relation to the rain-bearing influences, but another contributory cause is the tendency of depressions to be diverted

either along the north coast or along the south coast by the barrier
of the Meseta block and by the high pressure which tends to establish itself over the peninsula in winter.   This high pressure develops
in response to the continentality of the peninsula and the elevation
of the plateau.   In fact most places in the interior have two precipitation maxima, one in spring and another in late autumn.   By the
end of June a north-easterly extension of the Azores high establishes
itself over Iberia and southern France.   The Biscayan and north
Atlantic coastlands, which are cooler than any other region of the

Fig. 21.   IBERIA: GEOGRAPHICAL REGIONS

peninsula in summer, continue to be visited by Atlantic depressions,
but the rest of Iberia is subject to the desiccating influence of Tropical
Continental air moving in from the south.   Although a weak low
sometimes develops over the Iberian land mass the associated inward-
moving air tends to rise in temperature and in consequence no rainfall results.

Although some sections, particularly in the south-east, were never
much better than steppe, most of the Meseta was originally lightly
forested with evergreen oaks.   Much of this forest cover fell a

victim to the reprisals carried out by both sides during the wars of the Reconquest, and subsequently the woodlands dwindled further as a result of the dominance of powerful pastoral interests in the state and the demand for arable land. Considerable tracts of forest survive, however, particularly in the sierras and in Estremadura. Not all the deforested area has proved itself suitable for permanent tillage and vast areas are clothed with *garrigue* or *matorral* (cf. *maquis*) of little value even for grazing. Many areas of the Meseta are now receiving the active attention of the state forestry services.

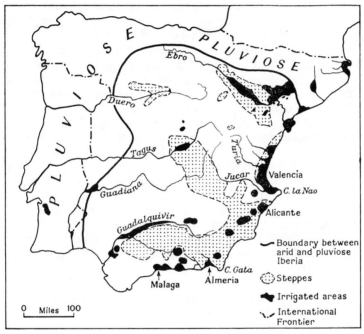

Fig. 22. STEPPES AND IRRIGATED LANDS OF SPAIN

Although there is a broad uniformity of climate throughout the Meseta, in the half of it north of the Central Sierras the slightly greater altitude and higher latitude result in more severe winters which are unfavourable to olive cultivation. The spring rains and the hot, dry summer favour extensive wheat and barley cultivation and viticulture. The low rainfall and its notorious unreliability increase the need for irrigation but the areas where this is possible are limited because of the incision of many of the main rivers into the plateau and the saline character of many of the soils. The climate of the Ebro basin is basically similar to that of the Meseta but the advantages of a somewhat lower altitude are offset by the chilling effect of cold air draining from the surrounding highlands.

A division of Iberia into two rainfall regions, pluviose and arid, is in some ways more helpful than that between its areas of Mediterranean and north-west European climate. The pluviose region, with over 600 mm or 24 in of rain, includes the western, northern, and north-eastern margins of the peninsula, i.e. most of Portugal, all Galicia, the Cantabrian and Basque region, the Pyrenees, and the Catalonian Mountains. The area which may be said to have a north-west European type of climate is rather more restricted, since it includes only the northern margins of Spain and Portugal as far as the River Douro, and the western and central Pyrenees.

The Biscayan coast-lands and northern Portugal are marked off from the rest of the peninsula by having their rainfall well distributed throughout the year and no dry season. Summer temperatures are rather lower than in the Mediterranean sections, but the warm dampness of the lowland and valleys is more oppressive than the drier heat of the Mediterranean. Fortunately the extensive mountainous country gives bracing air, and the region may be said to combine the advantages of both the north-west European and the Mediterranean types of climate from the point of view of plant life, as does the basin of Aquitaine in France which has a similar climate. The rainfall is heavy and constant enough for good cattle pasture and forest, and though the summers are not quite hot or dry enough for the olive they are long enough for the vine, while the characteristic fruits of central and western Europe also flourish, and both maize and wheat can be grown. The diversity of produce is obviously great.

All the rest of the peninsula can be classified as Mediterranean in climate, though the modifications on the Meseta and in the Ebro basin are great. There is an abrupt change on the southern side of the Cantabrian Mountains from a humid climate with small daily ranges of temperature to an arid climate with marked contrasts between day and night temperatures. The Meseta generally has scanty rain, clear skies, hot, dusty summer days, cold, sunny winter days, and a marked drop of temperature at sunset at all seasons.

The Catalonian Mountains resemble central Italy in climate and crops, but south of the Ebro the Mediterranean coastlands are drier than southern Italy, and especially in Murcia very little will grow without irrigation. The Andalusian depression is similar in climate to the Mediterranean coastlands, since it has high winter temperatures, though the rainfall is rather greater than on the Murcian coast (see statistics below).

The Portuguese lands south of the Douro have a heavier rainfall than the interior, greater atmospheric humidity, and higher winter temperatures. The climate favours a rather profuse development of Mediterranean vegetation, and there is even enough rainfall for maize, which is not a typical Mediterranean plant owing to the large quantities of water it demands.

| Station | Latitude | Mean monthly Temperatures | | | | Annual rainfall in inches |
| | | Jan. | | July | | |
| | | °F | °C | °F | °C | |
|---|---|---|---|---|---|---|
| Bilbao | 43° 20' | 46 | 7·8 | 70 | 21·1 | 46 ⎫ Biscayan type |
| Santiago | 42° 53' | 46 | 7·8 | 66 | 18·9 | 65 ⎭ |
| Lisbon | 38° 42' | 49 | 9·5 | 70 | 21·1 | 29 S. Portuguese type |
| Seville | 37° 23' | 52 | 11·1 | 85 | 29·4 | 19 ⎫ Andalusian and |
| Murcia | 37° 59' | 50 | 10·0 | 79 | 26·1 | 15 ⎭ Valencian type |
| Barcelona | 41° 23' | 47 | 8·3 | 74 | 23·3 | 21 Catalonian type |
| Burgos | 42° 20' | 35 | 1·7 | 64 | 17·8 | 22 ⎫ Meseta type |
| Madrid | 40° 24' | 40 | 4·4 | 77 | 25·0 | 17 ⎭ |
| Zaragoza | 41° 38' | 41 | 5·0 | 76 | 24·4 | 12 Ebro basin sub-type |

MEAN RAINFALL IN INCHES AND MILLIMETRES

| | Jan. | Feb. | Mar. | Apr. | May | June | July | Aug. | Sep. | Oct. | Nov. | Dec. | Total |
|---|---|---|---|---|---|---|---|---|---|---|---|---|---|
| Santiago | 7·8 | 6·4 | 6·7 | 5·3 | 5·2 | 2·5 | 2·0 | 2·4 | 5·2 | 6·7 | 7·3 | 7·6 | 65·1 |
| | 197 | 162 | 170 | 134 | 132 | 63 | 51 | 61 | 132 | 170 | 185 | 192 | 1653 |
| Lisbon | 3·7 | 3·3 | 3·8 | 2·8 | 2·1 | 0·5 | 0·2 | 0·3 | 1·3 | 3·0 | 3·7 | 4·0 | 28·7 |
| | 94 | 84 | 96 | 71 | 53 | 12 | 5 | 7 | 33 | 76 | 93 | 101 | 729 |
| Seville | 2·1 | 1·9 | 2·5 | 1·9 | 1·7 | 0·6 | 0·0 | 0·2 | 0·7 | 1·9 | 2·4 | 2·7 | 18·6 |
| | 53 | 48 | 63 | 48 | 43 | 15 | 0 | 5 | 17 | 48 | 61 | 68 | 472 |
| Murcia | 1·2 | 1·1 | 1·3 | 1·6 | 1·5 | 0·7 | 0·3 | 0·2 | 1·9 | 1·9 | 1·5 | 1·9 | 15·1 |
| | 30 | 27 | 33 | 40 | 37 | 17 | 7 | 5 | 48 | 48 | 37 | 48 | 384 |
| Barcelona | 1·4 | 1·5 | 1·8 | 1·9 | 1·7 | 1·5 | 1·0 | 1·3 | 3·0 | 3·1 | 1·8 | 1·4 | 21·4 |
| | 35 | 37 | 45 | 48 | 43 | 37 | 25 | 33 | 76 | 78 | 45 | 35 | 543 |
| Madrid | 1·3 | 1·3 | 1·6 | 1·6 | 1·7 | 1·3 | 0·4 | 0·5 | 1·5 | 1·8 | 2·0 | 1·6 | 16·6 |
| | 33 | 33 | 40 | 40 | 43 | 33 | 10 | 12 | 37 | 45 | 51 | 40 | 422 |

**The Heart of the Peninsula, the Meseta.** The term Meseta will here be used in its geographical sense to indicate the high tablelands of central Iberia, and not in the manner of many geologists who use the term to cover the whole of the so-called Archæan and Hercynian 'block,' regardless of relief.

The Central Sierras divide the Meseta into two sub-sections, that to the north lying in the old provinces of Old Castile (Span., Castilla la Vieja) and Leon, and that to the south in New Castile (Span.,

Castilla la Nueva) and Estremadura. These plateau basins, though mainly surrounded by higher and more rugged country, are themselves high, that of Old Castile and Leon averaging about 2,500 ft, and that of New Castile averaging about 2,200 ft. Considerable portions of these basins were once covered with saline lakes, and the floor of old rocks is therefore masked to a great extent by extensive deposits of Tertiary and later material; where these occur there are wide stretches of almost level plateau, particularly in the central part of Old Castile, in eastern Leon, and in the central part of New Castile, known as La Mancha. Elsewhere the relief is rather rugged, especially in Estremadura, to the west of New Castile, where the ancient rocks have only intermittent patches of Tertiary material overlying them, and erosion, working on the different bands of old rock, has tended to produce a ribbed effect parallel to the strike, which is here mainly north-west to south-east. Further, the land round the rim of the basins is usually well dissected by rivers coming from the surrounding heights.

*The Northern Meseta.* This plateau basin, which stretches for some 110 miles from east to west and some 140 miles from north to south, is mainly covered by horizontal Tertiary deposits consisting of clays, marls, limestones, and sandstones. Wide, tawny expanses of monotonous, treeless plateau have developed, but the different types of rocks have offered an unequal resistance to erosion, and so have given rise to contrasting types of land utilisation. The softer rocks such as the clays and marls, have weathered into extensive basins and plains, where, on very fertile red soils, cereals such as wheat and barley can be grown, as in the Tierra de Campos west of Palencia and the Tierra del Pan north of Zamora. The harder rocks, among which limestones predominate, form higher and drier tablelands, called *páramos*, often terminating in a *cuesta* or scarp overlooking the cereal lands. These limestone plateaus are devoid of water, and though at best they somewhat resemble the Apulian plateaus of Italy, usually they are much less productive and are used mainly for sheep pasture. Similarly unproductive are the great stretches of coarse gravels which surround the basin and which are formed of recent detritus from the mountain rim. The Duero and its tributaries which drain the basin are mainly incised into the plateau, though they are accompanied, especially in their lower reaches, by alluvial terraces, which give rise to fertile soil, and in a few places may be irrigated.

It appears that the plateau may once have carried a good deal of forest cover and there are remnants of pine woods and of evergreen oak woods. There is very little true steppe except in the region round Valladolid, where the annual rainfall averages less than

12 in. The limestone plateaus carry poor *matorral*. Bleak and frosty in winter, hot, dusty, and very dry in summer, the northern Meseta offers a hard environment.

Most of the northern Meseta is classed as *secano*, that is unirrigated arable land on which extensive wheat or barley alternates with a grazed fallow, but in Zamora and Segovia provinces there are extensive vineyards while elsewhere many areas are suitable only for sheep pasture. The population density is low, rarely much more than 100 per square mile and settlement is concentrated in numerous

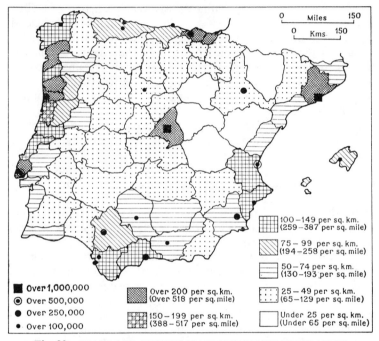

Fig. 23. SPAIN AND PORTUGAL: DENSITIES OF POPULATION

large villages and a few sizeable towns. Until recently these towns relied almost exclusively on their functions as communications, marketing, processing, and administrative centres, but recently with government encouragement and the development of hydro-electric power on the Esla and the lower Duero a few industrial enterprises have been established. For example, Medina del Campo has aluminium refineries, and Valladolid (145,000), a considerable communications centre on the main line from San Sebastian to Lisbon, once the capital of Castile and still the most important city of the northern Meseta, has added electrical and vehicle manufactures to its traditional food and processing activities.   The ancient city of Salamanca (90,000) is remembered chiefly for its university.   The small towns of Avila and Segovia, the former famous for its walls and the latter for its Roman aqueduct, are within easy reach of the capital and are developing a useful tourist trade.   Burgos (90,000) controls the main gap through the highland rim of north-east Old Castile, which gives access to both San Sebastian and the Ebro basin.

*The Central Sierras* rise gradually from the northern Meseta and drop abruptly on the southern side.   These mountains, consisting largely of granite and crystalline schists, reach a height of 8,501 ft in the Sierra de Gredos, carry snow in winter, and were sufficiently high for the highest summits to carry glaciers and to be carved by cirques in the Quaternary Ice Age.   As a rule, however, the pre-existing peneplain character is still sufficiently retained to give plateau-like and rounded forms.   There are a few fragments of the old pine and oak forests remaining, but generally the mountains are bare apart from scrubby pasturage.   Transhumant sheep and goats are driven up for the summer from the surrounding plateau, and human beings also take refuge in the cooler mountain air from the summer heat of Madrid.

The water resources of the Central Sierras, and in particular those of the Sierra Guadarrama, are being increasingly controlled for the benefit of the capital and for the extension of irrigation to the south of it.   In spite of their height the Central Sierras are not a great barrier to communications as there are many easy passes, some of them associated with faults.

*The Southern Meseta.*   Here there are two contrasted regions, New Castile with Tertiary sediments, level relief and monotonous aspect, and the more rugged and somewhat better-watered country to the west in Estremadura where the old rocks appear on the surface.

In New Castile the clays of the central portion, known as La Mancha, have an indeterminate drainage, and hold up water in lagoons which usually dry up in summer.   It is interesting to note that the new cycle of erosion has scarcely reached La Mancha, and river valleys, where they exist, are shallow and not incised.   The evaporation of these expanses of surface water has led to the development of widespread saline deposits in which only salt-loving vegetation flourishes.   Much of La Mancha may be classed as esparto steppe and may be compared with the Chott plateau of Algeria.   The tufty esparto is of some commercial value but sheep rearing, the traditional pursuit, is the main prop of the economy. Farther west, where the soils are less saline, secano cereal production is the dominant activity, although in Ciudad Real province there are vast areas devoted to olives and vines, the latter particularly in the Valdepeñas–Manzanares district. Sheep graze the extensive fallows and fit well into the economy of the secano areas. The settlement pattern is similar to that of much of Old Castile, large isolated villages set in an apparently empty and monotonous countryside. In the immediate vicinity of these villages, which are usually dominated by the church and the more recently built grain silo, there are often a few plots of irrigated land fed from wells, but the only sizeable irrigated areas in New Castile are to be found in the Tagus (Sp., Tajo) valley. The bluff-bordered floodplain between Toledo and Aranjuez has long supported a varied agriculture including fruit, maize, sugar-beet, and fodder, while the cultivation of the great expanse of alluvial wash to the south of Madrid is being increasingly intensified with the control of waters from the Sierra. East of Madrid, in the region known as La Alcarria, wide tablelands of infertile limestone separate the much more rewarding valleys of the Tagus and its headwater tributaries. This region is transitional to the Iberian mountains.

Estremadura is a region of greater variety of relief, soils, and agriculture, and of somewhat greater rainfall. On its large surfaces of old, often impermeable rock, such as slates, quartzites, and granites, extensive areas of cork and evergreen oak woodland survive. The trees provide their bark, loppings for making charcoal and above all acorns, which support large herds of pigs. Sheep are also grazed, particularly during the winter when Estremadura is one of the receiving areas for transhumant flocks, and at infrequent intervals the clearings are ploughed to produce a crop of wheat or barley. This apparently wasteful form of land use has stood the test of time and has the great virtue of conserving the soil cover. The traditional Mesetan type of agriculture based on cereals, olives, and vines, is practised on the more fertile Tertiary clays of the Tierra de Barros, to the south-east of Badajoz, and efforts are now being made to exploit more fully the irrigation potentialities of the Guadiana. The Badajoz depression is the scene of one of several schemes in the southern Meseta aimed at intensifying the agriculture by means of irrigation. Several multi-purpose dams on the Guadiana and its tributaries have been built and a planned recolonisation of the area is being carried out.

The towns of the southern Meseta, like those of the northern half, are modest in size and widely spaced. Essentially they are provincial market centres with few industries apart from agricultural processing. Such are Badajoz (99,000), set in one of the more favoured agricultural basins with routes into Portugal, and Albacete (75,000), controlling the gap through which the railway passes to Alicante and Murcia.   The repetitive uniformity of the demographic pattern is interrupted by the rapidly growing city of Madrid (2,260,000). Standing as it does on a bleak, sandy plateau poorly supplied with water, it seems to have few local advantages of site.   In fact, it owes its importance to its central position in the peninsula for which reason it was chosen in the sixteenth century as the capital of a state whose rulers, with few exceptions, have sought a solution to the centrifugal tendencies of the periphery in a highly centralised administration.   Inevitably with the development of railways and a modern road system Madrid became their focus, but until very recently, except for such activities as food processing, printing, and the transport services, the city has had little industry.   In recent years, however, Madrid has attracted a variety of industries including vehicles, electrical equipment, furniture, pharmaceutical products, and other consumer goods.   The city becomes more representatively Spanish each year as workers flock in from the provinces, particularly in response to the demands of the construction industry, which is the biggest employer of unskilled labour.   Despite these developments Madrid remains essentially a city of bureaucrats and of 'white collar' workers employed in banks, insurance offices, stores, and agencies of various kinds.   Industrially and even commercially, Barcelona, although smaller, is still of greater significance.

**The Sierra Morena** rises very gradually from the central Meseta and is only a little above the level of the high plateau.   On the south, however, it sinks abruptly by means of a great fault to the Guadalquivir depression.   Although it has the character of a highly dissected plateau and is barren and scantily populated, yet it is particularly rich in minerals, especially copper and iron pyrites, which are mined today mainly in the Rio Tinto district; silver-lead, mined in the Linares district; and mercury, from the famous mines of Almaden.   These deposits are largely associated with igneous intrusions.   The small coalfields of Carboniferous age, south-west of Ciudad Real (Puertollano) and north-west of Córdoba (Belmez), have some importance in an area which otherwise is very deficient in fuel.

**The Iberian Mountains.**   These folded ranges rise only gradually from the Meseta on the west but drop rapidly to the Ebro depression. They run for a distance of nearly 300 miles in a south-easterly direction from just south of Burgos nearly to the Mediterranean coast, where they overlook the plains of Valencia and Castellon. The ranges reach a height of 7,684 ft in the north where they are about 60 miles wide, and about 6,600 ft in the south, where, however, they average 100 miles in breadth.   Their height, width, and barren character make them a formidable obstacle; in fact they formed the frontier between the old kingdoms of Castile and Aragon. There are two gaps, however, which allow movement between the Ebro depression and the Meseta. Between the Iberian Mountains and the Cantabrian Mountains is the transverse depression of Burgos filled with Tertiary material, while in the middle of the system is the gap along the River Jalon. The Teruel depression allows communication between the middle of the Ebro depression and Valencia. All three are followed by rail, the Jalon valley taking the main railway line between Madrid and Zaragoza. These mountains have the melancholy distinction of having the lowest population densities of Spain, the Soria and Teruel provinces each having 39 per square mile.

**The Ebro Depression.** Wedged between the Pyrenees and the Iberian Mountains, and isolated from the Mediterranean by the massifs of Catalonia, lies the Ebro depression, once the core of the kingdom of Aragon. It is floored by thick, horizontal deposits of sandstones and marls which were laid down in the Tertiary era when the area was occupied by an inland sea. The Ebro and its tributaries have incised themselves deeply into these deposits to form a pattern of narrow floodplains separated by wide plateaus, which have been eroded into terraces and mesas. Although the climate is basically that of the Meseta, the Ebro basin has the great advantage of abundant supplies of water from the Pyrenees and to a much less extent from the Iberian mountains. The diversion of the rivers into canals to irrigate the floodplains was a comparatively easy matter and was achieved in the case of the Ebro by the Canal Imperial de Aragon and the Canal de Tauste. The irrigation of the lower interfluves in the Lerida area was more difficult but the construction of the Canal de Urgel (1861), from the Segre river, and of the Canal de Aragon y Cataluña (1910), from the Noguera Ribagorzana, marked important stages in the construction of a network of channels which enabled nearly 400,000 acres to be irrigated. Since then the irrigated area has been considerably extended with the construction of multi-purpose dams on almost all the Pyrenean feeders of the Ebro. Even so, vast areas of steppe remain; locally they produce a scanty crop of wheat or support a few acres of vines or olives, but the majority of their surface is of no value except as meagre grazing for flocks of transhumant sheep on their way up to the Pyrenean summer pastures. In some areas the state forestry services are planting these thirsty lands with drought-resisting conifers.

The extension of the irrigated area over the high interfluves is hindered by the terrain and by the porous and saline nature of so much of the surface; furthermore, there is obviously a limit to the amount of water which can readily be made available. In those areas which are well supplied with water a great variety of crops is grown including autumn-sown wheat, barley, oats, beans, lentils, and potatoes, and spring-sown sugar-beet, maize, hemp, tomatoes, and pimento. With the expansion of the meat and dairy industry, alfalfa, clover and other fodder crops are becoming increasingly important, and although field crops cover much the largest area, tree crops such as peaches, apricots, olives, and vines are an important element in the land use of the older established zones, which bear a marked resemblance to parts of Emilia. In some sectors, particularly where the reclamation from the steppe has been only recently or partially achieved, the supplies of water available are very restricted and the farmer has to be content with a few waterings which serve to ensure a satisfactory yield from the normal secano crops. On the whole the variety and the intensity of the cultivation achieved in the Ebro basin are less than in some of the coastal huertas; citrus fruit and early vegetables for export, for example, are not a commercial proposition. Vines, on the other hand, do well, and the Rioja Alta district, with Logroño at its centre, produces a large proportion of the table wines exported from Spain.

Despite the steady expansion of the irrigated area, the population density of the basin remains well below the average for the country; figures per square mile are: Lerida province 71·7; Zaragoza province 99·1; national average 158·2 – a fact which underlines the vastness and emptiness of the steppe zones. Among the towns, apart from Lerida, only Zaragoza (326,000), once the capital of Aragon, is of any size. A number of important routes followed by road and rail concentrate on its bridges, notably from Madrid down the Jalon river, from Miranda and the Basque coast, from Sagunto and Barcelona, and from south-west France through the Somport pass and Jaca. Zaragoza is also one of the few towns in the interior of Spain which are of industrial significance; apart from the agricultural processing common to most regional centres, it has a railway works, foundries and plants producing electrical goods and machine tools. The Virgen del Pilar in the cathedral has long been a centre of pilgrimage.

The Ebro itself, whose headwaters flow into the Reinosa reservoir, is of little navigational importance, but its power potential is being realised by the construction of dams at Mequinenza and Ribarrara, at the entrance to the defile by which the river escapes to the sea through the Catalonian mountains.

**The Catalonian Hill-and-Mountain Country.** Apart from the plains around Lerida which geographically belong to the Ebro depression, Catalonia (Sp., Cataluña) is essentially a region of hills and valleys. The coast is backed by a littoral chain edged by rocky

5 The Galician landscape near Ferrol. Note the gorse and conifers on the undulating granite plateau, from which a quartzite outcrop emerges, and intensive cereal cultivation and dispersed settlement in the valley.

6 The landscape of the eastern sector of the Betic Cordillera; steppe with scattered tree crops and small patches of low-grade wheat.

SPAIN

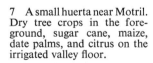

7 A small huerta near Motril. Dry tree crops in the foreground, sugar cane, maize, date palms, and citrus on the irrigated valley floor.

8 The Ebro basin near Zaragoza; on the left the barren, steppe-covered plateau of porous Tertiary deposits; on the right the irrigated flood plain. This photograph was taken in spring when much of the arable land was still under fallow.

SPAIN

9 The port wine country near Regua.

PORTUGAL

10 Boat-building yards and sardine boats at Vila de Conde and the mouth of the Ave river, north Portugal.

PORTUGAL

headlands, and the only sizeable areas of coastal lowland are the plain of El Ampurdan (inland from the Gulf of Rosas) and the deltas of the Ebro and the Llobregat. The coastal chain is succeeded inland by a series of tectonic depressions forming an inner valley, which is agriculturally very productive. It also contains a number of quite large towns, for example Gerona, Granollers, Sabadell (105,000), Villafranca, and Reus, most of which grew to importance in terms of textile manufacturing. The depression rises to the north-west to an inner mountain range which is considerably higher than the coastal massifs (Montserrat 4,054 ft). The Catalonian region as a whole forms a great contrast with both the Meseta and the Ebro basin, and in relief, climate, vegetation, density of population, and its active economic life, it closely resembles the northern Apennine peninsula. Most of Catalonia just falls within 'pluviose' Spain and its agriculture may be classed as Mediterranean polyculture with wheat, olives, vines, carobs, almonds, hazel nuts, stone fruits, and fodder crops well represented. The less productive hillsides are often covered with evergreen and cork oaks, the latter usually on the crystalline areas, for example the Montes Gavarras. Rice is of some importance in the Ebro delta and the plain of Ampurdan, while vines are the speciality of the Tarragona coastlands.

Since the Middle Ages Catalonia has engaged actively in the commercial life of the Mediterranean and in the mid-nineteenth century it began to develop as Spain's first and most important industrial zone. Its principal advantages, apart from the enterprise of the Catalans themselves, were a coastal position which facilitated the import of raw materials, water supplies and water power. With a protected home market and plentiful labour (cf. Italy), the first developments were almost exclusively in the textile sector, especially cotton, silk, and wool. The power resources soon had to be supplemented by steam raised from imported coal, and in this century hydro-electric power has become the dominant source of energy. Although Catalonia remains overwhelmingly the most important textile-manufacturing zone in Spain and has added rayon to its other spun and woven products, its interests are now much more diversified. Mechanical and electrical engineering, chemicals, cement, food processing, paper, and printing are all well represented; a recent development has been the establishment of a major car and lorry assembly plant near Barcelona. Despite Madrid's rapid growth, Barcelona (1,557,000) is still Spain's leading commercial and industrial city, and her busiest port. Raw materials and fuel for the manufacturing towns in the immediate hinterland provide most of the incoming traffic, and cement, fertilisers, and miscellaneous manufactures, mostly bound for other Spanish ports, figure largely in the outgoing trade. The harbour itself is entirely artificial. The main business and residential area of the city, which dates from the late nineteenth century, is remarkable for the regularity of its layout.

Since the war tourism, particularly on the Costa Brava (Palamos, S. Feliù, Tossa) which is very popular with foreign visitors, has become a very important item in the economy of the region and accounts for much of the heavy traffic passing through Barcelona airport.

Catalonia has a strongly pronounced regional consciousness, probably the most highly developed in Spain and certainly the most vocal. This consciousness is anti-Castilian and is based on profound differences of environment, language, and historical development between this bustling Mediterranean region and the aloof inland Castile.

**The Irrigated Mediterranean Coastlands.** From the Ebro delta south-westwards right round to the Straits of Gibraltar there extends a region of low rainfall and high temperature where oases of irrigation culture are backed and sometimes encircled by barren mountains. This long, narrow region shows some variation from north to south, but there is everywhere an essential contrast between the densely peopled, highly productive irrigation areas and the surrounding almost valueless and deserted mountains.

In the north, from the Ebro delta to Cape de la Nao in Valencia, the irrigated districts known as *vegas* and *huertas* (from Lat. *hortus* = a garden) are practically continuous along the coast, and the hills which back the region are not so barren as in the drier region of Murcia farther south. Whereas, however, the unirrigated land has a population density similar to that of the central Meseta (*c.* 70 per square mile) the huerta of Valencia has a density of over 2,000 per square mile. The vital resources are derived in part from springs issuing from the base of the limestone mountains inland, in part from wells, operated by the traditional *norias* or by mechanical pumps, and in part from rivers like the Turia and the Jucar whose rather erratic flow has been controlled by dams; the Acequia Real, the principal canal fed from the Jucar, is of particular importance to the Valencia huerta.

In contrast to those of the Ebro basin, the cash crops produced in the coastal huertas are mainly intended for export, traditionally to Britain and Germany, and have to face fierce competition from other producing countries. The diversity of crops within the huertas is remarkable. In the Valencia huerta, for example, the lowest zone, which in its natural state would be a marsh and still includes a sizeable lagoon (La Albufera), is entirely devoted to rice; the slightly higher alluvial area inland, which is easily irrigated by wells and gravity channels, produces oranges, lemons, stone fruits, tomatoes, potatoes, onions, and other early vegetables as well as maize, wheat and fodder crops for local consumption. On the edge of the huerta, where it is too high for systematic irrigation, tree crops, especially vines, olives, carobs, and almonds, dominate the land use.

Valencia itself (505,000), a port and the third largest town in Spain, depends largely on the collection, processing, and despatch of the agricultural products of its huerta, but it has also developed into a modest industrial centre with shipbuilding, engineering, textiles, and paper among its activities. Sagunto, an important railway junction and the site of the famous siege in classical times, has a small iron-smelting industry based on ores mined in its hinterland.

South of Cape de la Nao the climate becomes more arid, the heat of the summer is more intense, and the supplies of water available for irrigation are less plentiful, so that only part of the Murcian lowlands can be regularly supplied. The coast itself south of Alicante is edged with sandspits and extensive brackish lagoons parts of which have been converted into salt pans. The Murcia (249,000) and Elche huertas specialise in lemons, although Elche is perhaps better known for its date palms, which are an indication of the long, torrid summers of this part of Spain. Alicante (122,000) is the main port and commercial centre of the region. Cartagena (124,000) has the advantage of a good natural harbour and is traditionally Spain's main Mediterranean naval base. It also possesses one of the few oil refineries in the country and processes the lead, silver, pyrites, and iron mined in its immediate hinterland. The barrenness and aridity of the mountains of Alicante and Murcia amount almost to desert conditions and the steppes of La Mancha are continued across these gaunt uplands to the coast itself.

Along the south coast of Spain from Gibraltar to Almeria the rugged terrain and the scanty water supplies restrict the huertas to a few isolated pockets. Almeria (87,000) specialises in dessert grapes, Malaga (301,000) in wine and early vegetables, while Motril is one of several small huertas where sugar-cane is the dominant crop. With the advantage of easy and frequent air services to Gibraltar and Malaga, the western part of this coast, the Costa del Sol, is being rapidly developed as one of Europe's most important tourist areas. Gibraltar (24,000), with an area of only $2\frac{1}{2}$ square miles, is feeling the effect of the decline in British naval power (cf. Malta) but it is still of some importance as a bunkering station and as a port of call. Apart from its own attractions, not least the cheapness of many imported manufactures in a practically free port, Gibraltar is well placed for visits to Tangier and the Costa del Sol and is developing a flourishing tourist trade.  Some thousands of Spanish workers are employed in the colony and enter and leave it regularly each day.

**The Balearic Islands.**  These islands, which together cover some 1,936 square miles, lie on a submarine platform which is considered to be the continuation of the Betic Cordillera.  Menorca and Ibiza reach no great height, but in Mallorca the northern coast is backed by a high and rugged sierra (Sierra de Alfabia; 4,738 ft) composed of folded Mesozoic limestone.  Except for one or two small basins and a few coastal terraces, most of its surface is covered with *garrigue* or at best with evergreen oak.  Another limestone area inland from the south-east coast forms a broad upland of modest height; it is much less sterile than the Sierra and supports extensive areas of Mediterranean tree crops, mostly olives, almonds, vines, and carobs.  The central lowlands of the island, which reach their highest point in the Randa plateau, are also mainly devoted to dry tree crops, especially almonds and apricots, but there are a number of small huertas at the foot of the Sierra where spring and well water is available.  The region around Palma is also intensively cultivated with the aid of well irrigation.  In the smaller islands the opportunities for irrigation are few and the land use is a rather less productive variant of the Mallorcan central lowlands.  Apart from cement and fertiliser manufacture near Palma, the industries of the islands are mainly of handicrafts, for example, lace, pottery, baskets, and artificial jewellery.  Beautiful coastal scenery and a delightful climate have been important assets in the development of the tourist trade which since the war has grown to dominate the economy of the islands, particularly that of Mallorca and Ibiza.  Palma, which contains nearly half the population of the group (443,000), has excellent air communications with Barcelona, Valencia, and Madrid, as well as with several western European capitals.  There are also inter-island air services and regular sailings to Barcelona.  The rocky inlet on which stands Mahón was of considerable naval importance in the eighteenth century.

**The Betic Cordillera.**  This region stretches from the Cadiz coast, where it sinks beneath the waves of the Atlantic, to Cape de la Nao, where it disappears beneath the Mediterranean waters, only to reappear at intervals in the Balearic Islands.  Its length on the mainland is about 360 miles.  On its northern side it sinks to the Guadalquivir depression in the west, but farther east it abuts directly on to the Meseta.  Within the Cordillera two main east-west zones may be recognised; the first, the Sub-Betic zone, with its axis roughly along a line joining Cape Trafalgar and Alicante, consists of a narrow belt of Flysch succeeded southwards by a much broader belt of

Mesozoic deposits among which limestones are responsible for most of the higher relief features. The second is the crystalline zone which lies mainly to the south of a line joining Estepona, Granada, and Aguilas.

The crystalline zone which reaches its highest point in Mulhacen (11,421 ft) is made up of a number of isolated massifs (Sierra Bermeja, Sierra Nevada, Sierra de los Filabres) separated by deep-cut valleys which provide several fairly easy transverse routeways. In places cork oak and evergreen oak forests survive, but in general deforestation has been severe and the forestry service is attempting to remedy the situation by replanting with conifers. On the lower slopes, which are particularly steep and unstable in the areas composed of schists, tree crops, in the main almonds, olives, and vines, are the main element in the pattern of land use. Irrigation is restricted to a number of favoured patches, very often along river terraces. Although the Sierra Nevada is snow-capped for half the year, the potential water-power resources of the Cordillera are not impressive.

In the Sub-Betic zone high, barren limestone massifs rise up starkly above rolling plateaus of less resistant material, including large spreads of quite recent detritus. In the west the rainfall is just sufficient to support vines, olives, and extensive wheat, but the higher deforested sierras are of little value except as sheep pasture. Eastwards the rainfall declines and the cultivated areas dwindle until the landscape is dominated by wide expanses of steppe sweeping up to gaunt windswept sierras. The general unproductiveness of the zone is relieved by a number of high basins, for example those of Antequera, Granada, Guadix, and Baza. Except in the Granada huerta, which is favoured by the snow-fed streams draining the crystalline massif of the Sierra Nevada, the irrigated areas are very restricted and secano wheat and the Mediterranean tree crops are the traditional form of land use. Even the Granada huerta should not be compared with those of the coast; the main crops are cereals, sugar-beet and fodder, not citrus fruits and other specialised cash crops intended for export. Granada itself (157,000) lies above the southern edge of the huerta with its back to the Sierra Nevada. It is the main inland centre for the whole Cordillera region and is sharing increasingly in the tourist trade of the Costa del Sol. The Alhambra, the elegant palace buildings of the last Moorish kingdom in Spain, is its chief attraction.

**The Guadalquivir Depression.** This lowland, also known as the Andalusian or Betic depression, is a tectonic feature, some 200 miles long, about 100 miles wide at the seaward end, and some 50 miles wide at Seville. It is floored with Tertiary clays for the most part, but there are some residual limestones which form hills. Above Seville the lowland is lightly dissected, and the lowering of the base level of erosion has resulted in the formation of river terraces at various heights. Below Seville the country is still marshy in the region known as Las Marismas, on the site of a former lake. Sand-dunes fringe the marshes on the seaward side. The Andalusian depression shares the high temperatures of the southern coasts, and in contrast to the Meseta possesses much good soil, but is not the rich and productive region it has often been fabled. On the contrary large expanses of steppe are unproductive and the rainfall is generally only sufficient for secano cereals, olives, and vines. The monotony of vast, undulating expanses of wheat and olives is heightened by the absence of dispersed settlement, a feature associated with the latifundia system which has been blamed for much of the backwardness of this area. Several state-sponsored schemes aimed at intensifying the agriculture and reducing rural underemployment by means of a more rational use of the available water supplies, have been initiated, notably in Jaen province. Specialised viticulture is important in several areas especially near Jerez, the home of sherry. The irrigated zone of the Guadalquivir depression is limited to the rice area reclaimed from the Marismas and a narrow strip upstream on either side of the river. The mild winters and the long, hot summers make possible the cultivation of a wide variety of crops including wheat, maize, fodder, groundnuts, tobacco, sugar-cane, cotton, and citrus fruits. Except for the latter, which include oranges of the type suitable for making marmalade, production is aimed at the home market, a tendency encouraged by the autarchic policies in force in recent decades.

Seville (425,000) may be considered the commercial and cultural capital of Andalusia. It is also a modest port handling the mineral and agricultural products of the basin, but its outlet to the sea is constantly under the threat from the erratic behaviour of the channels and sandbanks at the mouth of the Guadalquivir, and part of the approach to the port is achieved by a ship canal. Cordoba (198,000), once the luxurious capital of Moorish Spain, is a bridging point and route centre on the main railway and road from Madrid to Malaga, and, like Seville, it enjoys a considerable tourist trade. Huelva (74,000) depends largely on the export of pyrites and, to a much less extent, copper from the mines of Rio Tinto. Cadiz (118,000), sited on a peninsula, is primarily a naval base and arsenal, but it is also the main port for sherry shipments.

**The Northern Coastlands of Spain.** These northern lands all possess a climate with abundant rain and equable temperature, but show considerable differences in their relief and in their inhabitants.

Three regions may be distinguished, the Basque lands on the east, the Cantabrian Mountains of the Asturias in the middle, and Galicia in the west.

*The Basque hill country* is composed of sandstones and limestones of Mesozoic, mainly Cretaceous, age, folded probably at the same time as the Pyrenees, and continuing in almost the same direction. It has three main lines of mountains running east–west and separated from each other by parallel depressions, but the mountains are highly dissected into small blocks by northward and southward flowing rivers, so that in spite of its considerable heights (c. 2,000–4,000 ft and more) the region offers a network of routes, and it has much easier lines of movement than either the Pyrenees to the east or the Cantabrian Mountains to the west. The northern side is rainy, well cultivated, and thickly peopled, whereas the southern side partakes of the aridity of the Ebro depression. The original vegetation consisted of forest (beech, oak, sweet chestnut, etc.), of which considerable fragments remain; cultivation is mainly concerned with fodder crops, meadow grasses, maize, and orchards of temperate fruits, such as apples. As in all the northern coast-lands, small holdings and a disseminated population are the rule, in contrast to the large holdings and aggregated dwellings of the mass of Spain. The rich Jurassic iron deposits between Bilbao and Santander have led to the growth of an iron and steel industry in Bilbao (298,000). Before World War II the bulk of the ore was exported to the British Isles, the return cargo being Welsh coal. Bilbao, 8 miles up the drowned estuary of the Nervion, with its out-port at Portugalete, is an important banking and commercial city and the main centre of shipbuilding and heavy engineering in Spain. Easily accessible from France by the busy route through Irun and magnificently situated on an enclosed bay, San Sebastian (135,000) is a prosperous summer resort. It has an important fishing industry and with its port, situated a few miles east of the town itself on a sheltered inlet, it is the focus of a group of small towns manufac-turing paper, woollens (Tolosa), rubber (Lasarte), and light metal goods. One of the principal industrial advantages of the north coast, and of this area in particular, is the abundance of water available.

The same type of country is continued westwards into Old Castile, which here reaches the coast. Santander (118,000) also lies on a drowned estuary; it has an iron and steel plant and is the main terminal for the Spanish transatlantic shipping lines. It is connected by road and rail with Valladolid and Madrid via Reinosa, itself a centre of special steel manufacture; another road over the Puerto del Escudo reaches Madrid via Burgos.

*The Cantabrian Mountains of the Asturias* rise to much greater heights, the Peñas de Europa reaching 8,687 ft. The high mountains were glaciated during the Great Ice Age and show 'lofty summits lost in mist, toilsome passes, deep narrow valleys, gorges and ravines' (Dantin-Cereceda). It was behind these ranges, i.e. to the north of them, that the Christian resistance was first organised against the Moors for the reconquest of Spain. The folded Cantabrian Mountains extend westward for some 150 miles to the border of Galicia. They form a complex system both in relief and structure, with summit levels reaching between 6,000 and 7,000 ft as a general rule. At the western end, the mountains turn south-westward and divide to enclose the basin of the upper Sil. Generally speaking, the rocks become progressively older from east to west, the eastern portion consisting mainly of Mesozoic limestone with a high proportion of dolomite, the middle portion of late Palæozoic limestones with some slates, and the western portion of still older rocks, mainly slates and quartzites. The mountains offer a formidable obstacle owing to the absence of low passes, few being under 4,000 ft, and this is to be associated with the prevalence of limestone and the lack of normal drainage due to the development of karstic conditions. There is only one main route across, via the Pajares pass, and the rail crossing involves 27 miles of railway line and 60 tunnels to traverse a distance of only 7 miles as the crow flies. The rail route from Madrid to Santander is not quite so difficult, but is really at the eastern end of the high Cantabrians. The mountains offer only a poor living to a scanty population, for although some forest remains, for the most part they carry only sheep pasture, as do similar karstic regions elsewhere in Europe, e.g. the Abruzzi, the Dinaric Alps.

On the north the Cantabrian Mountains drop down to an east-west rift valley filled with deposits of the Cretaceous period, beneath which Palæozoic coal measures are preserved. This depression broadens out round Oviedo (127,000), and is separated from the narrow coastal platform by a belt of hilly country. 'Here is the Asturias of the stories, the Asturias of light, free air, moderation, and balance. In the mild, humid, uniform climate central European vegetation flourishes side by side with the Mediterranean fig, the Asiatic orange and lemon; the rosy apple blossom decks the garden walls'. (Dantin-Cereceda.)

The region is also rich in minerals, the chief coalfield of Spain lying in the rift valley near Oviedo, though the annual output is only about 10 million tons. Considerable iron-ore deposits in the neighbourhood, and zinc towards the east have assisted the development of metallurgical and chemical industries at Oviedo. Gijon

(124,000) is the port for this area. At Avilès, sited on a navigable estuary, is Spain's most modern iron and steel plant, which at present accounts for over half the country's production. It relies on local coal and Basque ores. The considerable water power resources of the area are now receiving attention and an ambitious hydro-electricity project has been completed on the Navia river.

The Sil basin forms a productive and thickly populated area within a framework of the lofty Cantabrian ranges. Although at a height of some 1,500 ft, it is rich farming country, owing to the alluvium with which it is floored.

*Galicia* is a dissected peneplain composed mainly of granite, slates, and crystalline schists. It has many features in common with the other two regions of Europe that end in a 'Finisterre', namely, the south-western peninsula of England, and Brittany. Not only are all three dissected peneplains, but they all have a *ria* coast with a fishing industry, an equable rainy climate, and an active dairying industry. All are fairly densely populated in spite of wide areas of crystalline rocks of only moderate fertility, and all have suffered commercially from their remote, peripheral position.

A large proportion of the interior plateaus is covered with heath and with forests composed mainly of fast growing eucalypts and conifers. The population is concentrated on the coasts and in the valleys where an extremely intensive form of cultivation is practised on very small holdings. The alluvial valley floors, irrigated in summer, are used for maize, and for cabbages and rye in winter, while the lower slopes produce potatoes, oats, fodder, and fruit, including the vine. The more prosperous peasants keep a cow or two and perhaps a few pigs or sheep. This Miño type of agriculture is essentially a subsistence one and is indicative of rural overpopulation; emigration overseas and to other parts of Spain is traditional. The fishing industry, both short-range for sardines and long-range, for example to Grand Banks, for cod, is important in the economy of the area. Ferrol (83,000) is primarily a naval base and Vigo (166,000) and Corunna (Sp., Coruña; 177,000) are ports of call on the South American route.

In an attempt to provide this remote area with the power necessary for the development of industry the hydro-electric resources of Galicia are being realised and an oil refinery has been built at Corunna. An aluminium refinery, also at Corunna, has been one of the fruits of this policy.

**The Pyrenees.** The Pyrenees stretch for about 260 miles between the Mediterranean and the Bay of Biscay and attain a maximum width of about eighty miles. Like the Alps they contain an interior zone of hard crystalline rocks, such as granites, gneisses, and crystalline schists which weather slowly, and outer bands of little altered sedimentary rocks, generally of Mesozoic and Tertiary age, in which limestones predominate.  The higher peaks and the watershed lie nearer the northern than the southern side, so the northern or French slope is steep and narrow, but on the Spanish side the descent is more gradual.  The Pic d'Aneto (11,169 ft) in the Maladetta group is the highest summit of the chain, and the central Pyrenees between the Col de la Perche and the Pic d'Anie maintain a great average height, never falling below 5,000 ft.

Unlike the Alps, the Pyrenees have no glaciers of any size, only one or two little plateau glaciers on the northern side of the highest peaks, but they were abundantly glaciated during the Ice Age and bear all the marks of ice-work in the sharp arêtes, the U-shaped valleys, cirques, rock basins, and so on.

The western Pyrenees stretch from the Bay of Biscay to the Pic d'Anie, a distance of some fifty miles.  They present considerable differences from the central Pyrenees, since the middle crystalline zone is here very narrow, and its place is largely taken by Permo-Triassic sandstones.  South of this belt lies a band of early Tertiary material consisting of marls and conglomerates, generally easily eroded and forming lower ground.  In this zone on the River Arga stands Pamplona (98,000), the capital of Navarra.  The whole region has rounded forms, instead of Alpine peaks, and is fairly easily crossed, the best known pass being that of Roncesvalles (3,452 ft), which carries a motor road.  The only railway skirts the mountains by following the coast.  The rainfall is considerable even on the Spanish side, and some forest remains, though it has been much cleared to form arable land, as well as pasture.  On the south-west the Pyrenees merge into the Basque hill country.

The central Pyrenees extend for a distance of some 160 miles.  The broad central zone of crystalline schists of Palæozoic age, with numerous masses of granite, gives rise to impressive mountain scenery of steep-sided mountain blocks, with occasional towering crags, though true peaks are not very frequent.  Summit levels frequently exceed 10,000 ft and there is only one good trans-Pyrenean road in this sector, via the Somport pass from Jaca to Pau, although there is another, very much more difficult, linking the upper Noguera Ribagorzana and the upper Garonne through the Viella tunnel; another tunnel is planned to join Luchon and Benasque, on the upper Esera.  Two railway lines penetrate this part of the Pyrenees, one under the Somport, the other through the Puymorens tunnel, which provides a link between Barcelona and Toulouse.  The high Pyrenean backbone falls on the south to a zone of rugged but not quite so lofty country, formed of Mesozoic rocks, containing much limestone. This is followed by a zone of early Tertiary rocks, including marls and conglomerates, which form a belt of lower land. Farther south, overlooking the Ebro basin, a second zone of Mesozoic rocks forms the mountainous country of the sub-Pyrenean ridges, with summits of 4,600 to 6,000 ft. The rivers coming from the high central ranges break through all three zones, but often have longitudinal tributaries coming in from the Tertiary zone. These longitudinal depressions are shorter, less deep, and less broad than those in the Alps and offer less suitable sites for human habitation. Occasionally, however, they broaden out, as along the upper reaches of the Aragon river, in whose valley was formed the nucleus of the kingdom of the same name. On emerging from the Tertiary depression the rivers break through the sub-Pyrenean ridges in deep gorges. The central Pyrenees form a climatic divide, the French side having a heavy rainfall distributed throughout the year, while the Spanish side is dry and therefore much less productive. There is much steppe in the Tertiary depression and on the sub-Pyrenean ridges. Little cultivation is carried on and the scanty population derives a livelihood mainly from sheep and goat rearing. The main significance of the central Pyrenees in the Spanish economy lies in the water resources of the area which are being steadily controlled for power and irrigation.

The eastern Pyrenees stretch eastwards from the upper Segre river and the Col de la Perche for some sixty miles, and attain heights of over 9,000 ft in Puigmal and Canigou, the latter in France. They are, however, very attenuated near the coast, where they break down except for the narrow Mts Albères, which separate the tectonic basin of Roussillon on the French side from the similar but smaller basin of Ampurdan on the Spanish side. A railway follows the coast route.

Although less than half as long as the Alps, only about half as broad, and less high, the Pyrenees have always been considered more of an obstacle. The physical difficulties, however, have often been exaggerated, and the real reason for the lack of early roads and railways is to be found in the position of the chain. In the first place it does not lie athwart any great world route, as do the Alps, and secondly the traffic that existed could circumvent the chain either by the coast routes at either end or by the sea routes. Once the demand for routes arose in modern times with the coming of the tourist 'industry', hundreds of miles of roads suitable for motoring have been made, particularly on the French side, where the tourist industry is better organised, and, as already mentioned, two railways now cross the chain.

**Spain. Economic Summary.** In spite of its early entry into the civilised world and its great transoceanic conquests in early modern times, Spain is still, by western European standards, an economically backward country. Many explanations have been put forward to account for this. The long wars against the Moors, who were of Muslim religion and of Arab and Berber origin, are said to account for the fanaticism which led to the expulsion not only of the Moors but also of the Jews and Moriscos, who together formed the principal commercial and artisan classes. The discovery of America and the exploitation of the minerals of the New World drained the country of manpower and led to the neglect of the home land. The domination of the whole country, and between 1580 and 1640 of the whole peninsula, by the central Meseta was also detrimental to economic progress, since militant Castile, the chief champion against the Moors and therefore the most fanatical, was a poor country agriculturally and little interested in furthering agriculture apart from sheep rearing. Castile was also isolated from the sea and the Castilians showed little taste for commerce. On the other hand, Castile's central position and its good military organisation enabled it to dominate the more advanced parts of the country, such as Catalonia. But the marked differences between the various outlying regions of Spain encouraged the development of strong regional sentiments, which, being fundamentally anti-Castilian, hindered cooperation between all the regions.

When the rest of western Europe was industrialising rapidly on the basis of coal and steam, Spain's progress in this direction was baulked by recurrent periods of political instability. The nineteenth century ended disastrously with the Spanish-American war, but the early part of this century saw the stirrings of new life in Spain, and there was undoubted progress, particularly during and after the war of 1914–19, when Spain's neutrality was profitable at the time and left her without the heavy debts and loss of manpower incurred by the belligerent states of Europe. The tragic civil war, which followed the republican experiment of the early 1930s, more than wiped out the gains which had been made since 1914, and for nearly fifteen years Spain remained in political isolation, deprived of the cooperation of her European neighbours and of the American aid which had done so much to put the rest of Europe on its feet again. In the circumstances Spain had little alternative but to fall back on a policy of economic autarchy and strive to rebuild the economy on the basis of her depleted resources. Since 1954, however, Spain has benefited from her military agreements with the United States and the isolation of the postwar decade has begun to break down. One practical result of the renewal of contacts with the rest of Europe has been a spectacular development of the tourist trade which has helped very substantially in easing Spain's balance of payments difficulties.

Important as have been the historical and political vicissitudes through which Spain has passed, any explanation of her economic backwardness would be incomplete without some appreciation of the difficulties presented by her geographical endowment. For example, Spain's position with seaboards on the Atlantic and the Mediterranean was most advantageous in the fifteenth and sixteenth centuries but much less so after the economic centre of gravity of Europe had moved to the north-west. Internally development has been handicapped by the sheer size of the country and by the vast expanses of unproductive steppe and mountainous land which attenuate the communications system without contributing traffic to it. These difficulties were increased by the absence of navigable rivers. Quite apart from the political uncertainties of the period, in the nineteenth century Spain's industrial growth was stunted by other factors: the unwillingness of the monied classes to invest in anything but land, the preoccupation of the small middle class with the armed services, the liberal professions and administration rather than with commerce and industry, and, not least, the shortcomings in the natural resources of the country. Outstanding among the latter was the poverty of the water supplies over so much of Spain and the nature of the mineral deposits; fuels in particular were poorly represented and most mineral deposits were expensive to mine and dispersed geographically. Some of the most valuable deposits (those at Rio Tinto for example) made little direct contribution to the build-up of Spanish industry because they were of a type which could be used only in an already highly industrialised country. As a result, these minerals were often worked by foreign companies and their output exported. In this respect Spain's economy was for long colonial in character.

Within its 195,000 square miles, the population of Spain, which stood at 30·4 millions in 1960, is increasing rapidly. Approximately 44 per cent of the labour force is still engaged in agriculture compared with about 24 per cent in manufacturing, but a marked drift from the land has begun in response to the increased opportunities available in the manufacturing, servicing and construction industries; there is also a steady stream of emigrants to the continental countries of western Europe, particularly to France and the Federal German Republic.

Spanish agronomists have calculated that only about 10 per cent of Spain is first-class agricultural land, another 10 per cent is rocky and useless, 35 per cent is practically unproductive owing to high altitude, aridity or poverty of the soils, and the remaining 45 per cent is of medium productivity. In the vast areas of 'arid' Spain yields are low and fluctuate widely from year to year with the vagaries of the weather. In a good year the cereal harvest is barely adequate for home needs. Although population density is low in these areas, given the unproductive character of so much of the land, it amounts to a state of rural overpopulation and in many areas seasonal unemployment is common. Most of the wheat crop is still sown and harvested by hand, and mechanisation is handicapped not only by lack of capital but by the demographic and social situation. In fact in these droughty lands the scope for intensification and for technical improvements on the western European pattern are limited. Apart from the elimination of surplus manpower on the land, the most useful development would seem to be the conversion of secano, as far as is economically possible, into partially irrigated land to ensure a higher yield of the traditional crops, as is being achieved in parts of the Ebro basin. In pluviose Spain, where the environment is more favourable to technical improvements, rural overpopulation is the principal obstacle to progress; in Galicia two acres, usually in several parcels, constitute a sizeable holding. The same problem occurs in the Mediterranean huertas on whose exports Spain relies for so much of her foreign exchange.

Although the State has been active in the control of water supplies for the extension of irrigation and has undertaken a number of colonisation schemes, there has been no land reform on the Italian pattern. Latifundia are still a feature of the south and centre of the country and systems of tenure, for example sharecropping, which give little security or encouragement to the peasant, are widespread.

In 1961 the production of the principal minerals in Spain (in millions of metric tons) was as follows: coal 10·2, anthracite 2·4, brown coal 1·9, iron-ore 6·0, potash (from Navarra and Catalonia) 1·7, pyrites 1·5, rock salt 0·6, lead-ore 0·3; copper, bauxite, tin and wolfram were also produced. The importance of Asturias, the Basque provinces and the Sierra Morena will have emerged from the regional account. In view of Spain's limited output of coal and the complete lack of home-produced oil, the state has been attempting to improve the energy situation by investing heavily in hydro-electric power schemes. The production of hydro-electricity rose in ten years to 15,000 million kWh in 1961, 75 per cent of the total.

The oldest and, from the point of view of the labour employed, the most important manufacturing industries are the agricultural processing group and the textile group, but in recent years, with government support, direct or indirect, there has been a notable expansion in the steel output (2·8 million tons in 1961), thanks very largely to the contribution of Avilès, and in that of fertilisers, cement and vehicles. Although it has been government policy to encourage, as far as possible, the industrialisation of the traditionally agricultural areas, industrial activity is still overwhelmingly concentrated in Catalonia and on the Biscayan coast eastwards from Asturias.

In spite of the undoubted expansion of Spanish industry in recent years and the relative stagnation of agriculture, the country's exports are still dominated by agricultural products, especially citrus and other fruits, nuts, early vegetables, and wines which depend heavily on the British, German and Scandinavian markets. Sardines and cork are also of some importance but minerals and manufactured exports make no great contribution. Among the imports oil is the biggest single item but all types of manufactures, textile raw materials, colonial foodstuffs (especially tobacco and coffee) and even temperate foodstuffs, such as maize, figure largely in the list. Spain's exports find a market in the United States and in the western European countries; these too are her main suppliers together with the oil-producing countries of the Middle East and the Caribbean. The South American trade is comparatively unimportant.

Although there has been some relaxation recently, Spain has still a highly protected economy and it is doubtful whether either her agriculture or her industry is competitive enough to enable her, even if it were politically feasible, to enter an association of the nature of the Common Market.

## PORTUGAL

Portugal is in many ways more favoured by nature than Spain. Although the main structural lines of the western part of the Meseta are continued into Portugal, yet the highlands and uplands are generally at a lower altitude and they slope down to coastal lowlands threaded by navigable rivers. Since the country has also the advantage of being to windward of the landmass and of having an equable maritime climate, with adequate supplies of rain, it is potentially more productive than Spain, and its population density is higher, being 249 per square mile in 1960, having risen from 186 per square mile in 1930.

**Portugal's Seaward Outlook.** Portugal's geographical outlook is seaward and this gives the country an individuality quite different from that of Spain. Portugal was held together by the attractive force of the sea, and it maintained its independence by means of the English alliance, which dates from the fourteenth century. Separated from Spain by a belt of barren, scantily populated country, Portugal extends inland only to the head of navigation of the Rivers Douro[1]

[1] Duero in Spain.

and Tagus. Along the Hispano-Portuguese frontier the Douro and Tagus run in stupendous gorges, and there is not, and never has been, a road along the Tagus connecting Lisbon and Madrid, though this seems the obvious route on the map. Portugal takes its name from the old Roman port on the Douro of Portus Cale (the modern Oporto), the first capital of the country. The capital was moved to a more southerly port, Coimbra on the River Mondego, and finally to the best port of all, Lisbon on the River Tagus, when the latter town was recovered from the Moors in the twelfth century. The association of the capital with navigable waterways was of first-class importance in the development of the country, and this small land of 35,000 square miles (about the size of Ireland) still has a colonial empire of *c*. 800,000 square miles, in addition to the 'Adjacent Islands' of Madeira and the Azores which cover about 1,200 square miles. Another aspect of the oceanic outlook, the English alliance, was foreshadowed as early as 1217, when an English contingent helped the Portuguese to drive the Moors southward across the Sado river, but this historic treaty came in 1386, after the Portuguese had defeated the Spaniards with the aid of English bowmen. This treaty was accompanied by the marriage of Philippa of Lancaster (daughter of John of Gaunt) with the ruler of Portugal, and their more famous son became known to history as the patron of explorers, Prince Henry the Navigator. The English connexion was renewed at the beginning of the eighteenth century when Portuguese wines were given preferential treatment in the English market and the English upper classes took to port wine.

**Geographical Regions.** Although the complexity of the relief and structure seem to demand a division of the country into a number of geographical regions, the fundamental division is imposed by the climatic contrast between the provinces north of the Tagus and those to the south of it, which is reflected in almost every aspect of the environment. Portugal extends through latitudes which would naturally tend to give her an Altantic climate in the north and a Mediterranean climate in the south; this contrast is emphasised by the mountain character of much of the land north of the Tagus, with the consequence that high relief provokes even heavier rainfall, and a good deal of winter snow, whereas the south consists mainly of low plateaus with much level plain, so that the natural tendency to summer drought and a smaller total precipitation finds nothing but the low Algarve Highlands to counteract it. In consequence the north is a land of profuse vegetational growth, both hills and valleys being originally covered with deciduous forests, while in the south only drought-resistant vegetation will flourish. The crops also show a contrast, maize and rye being staple cereals of the north, and wheat and barley of the south. The distinction between north and south is further emphasised by the fact that the country north of the Tagus is *old* Portugal, while that to the south is *new* Portugal, and in contrast to a high density of population in the north, living on small holdings and in small villages or isolated farms, one finds a scanty population in the south, living on large holdings, and mainly in large nucleated villages.

**Lands North of the Tagus.** *The Douro Highlands or Plateaus.* Within the Douro Highlands there is a marked contrast between the interior zone of Tras os Montes and Beira Alta on the one hand and the coastal zone of Minho and Douro Litoral on the other. The former is composed largely of infertile schists, and to some degree shares the severity of the Mesetan winters. Much of its surface is covered with heath and, with the exception of one or two small irrigated zones, for example at Chaves, large areas are abandoned to pastoralism and the main crops are potatoes and rye. The whole area is difficult of access and scantily populated. The rivers Sabor and Tuella lead down to the famous port–wine country which has its centre at Peso da Regua.

In Minho and Douro Litoral granite is the dominant surface rock. Nowhere is it more ingeniously employed; it is used in buildings, the sets for the roads, walls, fences and vine posts. In this climate it weathers deeply and in the valleys and on the lower slopes forms a thick, disintegrated layer which is permeable but is also capable of retaining moisture. In such areas an extremely intensive form of agriculture is practised, and supports, largely on a subsistence basis, a population density of over 400 per square mile. The holdings are extremely small (*minifundia*), often no more than an acre, and the settlement is usually dispersed. The irrigable areas are occupied by maize in summer and by rye or cabbages in winter. On the slightly higher slopes, where irrigation is more difficult, a variety of crops is produced including potatoes, fodder, stone and hard fruits, and vines; olives are relatively unimportant. Cattle, pigs and poultry provide an essential element in this Minho economy. The high granitic interfluves, which were once clothed with deciduous forests, have been replanted with eucalypts and, higher up, with conifers. Where the forest has not been re-established the vegetation consists of a *maquis* of gorse and broom.

The Lisbon area excepted, industry is better represented in this part of the Douro Highlands than in any other part of Portugal. Oporto (303,000), which is the main centre for the processing and shipment of port wines, also produces woollen, silk and rayon textiles, electrical equipment, tires and metal goods. The town itself is sited on a spectacular gorge where the river cuts through the last hilly barrier, but a bar at the mouth of the Douro prevents the entry of large ships, and a modern artificial harbour and trading estate have been built at Leixões, a mile or two to the north. Guimaraes and Braga have textile and light metal industries while the coastal towns are concerned mainly with fishing. The industrial prospects of the area have been enhanced with the construction of a number of hydro–electric installations in the interior of Minho province.

*The Serra da Estrela.* This faulted highland, which consists of two main ridges, continues the line of the Central Sierras of Spain and attains heights of over 6,000 ft. In spite of snowy winters, the vegetation contains numerous Mediterranean elements and although reafforestation is being carried out, cistus *matorral* and heath cover wide areas. The region, which is very scantily populated, is a receiving area for transhumant flocks in summer. The main economic significance of the Serra lies in its hydro-electric power which has been developed on the Zezere and its tributaries.

*The Portuguese Coastal Foreland North of the Tagus.* As already mentioned, there are only discontinuous lowlands north of the River Douro. South of that river, the lowlands are marked off from the highlands by a great fault which runs from Oporto to Abrantes on the Tagus, though there is an extension of the lowlands east of this line, up the valley of the Mondego. Even this 'Foreland' west of the great fault was not immune from the earth swells connected with the Alpides movements, and the line of the Serra da Estrela is continued at a lower level and with younger rocks (mainly Mesozoic limestones) towards the south-west, in hills which run parallel to the Tagus and terminate in C. da Roca. Between these hills and the mouth of the Douro there is a tri-angular lowland, mainly below 600 ft, where broad, shallow valleys alternate with low limestone hills and plateaus. It is fronted on the seaward side by sand-dunes, behind which are lagoons and large expanses of sandy flats, so that the region resembles the Landes of France, and the dunes are similarly clad with pine forests, which are cut over for pit props and tapped for turpentine. Some of the swampy land near the coast has been drained for rice-fields, but the characteristic crops of the greater part of the Foreland are maize, beans, vines, and fruit trees. The central or coastal hills of the Tagus peninsula, which shut in the lowland on the south, seldom rise above 2,000 ft, and usually consist of tablelands at heights of 750–1,500 ft where karstic conditions have developed. The sides of the hills, however, are devoted to vineyards, about 40 per cent of all the wine produced in Portugal coming from the Tagus peninsula. It was across this peninsula, to the north-east of Lisbon, that Wellington constructed his famous defensive lines of Torres Vedras.

Lisbon (Port. Lisboa; 802,000), the focus of Portugal's commercial and financial life, is also the country's chief industrial centre and handles most of the overseas trade. It is a convenient port of call, particularly for liners operating between the Mediterranean and the United States, and it maintains regular services with Portugal's overseas territories, which contribute to the city's entrepôt activities. Food processing, textiles, ship repairing, metal goods, chemicals and oil refining are among the industries of the capital. Many of the newest enterprises have been sited on the marshy, and formerly neglected left bank of the estuary. For example, the new iron and steel plant, using mainly home-produced ores and American coal, is located at Seixal. A bridge spanning the Tagus is under construction.

Coimbra (46,000), pleasantly situated above the Mondego where it leaves the highlands, is a bridge town but is chiefly notable for its ancient university.

**Lands South of the Tagus.** South of the alluvial flats of the lower Tagus, the land rises to rolling plains which stretch southwards for some ninety miles, but have a breadth of little more than thirty miles. To west, east and south they rise to plateaus, which are comparatively low on the seaward side, rise gently on the east to over 1,200 ft. in Alemtejo, and to 1,885 ft on the south in the Highlands of Algarve. East of the Alemtejo plateau the land sinks again to the Guadiana valley. The Setubal peninsula and the province of Algarve stand somewhat apart and are best treated separately.

*The Plains and Low Plateaus of South Portugal.* These lands lie mainly in the drainage areas of the Sado and Sorraia rivers, which carry little water, especially in summer. They are floored with almost undisturbed sandstones and clays, and owing to the summer drought and to lack of facilities for irrigation, they are devoted to the extensive cultivation of cereals, chiefly of wheat. The climate is too dry for maize. The cork oaks for which the region is famous often grow as isolated trees in the midst of the wheat fields, though they grow in closer formations on the plateaus, particularly on the western Serra de Grandola. The olive is the only other tree grown to any considerable extent, though there are fruit trees in favourable localities, for example, the plums of Elvas in the Guadiana valley. The higher and less productive parts of the plateaus are covered by cistus *matorral*, alternating with various heath and other plants, on which sheep manage to pick up a living.

The coastal strip is dune-edged and unproductive except where it is broken by a volcanic outcrop at Cape Sines, and along the lower Sado river, where former swamps have been drained for rice cultivation.

The population is generally less than a hundred to the square mile.

*The Setubal Peninsula.* The limestone Setubal peninsula faces the similar Tagus peninsula across the estuary. Although its centre is unproductive and covered with *matorral*, it has a fertile and densely peopled strip on the north along the Tagus estuary, and another on the south, margining the sea and the Sado estuary. Setubal (44,000), at the mouth of the Sado, is the largest town south of the Tagus; it is a centre of the sardine fishery, and exports locally produced oranges and wine, together with large quantities of cork from the interior. A recent development has been the establishment of a vehicle assembly plant.

*Algarve.* Two strongly contrasted environments are found in this province. Along the southward-facing coast is a fertile, densely populated strip, which is backed by the unproductive, scantily peopled Algarve Mountains. The latter, of Hercynian age, are mainly composed of Carboniferous slate, and continue the line of the Sierra Morena, though they are separated from the latter by the Guadiana valley. They are covered with dense *matorral*, though there are some trees in places.

The Algarve coastlands still have a Moorish appearance and resemble the southern coastlands of Spain, with their white, often flat-roofed houses set among palm trees, pomegranates, figs, oranges, and almonds. Fruit is produced in abundance, but the salt pans and tunny fishing also have some importance.

**Economic Summary.** In recent decades the economy of Portugal (8,889,000) has made steady if unspectacular progress. In the agricultural sector, although output has increased only slowly, there has been a considerable extension of the irrigated area, notably in the Sado valley, and a number of colonisation schemes on the Spanish pattern have been undertaken. Unfortunately, the opportunities for intensification and for the extension of the cultivable area are limited and Portugal is obliged to import wheat and meat as well as such tropical products as sugar and coffee. In many areas rural overpopulation has become very severe; emigration to Brazil and the Portuguese African territories is traditional, and a marked drift to the towns especially to Lisbon has set in.

Portugal's forests, which cover over a quarter of the land surface, are important in the economy and provide a major item in the export list. The conifers of the north and of the coastal dunes produce resin and pit props while the oak woodlands of the south furnish cork and tannin. Quick-growing eucalypts are mainly used for paper.

Fishing is one of Portugal's traditional occupations. Cod, which in its dried form has long been a staple article of diet in the country, is caught by the distant water fleet on the Grand Banks. Sardines from home and Moroccan waters are a major export.

Until comparatively recently Portuguese industrial activity was dominated by textiles and by the processing of agricultural produce. Since the war there has been a determined drive to industrialise the country and broaden the basis of activity. As a result there has been a notable increase in the output of steel, cement, chemicals, oil products, metal goods, electrical equipment and vehicles, the last named mainly from imported components. Portugal's main assets are a cheap and abundant labour supply and hydro-electric power. Her mineral endowment is extremely modest and the deposits on the whole are poor in quality and are dispersed geographically. 600,000 tons of poor quality anthracite are produced annually near Oporto and small quantities of iron-ore and pyrites are mined in the S. Domingos area, which is a continuation of the Sierra Morena mineralised zone. In the north of the country some tin, wolfram and iron (at Moncorvo) are mined.

The pattern of Portuguese trade holds no surprises. Wines, olive oil, sardines and forest products, with some support from minerals, especially pyrites and wolfram, dominate the exports. Raw cotton, wheat, tropical foodstuffs, fuels and manufactures of all kinds, especially vehicles, make up the majority of the imports. The United States and the countries of western Europe, especially Britain, the Federal German Republic, France and the Benelux countries, are Portugal's main trading partners. In recent years trade with the overseas territories has accounted for about one-sixth of the total.

Portugal is a member of the European Free Trade Association but under a special agreement she is allowed to retain her protective measures against imported manufactures. The tourist trade is making an increasing contribution to the balance of payments.

### REFERENCES

Two books are available in English on Iberia, namely W. B. Fisher and H. Bowen-Jones, *Spain,* New York, Praeger, 1966, and R. Way, *A Geography of Spain and Portugal,* London, Methuen, 1962. See also D. S. Walker, *The Mediterranean Lands,* London, Methuen, revised ed. 1962; M. I. Newbigin, *Southern Europe,* revised by R. J. Harrison Church, London, Methuen, 1949; N. J. G. Pounds, *Europe and the Mediterranean,* New York, McGraw-Hill, 1953; J. M. Houston, 'Irrigation as a Solution to the Agrarian Problems of Modern Spain', *Geog. Journal,* 116, 1950; J. M. Houston, 'Land Use and Society in the Plain of Valencia', contribution to *Geographical Essays in Memory of A. G. Ogilvie,* London, Nelson, 1959; H. H. Bennett 'Soil Erosion in Spain', *Geog. Review,* 50, 1960; R. D. Hayes, 'A Peasant Economy in North-West Portugal', *Geog. Journal,* 122, 1956; E. H. G. Dobby 'Galicia, Spain', *The Geographical*

*Review*, 26, 1936; J. Naylon, 'Land Consolidation in Spain', *Annals of the Association of American Geographers*, 49, 1959, and 'Progress in Land Consolidation in Spain', ibidem, 51, 1961.

Among the works on Iberia published in other languages the following may be profitably consulted: P. Birot and J. Dresch, *La Méditerranée et le Moyen Orient*, Vol. I, Paris, Presses Universitaires de France, 1953; P. Birot, *Le Portugal*, Paris, Colin, 1949; M. de Teran, *Geografia de España y Portugal*, Vol. I, *Geografia Fisica*, Barcelona, Montaner y Simon, 1952; M. Sorre, *Géographie Universelle*, Tome VIII, Part 1, Paris, Colin, 1934; H. Lautensach, 'Portugal auf Grund eigener Reisen und der Literatur', in *Petermanns Geographische Mitteilungen*, Gotha, 1932–37.

# THE GREEK PENINSULA AND ISLANDS

THE total area of Greece amounts to only 51,000 square miles, but this small area of land is spread over a large range of latitude and longitude owing to the manner in which it is either interpenetrated or surrounded by the sea. From the northern boundary in Macedonia (about $41\frac{1}{2}°$N) to the southern coasts of Crete (about 35° N) is a distance of some 450 miles, or as far as from Dover to Inverness, while from the west coast of Corfu (c. $19\frac{1}{2}°$ E) to the east coast of Samos (c. 27° E) is an almost equal distance.

**Growth of the Modern State.** The modern Greek state dates from the Wars of Liberation of 1821–29, when a small southern portion of the present state won its freedom from the Turks. The parts freed at that time were the Morea, Attica, and the adjoining lands south of a line from the mouth of the Aspropotamo (Akheloös) river to that of the Spercheios river, together with the islands of Eubœa, the Cyclades, and the Northern Sporades. These had constituted the major part of the European Greek lands of classical antiquity, but there were many people of Greek speech further north in Thessaly, Macedonia, and Thrace, as well as along the coast of Asia Minor.

Greece fell to the Turks in the fifteenth century at the time of the overthrow of the Byzantine Empire, but for the previous two centuries it had been under the rule of the so-called Franks, who were adventurers of French origin, and of the Venetians, who together had turned the Fourth Crusade against Byzantium in 1204. The Frankish feudal lords, who had divided up the country amongst themselves, so impoverished the land by incessant warfare against each other that it could offer no resistance to the Turkish conquerors.

There are few Turks remaining in Greece at the present time, but from the remotest times there seems to have been an intermittent pressure of population from the north, so that the population of modern Greece is racially more mixed than that of ancient Greece, which was apparently even then of mixed Mediterranean and northern origin. Apart from the prehistoric invaders, who brought iron weapons and stimulated the great flowering of Hellenic civilisation, there have been 'Macedonians', Albanians, various types of Slavs, Vlachs, Turks, 'Franks', Venetians, and other

Italian settlers.   Few of these have left any obvious cultural traces, and Greek speech (to be distinguished from classical Greek) and a Mediterranean mode of life have quietly prevailed.

It may be worth noting here that before 1830 there had never been a single united Greek state, for the city states of ancient Greece, though allied at times, were independent of each other.   Also from the time of the Macedonian conquest onwards (338 B.C.) the Greeks had never had self-government, but had always been ruled by aliens.

From 1829 to 1919 the area under Greek rule greatly increased. Greece obtained the greater part of Macedonia as a result of the Balkan Wars against Turkey (1911–13), and thereby doubled in size.   It then became ambitious to bring all the Greek-speaking people under one flag; hence the attempt to obtain possession of the western part of Asia Minor.   Greek-speaking people had occupied these shores since prehistoric days, though in course of time they had become much intermingled with Anatolian stock. The result of the 1918–23 attempt to bring these lands under Greek rule resulted in vigorous Turkish resistance and the final expulsion of all Greeks from Turkey, with the exception of those in Constantinople (Istanbul).   These emigrants, who numbered nearly one and a half millions and were mainly farmers, carpet-weavers, artisans, and merchants, greatly swelled the population of the Greek state, and would have proved a very difficult problem if money had not been forthcoming from British, American, and French sources to prepare the sparsely peopled northern basins of Macedonia, Thrace, and Thessaly for their reception.

**Contrasts between Southern Greece and the Rest of the Country.** Modern Greece presents two main types of environment, the true Mediterranean one of southern Greece including the islands and the sub-continental one of northern Greece, though the coastal strips even in the north feel the sea influence sufficiently to make this distinction somewhat unsatisfactory.   The northern basins and mountains of Macedonia, Thrace, and Thessaly have too severe a winter climate to permit of typical Mediterranean farming, while the mountain massifs (e.g. Pindus) tend to be the domain of Vlach shepherds, who speak a tongue descended from Latin. The swampy basins, even when drained, demand a farming technique not suitable to the rest of Greece, and can grow cereals in abundance, whereas from the time of classical antiquity the true Greek lands have habitually suffered from a shortage of cereals and have had to import these from over the sea.   Less than one-fifth of the southern area can be cultivated owing to the mountainous relief, consequently the region is agriculturally poor, and the resources of the inhabitants have been supplemented from the dawn of history by utilising the surrounding sea. As the Mediterranean Sea is rather poor in fish, this activity mainly took the form of a carrying trade, together with the marketing of the goods carried. In addition, the ancient Greeks, particularly the Athenians, whose tillable land was exceedingly small, exported manufactured articles as well as olive oil and wine in exchange for cereals.

**Structural Outlines.** The Greek lands continue the main structural lines of the country farther north (see Fig. 3 and Chapter 28), but round the Ægean Sea and in the southern part of the country, they may be looked upon as a drowned mountainous area, with little more than the tops of the mountains standing above sea-level.

The Dinaric system on the west extends through Epirus southwards to the peninsula of the Peloponnesus or Morea, with the single transverse break of the Gulf of Corinth. The direction of the strike, which is followed by that of the mountain chains, is mainly north-west to south-east. An old massif, known as the Pelagonian massif, extends on the east as far south as Mount Pelion on the mainland and a similar massif appears at the south-east end of Attica and in the Cyclades, though here it is much dissected. The rest of the islands mainly belong to the system of young folded mountains, with occasional young volcanic material. In Crete the direction of the folds has obviously changed to an east–west direction, and in Rhodes to south-west to north-east. The various formations of the Dinaric system are so crowded together in Greece that there is a very great diversity of rock, which can be easily seen owing to the general scanty covering of soil and vegetation.

**Geographical Regions.** Greece may be divided into two main geographical regions, (a) the southern part of the mainland, together with the islands, which are wholly Mediterranean in climate and outlook, and (b) the central and northern sections which are scarcely Mediterranean in climate and lack the sea influence. The distinction made itself felt in the days of classical antiquity, for the greater part of the mountainous region between the Gulf of Corinth and the Albanian frontier lay outside the city states of ancient Greece and was regarded as semi-barbaric. Both these regions require some subdivision on ground of relief.

**Southern Peninsular Greece and the Islands.** This may be looked upon as classical Greece *par excellence*. The climate is purely Mediterranean, the summers are hot and very dry, the winters mild at low altitudes.

Even on the higher ground, where winter temperatures are lower, summer temperatures remain fairly high and drought

| | Mean temperature | | Rainfall<br>Per cent of total falling<br>in June, July, August |
|---|---|---|---|
| | January | July | |
| Corfu | 50° F (10° C) | 78° F (25·5°C) | 4 |
| Athens | 48° F ( 9° C) | 80° F (26·6°C) | 8 |

prevails, for example Tripolis at a height of about 2,000 ft has a January temperature of 40° F, (4·4° C), but a July temperature of 73° F, (22·7° C).

The differences in relief call for a subdivision into (a) the region centred on Attica, (b) the Morea or Peloponnesus, and (c) the islands.

The first of these regions is characterised by a large number of small basins, mainly tectonic, and by discontinuous heights, which, however, can be fairly easily circumvented so as to allow of communication between one basin and the next.

The typical Greek landscape of Attica and the Peloponnesus consists of a small tillable plain above which rise arid foothills with a scanty cover of scrubby *maquis*. Since the plains are tiny, the foothills play an important part in the rural economy. These foothills rise in turn to towering mountains, whose bare bones show through the scanty vegetation, and afford pasture only for sheep and goats. Even on the heights there are few tall trees, although many mountains rise sufficiently high to carry a winter snow-cap: notably the western peaks of Vardussia, Giona, and the celebrated Parnassus, seat of the ancient Delphic oracle. All these are over 8,000 ft, while Helicon, farther east, rises to nearly 6,000 ft from the waters of the Corinthian gulf, and Hymettus and Pentelikon raise their heads high above the Athenian plain. The close juxtaposition of mountains, sea, and plain is a characteristic feature of the landscape of classical Greece and forms one of its main charms.

'The mountains look on Marathon,
And Marathon looks on the sea.'

*The Region centred on Attica.* The general strike of the rocks is from west-north-west to east-south-east, and differs slightly, therefore, from the north-west to south-east direction farther north and west. The climate is Mediterranean, but the low rainfall (cf. fifteen inches at Athens) means that the vegetation is poor *maquis*, inclining to steppe in the most northerly basin, that of Lamia, through which flows the River Spercheios.

A southerly row of basins traversed by the River Cephissos (Kifissos) formed the ancient lands of Doris, Phokis, and Bœotia, with

Thebes (now a tiny town of only about 7,000 people) as the chief city of the latter. By the drainage of Lake Copais, into which the River Cephissos flowed, an area of 50,000 acres has been acquired for agriculture. These basins are traversed by the Athens-Salonika railway, with an eastward branch to Chalcis (24,000) on the narrow 70 ft channel which separates the island of Eubœa (Evvoia[1]) from the mainland. Eubœa contains mountains which rise to at least 6,000 ft in the middle of the island, but the foothills of young Tertiary material are moderately fertile and well cultivated. The peninsula of Attica has the advantage of being centrally placed with regard to the three most productive parts of old Greece, (*a*) the Cephissos basins and the Eubœa, (*b*) the Peloponnesus, and (*c*) the Cyclades Islands. In itself it is not very fertile and suffers severely from drought.

*Athens.* Today, as in the past, Athens (Athinai) is the centre of Greek commercial and intellectual life. In ancient times Corinth was equally placed for trade but lapsed into obscurity, partly because of the liability of the site to earthquakes, and partly because it lacked the ancient prestige which caused Athens to be chosen as the capital of an independent Greece at the close of the Wars of Liberation (1821–29). Athens and Piræus together have nearly two million inhabitants, roughly a quarter of the national total. The drift of population from the provinces into the capital inevitably raises a number of problems, among them employment, housing and the provision of water supplies. This last has been solved by the construction of the Marathon barrage but there is much talk of the need to decentralise population. Athens itself is mainly concerned with administration and the similar functions associated with a capital, but tourism contributes substantially to its economy. Piræus is its industrial and maritime adjunct; it handles the vast majority of the country's overseas trade and is the main collecting centre for the numerous coasting vessels, which play such an important part in the communications of Greece. At one time the industry of the Athens–Piræus area was very poorly developed and was concerned largely with such activities as tobacco processing, soap manufacture, textiles and carpet weaving, but in recent years there has been heavy investment in shipbuilding, ship repairing, engineering, chemicals, cement and oil refining.

**The Peloponnesus, or Morea.** Since the construction of the Corinth Ship Canal in 1893 this peninsula composed of peninsulas may perhaps be looked upon as an island. Although mainly mountainous, it contains a relatively important coastal plain on the north and north-west coasts, and three quite fair-sized plains (for

[1] The modern forms of Greek place-names are given in parentheses.

Greece) continuing the lines of the three southern gulfs. Of these plains Messenia in the west has the greatest rainfall and the densest population and is the only one growing oranges in considerable quantities. The plain of Laconia along the River Eurotas is the longest, being about thirty miles in length, but is only a few miles wide. Its northern interior part is very dry, and the plain of ancient Sparta is now a thickly planted orchard of olive trees. The plain of Argos is engaged at the present day in the production of green vegetables for the Athens–Piræus market, the necessary irrigation water for this arid plain being obtained from wells. Even the central highlands are interrupted by tectonic basins, e.g. those of Tripolis and Megalopolis, both traversed by the railway from Corinth via the plain of Argos to the Messenian basin and coast. Also there is some useful cultivated hill country, especially in the north-west in Elis. The Peloponnesus is noted mainly for a particular kind of small grape, which are dried and sold as currants, and take their name from the town of Corinth. These grapes are grown on the wetter side of the peninsula, chiefly on the narrow coastal plains and terraced foothills of the north and west and in Messenia, and the currants are exported principally from Patras (Patrai; 95,000), the most important port on the west coast. The population in the western Peloponnesus is denser than in any other part of the Greek mainland, apart from Attica, and varies from about 200 to 300 per square mile (see Fig. 24).

**The Islands.** *The Ionian Islands.* The chief of these are Corfu (Kerkira), Leukas (Levkas), Cephalonia (Kefallinia), Ithaca (Ithaki), Zante (Zakinthos). They are composed of the same limestone and Flysch zones as Epirus, with some young Tertiary material, and the relief generally consists of low hill country, although Leukas has a considerable area above 3,000 ft. The westerly position favours a plentiful supply of rain, Corfu having an annual average of 52 ins, and in addition to good rainfall and soil the islands had the advantage of a long period of peace under Venetian and later under British rule which terminated only in 1863. All three factors favoured the growth of a dense population, Corfu having about 455 people per square mile. The islands are well cultivated, Zante and Cephalonia being noted for their currants, and Corfu for olive oil.

*The Cyclades (Kikladhes)* consist of very diverse material, but mainly of ancient rocks, such as granite, gneiss, marble, and crystalline schists, which contain a considerable variety of minerals. Milo (Milos) and Santorin (Thira) are, on the contrary, composed of young volcanic materials, and the south-eastern islands of limestone and Flysch. The interior plateaus and mountains are mainly unproductive, while cultivation is laboriously intensive on terraces

and on the tiny plains.   Generally speaking, the smaller islands of
Greece are the domain of the peasant proprietor, are very densely

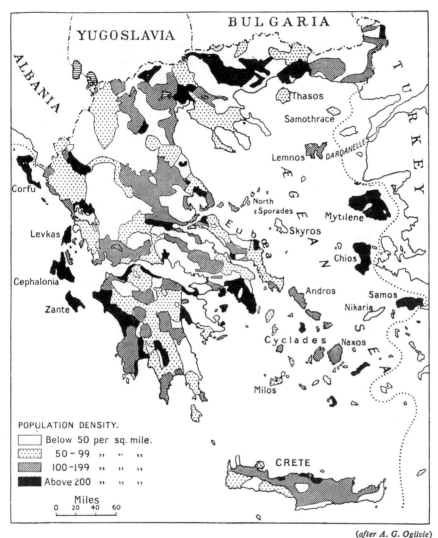

Fig. 24.   GREECE: DISTRIBUTION OF POPULATION

populated, but show no increase in population owing to emigration.
Siros is exceptional in possessing a ship repairing yard.

*The Cretan Arc.*   Crete (Kriti) with an area of 3,000 square miles is by far the largest of the Ægean islands.  Its limestone core forms three main mountain-masses, which lie nearer the south than the north coast, and which cause the steep harbourless south coast to contrast with the more gentle northward slope, whose fertile and well cultivated foothills sink seawards to convenient bays. Two cities, Candia (Iraklion; 64,000) and Canea (Khania; 33,000), lie on this favourable coast.  The island was in turn under Saracen, Venetian, and Turkish rule, but retained a predominantly Greek population and became part of Greece in 1913.

Rhodes is the second largest island of the Cretan arc.  Here the strike has assumed a south-west to north-east direction, but the young Tertiary rocks of which it is chiefly composed are infertile gravels, instead of the fertile soils which characterise the northern slopes of Crete.  Limestone mountains rise above these hills.

**The Islands of the Eastern Ægean.**  These large islands are detached portions of the western peninsulas of Asia Minor.  Samos consists partly of crystalline schists and limestone and partly of fertile young Tertiary hills and plains.  The islands are intensively cultivated and the population density approaches 250 per square mile.  Chios (Khios) consists mainly of Palæozoic shales and mountain limestone, and only in the south-east is there a stretch of young Tertiary hill country, but citrus fruits, olive oil, and mastic are produced in considerable quantities.  Lesbos (Lesvos) or Mitilini has a variety of structure with volcanic rocks in the west, serpentine in the centre, and crystalline schists in the east.  It specialises in olive oil and tobacco.  Its chief town, Mitilini, has a population of over 25,000. Lemnos (Limnos) and Imbros (the latter being Turkish) are composed partly of sandstones and shales, which give gentle land forms, and partly of volcanic trachyte, which gives rise to infertile hills. Both are rather low-lying.

These islands came under the Greek flag in 1913.

Of the remaining groups of islands, the Dodecanese or Twelve Islands and the Sporades lie near the shores of Asia Minor, and belonged to Italy between the two world wars.  The infertile Northern Sporades, however, lie towards the European side of the Ægean, though the division into Europe and Asia in this area has little significance.

**Northern Greece.**  Only the coastal strips of this region allow of the characteristic Mediterranean horticulture, since the interior parts are sufficiently high to give rise to low temperatures, particularly in winter, while the low-lying eastern basins are either cut off from sea influences by coastal mountains, as in Thessaly, or exposed to cold northern winds in winter as in Macedonia.

Northern Greece falls into four or five sub-regions: (a) the western coastlands of Epirus and Akarnania, (b) the central mountain mass of Pindus and the Vlach Highlands further north, (c) the eastern coastlands, comprising the basins and mountains of Thessaly, and (d) the basins and mountains of Macedonia and western Thrace.

(a) *The Western Coastlands.* Epirus (Ipiros) consists of a series of limestone ridges and moderately fertile valleys sometimes Flysch-filled, running parallel to the concordant coast. The structural lines are continued from Albania, and there has been some inter-mingling of population, with the result that disputes about the frontier have arisen. Epirus is terminated on the south by the Gulf of Arta (Amvrakikos), where the sea has breached the coastal ridge at a weak spot and has flooded the interior valleys, but the structural lines are continued to the south of the gulf in Akarnania, though the proportion of lowland increases. To the south, this region is cut across abruptly by the fault lines bounding the Gulf of Corinth. These western mountains, which attain heights of over 5,000 ft, receive the heaviest rainfall of Greece owing to their height and relatively northern latitude (c. 39° to 40° N), and though Mediter-ranean vegetation extends to a height of some 1,000 ft, above that level the winter cold is too great. Yanina (Ioannina), chief town and regional capital of Epirus, at a height of 1,600 ft, has a mean January temperature of 41° F (5° C), and a mean minimum temperature of only 17° (–8°C). Above the Mediterranean vegetation come deciduous trees such as the sweet chestnut and beech and also conifers, though the timber has been largely cleared for cultivation and pasture. Patches of cultivation extend up to nearly 5,000 ft. Subsistence agriculture and the keeping of transhumant livestock prevail over most of the interior. Vines and olives grow in the coastlands, and other tree crops on the lower slopes, while the few plains specialise: for example, the densely-populated deltaic plain north of the Gulf of Arta specialises in oranges, and the Agrinion plain of Ætolia (Aitolia) in tobacco.

On the whole, the north-western mainland of Greece is one of the most isolated and poverty-stricken areas in the country. There is only one short section of railway, from Agrinion to Missolonghi, and one major road, that from Yanina to the Gulf of Corinth. The development of the car ferry service from Brindisi to Igoumenit-za is helping to break down this isolation and the Louros hydro–electric power plant should improve the economic prospects of the region.

(b) *The Pindus (Pindhos) Zone,* a compact mountain system rising to over 7,000 ft, cuts this region off from land communication with eastern Greece, though transhumant shepherds of both Greek and Vlach speech pasture their flocks here in summer, having come up from their winter quarters in the basins of Thessaly. The region is continued northwards by a rather narrower but even higher mountain mass, which may be termed the Vlach Highlands, culminating in Mt Smolikas which reaches about 8,736 ft. No railway crosses these high dividing ranges, but a road connects the eastern Thessalian basins via Trikkala with the western basin of Yanina, by skirting the north of the Pindus massif. Very sparse population densities characterise these mountains, where life remains exceedingly primitive. The power potentialities of the Akheloös are now being exploited.

(c) *The Eastern Coastlands.* The Thessalian basins are girdled by mountains even on the seaward side, where the mountains of the Pelagonian massif are here mainly composed of crystalline schists and limestones. The most imposing of these mountains is Olympus (Olimbos), the mythical home of the Gods, which lies on the north-eastern border of Thessaly and raises its snow-capped head mightily above sea and plain to a height of 9,548 ft. Separated from Mount Olympus by the narrow Vale of Tempe, through which flows the River Peneus (Pinios), lies Ossa (6,457 ft), while Pelion (Pilion; 5,308 ft) lies farther south. The Vale of Tempe is traversed by a railway from Athens to Salonika, constructed after the Balkan Wars (1911–13), before which there was no rail communication between Greece and the rest of Europe.

The two tectonic basins of Thessaly, those of Trikkala and Larisa, linked by the Peneus, contain the largest area of level land in Greece apart from Macedonia, but they are not very thickly inhabited. The winters are cold and the rainfall low owing to the exclusion of sea influences by the surrounding mountains, and although with large-scale farming under Turkish overlords they were at one time quite important grain-producing regions, their treeless, steppe-like expanses are not adapted either in climate or relief to Greek horticulture. With assistance from the League of Nations, the Greek refugees from Asia Minor, who were more accustomed to agriculture as distinct from horticulture, began to transform these basins, which grow good grain and tobacco. Two small towns, Trikkala (24,000) and Larisa (56,000), are respectively the markets for the two basins, and where the Gulf of Volos makes the only gap in the south-eastern rim of the basin of Larisa there occurs the only harbour and the largest town of Thessaly, Volos (67,000).

It will be seen that central Greece has little of the Mediterranean type of agriculture and even less of the sea life that characterise the southern part of the peninsula and the islands.

(d) *The Basins and Mountains of Macedonia and Western Thrace.*

11 Hydroelectric station
at Ladon, Peloponnese

12 Temple of Apollo, Delphi. The view from the ruins of the temple is typical of much of Greece: barren limestone hillsides, with only thin useless scrub cover and much heavier vegetation on the valley floor. Note the alluvial flat in the valley and the regular rows of trees in the valley floor; these are almost all olives.

13 View of Rouen and the Seine. Note the steep valley sides, the island in the river, and the factories along the river valley.

FRANCE

14 The basin of Le Puy in Velay. The volcanic plug on the left is capped by a church and the other by a statue. Note the very steep sides of the plugs.

This region consists of the Ægean end of the central 'corridor lands' of the Balkan peninsula, together with the Chalcidice peninsula and the low seaward frontage of the Rhodope massif. Central European and Mediterranean modes of life here intermingle, and owing to this factor and to the convergence of routes, the region is a meeting place for many people, Greeks, Bulgars, Yugoslavs, Turks, Vlachs, and even Albanians. For these reasons it is a much disputed area. Greeks predominate in the peninsulas and along the coasts, and though their hold was precarious in Turkish times, it was strengthened through the establishment in the 1920s and 1930s of about a million Greek refugees from Asia Minor.

The proportion of lowland to mountain is here higher than in any other part of Greece, and in particular there are large level plains, though these, until recently, were mainly lake-covered or swampy and therefore malarial. These plains mainly lie in tectonic basins which were arms of the sea even in geologically recent times and have been partially filled up owing to a change in the sea-level and by silt deposited in the deltas of the rivers Vardar, Struma, Maritza, and others. Rising from the swampy, alluvial plains are dissected terraces of the old lake basins and gulfs, and above these rise the rounded slopes of barren or *maquis*-covered mountains. The higher and healthier parts of the lowland have been important agricultural land for centuries, for example, the Drama plain, with its specialised tobacco cultivation, which maintains a population density of some 350 per square mile.

The extensive plains along the lower Vardar (Axios) and Struma (Strimon), however, which contained large lakes and swamps, were extremely malarial and very scantily populated until the Refugee Settlement Commission began work in 1923. With the aid of the League of Nations and of loans raised in England and elsewhere, large-scale drainage works were carried out, especially in western Macedonia. The lakes Yiannitsa, Akhinos and others were entirely drained, precautions were taken against malaria, dams (e.g. the great Kerkini dam on the Struma) were built to control the rivers for irrigation, and entire villages were constructed, together with roads and all the necessary public utility services. Together Macedonia and western Thrace contain about one-third of the country's cropped area and account for an even higher proportion of the total cash value of its agricultural output. Tobacco and cotton are the principal cash crops but the area also produces large quantities of wheat, fodder and rice.

Thessaloniki (Salonika) (307,000), sited away from the Vardar delta, is the main commercial and industrial centre of 'new' Greece. It is also the busiest Greek port after Piræus but its advantageous

position in relation to the Vardar–Morava corridor has never been
fully exploited because of recurrent political differences with Yugoslavia.   There is, however, a Yugoslav free zone within the port area.

**Economic Summary.**   Although Greeks are to be found all over the
world pursuing their ancient trades of merchant, shipowner and
shopkeeper, those who remain in their own land derive their living
chiefly from agriculture, with some support from fishing, usually
on a part-time basis, if they happen to live on the coast.   Out of a
working population of about 4 million (total population 8·4 millions
in 1962), some 46 per cent are engaged in agriculture, which has
also been responsible for about 80 per cent of the value of the exports
in recent years.   Greece's natural endowment for agriculture is a
meagre one; only one-quarter of the land surface is cultivable and
much of that is poor land; the rest of the country is either too high
or too rocky to be of any value.   The maximum permissible holding
under the latest land reform is 25 acres and the vast majority of the
farms, few of which constitute a consolidated holding, are well
below this figure.   In the less accessible areas the rural economy is
mainly a subsistence one with wheat, beans and tree crops dominating the land use.   Where communications are good, however,
particularly on the plains and where water is readily available, there
has been marked progress in recent years.   Yields of the staple
foodstuffs have risen with the increased use of fertilisers and Greece
is now very largely self-sufficient in wheat; the irrigated area has been
doubled in the last decade and there has been an encouraging
increase in the production of rice, fodder crops and citrus fruits,
and of high-grade cotton for export.   Two other staple agricultural
exports, tobacco and currants, have made less progress, and the
olive yield is notoriously susceptible to weather conditions.

The high degree of rural overpopulation in much of Greece, for
which emigration has long been the traditional 'remedy', underlines
the need for industrialisation.   Until 1950 when Greece first began
to struggle out of a decade of war and civil upheaval, textiles and,
to a less degree, food processing were the only 'factory' industries,
although there was a host of enterprises on a workshop basis
producing a wide range of goods from caiques to handicrafts.   In
the last ten years advantage has been taken of the political stability
of the country to provide some of the basic elements necessary for
a wider and more thorough industrial development.   Large amounts
of capital, much of it from foreign sources, have been invested in
the provision of adequate water supplies and in the production of
electricity from both rivers and brown coal; output in 1961 reached
2,461 million kWh.   Among the hydro–electric schemes those on
the Ladhon, Akheloös, Megdhova, Louros and Loudhias **are**

noteworthy; the two main thermal stations, fed on brown coal, are located at Ptolemaïs in Macedonia and at Aliveri in Eubœa.

Although Greece yields a wide range of minerals, they are widely dispersed and both reserves and output are quite small. So far most of the production of iron-ore, lead, silver, chrome, manganese and pyrites is exported, but the brown coal (production 1·2 million tons) is usefully employed at home for chemicals as well as for power, and an aluminium refinery is being built to utilise the Elevsis bauxite deposits (0·6 million tons) at present used for cement. A small iron and steel plant using home-produced ore is also envisaged. Among the notable industrial ventures established recently are shipbuilding and repair yards and an oil refinery, both near Piræus. There has also been expansion in the cement, chemical, light engineering and vehicle assembly sectors. Even so textiles and construction work, much of it in connexion with the tourist industry, remain the largest employers of labour.

The Greek export trade is dominated by a limited group of agricultural products which include dried fruits, wines, cotton, citrus fruits and, most important of all, tobacco. The problem has long been to find steady and profitable markets for these products which have to face considerable competition in the traditional western European markets. No doubt it is hoped that Greece's associate membership of the European Economic Community will provide not only capital and technical assistance for her industrialisation, but also an easier outlet for her agricultural exports. The association agreement is so designed that Greek industry will not be obliged to face the full force of competition from the industrial products of the Six for some twenty years. In 1961 the Federal German Republic, the United States, the United Kingdom, Italy, and France were Greece's main suppliers and customers, but the USSR has also made its appearance in the list. The Greek balance of trade shows a large deficit which is made good, in part at least, by invisible items, notably emigrant remittances and earnings from the rapidly expanding tourist industry and from the carrying trade. The repatriation of large numbers of ships from flags of convenience has been responsible for the spectacular increase in the tonnage registered in Greece (7 million GRT in 1963).

## REFERENCES

*The Greek Commonwealth*, by A. Zimmern (5th ed., Oxford, 1931), gives an excellent account in the introductory chapters of the unchanging elements of the Greek land and life. 'Population Density in Greece', by A. G. Ogilvie, in *The Geographical Journal*, Vol. CI, 1943, is accompanied by a detailed map. *La Macédoine*, by J. Ancel, Paris, 1930, deals with developments in that area.

*La Grèce* in Mémento Economique series, published by L'Institut National de la Statistique et des Etudes Economiques, Paris, 1952, and *La Grèce*, Geographie Universelle, Larousse, Paris, 1958, are probably the most up-to-date works.

# SECTION II – WESTERN EUROPE

CHAPTER 9

## GENERAL INTRODUCTION TO WESTERN EUROPE

WESTERN Europe is a highly distinctive region through the mutually advantageous co-existence of land and sea. Its location in respect of the Atlantic Ocean, its configuration, climatic type, and vegetation forms, its continental shelves, tidal conditions, and navigable rivers have all combined to characterise this area and to mark it off from three adjoining major regions of the Continent: northern Europe, southern Europe, and central Europe. Certainly it presents sharp contrasts and varieties of landforms which result in contrasting environments – notably between the lowlands and highlands which compose it, although the North Sea, the Irish Sea, and the English Channel act as unifying agencies. In its human geography, western Europe stands out as an area of intensive farming – mainly mixed farming – on its lowlands and reveals an outstanding development of industry and trade. Full use has been made of its maritime location, not only for fishing, but also for international commerce, as formerly for imperialist achievements. A remarkable convergence of sea and air routes focuses on the ports and cities which lie near the Straits of Dover. Another salient characteristic of the region, associated with industrial development, is its high degree of urbanisation and its high population densities, although these apply only to specific lowland parts. Western Europe played a striking role in spreading its peoples and civilisation throughout the world, to which, in more recent times, it has contributed the knowledge of western industrial economy. But if it can claim a certain unity of culture, it is nevertheless much divided – in respect of nationality, language, political organisation, and even economic attachment – to such bodies as EEC and EFTA (see p. 622 and 623). While the decline of western Europe has often been discussed and proclaimed, it is none the less true that, despite the destruction which it suffered in major wars and the loss of valuable colonial holdings, it maintains a high status in the world and even expands its vigorous economy.

The United Kingdom, Ireland, France, Belgium, the Netherlands, and Luxembourg are the political units which make up western

148

Europe. The region is not so clearly a unit as southern Europe, but the various countries have certain similarities. For instance, climatically they all have a similar oceanic régime, structurally they lie mainly within 'Hercynian' Europe, and in relief they consist mainly of ancient horsts alternating with fairly extensive plains. The main exceptions are the southern and south-eastern parts of France, which lie within the region of Mediterranean climate or of Alpine folding or of both, and the northern parts of Scotland, which resemble Scandinavia in respect of geological structure and relief. The various countries have also been closely bound up with each other in their political and economic history, and developments have taken place there which have profoundly changed the face of the world during the past two centuries and which continue to make their influence felt.

Western Europe was fortunate in coming in contact with Roman civilisation at an early date, an occurrence which was aided, no doubt, by the facility of access from the Mediterranean Sea through France by the Rhône–Saône corridor and the Aquitaine basin, whilst the mild oceanic winters were not unkind to a southern people. Moreover, in spite of the barbarian invasions of the fifth and later centuries, civilisation was not completely swept away, and in many cases the barbarians themselves had been already in contact with Roman ways of life. Since the intruders came mainly from the east, the westerly position protected the region from receiving the most uncivilised type of invader, and saved it completely from some of the invasions, the brunt of which fell on the people of central and eastern Europe. Consequently western Europe was able to develop with relatively few checks, once it had recovered from the long series of invasions which ended about the beginning of the tenth century, whereas aggression on the part of invaders in eastern Europe continued right down into the seventeenth century, and even later, for example the Tatars roamed Bessarabia as late as 1800.

In spite of the fall of the Roman Empire, the pattern and inspiration for western civilisation all through the Middle Ages continued to be the Mediterranean lands, whose people also took the lead in the discovery of America and of the sea route to the Indies, though the English, Dutch, and French and, particularly the English, reaped much of the benefit. It was not until the end of the eighteenth century that developments took place in western Europe which gave an entirely new turn to civilisation, and which also gave the countries of western Europe a decisive lead. These developments were associated with three 'revolutions', usually known as the French Revolution, the Industrial Revolution, and the less widely known Agricultural Revolution. It is true that the ferment which became obvious during the eighteenth and early nineteenth centuries had been working silently for a long time, but the rest of the world had hitherto paid little attention.   The French Revolution brought to the notice of the greater part of Europe the idea of personal liberty, which had slowly become established in England and the Low Countries (Belgium and Holland) during the previous five centuries, whereas up to the time of the French Revolution individuals in most of the

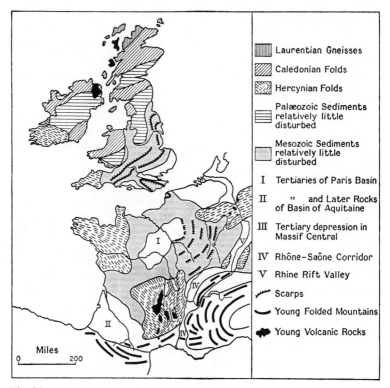

Fig. 25. STRUCTURAL DIAGRAM OF THE BRITISH ISLES AND FRANCE

other countries, including France itself, were still bound by feudal restrictions, which among other things hindered their free movement from place to place, and imposed severe restrictions on the occupations they could adopt.   These restrictions applied not only to serfs, who were economically bound to the soil, but also to other ranks; for instance, a German noble was not allowed to practise a trade or to become a manufacturer, and a German burgher was not allowed to own a landed estate.   The liberation of the individual, though it took place in England and Belgium from no humanitarian motive, set free an abundance of talent and enterprise, which first made themselves felt in those countries where feudal restrictions first disappeared.   Without the break-up of the feudal organisation of society it is doubtful whether the Agricultural and Industrial Revolutions could have taken place.

The Agricultural Revolution led to a great increase in the yield from the soil by substituting an improved system of agriculture for the old methods which had been practised with little alteration from Roman times and even earlier.   The chief change lay in the abolition of the wasteful biennial or triennial fallow, and usually involved also the abolition of what is known as the 'open-field' system of farming.   The great hedgeless arable lands of each village had been divided generally into three fields, one of which was devoted to wheat, the second to a spring-sown cereal, while the third lay fallow, the rotation usually being rigidly enforced.   Each landowner held one or more strips in each section of the field, instead of holding all his land in one continuous farm.   In addition, each village possessed common land for the grazing of livestock, though the fallow land was also largely used as common pasturage; but as there was insufficient winter grazing for the cattle, many had to be slaughtered every autumn; scientific cattle breeding and fattening were almost unknown.   This old system persisted in parts of eastern Europe well into the present century, but was done away with in England mainly under the Enclosure Acts of the eighteenth and early nineteenth centuries, while in western and southern England it had disappeared much earlier.   The new methods had indeed been evolved in Flanders as early as the thirteenth century, but were first adopted on a large scale in England, later in the other lands of western and central Europe, and finally spread to Russia in the twentieth century.   The abolition of the wasteful one-third fallow was made possible by the introduction of clover and root crops, of heavy manuring and of the development of scientific rotations.   The growing of clover on land previously kept fallow actually increased the yield of cereals in the following year, and together with the root crops provided winter fodder for livestock, which in turn made available a greatly increased supply of manure. The new methods brought more land under cultivation, resulted in much heavier yields, allowed a great increase in the quantity and quality of livestock, and therefore provided more and better food for a rapidly increasing population which was indeed the stimulant of improvement.   They also involved a great diminution in the common grazing lands, for poorer soils could now be brought under cultivation, and of course they brought about the abolition of the compulsory rotation. Though the wasteful strip-system of land-holding still persists in many parts of Europe, much progress has been made towards land consolidation in France and the Low Countries (see p. 279).

This revolution put Europe in the forefront of agricultural production. It is not always realised that Europe in normal times is a greater producer of foodstuffs than the great exporting continents, such as North America and that Europe, including the USSR, produces over half the world's wheat, meat, barley, potatoes, and dairy produce. It also produces nearly half the world's sugar.

In spite of this large home production, Europe has to import more food than all the other continents combined, in order to feed the large industrial population which has come into being as a result of the Industrial Revolution, and enjoys high living standards.

The Industrial Revolution originated in England, and is perhaps the most important of the three revolutions mentioned. It caused, and is still causing, immense changes in the distribution of population, in the methods and localisation of industry, in the methods and routes of transport, in the type and quantity of raw material needed, and indeed in practically every aspect of human life.

## GREAT BRITAIN AND THE INDUSTRIAL REVOLUTION

The Industrial Revolution hinged chiefly on the invention of steam-driven machinery, which required coal to feed it and iron for construction if it was to stand the strain of the new driving power. Since the mechanism of the steam engine is supposed to have been known to the ancient Greeks, but remained neglected for nearly 2,000 years, its reinvention in England might have remained equally local and unknown but for a series of favourable factors, which led to its great improvement and its rapid adoption for different kinds of work, including the mechanisation of the iron and textile industries and of transport. This rapid adoption seems to have been due to the fact that Great Britain had already developed overseas markets (mainly for textiles) which were expandable at such a rate that any invention which would speed up production and cheapen costs was seized upon with avidity. This market consisted largely of colonies, founded by widespread settlement overseas of people from the British Isles, and partly obtained at the expense of the Dutch and French during the seventeenth and eighteenth centuries. when the English established themselves as supreme at sea. With the mechanisation of production, increased quantities of manufactured goods became available at such low prices that the British

Isles were enabled to secure the 'whole world' as a market for nearly a century, though other regions, equally well equipped by nature, have since successfully challenged her monopoly.

Two of the fundamental necessities for the mechanisation of industry were coal and iron, which occur in Great Britain, though not in Ireland, in large quantities. The steam engine was invented in 1710 to pump water out of coal mines, a significant fact because very few other parts of the world at that time were using coal for fuel, timber being the usual fuel in the forest belts, and straw or dried dung in the non-forest areas. England however was suffering from a shortage of timber as early as the seventeenth century in spite of being in the forest belt, a shortage which may at first sight seem surprising. It should be remembered, however, that the soils of the south-eastern lowlands were good enough to be cleared for agriculture, apart from the growing of the great oaks needed for shipbuilding and other constructional purposes, and, on the other hand, the bare uplands and mountains of the north-west seem never to have been forested within historic times. Moreover, the British Isles have only one quick-growing native conifer, the Scots pine, and this seems to be a survivor from prehistoric climatic conditions but now reproduces itself with difficulty. As early as Cromwellian times the Baltic lands were supplying England with timber products such as masts, tar, etc. Coal, on the other hand, was plentiful, so near the surface in parts that it could be mined by means of adits or shallow pits, and so near the sea-coast that it could be transported conveniently and cheaply for hundreds of miles, for example from the Durham coalfield to London where the demand was greatest, hence the old term 'sea-coal'. Land transport for such a heavy and bulky commodity was difficult and costly before the Industrial Revolution, and Great Britain lacks large navigable rivers for successful inland water transport.

The steam engine did not become a really useful generator of energy until the improvements by Watt in 1782 reduced the amount of coal required and enabled the engine to be used at a distance from the actual coal mines and for divers purposes. By that time methods of smelting iron by means of coke, in place of the scanty supplies of charcoal, had not only been invented (c. 1730) but had become generally known (c. 1750), while the canal system had been started mainly with a view to transporting coal, the first canal being built in 1761. The manufacture of cotton goods had already begun, the invention of the spinning 'jenny' (1767) and Arkwright's water-frame (1768) had speeded up the production of yarn, and the latter had brought in the use of water power. Crompton's 'mule' (1775) combined the virtues of the jenny and the water-frame and enabled very fine yarns to be spun.

The change from small, home hand-manufactures to large-scale factory industries using steam power, and the development of great industrial agglomerations, came slowly, but the Revolution had been achieved in its essentials by about 1830. The building of the canals and the invention of railways and the steam locomotive allowed food to be transported to the new densely populated industrial areas, raw materials to reach the factories, and the finished product to be distributed to internal markets or the seaboard. The rapid increase in wealth during the period depended mainly on the export of textiles, of coal, and of iron and steel goods, to the rest of Europe and to the Americas. Once mechanisation was started, one branch of mechanised industry helped another. Never before had the world seen such a brilliant outburst of inventive genius combined with plentiful labour and adequate capital.

It may perhaps be argued that a series of fortuitous events combined to start the Industrial Revolution in Britain rather than in any other part of the world, but since the question involves the whole problem of the origins of culture and the whole area of the world, it is too vast to be treated here, except in bare outline and as regards Europe.

England's possible economic competitors at the end of the eighteenth century were those countries of Europe which already possessed considerable manufacturing industries at home, foreign or large home markets, some kind of transportable power capable of driving machines, and capital and labour available for expanding industries. A little consideration will show that the countries possessing these advantages at that time were very limited in number. Germany, which subsequently became England's chief European rival in industry, was only a 'geographical expression' a mosaic of over three hundred states divided from each other by separate customs-barriers, and still so completely in the feudal age that the bulk of the population was tied to the soil in serfdom and therefore unable to engage in manufacturing, while the manufacturing guilds of the towns were sufficiently strong to prevent any innovations and to prevent others from competing. On geographical grounds the great Ruhr coalfield of Germany offered possibilities for the development of early mechanised industry, since the coal occurred at the surface, near iron deposits, near old-established iron and textile industries, and near the navigable waterways of the Rhine system. (See Chapter 19.) These advantages, however, were negatived for a time by social and political factors, though they ultimately prevailed.

Of the countries with considerable seaboard, overseas possessions, and trade, only France possessed any considerable deposits of coal, but, like Germany, was still hampered by the survival of feudalism and the lack of an adequate banking system.    However, before the great

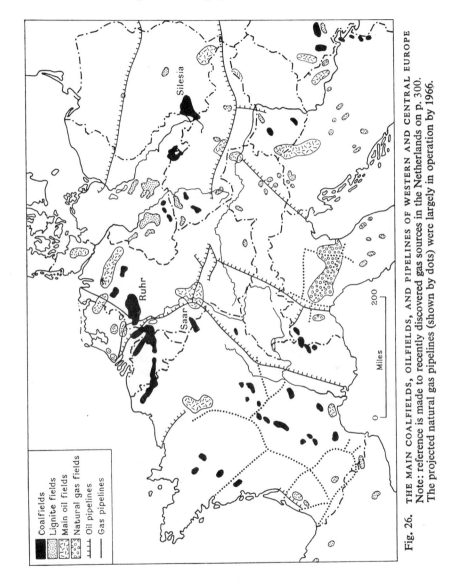

Fig. 26.    THE MAIN COALFIELDS, OILFIELDS, AND PIPELINES OF WESTERN AND CENTRAL EUROPE
Note: reference is made to recently discovered gas sources in the Netherlands on p. 300.
The projected natural gas pipelines (shown by dots) were largely in operation by 1966.

disturbance given to economic life by the French Revolution, France had copied England's example and had begun the mechanisation of the cotton industry, using water-driven machinery as in England, and had also begun the smelting of iron by coke; in both cases using smuggled English designs. The French Revolution and the Revolutionary Wars put a stop to the normal economic development, and by the time peace was restored on the Continent, England had definitely established her world lead.

The inventions made in England and Scotland in connexion with the Industrial Revolution were gradually introduced into other countries of Europe, and into the USA. This process was slow, partly owing to Britain's efforts to stop the leakage of information in regard to the new machinery, partly owing to the tremendous start gained by Great Britain, partly owing to internal disturbances and cultural backwardness in the southern and eastern parts of Europe. In one way or another, however, practically the whole of Europe was influenced by the Industrial Revolution by the end of the nineteenth century, Russia being the last of the great countries to be affected. Those countries which were well endowed with coal and iron deposits, particularly Germany, Belgium, and France, established great industries on similar lines, mainly behind defensive tariff walls. Those countries which had little or no coal either imported British coal for their manufacturing industries, or found their own expensive hand industries killed by the cheaply produced factory goods. In many countries both processes took place almost simultaneously, e.g. in Sweden and Italy. The invention of railways and the steam locomotive on the whole helped Britain's economic rivals, particularly the more continental powers, and to some extent negatived Britain's initial advantages, by enabling widely separated iron and coal supplies to be brought together.

The great new urban agglomerations made demands for foodstuffs on a scale hitherto unknown, while the new improvements in transport enabled foodstuffs to be imported from a great distance. In response to this demand, large-scale farming for export began on the prairies of south-eastern Europe even before it began in America, and the new cheap foodstuffs sounded the death-knell of grain production in those parts of Europe less favoured by climate, relief, and soil. Thus in Great Britain and Ireland, the Scandinavian countries, Denmark, the Low Countries, and parts of France, in fact, in all the rainy areas of north-western Europe, cereal production declined, to be replaced by specialised farming, for dairy produce, high-grade meat, fruit, flowers, and vegetables, which found a ready market in the manufacturing towns. In the country rural depopulation set in.

Changes which have taken place during the twentieth century have not diminished the importance of the coalfields. The substitution of electrically driven machinery for steam driven machinery has made less difference than might be expected, for in spite of the great development of hydro-electricity, the fact remains that much of the electricity supply of Europe is generated from solid fuels.    Moreover, in modern times, coal has acquired an additional importance; it is now not only a source of power but a raw material.    From coal and petroleum the heavy chemical industries derive numerous products, including synthetic oils and rubber, dyestuffs, fertilisers, explosives, solvents, plastics (including nylon), and other synthetic commodities whose number increases continually from day to day. Coal is actually in greater demand than ever, though the markets have changed somewhat with the development of hydro-electricity in the Alpine and Scandinavian countries, but as the most accessible and easily worked seams have already been exhausted in the older coalfields of Europe, the cost of extraction is likely to increase.    This change affects many of the fields of Great Britain, France and Belgium most acutely, but is beginning to be felt in the coalfields of Western Germany also.

Perhaps the most extraordinary aspect of the industrial development of western Europe is the large amount of imported raw materials used.    This is particularly applicable to Great Britain, which has to import most of the raw materials for its great textile industries, nearly all its timber requirements, the greater part of its non-ferrous metals, and in recent years large quantities of iron-ore and all its petroleum.    So firm was Britain's control of the sea that it does not seem to have occurred to nineteenth century economists that there was anything peculiar or precarious in Britain's reliance on the sale overseas of manufactured commodities made chiefly from imported raw materials.    The period 1815 to 1914, when Britain was undoubtedly the leading manufacturer of the world, was a century of relative peace and rapid progress, with a growing population and a rising standard of living in most countries; consequently world markets were able to absorb large quantities of high quality goods.    Nevertheless, the development of industries in other countries (e.g. USA, Germany, Italy, Japan, India) was forcing Great Britain to abandon the manufacture of certain products which could be made more cheaply elsewhere, notably cheap textiles, and to concentrate on branches of industry which demand the utmost skill, precision, organisation, and experience, such as the engineering and chemical industries.    The same is true to a large extent of the other countries of western Europe, including Western Germany.    The maintenance of millions of people by the sale abroad of manufactured commodities and their dependence on imported foodstuffs obviously involved grave risks which are all too apparent today.   Not only is peace essential, but even in times of peace, the smooth workings of the foreign exchanges and the reduction of tariffs to a reasonable level are prerequisites.   The great slump in world prices, which took place around 1930, the world-wide unemployment among factory workers, and the so-called over-production in agriculture seem to have been due to a breakdown of the means of exchange rather than to any real over-production of either industry or agriculture.

It is clear that the relatively high standard of living, achieved both by industrial and agricultural workers in western Europe as a result of the Industrial and Agricultural Revolutions and raised still further as a result of economic rehabilitation after World War II, depends upon the full working of mines and factories, upon the full use of all the means of communication and exchange, and upon the full exploitation of scientific and technological skills.   Any retrogressive movement towards a simpler economy would bring disastrous results.

## REFERENCES

On western Europe as a whole, A. G. Ogilvie, *Europe and its Borderlands* (Ed. by C. J. Robertson) Edinburgh, Nelson, 1957 and F. J. Monkhouse, *A Regional Geography of Western Europe,* New York, Praeger, 1967, are recommended.

On the Industrial Revolution J. H. Clapham's great work entitled *An Economtc History of Modern Britain,* Vol. I, *The Early Railway Age,* Cambridge University Press, 1926, and the same author's *The Economic Development of France and Germany,* 1815–1914, 4th ed., Cambridge, 1936, give a wealth of interesting detail.   L. C. A. Knowles' *The Industrial and Commercial Revolutions in Great Britain during the Nineteenth Century,* London, 1911, gives a shorter account. The first of the above-mentioned works also gives some account of the Agricultural Revolution, but the contemporary writings of Arthur Young and Cobbett (*Rural Rides*) are easily accessible and give vivid pictures.

On the British Isles, H. J. Mackinder, *Britain and the British Seas,* 2nd ed., Oxford, Clarendon Press, 1906; A. G. Ogilvie (ed.), *Great Britain; Essays in Regional Geography,* 2nd ed., Cambridge University Press, 1953; A. Demangeon, *Les Iles Britanniques,* Paris, Colin, 1927, trans. E. D. Laborde, London, 1939; and L. D. Stamp and S. H. Beaver, *The British Isles,* London, Longmans, 1957, are standard works.   See also L. D. Stamp, *The Land of Britain; Its Use and Misuse,* London, 2nd ed., Longmans, 1962; and *Britain's Scenery and Structure,* London, Collins, 1946; W. Smith, *Economic Geography of Great Britain,* 2nd ed., London, Methuen, 1953; G. J. Mitchell (ed.), *Great Britain; Geographical Essays,* Cambridge University Press, 1962.

### CHAPTER 10

# THE UNITED KINGDOM

ENGLAND, Wales, Scotland, the Isle of Man and the Channel Islands are collectively known as Great Britain (see Fig. 27). The wider term United Kingdom includes also Northern Ireland, which was created in 1920 by the Government of Ireland Act when the Republic of Ireland was constituted (see p. 227). The supreme legislative authority for the UK (though excluding the Isle of Man and the Channel Islands) is vested in Parliament in London. Wales and Scotland each has a Minister of State responsible for specific aspects of their affairs. While Northern Ireland is represented in the British Parliament, it has its own Parliament for domestic affairs. The Isle of Man is administered by the Manx Legislature (or *Tynwald*) and has its own budget, taxation system and tariffs. Similarly, Jersey and Guernsey in the Channel Islands have their own 'States' for internal administration, each with a Lieutenant-Governor appointed by the Crown.

The UK lies off the north-western coast of continental Europe between latitudes 50° and 61° North. The islands rise from a gently sloping continental shelf, and at their nearest are only twenty miles from the Continent, separated by a stretch of water that has been of critical importance throughout history and as late as 1940. This insular position, together with the numerous natural harbours, ice-free coasts and offshore fishing-grounds, has stimulated a maritime outlook which has played a great part in the development of Britain's naval, colonial and commercial interests. Only the last of these is important today, as Britain's world influence and power inevitably have declined, especially in comparison with those of the USA and the USSR.

Great Britain may be divided into two main relief units by a line from the estuary of the Tees to that of the Exe (see Fig. 28). To south and east of this line is 'Lowland Britain', consisting for the most part of Mesozoic and Tertiary (or Kainozoic) rocks, with a veneer of superficial deposits. It is rarely flat, except around the Wash, but it comprises low cuestas of limestone, chalk and sandstone, separated by vales and basins floored with clay, sand and alluvium.

159

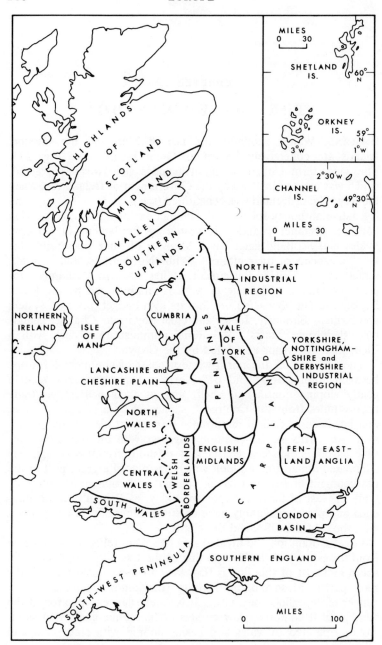

Fig. 27.  THE MAJOR REGIONS OF GREAT BRITAIN

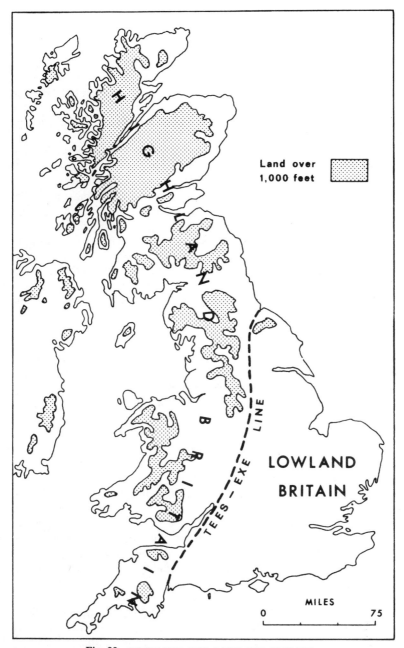

Fig. 28. HIGHLAND AND LOWLAND BRITAIN

To the west and north of the Tees-Exe line are the worn-down remnants of the ancient folded mountain systems (see p. 161 and Fig. 28), composed of Palæozoic rocks: the Highlands of Scotland, the Southern Uplands, the Pennines, the mountains of Cumbria, most of Wales, and the upstanding plateaus of the South-west peninsula. Several coalfields, the basis of Britain's rapid development during the Industrial Revolution (see pp. 152–158), have been preserved in basins on the Pennine flanks and in the Midland valley of Scotland. Among these uplands lie several areas of lowland of high agricultural productivity, notably the Lancashire and Cheshire plain, the South-west peninsula, and eastern Scotland.

The Quaternary ice-sheets at their maximum extended over Britain north of a line from the Severn to the Thames, and over Ireland (see p. 14 and Fig. 6). They had profound erosive effects on the uplands, deepening the pre-existing river valleys, creating cirques, arêtes and sometimes prominent peaks, and elsewhere rounding off the summit levels and leaving bare, rocky surfaces. Huge quantities of material were carried southwards and eastwards, and deposited over the lowlands as sheets of boulder-clay, sands and gravels; in East Anglia, for example, most of the solid rocks are thickly mantled with this drift. The withdrawal of the ice-sheets and their melting were accompanied by a gradual rise of sea-level, during which Britain was finally separated from the Continent, and numerous estuaries were formed, some penetrating far into the land.

The main factors responsible for the varied British climate include Britain's mid-latitude position on the eastern margins of a large ocean and on the western margins of a continental land-mass. Its insular location is emphasized by the North Atlantic Drift, which is warm for its latitude, hence responsible for a 'Winter Gulf of Warmth' over north-western Europe. Britain is subject to the influence of a succession of air-masses, with varying characteristics of temperature and humidity, though it is most dominantly affected by Polar Maritime air-streams from over the Atlantic; these bring cloudy conditions and a considerable precipitation, especially to the uplands, which lie mainly along the western margins. In a broad sense, therefore, Britain can be divided into quadrants. In the north-west, winters are remarkably mild for the latitude, though summers are rather cool, with a high degree of cloudiness and a considerable, well-distributed precipitation, especially on the mountains, where the total may exceed 150 in. In the south-west, winters are mild and the summers appreciably warmer, though the precipitation is still quite high. By comparison, the two eastern quadrants are distinctly drier, with 30 in or less annually, for they lie in the rainshadow of the western uplands. They are less cloudy, with higher seasonal ranges of temperature, and warm summers, with means of 60° to 64° F (15.6° to 17.8°C), in the south-east. These climatic variations, superimposed on the diverse relief, have distinctive results on the pattern of agriculture.

# ENGLAND

**The Pennines.** Almost half of the total area of northern England is occupied by the Pennines, which with the Cheviots and the uplands of Northumberland extend for almost 170 miles from the Scottish border to the valley of the Trent. In the north-west the Pennines are linked to the Lake District massif by the Howgill and Shap Fells, while farther south the Bowland and Rossendale 'Forests'[1] project towards the Irish Sea. On the eastern flanks are the coastal lowlands of Northumberland and Durham, the Vale of York and the Trent valley, and to the south-west is the Lancashire and Cheshire plain.

The Pennines consist of three main types of rock of Carboniferous age (except for a few exposures of the pre-Cambrian and early Palæozoic basement rocks): Carboniferous limestone (the oldest), millstone grit and Coal Measures. These rocks were complexly affected by both folding and faulting during past orogenic periods, notably that of the Hercynian (see p. 11), which arched them into domes and fractured them into individual blocks, for the most part tilted gently downwards towards the east. Long-sustained denudation removed the overlying Coal Measures from the central parts, so that they survive only on the flanks: the Northumberland and Durham coalfield in the north-east, the Yorkshire, Derbyshire and Nottinghamshire coalfield in the south-east, and the Lancashire and North Staffordshire coalfields in the south-west. Denudation also produced several distinct plateau surfaces, from which a few monadnocks rise prominently.

Two distinctive types of scenery can be distinguished, according to whether the limestone or the gritstone appears on the surface. In the northern Pennines, sometimes called the Alston Block, is Cross Fell, the highest peak in the whole range (2,930 ft), situated on the edge of the prominent fault-line scarp which overlooks the Eden valley (see p. 166) to the west. Limestone is also widely exposed farther south in the Askrigg Block and in the Derbyshire 'Dome'; the latter is sometimes known as the 'High Peak' or the 'Peak District'. Here can be seen characteristic features of Karst

---

[1] Such forests were historically areas reserved for hunting and were not necessarily well wooded.

scenery: bare rock pavements, sink holes, underground drainage systems and narrow gorges. In the Northumberland hills the limestone is impure and inter-banded with coarse sandstones and shales.

The coarse, impermeable gritstones form isolated monadnocks rising above the general level of the Askrigg Block (Ingleborough, Whernside and Pen-y-Ghent, each above 2,000 ft). In the central Pennines the gritstones comprise more extensive plateaus, part of an asymmetrical anticline with a step-faulted western margin and a gentle slope to the east, and in the south they make sharp 'edges' which surround the limestone 'dome'.

Various igneous intrusions make significant contributions to the relief. The Cheviot Hills consist of a mass of reddish granite, culminating in The Cheviot (2,676 ft) on the Scottish border. The Great Whin Sill is a near-horizontal intrusion of dolerite of Carboniferous age, which can be traced westwards from the Farne Islands off the coast of Northumberland as a line of north-facing craggy cliffs, along which the Romans built Hadrian's Wall; in the Alston Block the intrusion trends south and is revealed where the river Tees crosses it as a fine waterfall (High Force) in a deeply-cut gorge. In the High Peak horizontal intrusions of dark basaltic rock are known as 'toadstone', which is associated with mineral veins.

The general tilt to the east of the various Pennine blocks has induced a pattern of drainage in that direction, though some shorter rivers (Lune, Ribble and Mersey) flow to the Irish Sea. The valleys of the east-flowing Tyne, Wear, Tees and the 'sheaf' of the Yorkshire rivers focusing on the Humber were enlarged by glaciation and floored with boulder-clay, subsequently with alluvium; the valleys, known as the 'Dales', penetrate far into the uplands. Some are used by trans-Pennine railways (though tunnels are generally required at their heads) and by roads, the higher parts of which are sometimes blocked by snow for short periods in winter. Trans-Pennine routes are not easy, except for the 'through-valley' of the Tyne in the north.

*Agriculture and Settlement.* Soils on both limestone and gritstone are thin, except where the surface is plastered with boulder-clay. The limestone carries a covering of sparse but sweet grass, while the gritstone country has a more sombre appearance with stretches of moorland of coarse tussock-grass, heather and ling, with cotton-grass and sphagnum moss on the plateaus frequently forming areas of bog. Sheep are grazed on the upland pastures, which are divided by the remarkable dry-stone walls. Cattle, both store and dairy animals, are kept on the valley floors to provide milk for the industrial cities to the east and for making some well-known local cheeses, notably Wensleydale.

Settlement is scanty, consisting of isolated farms and attractive stone-built villages in the Dales; this is a popular tourist area, and the Dales have been designated a National Park. Some small resorts (Matlock, Buxton, Harrogate) owe much of their original popularity to their mineral springs of medicinal value. Other towns are market and servicing centres (Alston, Settle and Skipton), with some local light industry.

The Carboniferous limestone formerly contained large deposits of lead, silver and other ores which have been mined since Roman times, leaving abandoned workings and spoil-dumps on the hillsides. Some mines are still in operation, notably in Weardale, but more important now is the quarrying of limestone for several large lime- and cement-works, and the working of barytes and fluorspar.

The abundant soft water from the gritstone supplies the textile towns on either side of the Pennines, and a series of dams across the Derwent (a tributary of the Trent) impound reservoirs, which supply Sheffield and the towns of the East Midlands.

**Cumbria.** This corner of north-western England, between the Solway Firth and Morecambe Bay, is so called after the British kingdom of the *Cumbri,* though it comprises parts of three modern counties. It consists of a central 'dome', flanked by the Eden valley on the east and by a narrow coastal plain along the Solway Firth, the Irish Sea and Morecambe Bay.

*The Lakeland Dome* consists mainly of Lower Palæozoic rocks (slates, andesites and granitic rocks), which have undergone a complex geological history of folding and uplift, denudation and renewed uplift. The result is a much dissected 'dome', elongated in an east-west direction. This was buried under newer rocks (Carboniferous limestone, new red sandstone, and possibly even chalk), on which radially flowing rivers developed their valleys. As the cover of newer rocks was worn away, the rivers maintained their courses, cutting valleys into the underlying ancient rocks, providing an example of superimposed drainage.

During Quaternary times glaciers flowed radially outwards from a central ice-cap which accumulated on the dome, deepening the valleys and giving them a characteristic U-profile. When the ice finally disappeared, long 'finger-lakes' (such as Windermere, Wastwater, Ennerdale and Ullswater) occupied parts of the radiating valleys; they owe their existence partly to glacial overdeepening, partly to damming by terminal moraines. Other features resulting from glaciation are the high-lying cirques (commonly containing small lakes known as *tarns*), craggy arêtes, and streams falling abruptly from hanging valleys in cascades to the floors of the main valleys. Much boulder-clay was deposited, in places in level sheets, elsewhere as a chaos of morainic hillocks. The weather and the rivers have continued their inexorable work; rivers and frost-shattered scree streams below the rock-buttresses deposit alluvium on the valley floors and in the lakes. Between the valleys radiate long ridges from which rise peaks, notably Scafell Pike (at 3,210 ft the highest in England), Scafell, Helvellyn and Skiddaw.

The Lake District has a heavy precipitation, the central parts well over 100 in yearly; the wettest inhabited place in Britain is claimed to be Seathwaite, with a mean annual total of 129 in. The soils on the slopes are thin or absent; those on the valley floors are derived from heavy boulder-clays, occasionally from alluvium. The hills are covered with short grass and heather, known as *fell-grazings,* on which the hardy Herdwick sheep subsist. Cattle are reared and a few fodder crops are grown on the floors of the valleys. Settlement is limited to isolated farms, with small villages in the lower valleys and market-towns (such as Cockermouth) and tourist centres (Keswick, Ambleside, Windermere) around the margins of the hill-country. Some 800 square miles constitute the attractive and very popular Lake District National Park. Five State Forests have been established by the Forestry Commission; several lakes are used as reservoirs (for example, Thirlmere and Haweswater supply Manchester through aqueducts); and slate and granite are quarried.

*The Eden valley and the Solway plain,* comprising a gently undulating lowland of mainly new red sandstone overlain with a veneer of drift and alluvium, is an area of productive mixed farming, with emphasis on dairying and on the cultivation of potatoes, oats and root crops. The main administrative centre is Carlisle (71,000), situated on the banks of the Eden seven miles from the Solway Firth. It is a road and rail focus (sometimes called 'the gateway to Scotland'), and has varied manufactures: cranes, waggons, textiles, biscuits and consumer goods, many of the last being made on an industrial estate south of the city. Other towns, such as Brampton, Wigton and Aspatria, are markets and centres for processing agricultural products.

*The Cumberland coalfield* lies to the west of the Lake District, extending along the coast and continuing under the sea. Coal was mined here as early as the sixteenth century, but the most accessible seams are exhausted, output has dropped to under 1 million tons annually, and only two collieries are now working. However, the presence of the coalfield and of valuable deposits of high-grade haematite in the Carboniferous limestone formed the basis of an iron and steel industry – a 'black industrial crescent' along the margins of the hills. Though most ore has now been exhausted, an integrated steelworks operates at Workington, where the world's first Bessemer plant was installed; ore is now imported from Norway. But in the 1930s the decline in demand for coal and steel caused widespread unemployment, and West Cumberland became a Development Area (see p. 225). Steel is made at Workington, notably for rails, and several industrial estates have been established where the new factories introduced to diversify the economy produce detergents, plastics, silk cloth, hosiery, buttons, footwear, antibiotics, thermometers and many more items. At Whitehaven a post-war and highly successful chemical plant employs over 2,000. At Sellafield, on the coast south of Whitehaven, are the Windscale Atomic Energy plant and Calder Hall, the world's first atomic power-station, which began to put electricity into the Grid in 1958. In the south-west of the region, Barrow-in-Furness (65,000) is a shipbuilding town, which has specialised in the construction of warships (notably Britain's first atomic-powered submarines) and tankers.

**The Isle of Man.** This island, only 220 square miles in area, lies in the Irish Sea forty miles west of the Cumberland coast. It consists of a mass of Palæozoic slates, culminating in Snaefell (2,034 ft), with flanking lowlands covered by boulder-clay. Where the slates reach the coast, they form striking cliffs, and many small streams have eroded deep glens opening abruptly to the sea. The slates contain mineral veins, and in the nineteenth century large quantities of lead and zinc were obtained, but the mines have ceased production as a result of the competition of large producers elsewhere in the world and of rapidly rising costs of extraction. Agriculture is mainly devoted to dairying and mixed farming, largely to supply the many tourists (coming from the industrial areas of the north of England), who provide some 75 per cent of the island's income. The island's favourable fiscal position compared with that of the UK has encouraged many people to retire there, and also has led to the establishment of light industry, including the manufacture of hosiery and light engineering goods. The chief town and resort is Douglas, with about 20,000 inhabitants, though this number increases three-fold during the 'season'.

**The Lancashire and Cheshire Plain.** Between the Pennines and the Irish Sea an undulating lowland extends southwards from Morecambe Bay to southern Cheshire, where it merges through the 'Midland Gate', a broad gap between the Pennines and the

Welsh mountains, into the English Midlands (see p. 174). Much
of this lowland consists of Permo-Triassic sandstones, with the
Coal Measures of the Lancashire coalfield in the south-east,
though for the most part the solid rocks are masked by a thick
mantle of boulder-clay left by the several advances of the Pleistocene ice-sheets from Scotland, the Lake District and the Irish Sea,
and by recent alluvium, sands and deposits of peat (the Lancashire
'mosslands'). Four main rivers cross the lowland: the Lune,
Ribble, Mersey (with its southern tributary the Weaver) and Dee,
each with a prominent estuary.

In this region live almost 7 million people, mainly in sprawling
industrial towns, which in south-east Lancashire and around the
Mersey estuary form almost continuous conurbations. By contrast, between these urban-industrial concentrations are considerable areas of prosperous farmland, particularly in south-western
Lancashire and in Cheshire.

*Agriculture.* The chief emphasis is on dairy farming, favoured
by the heavy, clay soils; the moist, mild climate; and the nearby
urban demand for milk. Cheshire, in fact, is one of the most important dairy-farming districts of England, though it was grievously affected by the foot-and-mouth epidemic of 1967–68. In
southern Lancashire a diversified and productive agriculture has
developed, largely because of urban demand; the peaty moss-lands
have been drained and the sands and silts heavily fertilised.
Vegetables are grown intensively, both for local consumption and
for canning and quick-freezing; Ormskirk, for example, is the centre for potatoes and green vegetables. The Fylde peninsula specialises in the rearing of poultry. Despite its productivity, agriculture suffers from the steady incursion of houses and factories
upon the available land.

*Industry.* The most important aspects are general engineering
and the manufacture of textiles and chemicals. The textile industry began on a domestic scale making woollens, using the abundant supplies of water from the Pennines both for driving the
machinery and for the bleaching, dyeing and finishing processes.
When Liverpool, with its connections with North America, developed as the chief port of the area, raw cotton became available,
coal was used to raise steam in the rapidly growing factories, and
inventive genius had full scope to develop machinery. The cotton
industry reached its peak by the first decade of the twentieth century. A degree of specialisation emerged, with spinning in the
towns of southern Lancashire (at Bolton, Wigan, Oldham, Roch-
dale) and weaving and the making of garments in the north (at
Preston, Nelson, Blackburn, Burnley, Colne). Manchester han-

dled finished yarn, cloth and garments, and emerged as the commercial centre of the whole industry. During the last half-century the cotton industry has steadily declined, and instead of its former dominance it now employs only a seventh of the working population. This has resulted partly from the competition of countries with lower labour costs and more modern machinery, such as Japan, India and Hong Kong, the last being particularly serious because it is within the Commonwealth and Lancashire cannot easily be protected from it.

Newer textiles (nylon, rayon) have also had adverse effects on the demand for cotton. In recent years the government has stimulated a policy of deliberate contraction: closing factories, scrapping obsolete machinery, modernising and concentrating in selected areas, and introducing under the plans for the Development Areas new industries in places worst affected. The town of Blackburn, once called the 'weaving centre of the world', exemplifies the nature of the change; as late as 1938 there were 135 active cotton mills, now there are only 26, most with modern, automated techniques. The new industries include electronics (TV tubes, valves and components) and the making of tufted carpets (which has led to the establishment of the largest factory outside the USA for producing machinery for making tufted carpets), chemicals, batteries and mechanical shovels. Much of the town centre has been redeveloped, with new shops and multi-storey car parks, though there are still areas of decaying mills and old, terraced houses.

Engineering is now the most important branch of activity in south-eastern Lancashire. At Trafford Park, Manchester, heavy electrical engineering is carried on; Crewe is a centre of railway engineering; machine tools, textile machinery, and a wide range of metallurgical products are made in the many cities and towns.

Chemicals are produced in central Cheshire and in the Mersey valley, based on underground deposits of rock salt, pumped up as brine in the neighbourhood of Northwich, Middlewich and Winsford. These towns, together with Winnington (the headquarters of I.C.I. Alkali), have developed the large-scale production of heavy chemicals. The middle Mersey valley, at Runcorn, Widnes and Warrington, is another centre, as is the Cheshire side of the estuary, including soap made at Port Sunlight (using imported oilseeds), oil-refining at Stanlow and Ellesmere Port (with crude oil piped from a terminal at Eastham docks), and associated petrochemicals. St Helens is the main centre in Britain for making glass. Warrington also has chemical factories and its diverse activities include the making of leather, wire and wire ropes, and paint.

The two major cities in southern Lancashire are Manchester and Liverpool. The former, the centre of a conurbation of nearly 2·5 millions, is linked to the Mersey estuary by a 36-mile-long ship canal, and is the fourth British port in value of trade; it is the financial-commercial centre of south-eastern Lancashire; and has extensive and varied manufactures. Liverpool has grown up on the eastern shores of the Mersey estuary; before about 1700 Chester was the major north-western port, but the shallow and silt-filled Dee estuary could not compete with the Mersey as the tonnage of shipping increased. Helped by growing trade with America, the construction of a long line of docks, and the development of roads and railways, Liverpool in due course established itself as Britain's second port. Its industries include the processing of imported raw materials (flour-milling, sugar-refining, vegetable-oil extraction, timber-working), and Birkenhead on the opposite shore has large shipyards; here have been built liners, carriers and recently nuclear submarines. But Merseyside has suffered unemployment and is scheduled as a Special Area (see p. 225); industrial estates have grown on the outskirts of Liverpool with varied manufactures, including the assembly of motor vehicles.

A feature of the urban landscape has been the rapid growth in the nineteenth century of industrial towns, the decay of their centres into slums (affording problems of re-development and urban renewal), and the movement outwards from them ('overspill') of people to live in 'dormitory towns' and rapidly expanding suburbs which have engulfed small towns and villages and are linked by a dense network of communications. Another development is that of resorts along the coast to cater to this dense population, notably Blackpool, Morecambe, Lytham St Annes and Southport; the last is also a residential town for Lancashire executives. The administrative centre for Cheshire is Chester, established as a Roman city (*Deva*) at the lowest bridge-point of the Dee on a low sandstone hill above the river. It retains its old city wall and is a pleasant shopping and servicing centre.

**The North-east Industrial Region.** The eastward-dipping Coal Measures on the Pennine flanks are overlain east of Durham city by Magnesian limestone and other Permian rocks. The surface consists of low, undulating plateaus, in many places covered with drift, and ending in a coastline of rocky headlands and cliffs, sandy bays and prominent estuaries. Several rivers, notably the Tyne, the Wear and the Tees, entrenched in steep-sided valleys, flow eastwards to the North Sea. The Tyne has developed an extensive drainage system by 'capturing' the headwaters of former consequents, leaving their stunted 'trunks' as the Coquet, Wansbeck and Blyth rivers.

While a large part of the Northumberland and Durham coalfield is exposed, in the north the Coal Measures dip gradually under the North Sea and in Durham they are concealed under newer rocks. The exposed section has been worked for many centuries, yielding 'sea-coal' which was shipped along the coast to London, while the newest collieries are near the coast between Blyth and Seaham Harbour. The field produces about 30 million tons annually, much of which is high-quality steam- and coking-coal. Other industrial advantages are deposits of iron-ore (though low-grade and phosphoric) in the nearby Cleveland Hills, and large amounts of salt and anhydrite south of the Tees valley.

An industrial region has developed between the Tyne and the Tees, the basic activities being coal-mining, steel manufacture, heavy engineering, shipbuilding and the production of chemicals. Shipbuilding originated with the demand for wooden 'colliers' to export coal, and yards were established on the banks of the rivers. As the production of iron and steel developed on Tees-side, notably at Middlesbrough, first iron and then steel ships of increasing size were built (colliers, cargo vessels, warships and tankers), and marine engineering became an obvious ancillary. The steel mills (now largely dependent on imported ore) supply raw steel for girders, bridges, cranes and structural purposes.

Dependence on these basic industries was emphasised during World War I, but in the post-war years, especially during the depression of the 1930s, they suffered severe slumps, and unemployment rates soared. As a result, the North-east Special Area was established, and 'trading estates' were developed; the first was set up at Team valley west of Gateshead. World War II again stimulated heavy industry, but afterwards several more estates were created, with carefully planned 'new towns' (such as Newton-Aycliffe and Peterlee) to house their workers. The field now produces much less coal than it did before the war, but its efficiency has increased; similarly, steel-making, heavy engineering and shipbuilding (tankers) have been rationalised and modernised. The chemical industry has grown enormously, with modern plants at Billingham and Wilton, and with a new oil refinery at Tees-port, five miles from Middlesbrough.

The three main urban agglomerations are on Tyneside, Teesside and Wearside. Along each bank of the Tyne is an almost continuous conurbation: on the north, Newcastle, Wallsend, North Shields and Tynemouth; on the south, Gateshead, Jarrow and South Shields, with a total population of nearly 1 million. Newcastle is a regional focus, a shopping, business and servicing centre, with several bridges spanning the Tyne.   The attractive city of Durham, the administrative centre of Durham county, is situated on and around a meander-core of the Wear, dominated by a castle and cathedral.   On the Wear estuary Sunderland has varied industries, including shipbuilding and engineering.   Middlesbrough (157,000) is the centre of the Tees-side conurbation, which extends from Stockton to Redcar, with steel and engineering works and chemical plants.   Outlying centres are Consett (steel-making) and Darlington (engineering and locomotives).

**The Yorkshire, Nottinghamshire and Derbyshire Industrial Region.**   Along the eastern flanks of the Pennines, between the valleys of the Trent and the Aire, a distinctive region is based on a large coalfield.   In the west the Coal Measures are exposed on the surface, dipping gently eastward beneath the Permian, Triassic and younger rocks as a concealed field.   Coal has been mined for many centuries, mainly in the thick, relatively undisturbed seams between Barnsley and Sheffield, though in recent years new activity has been concentrated on the concealed eastern section from Doncaster southwards through Worksop, Ollerton and Mansfield.   The coal occurs in variety, including high-quality gas- and coking-coal and hard, semi-anthracite steam-coal.   This is the largest field in Britain, responsible for about 70 million tons annually, and has by far the greatest reserves.   More than 3·5 million people in the region are concentrated in the west in cities and towns along valleys separated by spurs of Pennine moorland, and more widely distributed in the east among a prosperous agriculture on fertile loams and clays.   Three industrial-urban concentrations may be distinguished: West Yorkshire, the Don valley and the Derby-Nottingham district.

*West Yorkshire,* comprising the valleys of the Calder, Colne and middle Aire, is the major British centre of woollen manufacture. Though dominated by Leeds and Bradford, the conurbation comprises a number of contiguous towns.   The making of cloth started as a 'cottage industry' using local fleeces from the Pennines, soft water from the millstone grit and water-powered mills.   The Industrial Revolution made available coal-raised steam-power to the mills with their new machinery, and West Yorkshire rapidly outstripped its rivals, using wool imported through London and Hull. Some specialisation has developed, with worsteds in Bradford and Halifax; woollens in the Calder valley (not so much in Halifax); 'shoddy' around Dewsbury, Ossett and Batley; carpets in Halifax; and ready-made clothing in Leeds. Increasingly, however, branches of the industry have become intermingled.   Huddersfield, for example, produces both woollens and worsteds, and the manufacture of knitting wool and knitwear is widespread. In recent years the district has felt the competition not only of man-made fibres (indeed, mixtures of wool and synthetics are used for suitings), but of modern mills established in Development Areas elsewhere in Britain. Several towns in the west, such as Todmorden and Hebden Bridge, have cotton mills, the result of their proximity to Lancashire (see p. 169). Engineering works make textile machinery, and chemical plants produce scouring materials and dyes.

The two chief towns are Bradford (295,000), the commercial centre, and Leeds (510,000), which grew up as a route-focus in the Aire valley; each is a congestion of houses, factories, shops and offices. Wakefield is the administrative centre of the West Riding, one of three administrative divisions of Yorkshire.

*The Don valley,* with that of its tributary the Dearne, contains concentrations of various aspects of metallurgical industry. Iron nodules in the Coal Measures were smelted as early as the twelfth century, using charcoal from local forests; later, water-power worked bellows, hammers and grindstones. By the Middle Ages, Sheffield steel had a high reputation, though by the time of the Industrial Revolution the depleted low-grade local ores had given way to imported ores, and soon Sheffield ceased iron-smelting; Rotherham, at the Don-Rother confluence, has become the main centre of iron production. Sheffield's traditional skills kept pace with technological developments not only in the lighter, specialised steel-using industries (cutlery, tools and surgical instruments) for which it has a world-reputation, but also in the production of alloy-steels and heavy products such as castings, forgings and electrical machinery. Chesterfield, to the south in Derbyshire, makes pipes and tubes for mains and pipelines. Barnsley and Rotherham are still mining centres.

*The Derby-Nottingham district* is commonly included in the Midlands, but it is marginal to the Pennines and is clearly associated with the coalfield. Its activities are diverse, often based on local traditions though using modern technology. Nottingham (311,000), on a bridge-point of the Trent, still makes the traditional lace, though now there is greater concentration on hosiery, pharmaceutical chemicals, tobacco and cigarettes, and bicycles. Derby (132,000), on the Derwent, makes rayon textiles, the world-renowned Rolls-Royce cars and aero-engines, locomotives and rolling-stock, and porcelain ('Crown Derby'). Much of this activity is in modern factories on the outskirts of these two cities and in the numerous small towns between them.

**The Vale of York.** Between the Pennine margins and the low escarpments to the east (see p. 180) lies a lowland underlain with Triassic rocks, for the most part covered with boulder-clay, outwash sands, lacustrine materials deposited in former proglacial lakes, and alluvium. The boulder-clay is mostly in hummocky sheets, though several terminal moraines can be traced, as at York. The north-south axis of the Vale is drained by the Ouse, which receives the Swale, Ure, Nidd and Wharfe from the Pennine dales (evidently the result of several phases of capture), and the Derwent from the east, which rises not far from the North Sea on the Yorkshire Moors and curves through the Vale of Pickering. The valleys reveal a series of distinct terraces.

The diverse if subdued relief of the Vale has resulted in a prosperous pattern of agriculture, with an emphasis on mixed farming. Dairy cattle are grazed on rotation pasture on the clays, supplemented by fodder crops; wheat, oats and malting-barley are grown on the better loams; potatoes, sugar beet and carrots on the sandy loams. Intensive market-gardening is practised on the alluvium. Farms are frequently large and prosperous, with attractive stone buildings.

The Vale is dominated by York (107,000), situated on the higher ground of a moraine which transversely crosses the Ouse valley. Founded as the Roman city of *Eboracum,* it flourished throughout medieval times as an administrative, military, commercial and ecclesiastical centre, the focus of a web of roads. After some decline the city regained importance as a railway junction on the main line between London and Edinburgh, which unlike the Great North Road (fifteen miles to the west), follows the axis of the Vale. The city continues to flourish as a commercial and ecclesiastical centre (the see of an archbishopric), and its industries include the processing of agricultural produce and the manufacture of leather, chocolate and agricultural implements.

Other settlements comprise small, pleasant market-towns along the main roads, railways and rivers, especially where the Pennine dales open into the Vale: Catterick on the Swale, Ripon on the Ure, Knaresborough on the Nidd, and Wetherby on the Wharfe. Lower down the Ouse from York is Selby. These are attractive towns, with houses built of brick on the clay and alluvial lands, and of stone where Jurassic or Magnesian limestone outcrops; many fine houses stand in their park-like estates. In all, the Vale of York is a pleasant and prosperous part of rural England.

**The English Midlands.** Situated between northern and southern England is a transitional region, with the Welsh borderlands on the west; the Pennines, the Trent valley and the Midland Gap on the north; and the Jurassic escarpments on the south-east. This is sometimes referred to as the 'Midland Triangle', since it tapers southward towards the confluence of the Severn and Avon, comprising all or most of six English counties, the 'core-region' of England.

*Structure and Relief.* Much is an undulating lowland, generally below 400 ft, covered with red Bunter sandstones and Keuper marls (calcareous clays) of Permo-Triassic age, and in the southeast with a broad outcrop of Lias clays (Jurassic). These rocks have undergone much denudation; the softer ones have been eroded into broad vales, while the more resistant sandstones and breccias stand out as low plateaus, such as the 'Birmingham Plateau' and Cannock Chase (the latter made of the Bunter Pebble Beds). In places the underlying older rocks stand out quite prominently; pre-Cambrian slates, grits and igneous rocks compose the rugged and dissected Charnwood Forest, the Lickey Hills south of Birmingham, and the quartzitic Nuneaton Ridge to the east. Distinct exposures of Coal Measures form the North and South Staffordshire, Leicester and Warwickshire coalfields. Apart from coal seams, the Coal Measures include resistant sandstones which form dissected hilly country, such as the undulating plateau of the South Staffordshire coalfield west of Birmingham, culminating to the south-west in a capping of compact breccia as the Clent Hills (1,036 ft). Some ancient exposures are quarried for road metal, as at Mountsorrel in Leicestershire.

These uplands are separated by broad alluvium-floored valleys eroded out of the less resistant clays and marls: the Severn curving around the western margins, with its left-bank tributaries the Stour and the Avon, and in the north the Trent, joined by the Tame and the Soar. These two systems are separated by a low, indeterminate divide in the heart of England. One of the best-defined valleys is that of the river Avon, which swings in great meanders across its flood-plain, bordered by distinctive terraces; this is known as the Vale of Evesham.

In the Quaternary era, a considerable mantle of boulder-clay, sands and gravels was laid down in undulating sheets and low ridges; though much has been removed, cappings remain on the interfluves, adding variety to the landscape.

*Agriculture.* Despite a long association with industry, much of the Midlands has an attractively rural aspect. The soils range from light sands to heavy clays, and land-use varies likewise, though mixed farming is dominant, with an emphasis on dairying. The heavy clay-lands and marls nurture rich permanent pasture, and both dairy cattle and fat bullocks are kept in a close-grazing system, together with sheep (notably the English Leicester breed). Milk is bulk-handled for despatch to neighbouring towns, some is made into cheese; the famous Stilton, once a domestic product, is now factory-made at Melton Mowbray. Fodder crops such as kale, wheat (on the better loams), potatoes and sugar beet are grown, and market-farming flourishes on the heavily fertilised light sands, stimulated by urban demand. The Vale of Evesham is one of the most prosperous districts: the loamy soils on well-drained terraces, a sheltered valley where spring comes early, and past traditions combine to favour an intensive, well-organized cultivation of tree-fruits (plum, damson, apple), bush-fruit (black currant, gooseberry) and vegetables (notably asparagus and peas). But much of the upstanding old rocks remains under forest, scrub and bracken, and large areas of land have inevitably disappeared under the sprawl of towns and factories.

*Industry.* The four coalfields have been responsible for the growth of the main industrial districts, though these have expanded well beyond the outcrops. The dense West Midland conurbation, with a population of 2·5 millions, includes the 'Black Country', so called because of the effects of smoke from coal, with the contiguous towns of Wolverhampton, Walsall, Dudley, West Bromwich and Smethwick, and the city of Birmingham to the east. This area nurtured an early iron industry, using ore from the Coal Measures, charcoal for smelting, and later coal for heating bar-iron before rolling and cutting. By the early nineteenth century, the Stour valley was the main English iron-making district, producing two-fifths of the pig-iron, notably at Halesowen and Stourbridge; from it nails, screws, chains, bolts, ploughshares, springs, knives, horseshoes and pumps were made. But now most pig-iron for the steel mills is imported from Northamptonshire. Similarly, coal-mining has declined in importance, except in the northern concealed part of the Cannock Chase field, where about 5 million tons are extracted annually. The Black Country–Birmingham district has remained a major source of steel and non-ferrous articles in great diversity, retaining the traditional, localised specialisations, an example of industrial momentum, but developing in modern times electrical engineering, the making of cycles and cars (now employing over a fifth of the region's labour force), chemicals, rubber, chocolate and cocoa (at Bourneville), beer, and glass (at Stourbridge). Though the Black Country in parts still retains the drab appearance of derelict land – spoil-dumps, slag heaps and depressing slums — much land has been reclaimed and levelled.

Birmingham (1·1 million), the second city of Britain, covers an immense area, having expanded to overwhelm neighbouring towns

## UNITED KINGDOM

15 Modern London, looking north-eastwards down the Thames. In the center foreground is Westminster Abbey with the Houses of Parliament to the right. Westminster bridge is at the far right; across the river are the County Hall, Waterloo Station and the 1962 skyscraper of Shell Centre.

16 The large plant of Morris Motors, Ltd, at Cowley, near the centuries-old university town of Oxford.

17 Clean coal, in 21-ton hopper wagons, awaiting collection outside the washery at Lynemouth Colliery, Northumberland.

## UNITED KINGDOM

18  Kirkstone pass in England's Lake District. The soils on the slopes in this region are thin or absent; those on the valley floors are derived from heavy boulder-clays, occasionally from alluvium. The hills are covered with short grass or heather.

## REPUBLIC OF IRELAND

19  Killarney's lakes lie along a broad valley running through the highest mountains in Ireland and are surrounded by woods of birch, oak and arbutus. Their colourful charm makes this a popular tourist area.

20  Dublin is situated on a bay into which the Liffey flows; it is a major centre of brewing. Here, a ship of the Guinness brewery is docked at the Custom House Quay.

and villages; in recent years the old city-centre has been demolished and rebuilt. 'Overspill' is a major problem, and many people have moved to expanding towns around, or have been rehoused in 'new towns' such as Redditch and Dawley; efforts are made to preserve a 'green belt'.

A second industrial district lies east of Birmingham in and around Coventry and Nuneaton in the northern part of the Warwickshire coalfield. From early medieval times Coventry has been a manufacturing town, using traditional skills to adapt itself to changing circumstances: first textiles, later iron articles, then the modern expansion of engineering, especially cars, motorcycles, aero-engines, cycles and machine tools. The centre of Coventry was largely destroyed by bombing in 1940, but it has been attractively rebuilt, its dominating feature being the new cathedral. Many other towns have specialist industries, such as Atherstone, second only to Luton as a hat-making centre. Some coal is still worked between Tamworth and Baddesley, and the fire-clays and pipe-clays of the Coal Measures have long sustained the production of earthenware, glazed pipes and drains, and refractory bricks, though the flooded clay pits and the spoil-dumps in many places mar the landscape.

Farther to the north-east the small Leicestershire coalfield has Coalville as its centre. The city of Leicester (273,000), twenty miles to the east, grew on the terraces of the river Soar; it too had an early woollen-textile industry and has continued to thrive as a market-town and route-centre. During the Industrial Revolution new types of textile-making machinery were installed, and a range of hosiery and kindred activities developed. Leicester is now one of the most prosperous cities in Britain, with an enviable record of full and well-paid employment, the result of its diverse manufactures: hosiery and underwear, footwear, plastics, machine tools and electrical equipment. Factories have been installed at neighbouring small towns, such as Hinckley and Loughborough.

The fourth major district, based on the North Staffordshire field, specialises in ceramics, hence its name of the 'Potteries'. Early local advantages included clay from the Coal Measures and plentiful wood, later long-flame coal (to fire the kilns), with lead and salt for glazing available from Derbyshire and Cheshire respectively. But its tremendous development was really the result of individual enterprise and the creation of a reputation. The Wedgwood family built their original factory near Stoke, bringing kaolin from Cornwall and ball-clay from Dorset by coasting steamer to Liverpool, then by barge along the Trent and Mersey Canal. The industry spread throughout the adjacent towns (Stoke, Burslem, Hanley,

Tunstall, Longton and Fenton), which in 1909 were administratively grouped as the county-borough of Stoke-on-Trent (266,000).
Following the Industrial Revolution the characteristic 'Pottery landscape' developed in the upper Trent valley, with rows of terrace
houses, a sprawl of grey buildings among which rose the black
bottle-shaped kilns, interspersed with dumps and crossed by canals,
with clay holes and piles of pottery waste.   But the industry has
been modernised and rationalised, and new electrically-fired kilns
have replaced coal-fired ones; the Wedgwood factory is in a
'garden-city' south of Stoke at Barlaston.   The number of individual manufacturers has been reduced from 250 to 78, and a
dozen companies produce two-thirds of the output; diversification
has resulted in such associated products as ceramic wall-tiles, two-
thirds of the British output.   Mining yields some 5 million tons
annually, though the number of collieries has been reduced from
40 to 5.   There is a variety of engineering, including a large plant
making computers in Stoke.

*Other Towns.*   Apart from these four concentrated industrial-
urban districts, there are other prosperous towns in the Midlands.
In the south-east is Rugby, with electrical and electronic industries.
Several pleasant residential and market-towns, with some light industry and tourist attractions, include Warwick (a strong point,
with its castle, during much of English history), Kenilworth, Leam-
ington and Cheltenham, the last being spas, and Stratford-upon-
Avon with its profitable Shakespearean associations.   Evesham
is the centre of the fertile Avon valley, with fruit-packing and preserving; Worcester is a county-town with light industries such as
textiles, porcelain and gloves; Tewkesbury has milling; and Glou-
cester engineering, as well as several large markets.

**The Welsh Borderlands.**   This varied region extends along
the eastern margins of Wales from southern Cheshire through
Shropshire and Herefordshire into Monmouthshire, and including
the western margins of Worcestershire and Gloucestershire.   For
the most part, this area comprises the basin of the Severn and its
right-bank confluents Teme and Wye, though these rise in the
Welsh uplands.   The Severn has had a complex history, as shown
by its curious curving course.   From its source on the slopes of
Plynlimon it flows north-eastwards through the Vale of Powis, then
meanders eastwards past Shrewsbury and southwards through a
gorge near Ironbridge before entering the plain of Worcester, and
so to its estuary.   This gorge was cut by melt-water which over-
flowed from a proglacial lake between the Shropshire hills and the
margins of the Quaternary ice-sheet to the north; the mid and
lower Severn were rejuvenated and several distinct sets of terraces

formed. The Wye also rises on Plynlimon, and in its lower course follows a series of incised meanders across the old red sandstone and Carboniferous limestone before entering the Bristol Channel.

The relief is quite diverse. In southern Shropshire several complicated groups of uplands include the pre-Cambrian mass of the Long Mynd (1,696 ft), which forms a fairly flat-topped plateau. Its eastern slopes descend sharply into a distinct rift-valley near Church Stretton, whose eastern edge in turn is bounded by a ridge of pre-Cambrian igneous rocks, culminating in Caer Caradoc (1,506 ft). The prominent Wrekin (1,385 ft) stands solitarily on the northern edge of the Severn valley. To the east of Caer Caradoc is the west-facing double escarpment of Wenlock Edge, of Silurian limestone. South of the Long Mynd Clun Forest is an old red sandstone plateau of over 1,400 ft, and another outcrop of the same rock, capped with resistant Carboniferous rocks and dolerite, forms the undulating plateau of the Clee Hills, where two summits exceed 1,700 ft. Finally, the long narrow line of the Malvern Hills marks the dissected remains of a mass of rocks upfolded by Hercynian earth movements.

These uplands separate two extensive lowlands. Central and northern Shropshire and southern Cheshire consist of an undulating plain drained by the Severn; though underlain by Triassic sandstones and marls, the surface for the most part is thickly covered with boulder-clay, outwash sands and gravels, with gentle slopes and meandering rivers. The other lowland, south of the Shropshire hills, is the dissected 'saucer' of the Plain of Hereford and is drained by the Wye; it is covered by red marls (derived from the old red sandstone) which have weathered into deep, fertile loams. Central Monmouthshire consists of the basin of the Usk, similar in character to the plain of Hereford.

In the angle between the Wye and the Severn estuary lies the Forest of Dean, a much dissected plateau of Coal Measure sandstones and shales, now mostly under conifers planted by the Forestry Commission. The rocks include coal seams, though these now yield under a half-million tons annually.

*Agriculture.* The various uplands are covered with moorland or rough pasture, supporting sheep and some store cattle. By contrast, the lowlands, situated in the rainshadow of the Welsh plateau, have a pleasant, sunny climate and rich soils, and so nurture productive agriculture; dairying is dominant on the heavy clay soils, with sugar beet and fodder crops on the lighter ones. The rich red loams of Hereford have much permanent pasture on which graze the famous Hereford beef cattle (exported to many parts of the world), as well as dairy animals. Sheep are brought down from the Welsh uplands to be fattened, and several distinctive breeds (such as Clun Forest) are native to these borderlands. Mixed farming includes the growing of cereals and potatoes, apples (notably cider varieties), plums, damsons and hops.

*Towns.* The most important town in the north is Shrewsbury (49,000), situated on a prominent hillock within an incised loop of the Severn; its dominating site has given it an important place in English history as the scene of several battles. The newer parts of the town, with housing-estates, factories (notably for agricultural implements), and a large animal-market, have spread on to the surrounding lowlands. It is an important route-centre, both for the West Midlands and for much of Wales. Hereford (40,000) is also a route-centre and market-town, with a fine cathedral; like the smaller Ludlow to the north on the Teme, it has a Norman castle, one of the 'strong points' along the Welsh marches. Industrial activities are associated with the processing of agricultural commodities (the making of cider, jam and preserves, and brewing), but newer categories include light consumer goods, furniture and electrical appliances. Other small market-towns are Wellington, Bridgnorth, Leominster and Monmouth. At times in the past the Borderlands contained iron-making districts; in fact, during the early Middle Ages the Forest of Dean was England's chief producer of iron, using local haematite and charcoal from the Forest. At Coalbrookdale in the Severn valley Abraham Darby successfully smelted iron-ore with coke in 1709; the world's first iron bridge still stands at Ironbridge across the Severn.

**The Scarplands.** This composite region extends diagonally across England from the North Sea coast of Yorkshire to the Channel coast of Somerset and Dorset; its identity, in fact, is mainly geological. The varied Jurassic and Cretaceous strata were tilted to the east and south-east by the mid-Tertiary earth movements. Long-sustained denudation, involving the evolution of complex river systems, has left the more resistant limestones, sandstones and chalk upstanding as cuestas, with their escarpments facing north-west, their long gentle back-slopes south-east. The less resistant clays have been worn into broad vales between the two main cuesta-lines.

*The Jurassic cuestas* start as a complicated series of hills in the south-west, but become more clearly defined in the Cotswolds, where the escarpment is steep and impressive, overlooking the valley of the lower Severn. The face is deeply dissected by dry valleys, at the bottom of which issue powerful springs. The rocks consist of Oolitic limestone and sandstone, quarried for building the attractive Cotswold houses and dry-stone walls. The back-slope is covered with thin, stony, brown soils, and springs emerging on this slope form the headwaters of the Thames, as at Seven Springs.

In succession to the north-east several almost parallel cuestas are known as the Northampton Uplands; in the main cuesta the Northampton Sands are the dominant strata, containing extensive beds of ironstone which affords an important source of ore.

In southern Lincolnshire the Jurassic outcrop thins out and disappears under the boulder-clay cover, but reappears as the steep though low Lincoln Edge. This is cut through completely by the valley of the river Witham, which flows to the Wash. Much of the surface of the Edge is covered with boulder-clay.

The Yorkshire Moors consist mainly of sandstone, forming a much dissected plateau rising to over 1,400 ft, and in places reaching the coast as cliffs. Several deeply eroded valleys divide the uplands into distinctive groups: the Cleveland Hills in the north-west, the Hambleton Hills overlooking the Vale of York in the west, and the Moors proper in the south, mostly draining to the Derwent. During the Quaternary, proglacial lakes were ponded up, notably in the valley of the Esk; the melt-waters, forced to escape southwards, cut a prominent overflow channel, Newton Dale, right across the Moors. As in the Northampton Uplands, the sandstones of the Cleveland Hills contain iron-ore.

*The Chalk cuestas* are formed of a pure white limestone, the strata varying in thickness between 600 and 1,000 ft. They begin in Dorset and Wiltshire as several groups of downland, continued north-east of the Goring Gap (through which the Thames breaks from the Jurassic clay-vale into the London basin) as the Chilterns. The gently undulating back-slopes form the margins of the Hampshire basin (see p. 193) and of the London basin (see p. 189).

The uplands south of the Goring Gap are rolling downland, with rounded slopes; occasional, impressive escarpments (as in the White Horse Hills); numerous dry valleys and thin chalky soils. In some parts the chalk was folded to form short elongated domes (*periclines*), as in the Vale of Pewsey, but denudation has removed the chalk from the centre of the axis, revealing older rocks between infacing escarpments.

The Chilterns are deeply dissected by dry valleys, affording several prominent 'dry-gaps' through which pass roads, railways and even canals between London and the Midlands. The uplands have an uneven cover of clay-with-flints – a mass of reddish-brown clay containing flint fragments – in part the indissoluble residue of chalk weathering, in part derived from the now vanished overlying Tertiary rocks. Then the chalk curves around the eastern margins of the Fenland as the East Anglian Heights, mostly covered with boulder-clay; though geologically part of the scarplands, this upland is most conveniently included in East Anglia (see p. 186).

After a break formed by the Wash, the chalk reappears in the Lincoln Wolds, which trend west of north towards the Humber, a long estuary into which flow the combined waters of the Ouse and the Trent. To the north ·the escarpment again becomes prominent as the Yorkshire Wolds, ending at the coast in the fine cliffs of Flamborough Head.

*The Clay Vale,* between the two lines of cuestas, is for the most part floored with Upper Jurassic beds (the Oxford and Kimmeridge clays), though in the south these outcrops are separated by a thin stratum of Corallian limestone, which in places forms a low but prominent ridge. In the south, too, much of the clay is exposed on the surface, affording heavy, poorly drained soils, except where the Thames and its tributaries have formed terraces, on which are river gravels and alluvium. Farther north the Jurassic clays are covered with the peat and silt of Fenland (see p. 184), and in Lincolnshire (the upper Witham valley) and Yorkshire (the Vale of Pickering) by alluvium and glacial deposits.

Though lying east of the scarplands, it is convenient to include two adjoining lowlands on either side of the Humber: eastern Lincolnshire and Holderness. Each is in general low-lying, formerly very marshy, with a considerable extent of boulder-clay, alluvium, marine silts and gravels, and coastal dunes. Erosion by the sea goes on steadily in spite of protective works, though the southward longshore drift has formed a long curving spit, Spurn Head, across the mouth of the Humber, and Gibraltar Point in Lincolnshire.

*Agriculture.* The higher parts of the Jurassic escarpment, particularly in the Yorkshire Moors, have thin sandy soils bearing moorland and rough pasture, which support only sheep. The back-slopes of the chalk — also traditional sheep pastures with their crisp downland turf – once supplied fleeces not only to the West Country woollen industry but also to Flanders. Now the thin chalk-soils are enclosed in large fields growing barley, wheat, rotation grass, clover and kale, using heavy applications of fertiliser; permanent grass is rare. Cattle, both dairy animals and stores, are grazed on the temporary leys, supplemented by fodder crops, and sheep are folded as part of good farming practise.

Much of the damp, rather cold and heavy soils derived from the Oxford and Kimmeridge clays in the south are under permanent pasture, though farther north, where outcrops of the lower greensand or outwash sands appear, arable farming is practised, with market-gardening on favoured areas of light warm soil, for example, near Biggleswade in Bedfordshire. In eastern Lincoln-shire and Holderness, especially where drained, the drier climate of the east coast favours arable farming, though rich permanent pasture supports dairy cattle.

*The Iron and Steel Industry.* Ironstone beds in the Jurassic rocks of the Cleveland Hills, in Lincolnshire, north-eastern North-amptonshire and adjacent parts of Oxfordshire contain ore with a metal content of only 25 to 30 per cent; however, the deposits are near the surface and easily worked. The dwindling Cleveland ores have long supplied the steel industry of Tees-side (see p. 171). Farther south the main steel-making centres are at Scunthorpe (in northern Lincolnshire) and at Corby, Kettering and Welling-borough in Northamptonshire.

*Towns.* A series of settlements can be traced through the scarp-lands, serving as market-towns and servicing centres for the pros-perous agricultural districts around: Cirencester, Newbury, Ayles-bury, Banbury and Gainsborough. Their siting usually involves the presence of water-supplies (near spring-lines or rivers), or they are on 'dry-site' terraces, or they are bridge-towns, or gap-towns commanding routes through the cuestas. Others, because of their centrality, have become administrative county and cathedral towns, such as Oxford, Northampton, Bedford and Lincoln. Most have developed light industry of some kind, apart from the steel-making towns; activities include leather-tanning (Northampton is an im-portant centre of shoe-making), the manufacture of fertilisers, the making and servicing of agricultural implements, and food-process-ing (both long-established milling and brewing and newer cate-gories such as quick-freezing, the making of potato crisps). Some towns have inherited legacies from the past, such as the making of high-quality woollen cloth at Stroud at the foot of the Cotswold escarpment, and carpets and blankets at Witney. The quality of the London clay has led to large-scale brick-making, centred in Peterborough and Bedford, with many yards surrounded by clay pits in the countryside around. Several cement-works are on or near the chalk cuestas, notably in south-eastern Bedfordshire and near the Humber estuary. Light industry has been established in pleasant towns with adequate sites and labour resources. Luton (132,000), in a gap in the Chilterns, is the headquarters of the Vauxhall Motors, one of the General Motors group; its old tradi-tional industry is hat-making. Swindon (92,000) is the centre of locomotive repairing for the Western Region of British Railways, and recently established industrial estates make a variety of light products, as well as car bodies. Oxford (106,000), for centuries a university town and cultural centre, has the large plant of the British Leyland Motor Corporation at Cowley. Cambridge (95,000), a transitionally placed city on the edge of both the Fenland and East Anglia, has also long been a university and market town, and has developed such light industries as electronics, radio and television, calculating machines and instruments.

The scarplands include much delightful rural scenery, and some Cotswold towns, built of the mellow limestone, are favourite tourist venues. Bath, situated where the Avon breaks through the Cotswolds, was founded by the Romans on the site of warm mineral springs; in the eighteenth century it became a fashionable spa, with crescents of stone houses tiered on the hill-side, and it is still an attractive residential town. Seaside resorts flourish at either end of the region. On the Channel coast, Sidmouth, Lyme Regis, Bridport and Weymouth take advantage of the cliffs and bays formed where the different rocks reach the sea. In the north-east visitors from the industrial areas of Yorkshire and the Midlands came to Whitby and Scarborough, while on the coast east of the chalk cuesta are Bridlington and Hornsea in Yorkshire, and Cleethorpes, Mabelthorpe and Skegness in Lincolnshire.

There remain two important towns on the Humber. Hull (303,-000), known officially as Kingston-upon-Hull, is situated where the little river Hull enters the estuary from the north. Making use of the deep-water channel which here swings near the northern shore, it has developed as a port for industrial Yorkshire (importing wool, timber, petroleum, oil-seeds), Britain's third in terms of tonnage of freight. It is also the premier fishing port, from which deep-sea trawlers operate far away in the Atlantic and Arctic grounds. Hull has developed a range of port industries (milling, oil-seed crushing). Grimsby (97,000), on the Lincolnshire coast of the Humber, is second to Hull in weight of fish landed, though it is actually ahead in value; its fleet supplies fish for curing and quick-freezing as well as for sale fresh, and ancillary activities include by-products (fertiliser, meal) and ice- and box-making. The shore between Grimsby and Immingham (constructed five miles to the west in 1912 by a railway company to export coal and import timber) has become a large industrial district ('Humberside'), with oil-refining and the manufacture of petrochemicals, paint, fertilisers (superphosphates) and titanium oxide.

**Fenland.** The Wash is a rectangular opening, some twenty miles square, into which flow the Witham, Welland, Nene and Ouse, draining a large part of eastern and central England. For thousands of years the land around the Wash was the largest area of fen in Britain; now it is one of the most fertile and intensively farmed regions. Although the danger of flooding has been much reduced, it has not been eliminated; after 2,000 years drainage works are still in operation, and pumping away the excess water is still required.

Fenland is a shallow basin floored with Jurassic and Cretaceous clays and sands, patches of which protrude through the newer deposits. During the Quaternary glaciation the level of the shrunken North Sea was appreciably lower than at present, but as this rose and the climate became milder, layers of peat were formed in the marshes; this peat is mild and alkaline because of water draining onto it from the surrounding chalk. Later still, between about 2000 and 500 B.C., the sea invaded the seaward parts of the basin, depositing silt and clay. Thus the section of Fenland nearest the Wash is mainly covered with silt, the more landward areas with peat; these are known respectively as the 'silt fen' and 'peat fen'.

*Reclamation.* At the time of the Norman Conquest, much of Fenland was still covered with marsh, meres and meandering streams, of value only to fishermen, cutters of reeds and wildfowlers. Such an area offered attractions and rewards for drainage schemes and a few sporadic attempts were made, notably by religious houses. But to be effective an integrated large-scale scheme was required, rather than piecemeal operations, and Dutch engineers, with experience in their homeland, were first employed in the seventeenth century. A major problem was the river Ouse, which brought large volumes of water from its catchment in the East Midlands, and made a great eastward bend before flowing north to the Wash. The engineers cut two parallel channels ('levels') directly across this bend, shortening the course and making a more direct outfall for the flood waters; the 'wash-lands' between are used temporarily as a reservoir to hold water until it can get away. Gradually more 'lodes' and minor drains were constructed, dividing the land into rectangular sections. Unfortunately, as the peat-fen dries out it shrinks, and in addition it wastes through accelerated bacterial action and oxidation as a result of cultivation, and even by wind erosion. As a result, parts of the peat-fen surface lie below that of the silt-fen nearer the sea, hindering outfall, and below that of the embanked rivers and drains; pumping, first powered by windmills, then by steam engines, now by diesel and electric motors, is necessary to remove water. Drainage schemes have been extended over all Fenland; indeed, no true fen remains except for the small Wicken Fen, specially conserved for its ecological significance by preserving a locally high water table.

But problems still remain, mainly the difficulty of outfall over the catchment at times of heavy rain and high tides in the Wash and its estuaries. In 1947 much of Fenland was flooded by rivers swollen by melt-water, which broke their banks; in 1953 a storm-surge in the North Sea caused the rivers to back up and flood large areas, as well as widespread inundation by the sea around the Wash itself. A new channel has been cut, taking Ouse water more directly almost to King's Lynn, and other drains were made to remove water from the right-bank tributaries of the Ouse.

*Agriculture.* The black humus and base-rich peat soils and the silty loams favour arable farming, with a high degree of specialisation in relatively small units. Wheat is the most important crop, occupying 25 per cent of the total farmland, followed by potatoes (though these have declined because of eel-worm), barley and sugar beet. The area under vegetables has increased rapidly, particularly peas, grown under contract to supply canning and quick-freezing plants, celery on the peat soils, carrots on the lighter sands, cauliflowers and cabbages. Wisbech is a centre of small-fruit growing for freezing, canning and jam-making, notably strawberries and raspberries, with blackcurrants for proprietary brands of juice. Flowers and bulbs are grown around Spalding.

*Settlements.* Fenland reveals a very dispersed settlement pattern, with isolated farms and small villages on the higher 'islands', strung out along the embanked rivers and roads, and on 'roddons', raised banks of silt indicating the courses of former streams. Some larger villages and towns have spread, as the danger of flooding has diminished, from around the usually fine church on the highest point, which was the original nucleus. The main towns are Ely on a higher patch of greensand in the south, with its fine cathedral, March with extensive railway marshalling-yards, Holbeach and Spalding. King's Lynn, Wisbech and Boston are minor, but quite busy, ports at the mouths of the rivers, handling petroleum, fuel oil, fertilisers and grain. Most towns are the centre of co-operative marketing and of industries associated with agriculture: sugar-refining, jam-making, the extraction of fruit juices, the canning and freezing of vegetables, the manufacture of fertilisers, pesticides, baskets and boxes for packing, and the maintenance of agricultural implements. However, the most important servicing towns, notably Cambridge, Peterborough and Lincoln, actually lie just outside the margins of Fenland.

**East Anglia.** This name applies to the counties of Norfolk and Suffolk, with the eastern part of Cambridgeshire. In the south it merges indistinguishably into the London basin; the Suffolk-Essex county boundary, following the river Stour, affords an arbitrary limit.

Much consists of a low chalk cuesta, known as the East Anglian

Heights, which reaches about 400 ft near Newmarket. The back-slope of the chalk dips so gently in an easterly direction that it is sometimes referred to as 'the East Anglian Plateau', or as 'High Norfolk' and 'High Suffolk'. Most is mantled with a thick layer of boulder-clay ('till') usually of a chalky nature, gravels and sands, and some compacted shelly sands known as 'crag'. Occasionally these surface deposits form low ridges, such as the Cromer Moraine which reaches the coast near Sheringham. The gently undulating surface of the plateau is crossed by the broad, shallow valleys of streams flowing to the North Sea near Great Yarmouth (Bure, Wensum, Yare and Waveney), and farther south by the Deben, Orwell and Stour.

The escarpment is flanked to the west by a 'bench' of gault clay and lower greensand, which overlooks Fenland. Some of these sands form undulating heathland, as between Sandringham and Downham Market, while in places the lower greensand consists of a compact brownish sandstone (*carstone*), used locally for building.

The details of the landscape, therefore, largely depend on the presence and nature of these superficial deposits, except where the chalk is revealed: the boulder-clay plateau of High Norfolk and Suffolk, the 'good sands' district of northern Norfolk, the 'sandlings' of eastern Suffolk, and the 'loam region' of the Bure valley developed on brick-earth. The district with perhaps most individuality is *Breckland,* across the borders of western Norfolk and Suffolk, an area of sands and gravels. Formerly it was a waste of heath and dunes, with occasional meres, but much has been improved and reclaimed or planted with conifers.

*The Coast.* In places low cliffs have developed as a result of wave action on the soft, unresistant deposits. The cliffs are composed of chalk near Sheringham and of glacial materials north of Yarmouth and along the Suffolk coast; moreover, slumping is common. Elsewhere shingle-spits and offshore sandbars have accumulated as a result of longshore drifting of material; the most striking is Orfordness, a shingle foreland with a spit trending across the mouth of the Alde southward for almost twenty miles. Behind these bars and spits, tracts of salt marsh and sand dune have developed. In Suffolk the river mouths have been converted into broad estuaries, with expanses of mud flat at low tide, as a result of the post-glacial rise of sea-level. North-west of Yarmouth shallow sheets of water inter-linked by the Bure and its tributaries form the Broads, most of which lie in hollows resulting from medieval peat-working.

*Agriculture.* With its diverse soils, a rainfall lower than in most parts of Britain though adequate for cultivation, and a sunny summer, East Anglia is one of Britain's major agricultural areas. In some parts, however, the soils are poor, notably on the greensand, in parts of the 'sandlings', and over much of Breckland. Parts remain under heath, other areas carry pasture, and some of Breckland is under the coniferous plantations of the Forestry Commission, its largest tract in England. Some areas of Breckland, by contrast, have been transformed by systematic liming, fertilising and marling, and produce remarkable crops of wheat, sugar beet and potatoes.

Over the better soils, farms are large and mechanised, growing barley (notably on the chalk), sugar beet and wheat. On the 'good sand' was first evolved the famous 'Norfolk four-course rotation' of crops. Farming is by no means exclusively arable; large numbers of cattle, both beef and dairy breeds, are reared on the permanent grasslands of the alluvial valleys and reclaimed coastal marshes, and on the temporary leys, supplemented by fodder crops in the rotation. Though sheep are not as numerous as in the past, they are folded on the stubble fields of the 'good sands'. Poultry is reared in large numbers, and Norfolk supplies a large proportion of Britain's turkeys. A feature of the chalklands near Newmarket (the administrative centre of horse-racing) is the number of stables and studs and a famous racecourse.

*Settlement and Industry.* The settlement pattern involves a fairly even distribution of small towns and villages, with occasional hamlets and isolated farms. East Dereham, Wymondham, Thetford, Bury St Edmunds (the county town of West Suffolk), and Stowmarket are market-towns, with some attractive houses and large impressive churches and abbeys, built when East Anglia was a textile region before the Industrial Revolution passed it by; the Norfolk village of Worstead actually gave its name to worsteds. Some towns have cattle- and corn-markets; agricultural engineering and servicing; sugar refineries; breweries; malt houses; factories engaged in the manufacture of fertilisers, sacks and boxes; canneries and quick-freezing plants. At Sizewell, on the coast near Ipswich, is a nuclear power-station.

Norwich (120,000) is the premier regional centre of East Anglia, situated on slightly elevated ground near the Wensum-Yare confluence. The city has grown steadily since the thirteenth century, first as the focus of the East Anglian woollen industry, then of agriculture, and it has maintained its position as the administrative and servicing city of Norfolk, an expanding centre of light industry (footwear, mustard, machinery, food-processing), a commercial centre (marketing, insurance), and a cultural centre (with a cathedral, museum, art gallery and a recently founded university), in all, an attractive and flourishing city.

Ipswich (117,000) is the county-town of East Suffolk, with a port on the Orwell estuary handling coastal traffic, and with industrial estates, tanneries, flour mills, breweries, chemical works, and factories making agricultural implements.

Some small towns are situated along the coast. Harwich, at the mouth of the Stour, is a ferry port (Parkestone Quay) for Denmark and the Netherlands. Lowestoft and Great Yarmouth have long been fishing ports for the North Sea banks, though this has declined in recent years; however, fish-curing and canning are still of importance. Light industry has been diversified, and the quick-freezing of vegetables (especially peas) has expanded.

The East Anglian coast offers a number of resorts, with beaches, golf courses and sailing facilities. The estuaries near Harwich provide famed yachting waters; Yarmouth and Lowestoft are increasingly well-provided resorts; many small places have their own particular charm: Hunstanton, Wells, Cromer and Aldeburgh. But here, as so often in Britain, has developed a regrettable rash of caravan sites and holiday camps. Wroxham is the centre of popular sailing and cruising on the Broads.

**The London Basin.** This shallow downfold, with a west-east axis, was created during mid-Tertiary times, its margins formed by the 'chalk horseshoe' of the Chilterns in the north-west and the North Downs in the south, though it opens to the North Sea in the east. The chalk dips under the centre of the basin, and its strata provide a source of water; the wells were formerly artesian, but so much water has been removed that pumping is now necessary, and a much greater part of London's vast requirements is taken from the Thames at Teddington and from reservoirs in the Lea valley.

Overlying the chalk in the centre of the basin are Tertiary sediments, of which the London clay and the sandy Bagshot and Bracklesham beds (of Eocene age) are widespread. The surface in the north is further diversified by superficial deposits of boulder-clay and outwash sands of glacial origin, for the maximum advance of the Quaternary ice-sheets reached just across the north of the basin, together with masses of compacted angular flints ('plateau gravels'), which form cappings to the low sandstone hills at 300–500 ft, and various terrace-gravels (on one large area of these is London Airport), and brick-earth. The floodplain of the Thames and its tributaries is covered with alluvium, and the estuary is bordered with tidal flats and marshes.

The Thames breaks through a gap in the western chalk cuesta at

Goring, above Reading, and flows eastwards along the axis of the basin into its estuary, receiving tributaries both from the north (the Colne and Lea) and from the Weald (see p. 192). Changes of sea-level have resulted in the formation of several distinctive river-terraces, forming 'steps' of considerable importance in the pattern of London's growth. Though the Thames is tidal upstream to Teddington Weir, the estuary opens out into a broad funnel below Tilbury, diversified on the south by the irregular estuaries of the Medway and the Swale which separate the Isle of Sheppey. To the north the post-glacial rise of sea-level created the winding estuaries of the Essex rivers (Crouch, Blackwater and Colne).

The Thames estuary is bordered by lowlands extending north into Essex and south into Kent; these are mainly underlain with London clay and various Tertiary sands, diversified by a veneer of alluvium and in Essex by boulder-clay and brick-earth. A small isolated mass of chalk on the south-eastern margins, structurally separate from the North Downs, forms the Isle of Thanet. At levels between 1,500 and 3,000 ft below the surface in eastern Kent coal is mined and about 1·5 million tons is produced annually.

*Agriculture.* Not all the London basin is built over, though more land is swallowed every year; parks have been preserved, efforts continue to maintain a 'green belt' of open spaces and 'commons', golf courses and playing fields; and the outer margins are still important agriculturally. The clays and the back-slope of the western basin support dairy farming; cereals and sugar beet are grown on the Essex boulder-clay and brick-earth; and in northern Kent on the sandy loams are orchards of apples and other fruit, hop fields and market-gardens, though these inevitably decline in area every year.

*London.* The main feature of the basin is the rapidly expanding 'urban sprawl' of London, capital of the United Kingdom, with a tremendous grip on the nation's life; with a conurbation population of over 8 millions, it is the third largest city in the world. It was founded by the Romans as *Londinium,* at the lowest bridge-point of the Thames, and on it focused many roads. It grew rapidly, though Winchester for a time was the capital, and its importance increased as commercial links with the Continent developed after the Norman Conquest. London thus became the headquarters of trading and commercial companies, the foundations of its present world rôle in finance, commerce and insurance; these activities developed with the country's increasing power, wealth and colonial expansion. The city of London, near London Bridge, was the original commercial nucleus, while Westminster, with the Houses of Parliament, became the administrative area. As population grew, the built-up area expanded, first over the river-terraces, then after drainage and embanking on to the floodplain, later still towards the chalk margins. Some areas of sand and plateau gravels were avoided by the builders, which was fortunate, since this has left open spaces as parks and 'commons', which have been jealously guarded. Gradually the city and the eastern part ('the East End') became devoted to the commodity markets, offices and banks, forming the business district; the west-central part to government and administration; and the 'West End' to shops and places of entertainment. The residential districts moved progressively outwards, linked by a web of roads, suburban railways and the still-expanding electrified 'Underground', and since 1950 some administrative, residential and business facilities have also moved upwards in the form of 'high-rise' blocks. In the East End houses were usually small and crowded, the result of too rapid nineteenth-century expansion, and slums developed; many of these have been cleared, a process accelerated by wartime bombing. Vast, rather monotonous housing-estates spread to the south, with many high blocks of apartments, and more pleasant districts in the south-west and west; farther out still is the low-density attractive housing of the so-called 'stockbroker belt'. Outer towns have been drawn within the influence of Greater London, on the back-slope of the North Downs and the Chilterns and even on the South Coast, serving as 'dormitories' for more than 1 million commuters who surge in and out during 'rush hours' in a great, daily tidal flow. The shores of the Thames estuary have dormitory towns, some of which are also seaside resorts, particularly patronised by day-visitors from London: Southend in Essex, and Whitstable, Herne Bay, Margate and Ramsgate in Kent. The Greater London Council administers much of London proper, though the boroughs retain a degree of autonomy over local affairs.

London has continued to diversify and expand as a centre of administration, industry, education and entertainment. It is by far the largest manufacturing centre in Britain, with a large population that is a labour force and its own market, served by a major port and radiating roads and railways. Necessarily there are large utility industries: power-stations, gasworks, waterworks and sewage plants. These are located mostly along the shores of the estuary. One class of industry is associated with the immense volume of bulky imports: food-processing (flour-milling, sugar-refining), oil-refining (several large refineries are situated on the shores of the estuary at Shellhaven, Isle of Grain and Coryton), timber-working, paper-making and chemicals. The proximity of chalk outcrops to the south has resulted in plants which make half of Britain's cement.

Light industry can be divided into two groups: the older established types (printing, publishing, clothing in the East End, furniture, paint); and the newer consumer industries located along the arterial or ring roads and in estates such as at Slough to the west. Other towns in outlying parts of the basin have manufactures: biscuits at Reading, ship-repairing in the Medway towns, paper-making near Dartford, and various light industries at Chelmsford. On the Essex banks of the Thames near Dagenham is the American-owned Ford plant, an integrated unit sited where assembly space was available and where wharves could be constructed for importing coke and iron-ore for its blast furnaces. At Bradwell, near the mouth of the Blackwater in Essex, a nuclear power-station is owned by the Atomic Energy Authority.

*The Port of London.* The earliest harbour, used by the Romans, was well up the river, and in medieval times developed near London Bridge; this port, though lined with embankments and wharves, is now used mainly by lighters, small coasting steamers and pleasure craft. As ships grew larger, activity moved downstream, and the appreciable tidal range necessitated the construction of wet-docks in the alluvium and clay along the great loops in the river east of the Tower of London; the first group was the West India docks (opened in 1802), the latest the King George V (1921). To serve larger passenger liners, the outport of Tilbury, thirty miles below London Bridge, was constructed towards the end of last century and subsequently enlarged and modernised.

**Southern England.** To the south of the Thames basin are two major features: in the east the Weald, in the west the Hampshire basin. The former is the denuded remains of an elongated dome, the latter is part of a broad asymmetrical basin; each has a general east-west axis, though in detail the structures are complicated by numerous parallel upfolds and downfolds. The eastern part of the Weald and the southern part of the Hampshire basin have been destroyed, probably by prolonged marine denudation.

*The Weald.* The dome has been heavily denuded, removing the newer overlying rocks from the centre and revealing a series of older rocks. In the centre the Hastings Beds, the oldest of the Cretaceous system, forms a series of sandstone ridges rising to over 700 ft in Ashdown Forest; these are sometimes known as the *High Weald* or the *Central Forest Ridges*. On either side is a broad vale floored with Weald clay, its surface mainly below 300 ft, poorly drained and sometimes waterlogged; to both north and south, though most marked in the north, are outcrops of the lower greensand, a complex formation including sandstone, limestone and clay. The sandstone of the Hythe Beds forms an in-facing cuesta which culminates in Leith Hill (965 ft), the highest point of the Weald. Then follow to north and south narrow exposures of Gault clay, eroded into east-west vales, and the upper greensand, which appears as a bench, particularly marked in the west.

The northern and southern margins of the Weald comprise the North and South Downs respectively. The former can be traced westward from the white cliffs of Dover, forming a chalk cuesta rising 600 to 800 ft; the steep escarpment, scarred with quarries, overlooks the Weald, while the back-slope dips gently towards the London basin. Between Farnham and Guildford, however, the dip of the strata steepens strongly, forming a prominent ridge, the Hog's Back. The South Downs extend from the cliffs of Beachy Head to merge with the North Downs in Hampshire. Both lines of hills are characterised by smooth, rounded slopes; the absence of surface drainage; deeply eroded dry-valleys; and a profusion of springs emerging at the base of the escarpments.

Complicated river systems have developed, the main streams flowing northwards to the Thames (Wey, Mole, Medway), and southwards to the English Channel (Arun, Adur, Ouse, Cuckmere), joined by tributaries in valleys which have developed in the less resistant west-east outcrops; for example, the Rother flows eastwards to the Arun, the Beult westwards to the Medway. The main rivers have cut the Downs into individual blocks, separated by steep-sided gaps through which they meander; these 'water-gaps', with some 'dry-gaps' eroded by rivers which have now disappeared (probably as the result of capture), are utilised by the roads and railways between London and the South Coast.

Several other small relief units lie outside the Weald: the marshy alluvial flats of the Pevensey Levels and Romney Marsh, flanked seawards by the shingle foreland of Dungeness; and the coastal plain of Sussex, south of the Downs, which is covered with brick-earth and other recent deposits.

*The Hampshire Basin.* This greatly undulating lowland is enclosed by a rim of rolling chalk uplands 400 to 600 ft high: the Hampshire Downs in the east, Salisbury plain in the north, and the Wiltshire and Dorset Downs in the West. This rim forms part of the northern limb of the Hampshire basin syncline, cut into low plateaus by the valleys of the Avon, Bourne, Test and Itchen, and further diversified by dry valleys. Its outward-facing margins form distinctive escarpments, such as Cranborne Chase overlooking the Vale of Blackmoor.

The chalk dips gently southward under Tertiary deposits, but outcrops steeply in the south.    At one time this southern outcrop must have formed a prominent continuous 'hog-back', but breaching by the sea has left only the Purbeck Downs in Dorset and a ridge forming the east-west 'backbone' of the Isle of Wight; the Needles stand up prominently as sea-stacks at its western end.

The centre of the basin is floored with early Tertiary sands and clays, deposited over the chalk during a period of marine transgression.    They give rise to a low undulating relief, diversified by alluvium-filled valleys through which meander the Frome, Avon, Test and Itchen towards Poole Harbour and the Solent.    In places a compact layer of flinty gravels forms low plateaus, as to the north of Southampton and in the New Forest.

*The Coast*.    The coastline from Portland Bill to the Straits of Dover is of great variety and charm.    In Purbeck, the Isle of Wight, and near Eastbourne and Dover the chalk ends in impressive cliffs, and along the coast of Purbeck some surviving fragments of Jurassic limestone form cliffs, arches and reefs.    The Tertiary clays and sands also form low cliffs, rapidly attacked by the waves and downward slumping, so that measures of protection (piling, embankments and groynes) are needed.    The post-glacial rise of sea-level created several estuaries (Poole Harbour, Southampton Water and the Portsmouth 'Harbours'), and the Solent separating the Isle of Wight from the mainland.

*Agriculture*.    Some soils, such as those derived from the sandstones, are thin, acid and poor, carrying a vegetation of heathland (ling, heather, bracken, gorse), scrub-birch and coniferous plantations, as on the Forest Ridge and in the New Forest.    The chalk has a thin cover of rendzinas, while the clays are commonly heavy and waterlogged.    The best soils are the sandy loams developed on some of the Tertiaries and greensand, the alluvial soils in the valleys, and the brick-earths of the Sussex plain.    Other factors stimulating agricultural development are the generally pleasant climate, for this is one of the sunniest parts of the country, and the large markets in London and the coastal towns.    Conversely, the spread of these towns has taken much good farmland, notably on the Sussex plain and in southern Hampshire.

Though the chalk escarpments are generally too steep to cultivate, their back-slopes, once grazed by flocks of sheep, are now either ploughed for barley and wheat or are under short-ley pasture for dairy and beef cattle, for which kale, alfalfa and roots are also grown.    Water for the animals is piped to troughs on the Downs, and in some parts sprinkler irrigation is used, especially on alfalfa. Dairy cattle are also kept on the Wealden and Hampshire claylands, usually on permanent pasture.    Pig- and calf-rearing in houses, and poultry, usually in broiler houses, are widespread, and the number of sheep is again increasing, after many years of decline, as a diversifying contribution; sheep are especially important to Romney Marsh, where a distinct breed has evolved.

Market-gardening is widely practised, especially on the Sussex brick-earths and the Hampshire loams. The sunny climate has stimulated fruit-growing, including apples and pears in Kent on the greensand loams, cherries on the ragstone (limestone) outcrops, and strawberries between Southampton and Portsmouth.

*Settlements.* Much of this region is attractively rural, with pleasant villages, prosperous farms and considerable woodland on the Weald; the last once supplied the charcoal burners who provided fuel for the medieval iron industry. London exerts an increasing influence, and many small market-towns have expanded to serve as 'dormitories' (see p. 191); commuters even travel daily from the Sussex coast, using the fast, electrified rail services. Crawley was designated a 'new town' in 1946, and has expanded from a population of 11,000 in 1951 to about 60,000.

A series of market-towns stands in the gaps through the North Downs, bridge-points on their respective rivers: Guildford, Dorking, Redhill, Sevenoaks and Maidstone. Other towns act as market-centres: in the Weald, Tunbridge Wells and Ashford in the east, Haslemere and Petersfield in the west; in the Hampshire basin, Winchester (once the capital of England) and Salisbury with their fine cathedrals, and Andover farther north. Many towns have light industry, notably fruit-packing, brewing and milling, the servicing of agricultural machinery, and the recently introduced manufacture of consumer goods.

The earliest settlements along the coast were small ports. The Cinque Ports were established in the Middle Ages with special privileges and responsibilities; the original five were Hastings, Sandwich, Dover, Romney and Hythe, while Rye and Winchelsea were added later. Of these Dover remains a busy cross-Channel port to Calais and Ostend, while Folkestone (to Boulogne) and Newhaven (to Dieppe) are less important. As seaside holidays became an English habit, stimulated by royal example, an almost continuous line of resorts developed, with promenades, piers, hotels and guest-houses and large areas of bungalows, holiday camps and caravan sites. Of these resorts the largest in the east is Brighton (160,000), in the west the fashionable Bournemouth, which, with contiguous Poole, has a population of about a quarter-million. The diamond-shaped Isle of Wight, off Southampton Water, is in effect one large resort, with fine beaches, a sunny climate and its status as a yachting centre. Many people have retired to the South Coast, so swelling the population.

Portsmouth (220,000) developed as a naval base because of its extensive and easily defensible harbour on the Channel coast, but the progressive decline in the Royal Navy has inevitably affected the port and its inhabitants, and efforts have been made to introduce light industry. Southampton (205,000) has been a port since Roman times (*Clausentum*), situated at the convergence of the rivers Test and Itchen into the six-mile long Southampton Water. It has the advantages of shelter by the Isle of Wight, ready access to the Channel and the Atlantic, its famous prolonged high tide, a depth of water (minimum 35 ft) which needs little dredging because of the silt-free rivers (though this has been recently necessary to cope with super-tankers), a small tidal range obviating the necessity for wet-docks, and extensive frontages for constructing berths. Proximity to London has made Southampton a major trans-Atlantic passenger terminal, though air competition in recent years has been seriously felt. It also has regular services with South Africa, and an increasing amount of foodstuffs is imported (bananas, citrus fruit, grain, wine), with some timber. Several car-ferries operate to the Continent. On the western shores of Southampton Water is the Fawley (Esso) refinery, the largest in the Commonwealth, with deep-water tanker-berths along the oil-jetty, and linked by pipeline with London Airport and the Bristol district; various petrochemical industries and two oil-fired power-stations are located nearby. Southampton was grievously bombed during World War II but has been largely rebuilt, and several estates with light industry (including ocean cables and auto-accessories) have been developed.

**The Channel Islands.** Situated off the north-west coast of France, and formerly part of the Dukedom of Normandy, these include Jersey and Guernsey, with seven others of which the largest are Alderney and Sark; their total area is only seventy-five miles. The islands represent fragments of the Armorican-fold ranges of France (see p. 256), broken up by faulting, erosion and the post-glacial rise of sea-level, and they consist of complex igneous and metamorphic rocks (granite, gneiss, gabbro, schist) shot through with intrusive dykes.

The islands have suffered long-sustained denudation, so that their surfaces are gently undulating plateaus, ending in some parts abruptly in cliffs. Jersey rises to 400 ft in the north and slopes southward; Guernsey slopes northward up to nearly 350 ft and Alderney to 280 ft; Sark is a more uniform plateau. The rocks vary greatly in their resistance to marine erosion, and fine cliffs and coves have developed, with sweeping bays, sand and shell beaches, and numerous offshore stacks and jagged reefs.

The southern latitude and insular character of the group result in remarkably mild winters (40° to 44° F (4.4° to 6.7° C) January means), virtually frost-free, with warm, sunny summers (60° to 63° F (15·6° to 17·2° C), and a well-distributed rainfall of 30 to 40 in. These climatic factors are responsible for two main activities: intensive agriculture and horticulture, and tourism. Jersey specialises in early potatoes, vegetables, flowers, and tomatoes grown in small fields; Guernsey, rather farther north, has many more glasshouses, producing tomatoes and cut flowers. Holdings are usually small, terraced on south-facing slopes, surrounded by stone walls or earth banks. The well-known Jersey and Guernsey cattle are bred for their rich milk and for export. Some fishing is carried on, largely to supply local hotels.

Many visitors come to the islands, attracted by the pleasant climate, sandy beaches, charming towns, and the low-duty attractions of tobacco, wines, spirits and perfumes (of which a large 'personal export' has developed). Steamer services to St Peter Port (Guernsey) and St Helier (Jersey) are from Weymouth, though many people fly directly from London and other UK airports. Some people retire there from the UK, attracted by the low rate of income tax, and the absence of surtax and death duties. About 110,000 people live in the islands, of whom 63,000 are in Jersey, 45,000 in Guernsey.

**The South-west Peninsula.** In its broadest sense this region comprises the counties of Cornwall, Devon and Somerset; the city of Bristol on its margins is also included here for convenience. It consists mainly of Palæozoic rocks of Devonian and Carboniferous age, with some pre-Cambrian metamorphics (notably serpentine in the Lizard peninsula, the most southerly point on mainland Britain). These ancient rocks are flanked on the east by Mesozoic sandstones and marls.

The Palæozoic rocks were crumpled by the Hercynian earth movements into a series of west-east fold-ranges, and in addition several large masses of granite were intruded. Long-continued denudation, interrupted by *en masse* uplift and later flexuring, reduced these mountains to a series of uplands. Those in the west consist of granite batholiths, their upper surfaces exposed: Land's End, Carn Menellis, Hensbarrow, Bodmin Moor and Dartmoor (which rises to just over 2,000 ft); their upper parts are rounded and smooth, diversified only by tors, castellated piles of well-jointed granite blocks, standing out boldly as the highest points, and by deeply incised valleys on their margins. By contrast, farther east are Exmoor and the Quantock Hills of coarse Devonian sandstone, and the Mendip Hills of Carboniferous limestone. The sandstone uplands broadly resemble the granite country in appearance (except for the absence of tors), with thin, acid soil, and a moorland vegetation of coarse grass and bog. The Mendips reveal features of limestone Karst: underground streams, caverns, resurgences, sink holes and gorges.

For the most part the main divide lies well in the north of the peninsula, except for the Torridge and Tawe rivers, which rise on the northern slopes of Dartmoor, and for the Parrett, which drains central Somerset; these all flow to the Bristol Channel. The Fal, Tamar (which for much of its length demarcates the boundary between Cornwall and Devon), and the very complicated Exe rivers, reach the English Channel.

In the west, lowlands are limited to the valleys and along the estuaries; they are mostly floored with Devonian sandstones and the Culm Measures (shales and sandstones of Carboniferous age), which have weathered to give dark red loams and yellowish clays respectively. Farther east the gently rolling basin of the Exe, sometimes known as the Devon Lowland, is floored with Permian, Triassic and Jurassic marls, sandstones and limestones, which give rise to the characteristic red soils of Devon.

The most extensive lowland is the Plain of Somerset, drained by the sluggish Parrett, Brue and Axe rivers. Sometimes called the Somerset Levels, this near-flat area is floored with peat and silt; much has been drained and the rivers embanked, but flooding still occurs. The base-rich peat is worked in several places for horticultural use.

*The Coast.* Wave erosion of the strongly jointed granite has produced fine castellated cliffs, alternating with coves where the weaker rocks have been removed, and with offshore stacks and reefs; the Scilly Isles are the worn-down remnants of an almost submerged granite mass. In Devon, likewise, where rocks of differing degrees of resistance to erosion alternate, so also do bays and headlands. The post-glacial rise of sea-level inundated the lower courses of the rivers, creating winding ria-like indentations such as the Fal estuary (Carrick Roads) and the Tamar estuary (Plymouth Sound).

*Agriculture.* The climate of the coastal lowlands is equable, with very mild, virtually frost-free, winters, early springs, and well-distributed yearly rainfall of 40 in or more. The uplands, however, are bleak and may have heavy winter snowfall; here farming is limited to the grazing of beef cattle, sheep and ponies. On the lowlands the damp, mild weather and heavy soils favour dairy cattle, especially on the rich Somerset water-meadows. Milk is sent by road and rail to the Midlands and London, though much is processed into cheese (notably Cheddar), butter and cream; a large amount of 'Cornish clotted cream' is sold to visitors. The early springs along the coast favour the specialised production of early flowers such as daffodils (especially in the Scillies), new potatoes and broccoli, grown in small fields surrounded by sheltering stone walls. Southern Devon has more varied and larger scale market-gardening. Fruit is grown widely (with canneries at Bridgwater), and apples in Devon and Somerset yield the traditional cider, once consumed locally as a rough drink, now widely distributed as recognised brands. Most farming, in fact, has benefited by the improving of communications and the widening of markets.

*Fishing.* The peninsular character of the South-west, with its sheltered harbours and offshore grounds in the Channel, stimulated subsistence fishing, though this gradually became commercialised; for a time Brixham was a leading British fishing port. But the shoals of pilchards seemed to vanish, and the activity declined in comparison with the large east coast ports, though some of the catch still travels to London by special train. At many harbours fishing is little more than a picturesque adjunct of tourism.

*Mining.* Thermal metamorphism around the margins of the granite intrusions not only caused the injection of mineral veins, but 'kaolinised' the granite, which became kaolin (china clay) as the felspars decomposed by weathering. Tin and copper in Cornwall and lead in the Mendips have been worked for probably 2,000 years, and even a century ago Cornwall was a leading world producer as testified by the many ruined mines. Tin and wolfram are still mined in one or two places, but Cornwall cannot now compete with large-scale sources. At Camborne and Redruth mining machinery is made for export, and the School of Mines at Camborne is world-famous. Granite is quarried at Penryn near Falmouth and on Bodmin Moor, and slate is quarried at Delabole also on Bodmin Moor.

The working of kaolin thrives in the St Austell area, since it is of pure quality and can be shipped (as English china clay) from Fowey, not only coastwise to the Mersey, hence to the Potteries (see p. 177), but also to the USA. The results on the landscape are shown by the huge, white conical spoil-dumps.

*Tourism.* The South-west peninsula is one of the most attractive parts of Britain, with its sandy beaches and fine cliffs, moorlands, wooded valleys and picturesque harbours. It first became popular when the railway made it accessible to London; now many people come by rail, car and coach, and the main access roads from the east and the often steep, winding roads within the region are choked with traffic for much of the year; indeed, some feel that this growth in popularity is doing much to destroy the peninsula's charm.

*Settlement.* Most of the upland areas have little habitation, except for isolated farm houses and small hamlets built solidly of granite with massive slate roofs. The towns are of two categories: evenly spaced market-centres, often at valley junctions or bridge-points (Truro, Bodmin, Tavistock, Tiverton, Newton Abbot, Yeovil and Bridgwater); and many small harbours and resorts, including both the larger, more fully developed Torquay (83,000), Newquay, Paignton, Ilfracombe and Weston-super-Mare (43,000), and a multitude of minor places. In the past, some ports were much more important for coastal trade, when land communications were difficult or deficient, and as ports of call for sailing-ships. But larger ships began to go farther up the Channel to Southampton and London, and only Plymouth retains any importance, with neighbouring Devonport, as a naval base. Falmouth, once the last port of call for Atlantic crossings, has drydocks and repair facilities, and is a base for ocean-going tugs.

Three cities, each a major route-focus, have a wider regional importance: Plymouth (204,000), largely rebuilt after wartime destruction, the market and servicing centre for Cornwall and south-western Devon; Exeter (80,000), for the rest of Devon; and Taunton (35,000), for western Somerset. The last two are also county administrative towns. Exeter, founded at the lowest bridge-point of the Exe, with its surviving medieval walls, fine shops, offices, markets, university, light industries and pleasant residential suburbs, is one of the most attractive of the English 'provincial capitals'.

Bristol (436,000) grew up eight miles from the Severn estuary on a defensible site on the banks of the Avon; from its docks went sailing-ships and merchants to the New World, and its commerce throve. So too did industries based on imported commodities: sugar-refining, cigarette-making, tobacco, chocolate, and the bottling of wines and spirits; these are still of major importance. For a time its trade was second only to that of London, but the concentration of manufacturing on the coalfields after the Industrial Revolution and the increasing tonnage of ships were handicaps. Towards the end of the nineteenth century, docks were built at Avonmouth and Portishead to serve as outports. In recent decades its industrial importance has increased considerably. To the traditional activities have been added light engineering; the making of

aircraft; printing; the manufacture of paint, prefabricated buildings and many more items.   Bristol's position as a transport centre
has been helped by the construction of the Severn railway-tunnel
and the recently opened Severn road-bridge, and it has direct rail
links with London, Birmingham, South Wales, the South-west
peninsula and Southampton.

## WALES

The principality of Wales includes glaciated mountains, extensive plateaus, deep valleys and narrow coastal plains.   By contrast,
there is an industrialised and densely populated coalfield in the
south and a smaller one in the north.
The extensive uplands cause considerable difficulty to transport,
especially by rail.   A main line follows the northern coast from
Chester, crossing the Menai Strait to Anglesey, where Holyhead
is the packet station for Dún Laoghaire (Kingstown, the outport
of Dublin).   Another line from Bristol passes under the Severn in
a tunnel, and continues through the industrial towns of south
Wales to Fishguard, a port for Rosslare and Cork.   It is possible
to reach Aberystwyth on the coast of mid-Wales by a circuitous
rail route along the upper Severn and lower Dovey valleys, or from
the south through Carmarthen, but other lines are slow and circuitous.   To travel from north to south Wales, it is usually necessary
(and quicker) to go via Shrewsbury.   Some good roads cross the
uplands, but much of rural Wales is remote and difficult of access.
**North Wales.**   The highest mountains are north-west of the
Dovey estuary, particularly in Snowdonia, now a National Park;
these consist mainly of early Palæozoic rocks, great thicknesses of
slate and compacted volcanic materials.   During the Caledonian
earth movements, these rocks were folded into complex ranges,
trending from north-east to south-west, and also masses of granite
were intruded.   But long-sustained denudation has created a
series of distinctive erosion surfaces, from which clusters of higher
summits protrude.   The whole area was again uplifted, probably
in mid-Tertiary times, so that the rejuvenated rivers cut deep
valleys.   The Quaternary glaciation has left a distinctive stamp
on this landscape.   Snowdonia comprises three groups of mountains, with fourteen peaks exceeding 3,000 ft, separated by
glaciated through-valleys and cut into by cirques (known in Welsh
as *cwms,* pronounced like its English equivalent, 'coombes') separated by rocky ridges rising to prominent summits; the highest
is Snowdon (3,560 ft).   Several U-shaped valleys contain lakes
(*llyns*), and there are many small sheets of water similar to
the tarns of the Lake District (see p. 165).   Boulder-clay lies

in uneven mounds in the *cwms* and more extensively in the valleys and along the coastal plains. Farther south the range of the Arenigs reaches 2,800 ft, and the fine mass of Cader Idris (2,927 ft) rises between the Mawddach and Dovey estuaries. Along the coast rocky headlands alternate with bays and sandy beaches, backed by a narrow coastal plain.

*Anglesey* is a worn-down plateau of highly folded and metamorphosed rocks, some pre-Cambrians being among the oldest in Britain; in parts these rocks are visible, as in Holy Mountain and along the coast near Holyhead. Elsewhere they have an uneven cover of boulder-clay, sometimes in the form of drumlins, with sand dunes and marsh in the south-west.

*Agriculture.* The mountains, with their bare rock and scree, and with an annual precipitation exceeding 100 in, are used for grazing the hardy mountain sheep, many of which are wintered in the Conway valley or on the coastal plains. Cattle, both dairy and beef, are reared in the valleys and in Anglesey, and some fodder crops are grown.

*Industry.* Though north Wales cannot be called an industrial area, there are, nevertheless, survivals of long-established activities and some new ones. At Bethesda, Llanberis and Ffestiniog the Cambrian slates are quarried, leaving vast terraced holes in the mountain sides, and a granite intrusion which outcrops along the coast near Penmaenmawr is quarried for road-metal. Textiles are made from local wool at Trefriw, in the Conway valley. At Dolgarrog aluminium rolling-mills are powered by electricity derived from water stored in the Cowlyd reservoir, and a few small hydro-stations put power into the Grid.

A small outcrop of Coal Measures to the north-east in Flint and Denbigh forms the north Wales coalfield; its annual output has dwindled to under 2 million tons, most of which is now mined in the Wrexham district. This coalfield has been responsible for a small industrial region, with an integrated steel plant at Shotton, and smaller engineering works at Mostyn and Brymbo. This part of north Wales is now a Development Area, and light industry has been introduced into Flint, Holywell and Connah's Quay, notably rayon textiles and chemicals. Anglesey has a milk-processing plant, factories in Holyhead making light products, a plant for extracting bromine from sea water, and at Beaumaris a plant for making hovercraft. At Wylfa, in the north, a nuclear power-station is operated by the UK Atomic Energy Authority.

*Tourism.* North Wales is a popular area, for the close relationship of sea and mountain caters to a range of tastes. Along the coast west of Point of Air is an almost continuous line of popular holiday resorts (Rhyl, Colwyn Bay, Llandudno), and smaller ones on the Menai Strait (Bangor, Caernarvon) and around the Lleyn peninsula (Pwllheli, Criccieth). The Snowdonia National Park is visited by many walkers and climbers, catered to by such centres as Bettwys-y-Coed and by scattered hotels, farm houses and youth hostels.

**Central Wales.** The high, glaciated mountains give way southward to more rounded plateau surfaces, generally some 1,500 to 2,000 ft above sea-level, of Palæozoic sandstones and slates. The plateau is deeply dissected by rivers flowing westwards to Cardigan Bay (Dovey and Teifi) and eastwards as headstreams of the Severn, Wye and Usk; the first two rise on the eastern slopes of Plynlimon (2,469 ft), only twenty miles from the west coast. Other upstanding areas are Radnor Forest on the east, and in the south the escarpment edge of the Hercynian basin (see below): the lonely uplands of the Brecon Beacons (2,907 ft), now a National Park, and the Black Mountains, both mainly of old red sandstone, with moorland, heather and peat bogs, and rough hill-pasture.

The Welsh plateau has a heavy rainfall of 60 to 80 in, except in the eastern rainshadow. Water is accumulated behind dams, and Liverpool obtains water from Lake Vyrnwy in the valley of a headstream of the upper Dee, Birmingham from the valley of the Elan (a tributary of the Wye). Several reservoirs in the Brecon Beacons supply south Wales.

The high moorland supports only sheep, hardy mountain cattle, and herds of ponies, sometimes kept on a ranching basis. Some tracts have been planted with conifers by the Forestry Commission. Towns are few, including such market-centres as Newtown and Welshpool in the Severn valley, Llandrindod Wells and Builth Wells in the upper valleys of the Wye, and Brecon in the Usk valley; these are also pleasant resorts. The narrow coastal plain of Cardigan Bay supports dairy farming, and several small towns (Aberystwyth, Cardigan) are market and shopping centres and seaside resorts; Aberystwyth is the home of a college of the University of Wales.

**South Wales.** This region extends from the Pembroke peninsula eastward to the Usk valley; the Plain of Gwent, between the Usk and the Wye, is a transitional region in Monmouthshire.

*Relief.* Much consists of old red sandstone, Carboniferous limestone, millstone grit and Coal Measures; these were folded by the Hercynian earth movements into ranges and basins with a broad east-west trend. The area then suffered a long complex history of denudation, renewed uplift, and dissection by the parallel superimposed rivers flowing to the Bristol Channel. The main synclinal basin, containing Coal Measures, is oval in plan, though asymmetrical in section, with a gentler dip, more level seams and broader outcrops to the north of the central axis. The coalfield is flanked on the north by moorland plateaus of gritstone, shale and sandstone, on the south by the gently undulating Plain of Glamorgan, covered with newer rocks, drift deposits and alluvium.

On the western margins of the coalfield, the Gower peninsula is a mass of Carboniferous limestone covered with boulder-clay. Exposed to wave attack from the south-west, the coast of Gower consists of fine cliffs and sweeping sandy bays, easily accessible to visitors from Swansea and beyond.

Farther west again are lowlands surrounding Carmarthen Bay, into which drain the Towy and Taff rivers, and then the Pembroke peninsula, composed of Carboniferous limestone and ancient Palæozoic rocks, including some igneous masses rising above the general level as the Prescelly Hills. Pembroke has a fine rugged coastline, with headlands, bays and the ria-like deep-water inlet of Milford Haven.

*Agriculture.* A considerable amount of farming is carried on in the coastal plains, especially around Carmarthen Bay, in the Vale of Glamorgan and the Plain of Gwent. Its advantages are the fertile clay and alluvial soils, the mild climate with its south-facing aspect, and the local markets in the industrial towns. The emphasis is on dairying, the winter-grazing of sheep from the Welsh uplands, and market-gardening; early potatoes are grown on the Pembroke peninsula.

*The Coalfield.* The coal deposits are of varied quality: thick seams of bituminous coal, long-flame coals near the coast, and anthracite in the west and in the extension of the field in Pembroke, though the last is no longer worked. In the northern part of the field the seams are near the surface, thick, level or gently inclined, and little disturbed. Mining began in medieval times in the northern valleys, using adits where the seams outcropped on the sides. At the time of the Industrial Revolution most coal still came from the northern section near Aberdare, Merthyr Tydfil and Ebbw Vale, and was used for coke-making for the numerous small blast furnaces. In the latter part of the nineteenth century, increasing demand for steam-coal, especially for bunkering ships, led to developments in the centre of the basin, and Neath,

Rhondda and Pontypool developed as mining communities, with houses and collieries strung out along the narrow valleys. By the beginning of the twentieth century, output exceeded 60 million tons annually, of which about half was exported from Swansea, Port Talbot, Cardiff and the specially built docks at Barry.

Since World War I, output has steadily declined, partly because of the exhaustion of the more accessible seams, mainly because of the increasing use of other kinds of energy by former customers; anthracite is no longer used as smokeless fuel for warships, for baking or in central heating. Unemployment mounted as the collieries steadily closed, reaching a climax during the depression of the 1930s, and output is now less than 20 million tons annually, though since 1945 some collieries have been modernised, a few new ones developed by the National Coal Board, and some large-scale open-cast mining is used. The mining force shrank from 100,000 in 1957 to 53,000 in 1968. Several power-stations on the coast use small coal for heat-raising, and one development is the manufacture of smokeless fuels to meet modern regulations in smokeless zones, the by-products being used in the chemical industry. Large quantities of gas are put into the grid operated by the Gas Board.

Fire-clays from the Coal Measures are used to make refractory bricks, limestone is worked as a blast-furnace flux, and sandstones are quarried for building stone.

*Other Industries.* Four main categories may be distinguished. Imported non-ferrous ores are smelted, formerly by long-flame coals, now mainly by electricity. This is particularly important in the Swansea district and includes tin, zinc, and copper, more recently nickel, aluminium and titanium; ores once came from Cornwall, but now sources are world-wide.

The iron and steel industry originally developed on the northern coalfield, with small furnaces using clayband ores from the Coal Measures; activity was located in a string of towns from Pontypool to Hirwaun, notably Ebbw Vale and Merthyr Tydfil. As local ores were exhausted, the works closed down or changed to general engineering. Smelting and steel-making therefore moved nearer the coast to Newport, Cardiff and Port Talbot, using sea-borne ore and producing sheet steel in open-hearth furnaces. After the first world war this industry, like coal-mining, suffered severe decline, causing serious unemployment and many plants were shut down. But in 1935, as a measure to help south Wales, a large integrated plant was built at Ebbw Vale, using Jurassic ores from the East Midlands (see p. 183); its output was stimulated during World War II, and since then it has produced sheet steel, mainly for the car industry of the Midlands. After the war most of the remaining older plants were closed and replaced by two large units at Margam (east of Port Talbot) and at Llanwern (near Newport); the latter is one of the world's most highly automated plants. Thus most of the steel production is now concentrated in three plants, using local coke and imported ore.

The making of tinplate developed in the latter part of the nineteenth century with the increase of canning, and galvanizing became increasingly important. These activities have expanded as new outlets for coated sheet-steel have been found in the manufacture of refrigerators and washing machines, as well as vast increase in canned food and drinks. Nearly 1 million tons of tinplate is produced annually, of which a large part is exported.

Since 1950 south Wales has made great efforts as a Development Area to diversify activity in order to reduce dependence on the basic industries. New factories have been installed, many in new estates as at Trefforest and Hirwaun, and located both near the coast and in the northern valleys; special mention may be made of the production of nylon yarn at Pontypool. A B.P. oil-refinery at Llandarcy (near Swansea) is linked with the rapidly expanding tanker terminal at Milford Haven by a sixty-mile pipe-line, and on the shores of the Haven itself are two other refineries and the terminal facilities are being enlarged. Thus although unemployment in south Wales is still above the national average, there is no longer the black despair of the early 1930s.

*Settlements.* The pattern of settlement in south Wales is the result of the relief and of the development of industry. The northern margins of the basin, and the interfluves between the narrow valleys, are bleak moorlands used mainly for grazing sheep. Between them long 'ribbons' of almost continuous settlement line the valleys, with concentrations at Aberdare, Mountain Ash, Merthyr Tydfil, Rhondda and Pontypridd; Rhymney, Trede-gar, Ebbw Vale, Abertillery; and Pontypool. Cwmbran is a deliberately planned 'new town' south of Pontypool. Efforts are made to clear a legacy of the nineteenth century: housing of slum-like character, unused factories and unsightly spoil-dumps, though the latter are so enormous that the task is well-nigh impossible. In all, about 1·5 million people live in this urban-industrial complex.

The three main towns are Cardiff, Swansea and Newport, located where major river valleys crossing the coalfield reach the coast of the Bristol Channel. Cardiff (256,000), the administrative 'capital' of Wales, with its attractively laid-out civic centre, has numerous industries. Swansea (166,000) is the centre of the western basin and of the varied metallurgical and engineering district. Newport lies on the eastern coal basin, at the mouth of the Usk. South Wales has been helped by the completion of the 'Ross Spur', a section of motorway which links with the M5 to the Midlands, and also by the recent opening of a road-bridge across the Severn near Bristol.

## SCOTLAND

Scotland consists of three distinct regions. Across the centre lies an area of lowlands, hills and valleys; structurally it is a rift-valley, trending from north-east to south-west between two major fault-lines. In the north the Highland Boundary Fault can be traced from Stonehaven on the east coast, fifteen miles south of Aberdeen, to Helensburgh on the Firth of Clyde; north of this are the Highlands of Scotland. In many parts a distinct south-facing fault-line scarp results from the removal of less resistant rocks flooring the rift-valley, but its continuity is interrupted by the valley of the Tay (Strath Earn) and by the basin in which lies Loch Lomond. The southern boundary runs from Dunbar in the north-east to Girvan on the Ayrshire coast; though clearly defined on a geological map, this fault-line scarp is less obvious on the ground, for the land rises gradually into the Southern Uplands, except in the north-east where the Lammermuir Hills reach 1,733 ft in a prominent north-facing escarpment.

**The Midland Valley.** Though generally known by this name, it is in some sense misleading, since several valleys are separated by hill-masses, and there is little continuously flat land. Two main formations were deposited, surviving on the floor of the rift-valley: the grits and conglomerates of the old red sandstone; the sandstones, shales, limestones and coal seams of the Coal Measures. These rocks were folded into a complex synclinorium, though denudation has removed the higher undulations, leaving basins in which survive three main coalfields: the Ayrshire field along the west coast, the large Lanark-Clackmannan field in the centre, and the Fife-Midlothian field across the Firth of Forth. Further complications have resulted from later faulting, one result being the breaking up of coal seams, and from vulcanicity, responsible for many dykes, sills and plugs. Edinburgh Castle is built on a worn-down plug, and the nearby Salisbury Crags consist of a sill. A series of upstanding hill-masses of igneous rock lies along the northern edge of the Valley: the Renfrew,

Kilpatrick, Lennox, Ochil (2,363 ft) and Sidlaw Hills; on the south are the Pentlands. The northern line is separated from the Highway escarpment by a 'corridor' floored with old red sandstone, prominently defined in the east as Strathmore.

The Quaternary glaciation widened the valleys, scraped bare prominent masses of rock, and deposited sheets of boulder-clay, drumlins, outwash sands and gravel kames. The Clyde, rising far to the south-east in the Southern Uplands, flows north-west-wards into its long estuary, while the Forth, a misfit river far too small for its broad valley, wanders in a series of sweeping mean-ders across its floodplain into its firth, a re-entrant penetrating far into the Midland valley. Indeed, the two firths are only twenty-five miles apart between Glasgow and Grangemouth, the narrowest part of Britain. From the Grampians in the north-west flows the Tay, entering its firth between the Ochils and Sidlaws.

*Agriculture.* In spite of the narrowness of the Midland valley, climatic differences are quite pronounced, particularly as the hills induce distinct local effects. The west has mild winters and early springs, with over 40 in of precipitation, and a rather cloudy summer. The east has colder winters, often with bleak north-easterly winds, but it is appreciably drier (25 to 30 in of precipi-tation) and sunnier, especially where the sheltering effect of the hills is felt, as in Strathmore and the Carse of Gowrie on either side of the Sidlaws.

The hills are covered with moorlands and rough grazing, sup-porting sheep, with store cattle on their lower slopes. In the west, along the Ayrshire coast, the damp heavy clay-lands are under permanent pasture, with some rotation grass, oats and roots, supporting Ayrshires and other dairy breeds. Parts of the lower Clyde valley are market-gardening districts, with extensive glass-houses, to supply Glasgow.

The eastern part of the valley concentrates on arable farming: barley for the breweries and distilleries, oats (especially in Strath-more), potatoes and sugar beet (in the Fife lowlands), even some wheat. But much land is devoted to fodder crops for fattening beef cattle, especially the Aberdeen Angus breed. In favoured locations specialised cultivation flourishes, such as raspberries and other fruit in the sheltered Carse of Gowrie.

*The Coalfields.* Before the first world war, over 40 million tons of coal were produced annually, most from the Lanark field, utilised not only by the rapidly expanding heavy industries, but also for export (especially from the Ayrshire field). But as in other British fields, output has dropped markedly to little more than a quarter of its peak partly because of the decline in demand, partly because the more accessible seams are approaching exhaustion. The best are now in the eastern fields, but they occur at much greater depths than in Lanark; here most modern collieries are developed, as near the 'new town' of Glenrothes.

*Heavy Industry.* In the nineteenth century iron-ore was obtained from blackband deposits in the Coal Measures, and an iron and steel industry developed, concentrated on Clydeside; steel was made to supply shipbuilding and the making of machinery, bridges, locomotives and cranes. Most blast furnaces have now closed, and the steel industry uses scrap and imported pig-iron. A line of contiguous towns dependent on shipbuilding and marine engineering grew up on Clydeside below Glasgow: Clydebank, Bowling and Dumbarton on the north; Port Glasgow, Greenock and Gourock along the southern banks of the Clyde. The first successful steamship (the *Comet*) was launched in 1812, and since then the yards have built about a third of all British tonnage, including most of the larger liners. Unfortunately, shipbuilding is particularly susceptible to world depression and fluctuations in demand and to the competition of Japan, Sweden and West Germany; Clydeside's dependence on the state of its order books is dangerously vulnerable. The depression of the 1930s was alleviated by the building of the *Queen Mary* and the *Queen Elizabeth,* and then by the immense wartime construction. But in the post-war years rationalisation had been forced on the industry; many yards have been closed, others modernised, and the tonnage launched is much less than in its heyday. Other forms of heavy industry have adapted themselves to changed conditions; thus at Falkirk and Grangemouth the making of iron castings has developed into the production of solid-fuel stoves and ovens.

*Other Industries.* Textile manufacturing at first was based on local wool, plentiful water for power and processing, and coal for steam-raising. But competition, both from the Tweed valley (see pp. 212–13) and Yorkshire (see p. 172) has virtually eliminated the woollen industry, except for the making of carpets at Kilmarnock. The expansion of the port of Glasgow and its growing trade relations with North America helped the cotton industry, but this also has declined, leaving only the manufacture of sewing thread at Paisley and of high-quality shirtings in Glasgow. Linen has long been made at Dunfermline, though this has suffered from competition with synthetic fibres. Dundee also made linen, but turned to the processing of jute (imported from Calcutta) when supplies of Russian flax were interrupted during the Crimean War.

The city once had a near world-monopoly of sack-making, which is still important, though competition from new factories in the jute-growing countries has caused some decline. Perth is a centre of dyeing and bleaching, utilising the soft waters of the Tay; Kircaldy makes linoleum.

Heavy chemicals are made on the Lanarkshire coalfield from coal by-products. More recently petrochemicals have developed near the B.P. oil-refinery at Grangemouth, on the southern shores of the Firth of Forth. Crude oil was formerly discharged from small tankers which could negotiate the shallow Firth, but as their draught increased it was necessary to construct a deep-water terminal at Finart on Loch Long and pipe the oil across Scotland's narrow 'waist'. Oil-shale was worked in West Lothian, but production ceased in 1962. At Burntisland on the northern shores of the Forth bauxite is converted into alumina, using Fifeshire coal, which is sent by rail to the aluminium refineries at Fort William and Kinlochleven (see p. 217).

An important group of activities involves food-processing. Both Glasgow and Leith (the port for Edinburgh) have flour mills, biscuit factories and sugar refineries; Glasgow processes tobacco; and Dundee is known for its confectionery ('Dundee cake') and chocolate. Brewing and distilling are widespread, with concentrations at Edinburgh, Glasgow and Dundee. The manufacture of jams and preserves developed in Dundee from soft fruit grown in the Carse of Gowrie, though much fruit (including marmalade oranges) is now imported. Cupar in Fife has a large refinery for processing sugar beet.

Other long-established activities include those associated with Edinburgh's position as an administrative, cultural and educational centre: paper-making (using imported pulp and esparto grass), printing and publishing, and the manufacture of scientific instruments.

Though this account indicates a variety of widely dispersed activity, certain areas, notably the Glasgow conurbation, have remained heavily dependent on such staples as coal-mining, heavy steel and shipbuilding, and have suffered serious unemployment during periods of economic depression. Before World War II an estate for light industry was developed at Hillington outside Glasgow, and since the war Scotland has become a Development Area, seeking to attract an increasing diversity of light industry. Factories have been established in the 'new towns' of East Kilbride and Cumbernauld near Glasgow, Livingston in West Lothian, and Glenrothes in Fifeshire.

*Tourism* attracts many people, though this is rather a transit region to the Highlands. Edinburgh, with its attractive setting and buildings, its historic interest and its annual 'Festival', is a popular venue. Many parts of the coast have resorts, both in the west (Troon and Prestwick) and in the east (St Andrews and Carnoustie), famed for their golf courses. The waters of the Firth of Clyde are renowned among yachtsmen.

*Settlement.* The Clydeside conurbation contains over 1·8 million people, dominated by *Glasgow,* which now faces many problems of 'overspill', slum clearance and urban renewal. It was sited at the lowest bridge-point of the Clyde, and has become the sixth port in Britain by value of trade, though constant dredging is necessary to maintain a navigable channel. The city has merged with its neighbouring towns: Paisley, Hamilton, Motherwell, Coatbridge, Airdrie and others along the estuary, sharing in its industrial activities.

Edinburgh (468,000), in the Lothian plain, is now contiguous with its port of Leith, five miles away, on the Firth of Forth, which is spanned by a rail-bridge and a new road-bridge. Its nucleus is the castle, around which is the old city, which developed as the administrative 'capital' of Scotland.

Dundee (183,000), the fourth largest Scottish city, is on the northern shores of the Firth of Tay, linked to the south with a rail-bridge and a new road-bridge. Perth (41,000), at the head of navigation of the Tay, and Stirling (27,000), the original lowest bridge-point of the Forth in the gap between the Lennox and Ochil Hills, are centres of road and rail communication.

**The Southern Uplands.** Undulating plateaus extend from the southern fault-line to the English border, where they merge into the Cheviots. They consist mainly of Ordovician and Silurian shales, slates and grits, which underwent acute folding during the Caledonian orogeny, creating ranges with a north-east to south-west trend; several masses of igneous rocks were intruded, especially in the west. The ancient folded mountains have suffered long-sustained denudation, though they were later uplifted, and the net result is an extensive plateau with distinguishable surface levels at 1,500 to 2,000 ft and again at 500 to 1,500 ft. In the centre lie the convex surfaces of the Tweedsmuir Hills, made of resistant grits, culminating in Broad Law (2,754 ft) and Hart Fell (2,651 ft), strewn with angular rock debris. The highest and most rugged summit, however, is to the west, Merrick (2,764 ft), a ridge-like exposure of a granite intrusion, where glaciation has produced deep, U-shaped valleys, and cirques bounded by arêtes. Smaller masses of granite in the south-west stand out prominently, notably Cairnsmore of Fleet (2,331 ft) and the rounded hump of Criffel (1,866 ft) near the shores of the Solway Firth.

Rivers have cut deep valleys in the Uplands, creating a pattern of almost radial drainage, except in the south-centre where the Cheviots form a divide between the English and Scottish streams. On the south the 'dales' contain rivers flowing to the Solway across an undulating lowland (known in the west as Galloway): the Esk, Annan, Nith and Dee. On the north the Clyde follows a lengthy north-westerly course to its firth, while on the east the Tweed and its sheaf of near-parallel tributaries occupy a valley known in its lower, broader section as the Merse (of Berwick).

*The Coast.* In the east the Palæozoic rocks reach the sea at St Abb's Head, forming fine cliffs, though south of this the lowlands of the Merse continue into Northumberland. In the west a rise of sea-level has converted the lower valleys into tidal estuaries, with sandbanks and mud flats at low tide. The low ridge of the Rhinns of Galloway, in the extreme south-west, forms a hammer-headed promontory, with the broad Luce Bay and the narrower Loch Ryan on either side.

*Agriculture.* The Southern Uplands have a thin stony soil, though on the whole well drained, so that in the drier east (with about 30 in of precipitation) are ling and heather moors with vast expanses of coarse grass. In the more humid west (over 60 in of precipitation) rather bleak 'wet moorland' covers the slopes, with coarse grass, sedge, cotton-grass and bracken on lower areas, and sphagnum peat bogs in shallow depressions. Several extensive coniferous forests have been planted by the Forestry Commission.

The main use of the Uplands is grazing sheep – the Cheviot breed mainly for wool in the east, the Blackface primarily for mutton in the west. On the lower slopes black Galloway cattle are reared as stores to be moved away for fattening.

On the coastal and valley lowlands mixed farming is practised, with an emphasis on dairying in the west (the home of the Ayrshire breed of cattle), and on the production of fat stock (both cattle and sheep) in the east. Along the fertile Solway and west coast lowlands most farmland is under rich pasture and fodder crops; in the east are barley (for malting), oats and turnips, with some rotational grassland.

*Industry and Towns.* The towns in the valley of the Tweed, utilising advantages of local wool, soft water for scouring and dyeing, and fast-flowing streams for power, have manufactured woollen cloth for centuries. This was first a domestic industry, then it became concentrated in domestic workshops in such 'burghs' as Galashiels, Peebles, Selkirk, Melrose and Jedburgh, and is now carried on in small factories. In spite of the rapid competitive growth of the woollen industry in the West Riding during the Industrial Revolution (see p. 172), it has survived, even flourished, mainly by concentrating on high-quality tweeds, knitwear and hosiery. But it is a sign of the times that a rayon factory has opened in Jedburgh.

Most towns in the west are market-centres, strung out along the railway from Carlisle via Dumfries to Stranraer; the last is a rail terminus on Loch Ryan for the steamer route to Larne in Northern Ireland, and the coastal towns are resorts. Dumfries (27,000) is the regional centre of the south-west coast, situated at the lowest bridge-point of the Nith. It is an important market-centre, with old, established knitwear and hosiery industries, and with factories processing agricultural products. Several small hydro-plants operate in the west, and at Chapelcross near Annan is a nuclear power-station.

*Communications.* The Great North Road, the historic military route to Edinburgh, and the railway from Newcastle for the most part follow the east coast. The valleys extending into the Uplands form routeways for both road and rail between Carlisle, the 'border city', and Glasgow and Edinburgh. On the 'Caledonian' route between Carlisle and Glasgow, which uses the Annan and Clyde valleys, the railway crosses Beattock Summit at 1,014 ft, closely paralleled by a main trunk-road recently made double carriage-way, for it carries an enormous number of trucks.

**The Highlands and Islands of Scotland.** Beyond the northern edge of the Midland valley lie extensive mountains, plateaus and deep valleys, fringed on the north-west and north by islands. In the far north-west and in the Outer Hebrides the rocks are mainly pre-Cambrian gneiss, schist and Torridonian sandstone, the last including sandstones and felspathic grits. Father south the rocks are extremely varied, comprising metamorphosed sedimentaries of early Palæozoic age – mostly schist, quartzite and sandstone. In addition, intrusive masses of granite (mainly of Devonian age) form such mountains as Ben Nevis (though this has an inner 'core' of andesite), the Cairngorms and Lochnagar; these intrusions have greatly affected their surroundings by thermal metamorphism. Granite also reaches the coast near Aberdeen, in Buchan.

During Ordovician-Silurian times the Caledonian orogeny (see (Fig. 2, p. 5) upfolded ranges trending from north-east to south-west across western Scandinavia, Scotland and northern Ireland. The earth movements were so acute in north-western Scotland that wedges of Cambrian quartzites · and limestones were fractured and overthrust in slices (*imbricated structure*) between at least four major thrust-planes. This faulting has given a 'grain' to the country, which can be seen not only on the geological map, where different slices of rock appear, but on the pattern of valleys (*glens* and *straths*) eroded along the lines of weaker strata, some containing lakes, and of fjord-like openings along the west coast; both lakes and sea-inlets are known as *lochs*.

The major structural line of the Great Glen (a tear-fault, in which the rocks have been displaced horizontally as well as vertically) can be traced from the Moray Firth in the north-east to Loch Linnhe in the south-west, marked by a line of deep lochs, the best-known of which is Loch Ness; these are linked by the Caledonian Canal, though this is little used except by trawlers. This 'trench' separates the Highlands into two main parts: the Grampians and the North-western Highlands. Another more extensive area of down-faulting separated the Outer Hebrides from the Inner Hebrides and the mainland, forming the straits known as the Minch.

The Caledonian ranges have been subject to long-sustained denudation, interrupted by later faulting and uplift, so that they are now merely the worn-down remnants, a deeply dissected plateau with an average height of about 2,000 ft, interrupted on the one hand by valleys, on the other by residual masses forming the higher peaks. Two areas, Ben Nevis and the Cairngorms, exceed 4,000 ft, the former (4,406 ft) being the highest mountain in Britain; these groups are the surviving fragments of a formerly continuous plateau surface at 4,000 ft, and the Cairngorms have over 200 square miles at over 2,000 ft. More than 300 Scottish peaks exceed 3,000 ft. By contrast, the lower parts of the plateau form basins or 'sags', such as the Moor of Rannoch south-west of the Nevis massif; it is covered by a blanket-bog, through which project bosses of granite.

During mid-Tertiary times a period of igneous activity occurred, particularly in the Inner Hebrides. Much of these islands consist of the fragments of lava flows, forming step-like plateaus ending in sea cliffs; in Fingal's Cave on the Isle of Staffa, the lava has solidified in striking hexagonal columns, similar to those of the Giant's Causeway (see p. 220). The islands also include masses of granite and gabbro; in the Isle of Skye these form the Red and Black Cuillins respectively, and the main peaks of Rum are also of gabbro. The highest part of Arran, in the Firth of Clyde, consists of a much dissected intrusive mass of granite.

The Quaternary glaciation had a profound effect on the landscape, since this part of Britain was affected longest and most intensely. In many parts of the Outer Hebrides (especially Lewis), the surface consists of gently undulating, ice-worn bare rock, with 'whale-backs' alternating with water- or peat-filled hollows. Among the mountains of the mainland, many cirques (in Gaelic *coires*) were formed with high steep backwalls, notably in the Nevis and Cairngorm groups. The glaciers etched out shatter-belts of the faults, the preglacial valleys and other lines of weakness, eroding the U-shaped valleys now forming the glens and straths, many containing deep narrow lochs.

The drainage systems are complex, the results of superimposition, glacial diversion and breaching of watersheds, and capture. The longer rivers are in the east: the Tay, which drains much of the south-eastern Grampians, and the Dee and the Spey, their headstreams rising near each other in the Cairngorms.

The most extensive lowlands are along the east coast, largely made of old red sandstone covered with boulder-clay. Here, in contrast with the west, the coast is straight and unindented, except for estuaries which form the Moray, Cromarty and Dornoch Firths.

To the north of the mainland are two main groups of islands. The *Orkneys,* beyond the seven-mile-wide Pentland Firth, are composed mainly of sandstones and limestones of the old red sandstone formation, fragmented into more than a hundred islands, the southern ones around Scapa Flow (which was a naval anchorage). Most are low lying and gently sloping, though hills rise in Hoy to 1,565 ft, with some fine cliffs and stacks. A few intrusive sills of igneous rock add variety to the landscape. By contrast, the *Shetlands,* seventy miles north of the Orkneys, are formed of very varied rocks, with a low, undulating, ice-scraped surface, though one hill reaches 1,475 ft. Both groups owe their fragmented and indented outlines to a rise of sea-level over formerly irregular surfaces.

*Climate and Vegetation.* Precipitation is heavy, especially on the mountains in the west, where mean annual totals of 80 to 120 in or more are common, much in the form of snow. By contrast, the eastern lowlands, lying in the rainshadow, have 30 in or less; Nairn on the Moray Firth has only 25 in, Inverness 27 in. The west coast has mild winters, the result of oceanic influences, and frost and a snow-cover are rare at sea-level, though farther inland and with increasing altitude conditions become more extreme; snow lies on the higher peaks and in north-facing cirques for almost half the year. The east coast has mean winter temperatures some 4° F (2.2° C) lower than the west.

Soils are usually thin, developed on ancient rocks, or consist of boulder-clay, and great areas are covered with heather and coarse grass. Probably forest was once much more widespread, though it must be appreciated that in Scotland *forest* is often applied to an area of moorland, now mainly used for shooting, such as the Mamore Forest. Even so, there is evidence that a thousand years ago a large area was covered with the ancient 'Caledonian Forest', especially in the sheltered glens and straths, which was destroyed by ruthless felling for timber and charcoal. In recent years the Forestry Commission has established plantations of spruce and pine, especially south and south-west of the Great Glen.

*Agriculture.* The poor soils, steep rocky slopes, cloudiness and strong winds are unfavourable factors for farming, but at one time subsistence agriculture, based on keeping sheep and cattle and growing patches of potatoes, hay and oats, was widespread. This is shown by the many abandoned cottages, and by the numerous *head-dykes,* dry-stone walls separating upper hill-pasture from the lower arable and meadow-land, but now with no sign of farming activity. The holdings are known as *crofts,* the people as *crofters.* A croft consists of a patch of cultivated land, with grazing rights over a large area of moorland. But the number of crofters has steadily diminished, as they moved away to the industrial towns of the Midland valley or emigrated. Even now many young people leave the Highlands because of inadequate opportunity for employment. Those who remain usually have supplementary work as fishermen, gamekeepers or in public works schemes, or go away periodically as seamen. Hill-cattle and sheep are still reared, some on large 'ranches' (such as the Great Glen Cattle Ranch near Fort William), but many sheep runs have been turned into 'deer forests' or 'grouse moors'. Cattle and sheep reared in the north-west are usually brought to market at Inverness.

The most favourable lands are on the east coast plain, where the drift-cover affords good soils, and precipitation is 30 in or less. Oats, turnips and barley are grown, and beef cattle, notably the fine Aberdeen Angus breed, are kept. In the Orkney Islands there is some emphasis on dairying and poultry farming.

*Fishing.* This has long been a supplementary occupation to crofting, especially in the Outer Hebrides and the Shetlands, though increasingly it has been concentrated on a commercial basis in the larger centres: Aberdeen, Peterhead, Fraserburgh, Inverness and Wick on the east coast; Mallaig on the west; Thurso on the north; and Stornoway in the Outer Hebrides. Lerwick in the Shetlands was once a great centre of herring fishing, but this has greatly declined, largely because the fish do not come to nearby waters in such shoals as formerly. Herring are caught in the North Sea, and cod, hake and halibut between the mainland and the Faeroes.

*Industry and Towns.* Industry is of a limited, localised and specialised character, though stimulated by the Highlands and Islands Development Board. The hand-weaving of woollen cloth is concentrated in the island of Lewis, where it is highly organised under a co-operative system; wool is spun by machines in small mills in Stornoway, the yarn is distributed to the crofts for dyeing and hand-weaving, and the cloth is returned to the mills for finishing. It can be bought at tourist shops in Fort William and elsewhere, though a considerable amount, made into clothing and bearing the 'genuine Harris Tweed' emblem, is exported.

The heavy precipitation, large lakes and reservoir sites offer possibilities for the production of hydro-electricity, in places realised by the North of Scotland Electricity Board. About thirty power-schemes have been completed, as at Lochs Tummel, Rannoch and Sloy, linked by the 'Highland Grid'. On the north coast, near Thurso, is the Dounreay nuclear power-station, which also puts power into the Grid. At Kinlochleven and Fort William, hydro-electricity is used to refine alumina brought from Burntisland (see p. 210). Another industry recently introduced includes a large pulp and paper mill at Fort William, using timber from the State Forests. Mention must be made of Scotch whisky, of which about 120 million gallons a year are made, using the peat water which gives the many brands much of their identity. While there are numerous small distilleries (as at Fort William), the bulk of the whisky comes from large units in Inverness, as well as in Edinburgh and Glasgow.

Several towns in the east have varied industries, notably Aberdeen (185,000), the third largest city in Scotland, with marine and electrical engineering; the manufacture of woollen and linen textiles, chemicals and paper; and fish-processing. Granite is still quarried nearby, though to a lesser extent than in the past.

*Tourism.* For long the Highlands were remote, and communications were limited to a few tracks and military roads. In the latter part of the nineteenth century, some picturesque railroads were made, which penetrated the mountains to reach the west coast at Oban, Fort William, Mallaig and Kyle of Lochalsh, and the east coast at Inverness. The deer forests, grouse moors and salmon streams attracted wealthy visitors, as did the royal influence at Balmoral; luxury hotels were built and the various 'Highland Games' became ever more elaborate. But the main attraction remains the scenery, made more accessible by new roads and the increased number of cars. Motor-coach tours linking the main centres have developed enormously, bringing steady employment to hotels during the summer months. Resorts, many with golf courses, have developed, with hotels and shops selling tweeds and tartans: Oban, Fort William and Ullapool in the west; Inverness, Braemar and Blair Atholl in the east. A recent development has been winter sports in Glencoe and especially in the Cairngorms; the new Aviemore Centre has luxury hotels, chalets, ice rinks, artificial ski slopes to supplement the natural ones, ski lifts and access roads. But even so, much of the Highlands remains an area of lonely mountain and sweeping moorland, of rushing streams and deep lochs, of scanty and declining population.

## NORTHERN IRELAND

Northern Ireland, sometimes referred to as Ulster (although the ancient province with this name occupied a much larger area) consists of the counties of Antrim, Londonderry, Tyrone, Fermanagh, Armagh and Down, together with the County Boroughs of Belfast and Londonderry. It was constituted in 1920 (see p. 159 and Fig. 29).

*Relief.* The structure is broadly continuous with that of Scotland, though separated by the fifteen-mile-wide North Channel. The Highlands of Scotland are represented in Northern Ireland by the much lower Sperrin Mountains, rising to 2,240 feet; the Highland Boundary Fault can be traced along their southern edge. These are worn-down dissected stumps of older Palæozoic rocks, and for the most part are covered with thin acid soils and moorland vegetation.

In the south, in Down and Armagh, are several groups of uplands of Ordovician and Silurian rocks, the continuation of the Southern Uplands. They too are appreciably lower than in Scotland, only attaining 500 ft in a few places, much covered with undulating sheets of boulder-clay and swarms of drumlins. The

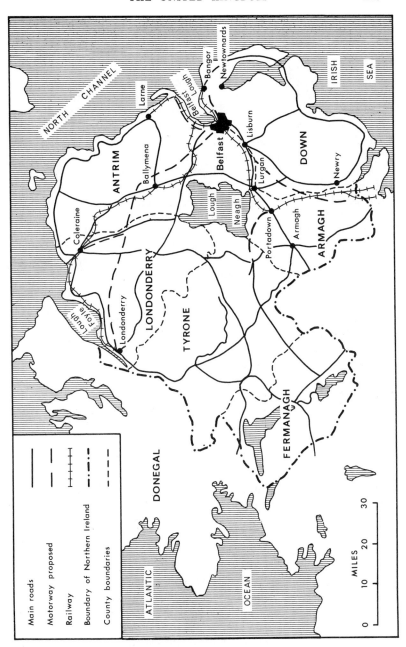

Fig. 29. NORTHERN IRELAND

highest group is the Mourne Mountains, rising to 2,796 ft near the Irish Sea; they are formed of an intrusive mass of granite, with rounded surfaces between the deeply cut cirques and the radiating valleys.

Between these uplands is the continuation of the Midland Valley of Scotland, underlain by old red sandstone and Carboniferous limestone, and in places covered with a layer of chalk. Except in the south-west, however, these rocks are rarely visible, for fissure eruptions in Tertiary times extruded sheets of basaltic lava over some 1,500 square miles. The basalt forms a plateau which has 'sagged' in the centre, within which lies shallow Lough Neagh (*lough* is the Irish name for lake), the largest lake in the United Kingdom. The surrounding lowlands are irregularly mantled with boulder-clay and alluvium; they drain into the lough, thence by the river Bann into the sea. By contrast, the basalt in the north-east rises to form the plateau of Antrim, with a prominent rim, interrupted by deep, steep-sided glens, along the coast; its highest point is 1,817 ft. Along the north coast the uniform surface of the basalt ends abruptly in the columnar cliffs of the Giant's Causeway; in places the underlying chalk strata, baked by thermal contact of the molten basalt, can be seen in the cliff faces and exposed in the sides of valleys.

A prominent feature is the presence of several wide estuaries: Lough Foyle in the north, Belfast and Strangford loughs in the east, Carlingford Lough in the south-east. These were formed by the post-glacial rise of sea-level and are generally shallow; the numerous oval islands in Strangford Lough are partially submerged drumlins.

*Agriculture.* This north-eastern corner of Ireland is to some extent a rainshadow area. It shares with much of western Britain the characteristic pattern of mild winters (44° F (6·7° C) January mean) and cool summers (58° F (14·4° C) July mean); precipitation, except on the higher uplands, is generally less than 40 in.

The hills are bleak and covered with moorland and rough pasture, used for grazing sheep, although considerable areas are now under coniferous plantations. The lowlands around Lough Neagh and extending towards Strangford Lough have generally good soils derived from boulder-clay, outwash deposits, and the underlying basalt, sandstone and limestone. The lowlands around Lough Foyle are floored with fertile red marls.

A prosperous mixed farming has developed, based on growing barley, oats, potatoes and turnips and on both permanent and temporary pasture of high quality. Dairy cattle are numerous, especially in the Lagan and Bann valleys; beef cattle and pigs are fattened for export to English markets, and poultry are reared. Market-gardening is active around the larger towns and soft-fruit cultivation on the southern shores of Lough Neagh.

*Industry.* Northern Ireland has had its traditional industries for a considerable time, though they have become concentrated in Belfast and to a lesser extent in Londonderry. The manufacture of linen was established here before the eighteenth century as a cottage industry based on locally grown flax and using the abundant supplies of water for retting and power. As the Industrial Revolution proceeded, linen manufacture became a factory industry; the machines were powered by steam raised with coal from Scotland and West Cumberland, and an increasing amount of flax was imported from Belgium and the Baltic ports. Most mills are now in Belfast, with a few in Lisburn, Portadown, Cookstown, Ballymena and Londonderry. But linen textiles have suffered decline in competition with cotton and nylon, though recently a determined advertising campaign ('real Irish linen'), together with rationalisation of production of quality goods in modern mills, has caused some revival in fine handkerchiefs, tablecloths, sheets, pillow cases and clothing, and high-quality shirtings are made at Londonderry. Many long-established firms have introduced cotton and nylon as a diversification. Another old activity is the making of rope and cordage at Belfast.

The second major industry is shipbuilding and marine engineering, mainly in the yards at the head of Belfast Lough. Unlike Clydeside or Tyneside, Belfast has no adjacent steelworks, but coal and steel can be readily imported from Scotland and northwestern England; liners, cargo ships, warships and tankers have all been built. But, as elsewhere, the competition of Japan, Sweden and West Germany has been seriously felt, and some yards have been closed, the remainder concentrating on the building of tankers.

A third group of activities comprises the processing of agricultural products; these include bacon-curing, brewing and distilling, the preparation of milk products and vegetable canning.

Since the second world war, Northern Ireland has experienced considerable depression in its industries and a rise in unemployment appreciably above the national average. It is scheduled as a Special Development Area, and as a result a considerable diversification of activity has taken place, utilising available sites and labour supplies and helped by government stimulation such as low rentals, de-rating and training grants; several industrial estates have been developed near Belfast and Londonderry (Maydown). These activities include aero-engineering and electrical engineering; electronics; the making of furniture, precision instruments, machine tools, record changers, vacuum cleaners and pharmaceutical chemicals. Tobacco-processing is a large employer of labour; two large factories are in Belfast, and another was recently opened at Lisnafillan near Ballymena.

*Tourism* has been promoted by the Northern Ireland Tourist Board, and many people travel by air or via the Stranraer-Larne or Liverpool or Heysham – Belfast steamers. The pleasant countryside, the mountains of Mourne and the picturesque coast are the main attractions.

*Settlements.* Small market-towns are fairly evenly spaced over the countryside; some also have factories for processing and packing agricultural products, and a few have branches of linen and clothing firms and some new light industries.

*Belfast* (416,000), the administrative capital and chief industrial centre, is situated at the head of the sheltered north-east-facing Lough. Its port is equipped with warehouses and cold stores for the bulk-handling of produce, including live animals, and manufactured goods, and for the import of raw materials, coal and oil. *Londonderry* (54,000), at the head of Lough Foyle, is much less important because of its peripheral location near the border with the Republic of Ireland and its limited hinterland.

## ECONOMIC SUMMARY

In 1966 the estimated population of the United Kingdom was 54·7 millions, of whom 45·4 lived in England; the average density per square mile for the UK as a whole was 589, though for England alone it was nearly 900, exceeded only by the Netherlands. Since the Industrial Revolution (see p. 152) the UK has been mainly a manufacturing and commercial country, unable to be self-sufficient in foodstuffs, despite some recent improvement, and very dependent on overseas sources of raw materials.

Of the total area of some 57 million acres, about 17 millions are classified as arable, the same amount as rough grazing, and 11 millions under permanent pasture. On the whole, British agriculture is intensive, mechanised and scientific, with high yields per acre and producing high-quality livestock. With the exception of a few areas, notably East Anglia and the Fenland, where there are some large arable units, farming is primarily mixed. The main cereal crop (by acreage) is barley, followed by wheat and oats; fodder crops and hay are grown widely to supplement the permanent grassland, and large areas are devoted to potatoes and sugar beet. Though horticulture occupies less than 2·5 per cent of the farmed area, it accounts for one-third of the value of all crops, an indication of its intensity. In favoured areas, such as Kent, the Vale of Evesham, Herefordshire and Fenland, fruit is grown. There is a considerable emphasis on dairy cattle (some 12 million head) to supply the dense urban-industrial population; the chief concentrations are in the Lancashire and Cheshire plain, Somerset and Devon, the West Midlands and south-western Scotland. While sheep are not as important as in the past, nearly 30 millions are kept, both within the mixed farming pattern and on marginal hill-pastures. The intensive rearing of calves and pigs in pens, and of poultry in batteries and broiler houses, has increased enormously in recent years. About 800,000 people are employed in agriculture, only some 3 per cent of the working population, but they enabled the UK in 1965–66 to produce about 70 per cent of its meat requirements, about 40 per cent of its wheat, bacon, ham and cheese, and to be virtually self-supporting in milk, eggs and potatoes. The chief food import is wheat, but even in this respect there has been considerable improvement, for output rose from 1·7 million tons per year in the years before 1939 to 4·1 millions in 1965; this is largely because of the breeding of strong-strawed, heavy-yielding varieties and the increased application of fertilisers. Though efforts have been made by the Forestry Commission to increase the area of woodland (this now covers about 6 per cent of the land surface, or 3·3 million acres), the UK is still obliged to import 90 per cent of its timber requirements.

The UK's position on a continental shelf and accessibility to distant grounds in North Atlantic and Arctic waters have stimulated the fishing industry, which employs 25,000 people and lands annually nearly 900,000 tons of fish, worth some 58 millions sterling. The main fishing ports are Hull, Grimsby, Aberdeen, Great Yarmouth and Lowestoft; many smaller ones are around the coast. Apart from the sale of fresh fish, the development of curing and quick-freezing and the production of meal for fertiliser and animal food are important. The industry supplies four-fifths of the country's requirements of fish.

In 1913 the UK's highest production of coal was reached: some 213 million tons. This was widely used as the basis of manufacturing industry, for domestic consumption, for fuelling locomotives and for bunkering ships; in some years as much as 90 million tons were exported. But the annual production has now dropped to 150 million tons, partly because of the competition of other forms of energy (especially oil, which accounted for only a fifth of the total energy consumed in 1958, but a third in 1966), and partly because of a big drop in exports, now only about 3 million tons annually. Mining was nationalised in 1947 under the National Coal Board, which has modernised some collieries and opened a few new ones, but it has been obliged to carry out a policy of closure of uneconomic mines, causing considerable unemployment; this has become a social and political, as well as an economic, issue. Some grades of coal are still required for making metallurgical coke, patent fuels, gas and chemicals, and for burning in thermal-electric generators; coal is now, in fact, much more efficiently used. Hydroelectricity, produced in the Highlands of Scotland and on a small scale in North Wales, contributes only 2 per cent of the total power. Fourteen nuclear stations are in production or under construction; in 1967 they were responsible for about 9 per cent of the UK's electricity, a proportion which will rise substantially. It is noteworthy that these stations have a larger output of nuclear-generated electricity than does the rest of the world combined.

The United Kingdom has virtually no deposits of petroleum, and imports some 70 million tons annually, mainly from Kuwait and Iraq; this dependence on the politically unstable Middle East is highly vulnerable. Since the closure of the Suez Canal in 1967, most oil has come round Africa, and the tanker-tonnage now forms a third of the UK's merchant marine. Twenty refineries, situated on or near tide-water, have a throughput greater than that of any other European country. Natural gas is imported in liquid form in tankers to a plant on Canvey Island in the Thames estuary, to be put into the Gas Board's grid system, together with refinery and coal gas. This situation may have been revolutionised by the discovery of gas fields under the floor of the North Sea; the initial work of development has been costly, but gas is now flowing ashore near the mouth of the Humber and on the East Anglian coast at Bacton; there may be a tremendous future.

The economic strength of the UK has been largely derived from two sources: its varied manufacturing capacity, and its volume of exports. For a long time, the main industrial areas have been on the coalfields, where fuel was available for steam-raising; these are the 'old' industrial regions, some of which developed specialisms of world renown. Because so much foodstuff and raw materials are imported, manufacturing has also developed at the ports, notably London, Liverpool, Glasgow and Bristol.

Some of the 'old' industrial regions suffered severe unemployment in the 1930s, because of world competition in their staple activities and the general economic recession. Though recovery was stimulated in many cases by the demands of the second world war, it has been necessary to help by designating them as 'Development Areas', where inducements are offered by the government and local authorities to attract new industry; much of Scotland, north-western England and Wales are so designated, with Special Development Areas (West Cumberland, Clydeside, South Wales, etc.) in parts most adversely affected. Moreover, as a complement there has been the active discouragement of new industry in south-eastern England and the Midlands. 'Trading estates' have been created, in which factories were built and leased to firms, especially in the 'new towns', of which more than twenty have been created to take the 'overspill' population from London and other cities. The UK's industrial production continues to rise at a rate of about 3 per cent per annum, and exports have likewise grown (though these proportions are not sufficiently high). About 58 per cent of the working population is engaged in the metallurgical and engineering industries (of which 10 per cent make cars and aircraft), 10 per cent in the chemical, glass and pottery industries, and 9 per cent in food-processing.

But the UK's economic position is far from sound, since the value of these exports, even with the addition of 'invisible' categories, has for several years been exceeded by the high and rising cost of imports, by large overseas' spending commitments (defence and foreign aid), by the necessary repayment of capital and interest on loans, and by the great rise in the cost of the social services. This adverse balance of payments situation has steadily worsened at a time of internal inflationary trends. In 1967 the weakness of sterling resulted in the devaluation of the pound, and the imposition of severe restrictions on spending in both the private and the government sector. The state has played an ever-increasing rôle in economic planning, and in the nationalisation of transport, industry and utilities. The general world political and economic situation has added to the gravity; it remains to be seen how effective the unpalatable measures of recovery prove to be.

## REFERENCES

The two standard and complementary works are L. D. Stamp and S. H. Beaver, *The British Isles,* London, Longmans, 1933, latest edition 1967; and J. B. Mitchell (ed.), *Great Britain: Geographical Essays,* London, Cambridge Univ. Press, 1962, revised 1967. See also L. D. Stamp, *Britain's Structure and Scenery,* London, Collins, 1946, revised 1967.

For a discussion by topics see J. Wreford Watson and J. B. Sissons (eds.), *The British Isles,* London and Edinburgh, Nelson, 1964; W. Smith, *An Economic Geography of Great Britain,* London, Methuen, 1949, revised 1953 and reprinted 1961, includes also historical background; L. D. Stamp, *The Land of Britain: Its Use and Misuse,* London, Longmans, 1948, 3rd ed. enlarged 1962, 2nd imp. 1963; R. H. Best and J. T. Coppock, *The Changing Use of Land in Britain,* London, Faber, 1962, 2nd imp. 1965; L. Symons (ed.), *Land Use in Northern Ireland,* Univ. of London Press, 1963; Emrys Jones, *A Social Geography of Belfast,* London, Oxford Univ. Press, 1960; E. G. Bowen (ed.), *Wales: A Physical, Historical and Regional Geography,* London, Methuen, 1957, reprinted with minor corrections 1965; J. T. Coppock and H. C. Prince (eds.), *Greater London,* London, Faber, 1964; J. E. Martin, *Greater London: An Industrial Geography,* London, Bell, 1966; E. Estyn Evans, *Irish Heritage,* Dundalk, Eire, Dundalgan Press, 1942.

See volumes in Regions of the British Isles series, London and Edinburgh, Nelson, edited by W. G. East, namely: *North England,* by A. E. Smailes, 1960, revised edition 1968; *The Highlands and Islands of Scotland,* by A. C. O'Dell and K. Walton, 1962, 2nd imp. 1963; *The East Midlands and the Peak,* by G. H. Dury, 1963; *Lancashire, Cheshire and the Isle of Man,* by T. W. Freeman, H. G. Rodgers and R. H. Kinvig, 1966; *Southwest England,* by A. H. Shorter, W. L. D. Ravenhill and K. J. Gregory, 1968.

### CHAPTER 11

# THE REPUBLIC OF IRELAND

FOR several centuries Ireland was an integral part of the United Kingdom and was represented in Parliament in London. In 1916 an insurrection (the 'Easter Rebellion') broke out in southern Ireland against British rule. After bitter hostilities, an Act was passed in 1920, establishing a separate parliament for the twenty-six predominantly Catholic counties of southern Ireland and another parliament for the six predominantly Protestant counties of northern Ireland. The 'Ulster Unionists' of the north accepted this, but the south refused. In 1921, however, a treaty was signed, by which the south became a Dominion known as *Saorstát Éireann* (Irish Free State) or *Éire*. The north chose to remain part of the United Kingdom (see p. 159). A boundary between the two was demarcated, and it has been the scene of countless incidents, mainly brought about by extremists who desire to re-unite the two parts of Ireland. In 1949 the Republic of Ireland (*Poblacht na h-Éireann*), as the south is now known, left the British Commonwealth.

Close commercial links have been maintained between the Republic and the United Kingdom. Both are members of ETFA and both have applied, so far to no effect, for membership in the European Economic Community (see Postscript, pp. 621–24). Much agricultural produce from the Republic is shipped to the United Kingdom, and a wide range of British manufactured goods is imported into the Republic of Ireland. Financial relationships are close, and currency is readily transferable and exchangeable. Large numbers of Irish work permanently or temporarily in the UK; no passports are needed in either direction. Officially, the Republic does not recognize the existence of Northern Ireland, and is pledged to attain the unity of all Ireland; in practise, there has been a growing acceptance of the situation, as evidenced by friendly visits of the Prime Ministers of the two divisions.

## THE MAJOR REGIONS

Ireland consists essentially of a low undulating plain, about 100 miles across from the Atlantic Ocean to the Irish Sea, with a

Fig. 30.  THE MAJOR REGIONS OF THE REPUBLIC OF IRELAND

number of upland masses around its margins (see Figure 30). These form a kind of rim to a central 'basin', though this is by no means continuous, and the lowlands reach the sea in many places, especially where rivers flow into wide estuaries or bays.

**The Central Plain.** This is underlain by a basement of Carboniferous limestone that is rarely visible on the surface, since it is mantled with an irregular cover of glacial drift. At its maximum the continental glaciation of Quaternary times overwhelmed the whole island; Irish Sea and Scottish ice merged with the ice which formed over the uplands. In the later stages the upland ice-masses formed separate small ice-caps, from which glaciers moved down, eroding numerous valleys. Widespread sheets of boulder-clay, diversified by lines of moraines and swarms of drumlins, were laid down on the lowlands, so producing a largely impermeable and irregular surface of hillocks and depressions. Further diversity results from the outwash sands and gravels, deposited sometimes in sheets, elsewhere in east-west lines of kame-moraines, commonly referred to as eskers (after their Irish name, *eiscir*). One such line can be traced across the country, from Dublin to Galway Bay, though cut through by the river Shannon near Athlone.

The boulder-clay cover is impermeable and liable to become water-logged; many irregularly-shaped lakes lie in the depressions, and are linked by wandering, indeterminate streams. Impeded drainage has resulted in extensive peat bogs, for the most part formed during the 'Atlantic' phase of climate — from about 6200 to 3000 B.C. — which was appreciably damper and warmer (by some 3° to 5° F) than at present. Under these conditions aquatic vegetation grew rapidly, accumulating as peat, sometimes so thickly as to form a 'blanket-bog'; one of the most extensive is the Bog of Allen.

To some extent the drainage may be described as radial, for rivers flow to the sea in many directions: the Boyne and the Liffey to the east; the Barrow, the Nore and the Suir southwards into Waterford Bay; and many small streams into the Atlantic. The master stream is the Shannon, 240 miles long, which rises far to the north-west. Before reaching its long estuary in the southwest, it widens to form a string of lakes (loughs Allen, Boderg, Forbes, Ree and Derg), which partly lie on the boulder-clay, partly in hollows created by solution of the underlying limestone.

*Agriculture.* Over much of the Central Basin the climate is mild with annual temperature extremes of 20° F (11° C) or less, and a mean annual precipitation of 40 to 60 in. The bogs are of little use for farming, and much of the rest of the area consists of ill-drained pasture, often remote of access.  Farms are therefore scattered and isolated, situated on morainic or gravel eminences, and concentrating on the rearing of beef cattle, formerly driven on foot all the way to Dublin, now more usually to the nearest road, by which they are taken in trucks.  Dairying is rarely practised, except for local consumption, because of transport difficulties, and arable farming is limited to small patches of potatoes and oats on higher and drier patches of land.

The most important farming areas are along the east coast, in the south-west near the Shannon estuary, and in the Golden Vale of Tipperary.  Near Dublin, store bullocks brought from central Ireland are fattened on the rich permanent pasture supplemented by fodder crops before shipment to the UK, and dairy cattle are reared.  The somewhat drier climate in the east enables cereals to be grown, notably barley to be made into malt for the breweries and distilleries, and even some wheat, together with potatoes and other vegetables, for the considerable urban population in and around Dublin.  Large numbers of race horses and hunters are bred and trained there.

The Limerick lowland, with its extension into the Golden Vale, has some of the characteristics of central Ireland, with boulder-clay, alluvium and peat bog, and a heavy precipitation which limits arable farming to potatoes and oats.  But here the pastures are rich, and the farms are much more accessible by road and rail to Cork, Limerick and Waterford than those in the centre.  Dairy cattle are kept in large numbers, their milk being taken by donkey-cart or, increasingly, by truck to the co-operative creameries.  The skimmed milk is returned to the farmers to feed pigs destined for the bacon factories.

*Industries.*  For the most part the Central Plain is of negligible importance, and industry is limited to the eastern and western margins; but it does afford two sources of energy: peat and hydro-electricity.  Peat has been laboriously hand-cut for centuries; the peat blocks drying among the bogs and the stacks outside each little cabin are familiar sights, for most homesteads and farms have rights to cut peat for a certain period each year.  On a vastly different scale the government has set up a board (the *Bord na Móna*) to construct and operate peat-fuelled thermal power-stations, which generate power for the nation-wide grid; the main ones are at Portarlington, Ferbane and Allenwood.  The peat is machine-cut on a large scale, and thus the surface of Ireland is being stripped at a rate of over 3 million tons annually.

The Shannon is for the most part a sluggish stream, descending only 55 ft in 125 miles into Lough Derg, but below this it crosses several masses of hard rocks in a series of rapids, falling in only 15 miles from about 100 ft above sea-level to tidewater above Limerick. A dam was constructed across the river below its exit from Lough Derg, and a head-canal takes water to the hydro-station at Ardnacrusha, just north of Limerick. The work, carried out by the German firm of Siemens, was completed in 1929; grid lines carry power to Cork, Dublin, Limerick and the Shannon development area.

Much activity is devoted to the processing of agricultural products, as in the creameries of the Golden Vale and in the bacon factories and meat canneries of Dublin and Limerick.

Modern industrial development has taken place in and around Dublin and Limerick and at Shannon Airport. Dublin, the capital city, has a population of 569,000, about a fifth of the country's total. Situated on the east coast opposite England, on a bay into which the Liffey flows, it is the obvious 'gateway' to the Republic, though constant dredging is necessary to maintain deep-water berths for cargo vessels. Its outport, Dún Laoghaire (Kingstown), is used by ferry steamers to Holyhead. Dublin is a focus of rail and road communications, though the Grand and Royal canals from the west are now but little used. Dublin is by far the most important industrial city in Ireland. It is a major centre of brewing (notably in the huge Guinness brewery). Irish whiskey is distilled, and biscuits, confectionery and chocolate are made. Dublin manufactures a variety of consumer goods, including clothing, footwear, paper and books, ropes, and light metallurgical products, together with the food-processing already mentioned. Exports comprise mainly agricultural produce (live cattle, meat, dairy produce, eggs, stout, whiskey; imports include oil, coal, machinery, cars and auto parts, raw materials generally, and animal feedstuffs. The city is an attractive shopping, cultural and administrative centre, as well as a venue for visitors with its fine hotels, theatres and general charm and interest.

Limerick suffers from the disadvantage of facing west, but it is the centre of a considerable region, with its food-processing industries, radiating roads and railways, cathedral and port. It has some of the same manufacturing activities as Dublin, on a much smaller scale. The quays and docks extend along the banks of the Shannon; however, the port is but little used, because it lies so far up the estuary, and it is easier to send commodities to Dublin. With a population of 56,000, it is the third city of the Republic.

At Shannon Airport a large custom-free industrial zone has been created, offering inducements to foreign firms, notably from West Germany, Japan, the Netherlands and South Africa: new factories for cheap rental, cash grants to assist initial installation, freedom from import duties on raw materials, tax-free profits until 1983, plentiful supplies of labour and power, and special jet-freight terms for exports.   Manufactures include transistor radios, buttons, electronic control mechanisms, wire netting, and even pianos.   Most of this output is shipped away by air.

**The Wicklow Mountains.**   These consist of an elongated granite batholith, which was intruded among the ancient Caledonian folds, incidentally changing the Lower Palæozoic rocks along its margins by thermal metamorphism; gold has been found in the mineral veins.   The rounded surfaces of the Wicklows form bog-covered moorlands, rising to a maximum of 3,039 ft.   The Quaternary glaciers carved several deep, steep-sided valleys (known as *glens*), notably that of Glendalough, with its two lakes, divided by the delta of a stream which has been built out into the original single lake.   There are also numerous water-eroded glacial overflow valleys.   The streams rising on the upper slopes plunge as rapids into the glaciated valleys; often they have eroded gorge-like courses into the boulder-clay deposits on their floors.

*Agriculture.*   The granites of the Wicklows weather to form thin coarse soils, sustaining a poor moorland vegetation, with heather on the better-drained slopes, and wet bog on the flatter areas.   The glens, sheltered and with deeper soils, retain a considerable forest-cover.   Farming on the moorlands is restricted to the rearing of sheep and a few hill cattle, which are brought down to the coastal plain in winter and for fattening for market.   The glens provide some arable lands, growing barley and potatoes, and dairy cattle are kept.

The valley of the river Liffey, rising on the northern flanks of the Wicklows, has been dammed to form the Pollaphuca reservoir, one of Dublin's sources of water.   Some small towns strung out along the coast are resorts and have various light industries, such as the manufacture of electric light bulbs at Bray, pottery at Arklow, and fertilisers at Wicklow.

**The Southern Uplands and Plains.**   Between the two Mizen Heads, one on the south-eastern coast, the other in the extreme south-west, are a number of uplands, separated by valleys and bordered by coastal plains.   In the east the Leinster Hills, south of the Wicklows, are structurally part of the worn-down Caledonian ranges, probably once continuous with those of Wales.   Their structural lines, from north-east to south-west, can be traced.

By comparison, the uplands along the south coast are structurally part of the Armorican folding, of east-west trend. Most are now merely worn-down stumps of Carboniferous limestone and old red sandstone, with plateau-like surfaces, reaching their highest points in the Knockmealdown Mountains (2,609 ft) and the Galtee Mountains (3,018 ft). The east-west trend is emphasised by the rivers; though they ultimately break through to the coast, forming ria-like estuaries, their middle and upper courses are aligned west-east; this is well shown by the Lee, which flows into Cork Harbour, and by the Suir into Waterford Harbour. The ranges have been heavily glaciated, and have some fine cirques with steep, rocky backwalls, usually containing small lakes.

*Agriculture.* Though the uplands are covered with moorland and rough grazing, the lowlands are floored with limestone and a thin mantle of drift, forming fertile soils. The climate, with a southern maritime aspect, is extremely mild (frost is rarely experienced); yet, because the region lies in the rainshadow of the southwestern mountains, the annual precipitation is for the most part less than 40 in. The permanent pastures are rich, and potatoes, oats, barley and in the east some wheat are grown. Dairy cattle and pigs are kept in large numbers, the produce being processed at large co-operatives. More than a third of the farmland in Wexford is cropped, the largest proportion of any Irish county.

*Industry and Towns.* Ireland's only coalfield of any size, the Leinster field, is in the south-east around Castlecomer. The seams are mainly of anthracite and have been worked infrequently, except during World War II, when English coal was difficult to obtain. About 179,000 tons were mined in 1966, and mostly consumed in a small thermal power-station.

Most market-towns contain the usual creameries and other food-processing factories. Otherwise, industrial activity is centred in the three ports of Cork, Waterford and Wexford. Cork (122,000), the second largest town in the Republic, is situated in the north-west of a large inlet at the mouth of the river Lee. Its port handles agricultural produce from its rich hinterland, with which it is connected by railway. Apart from processing agricultural items, factories make woollen textiles (Irish tweeds, rugs and blankets), beer and whiskey, leather, agricultural machinery and rubber articles; a shipyard builds small steamers; and there is a Ford assembly plant. An oil refinery is situated at Whitegate on the shores of Cork Harbour, and in 1938 a small integrated iron and steel plant went into operation on Haulbowline Island. The outport of Cork is Cóbh, (formerly Queenstown), on the southern coast of Great Island, where some of the smaller Atlantic liners call.

Waterford (29,800) and Wexford (11,500) are market and service centres; the latter has a long-established high-quality glass-making industry, a factory producing agricultural implements, and a recently opened industrial estate with light industries. Several other small towns have manufacturing activities, such as the making of razor blades at Enniscorthy and insulated cables at New Ross, at the head of the Barrow estuary.

The south coast is popular with tourists, and has many attractive bays and beaches. Blarney Castle, near Cork, probably attracts more tourists than any other single feature in Ireland.

**The Mountains of the South-west.** The Hercynian ranges end in south-western Ireland, where rugged ridges of old red sandstone are separated by valleys worn in the less resistant Carboniferous limestones. The post-glacial rise of sea-level converted the lower reaches of the rivers occupying these valleys into long, tapering rias: Dingle Bay, Kenmare River, Bantry Bay and Dunmanus Bay. Between them the ridges taper into rocky peninsulas, with steep cliffs and offshore reefs and islands; the Blasket Islands form the westernmost point of Europe. The mountains have been heavily glaciated, notably in the Macgillycuddy Reeks; these culminate in Carrantuohill (3,414 ft), the highest point in Ireland, a fine peak with radiating rocky ridges enclosing in the cirques several small deep lakes.

These mountains, projecting into the Atlantic, are one of the wettest parts of Ireland, with mean annual precipitation totals exceeding 100 in, and with 40 to 60 in along the coast. There is a high degree of cloudiness, and strong winds and gales from off the Atlantic are frequent. But the climate is exceedingly mild; frosts are rare and in some places have never been recorded, and as a result some famous gardens grow tree ferns and palms.

*Agriculture.* The predominantly sandstone mountains have much bare rock, and, elsewhere, only a thin coarse soil covered with poor grass and colourful stretches of heather. The valley soils, derived from boulder-clay and the underlying limestone, are sometimes rich, and carry permanent pasture of good quality. The dominant activity is the rearing of dairy cattle, their milk going to co-operative dairies in such small towns as Cahirciveen, Killorglin and Kenmare; pigs and horses are also kept. But much marginal land has been abandoned, as is evidenced by the many ruined cabins and overgrown plots.

*Other Activities.* Some subsistence fishing is carried on, still using the traditional tarred canvas boats, but many little harbours and jetties are in disrepair. The rugged mountains, lakes (notably those of Killarney), and superb coastline and the general colourful charm make this one of the most popular tourist areas in Ireland, for which Killarney, Tralee and Bantry are the centres. New hotels, golf courses (including several of championship quality), and much improved roads, notably the 'Ring of Kerry', a popular circuit from Killarney around the Kerry peninsula, have all contributed. Fishing for salmon and trout in the rivers and lakes and game-fishing in the Atlantic also attract many visitors.

Apart from food-processing, several manufacturing industries have recently been introduced, including the making of cranes at a German-owned factory in Killarney. A consortium is planning the development of Bantry Bay as a terminal for super-tankers, which will discharge into smaller vessels for delivery to refineries around the coast of Britain and in parts of Europe.

**The Uplands and Coastal Plains of the North-west.** From Galway Bay to Lough Foyle extends a series of uplands, remnants of the Caledonian ranges: the mountains of Connemara, Mayo and Donegal. They form rugged masses of early Palæozoic sandstones, limestones and schists rising to between 2,000 and 2,500 ft; the highest summit, Mweelrea (2,688 ft), overlooks Killary Harbour in Connemara. The uplands were heavily glaciated, leaving much bare rock, and the ice-scarred lowlands are studded with lakes. The coast is extremely rugged, exposed to the full force of the Atlantic waves; promontories ending in cliffs alternate with broad open inlets (Galway, Clew, Sligo and Donegal bays) and many minor indentations. Irregularly shaped islands lie off the shore, including the Arans in Galway Bay and Achill (with magnificent quartzite cliffs said to be the highest in Ireland and the UK) off the coast of Connemara.

*Agriculture.* This area is constantly swept by strong winds, restricting tree-growth to the sheltered valleys. Precipitation in many parts exceeds 70 in (with about 250 rain-days) on an average each year. Conditions are damp and cloudy, though the seasonal temperature range is only 16° F (9° C) or less; mean January temperatures vary little from 44° F (6.7° C).

Over the uplands, the soil is thin and acid, or even non-existent, and there are extensive moorlands and peat bogs. Farmland is limited to small patches along the coast and in the valleys, with a pattern of life generally similar to that of the Scottish crofters (see p. 216), one of unremitting toil. Potatoes are grown on small patches (especially in Donegal); sheep are grazed on lower slopes, and a few cows, pigs and poultry are kept. The most fertile areas are in the north, around Lough Swilly and on the western side of the river Foyle near the border. Fishing forms a supplement in some parts, as in the Aran Islands, but this is difficult and often dangerous in the stormy, rock-bound seas. Life in the north-west is more than usually hard, and many people have migrated, leaving only ruined cabins.

*Settlements.* The few small towns, notably Galway (24,600), Westport, Sligo and Buncrana, are on the coast, but their harbours are poor and exposed. Some have small-scale woollen industries, notably the manufacture of tweeds for export, and Galway has a small industrial estate with light manufactures. The picturesque ruggedness attracts increasing numbers of visitors.

**Economic Summary.** During the eighteenth and the first half of the nineteenth century, the population of Ireland expanded rapidly, reaching a peak of about 8·5 millions in 1845. But in that year occurred the first of a series of disastrous famines resulting from the failure of the potato crop, the country's food staple. Large numbers of people died of starvation; many others emigrated to Britain or America and formed a major labour source for building roads, canals, railways and dams in those and other countries; many girls went as domestic servants to Britain. This emigration still continues, though on a reduced scale; as recently as 1960 over a half-million first-generation American citizens were Irish-born. The population of the Republic continued to decline: 3·1 millions in 1921, 2·96 millions in 1946, and 2·85 millions in 1964; this is still largely because of emigration, for the natural increase of 10·7 per thousand is one of the highest in Europe. The decline has been most marked in rural areas, at the expense of which the four main towns (Dublin, Cork, Limerick and Waterford) have increased their population during the last half-century by 40 per cent, and together contain nearly a third of the country's total. However, the general decline may at last have been arrested, for between 1961 and 1966 the total actually rose by 2·2 per cent to 2·88 millions, as a result of the halving of the rate of emigration; the average density is now 108 people per square mile.

Much of the countryside retains its traditional and somewhat leisurely way of life, based on the family unit and on the cultivation of potatoes, with a few head of stock. This system, at best subsistent and marginal, in some parts, particularly in the north-west, results in outright poverty. Other districts are highly productive, favoured by rich soils, a mild humid climate, and communications allowing ready access to the ports of Dublin and Cork. The best areas are on the east coast lowlands and in the Golden Vale.

Of the total area of some 17 million acres, nearly 6 millions consist of mountain, moorland, peat bog and lakes, and only about 1·5 millions are classified as arable. The main crops, in decreasing order of acreage, are barley, oats, potatoes, wheat and turnips, though potatoes and turnips are the most important in yield by tonnage. In recent years the growing of wheat has been specially stimulated in order to reduce imports; the 1967 harvest (about 200,000 tons) showed a 40 per cent increase over that of 1966.

There are about 5·6 million cattle, 4·7 million sheep, 1 million pigs and 160,000 horses. The major exports (of which 80 per cent goes to the UK under a free-trade agreement) are live cattle, sheep and bloodstock horses; these exports have been stimulated in 1968 by the losses incurred in the UK by the foot-and-mouth outbreak of 1967–68. Other exports are butter, cheese and eggs, beer, stout and whiskey.

Strenuous efforts are made by the government to stimulate agriculture: by improving agricultural education by means of colleges, institutes and training schools; by developments in co-ordination of production, processing and marketing; by increased mechanisation; and by the creation of boards, such as the Irish Dairy Produce Board, as a unifying and stimulating influence. The Land Commission increases its efforts to create more viable and productive farms, on the one hand by eliminating small uneconomic holdings by purchase, on the other by acquiring large, poorly farmed estates to divide into efficient, intensive holdings.

The main problem faced by the Irish economy is its inability to maintain full employment, largely because markets for agricultural produce are difficult to expand (with competition from Denmark, New Zealand and elsewhere), and because industrial development is difficult as a result of the limited purchasing power of the home market and deficient or inadequate supplies of raw materials. However, by concerted efforts, industry, a former virtually stagnant section of the economy, has been improved, and by 1967 it accounted for 30 per cent of total employment, compared with 20 per cent in agriculture. Formerly industry was limited to the processing of agricultural commodities, and in value these are still dominant; the largest items (in decreasing order) are butter and cheese, tobacco, milled grain, bacon, biscuits, beer and stout, and canned meat. In net output value (gross output value less the cost of materials, power and fabrication) beer and stout are by far the most significant items. Some traditionally fine products, of considerable export value, such as silverware, hand-made shoes, furniture, hand-knit sweaters, glassware and tweeds, are still made.

In an effort to diversify and expand industrial production, the government has established a series of programmes, with growth targets, and has created state corporations, notably, in 1958, the Industrial Development Authority, which devotes much effort to attracting foreign firms by making factory sites available on favourable terms, particularly at Shannon, Cork and Waterford, and in the Dublin district. Since its inception eighty new factories have been installed, and the value of exported manufactures has tripled. As a result the gross national product has risen annually by an average of 4·3 per cent.

One major improvement has been in the production and transmission of power. Energy is derived from the large Shannon hydro-station and from smaller units on the rivers Liffey, Lee and Erne; thermal power is produced by generators fired with peat, coal (mostly imported) and oil. Water supplies about 40 per cent of the total energy; peat, about 30 per cent; and coal and oil, the remainder.

Recently there has been some development in mining, largely by Canadian companies; prospecting for copper, lead, zinc, silver and barytes is being pursued, and some mines have been opened. The open-cast Tynagh mine in Galway and the Gortdrum copper mine in Tipperary produced metals worth over $25 million in 1967; the Galway mine has its own concentration and smelting plant.

The Irish Tourist Board, aided by a large advertising campaign that stresses the tranquil beauty of the Irish countryside, has assisted materially in increasing greatly the number of visitors. It has been helped by the expansion of *Aer Lingus,* the Irish airline, by a considerable programme of road and hotel (recently also motel) improvement, and by the stimulation of festivals, of which there were in 1968 thirty-six, such as the Dublin Theatre Festival and the Cork Film Festival.

Changes are taking place, even if they are evident only in a small number of centres. But one of the charms of Ireland is the maintenance of the traditional picturesque and leisurely way of life over much of the countryside.

## REFERENCES

The standard text is *Ireland,* by T. W. Freeman, London, Methuen, 1942, 3rd ed. 1965. On geographical aspects of prehistoric culture, see E. Estyn Evans, *Irish Heritage,* Dundalk, Eire, Dundalgan Press, 1942. The periodical *Irish Geography,* the bulletin of the Geographical Society of Ireland, Dublin, 1944 onwards, includes short articles on aspects of the geography of Ireland. See also J. Wreford Watson and J. B. Sissons (eds.), *The British Isles: A Systematic Geography,* London and Edinburgh, Nelson, 1964.

### CHAPTER 12

# FRANCE

FRANCE is the largest country of Europe, with the exception of the USSR, and is nearly twice as large as the British Isles. Apart from the bordering chains of the Alps and the Pyrenees, France belongs structurally to the Hercynian region of Europe with its old massifs and its included basins and scarplands.

The advantages of its position and physical layout have often been stressed. It is the only country of Europe, except Spain, which has coastlines on both the Mediterranean and the Atlantic, and in the case of France these coasts are mainly bordered by lowlands, which allow easy access inland, whereas Spain is hampered by the presence of coastal mountains which hinder movement to and from the interior. Instead of the mountain rampart, which elsewhere borders the northern side of the Mediterranean Basin, there is here a great depression represented by the Gulf of Lyons (Fr., Golfe du Lion), from which two relatively easy routes lead northward into the great lowlands of northern and western France, the more important being the Rhône–Saône route leading due north towards the lowland known as the Paris Basin, and the other, leading north-west via the Carcassonne Gap, into the lowland basin of Aquitaine. These natural routes allowed the early spread of Mediterranean civilisation northwards into France beyond the range of Mediterranean climate, and in non-Mediterranean France Roman civilisation retained its hold despite the subsequent barbarian invasions.

The Rhône–Saône route in particular is still of great importance, since it puts the densely peopled lands of northern France, Great Britain, and the Low Countries (Belgium and Holland) into easy communication with the Mediterranean–Suez–Orient route. Not only does it immediately connect two natural regions of unlike climate and products, that is to say, the summer-drought region of the Mediterranean with the rainy region of north-west Europe, but it also provides a useful link in one of the great highways of the world. As already noted in Chapter 1, the only other easy natural route through the northern mountain-border of the Mediterranean Sea is via the Bosporus and Dardanelles, but the western route through France is more important commercially at the present time, because western Europe is more thickly populated and more developed commercially than eastern Europe. Passenger traffic is particularly important owing to the saving of time via the Rhône–Saône land route as compared with the long sea route via Gibraltar, round Spain and Portugal and through the Bay of Biscay. Water transport will increase with the improvement of the Rhône–Saône route.

Among the advantages of the physique of France the high percentage of lowland must take a foremost place. None of the large established countries of Europe has so much, with the exception of Russia, where the advantage of possessing a great expanse of lowland was reduced by adverse climatic and historical conditions. Moreover, the lowlands of France are in the main fertile, and further, there is easy communication between them.

A favourable climate is ensured both by the position and relief of the country. Lying between latitudes 42° N and 51° N France possesses only a narrow southern strip within the Mediterranean climatic province, while the rest has cyclonic rain throughout the year. Since, however, the southern coastlands of France lie on the northern edge of the belt of Mediterranean climate the period of winter rain is prolonged even here, and there is rarely excessive drought, while the near presence of high mountains provides water for irrigation. The relatively low latitude of even the rest of France gives the country a climatic advantage over the other parts of Europe which have also abundant cyclonic rain, since not only the fertile lowlands, but the slopes of the mountains themselves, can be cultivated. Whereas in England at latitude 55° cultivation ceases above about 700 ft, in the French Alps of Savoy about latitude 45° it can be carried up to 4,500 ft, and even above 6,000 ft in favourable exposures and slopes. Moreover, the hotter summers and shorter winters allow the cultivation of a greater variety of crops, including the heavy yielding maize and the valuable vine. Since about 1900, also, advantage has been taken of the early spring to cultivate early vegetables and fruit for the dense industrial populations of lands farther north, particularly of Great Britain. The disposition of the mountains and plains allows the penetration over the whole country of the rain from the west.

In addition to the rich agricultural possibilities of France, the country also possesses considerable wealth of minerals and water-power, though in regard to coal, the essential fuel of the modern world, the endowment is not very great, France being fifth among the coal producing countries of Europe. The only really important coalfield, moreover, is situated in the extreme north-east of the country, so that distribution to the south and west of the country is costly. Moreover, owing to the nature of the seams, the coal is difficult to mine and therefore expensive, and the cost puts a brake on industrial development under modern conditions, especially when the import of foreign fuel is restricted. Petroleum production is very small (2·3 million tons in 1962). Natural gas production is increasing, and over a hundred hydro-electric power stations have been built since 1946. The hydro-electricity available from the rivers of the French Alps and Pyrenees puts France third among European countries in regard to the amount of water-power utilised. In iron, however, the great present-day industrial necessity ranking second only to coal, France is the richest country in Europe, the iron mines of Lorraine yielding 67 million tons of ore in 1962 (see Appendix F and p. 628).

The advantages of size, position, relief, and climate, which helped to make France *la grande nation*, do not appear sufficient to sustain her as a great power in the present world, where the United States and the Soviet Union, so evidently command much greater economic potentials. France has not enough coal to sustain a really large industrial output and, like other west European countries, has lost her considerable oversea dependencies. However, she now enjoys large hydro-electric and iron ore resources and a growing labour force, which was augmented in 1963 by the absorption of French citizens from Algeria, from which she now imports petroleum and natural gas. Further, through the Common Market, she remains associated with former French African territories (see p. 276 and p. 622).

**Structure and Relief.** The main outlines of the structure and relief of France are simple.

There are four Hercynian horsts, namely the Massif Central, the Armorican Massif, the Vosges, and the Ardennes (see Fig. 25). The first three are wholly in France, the last extends through Belgium to join the Rhine Highlands. These horsts, in common with most of the other Hercynian massifs of Europe, were worn down to base level and generally submerged beneath the Cretaceous Sea, only to be raised again during the Alpine mountain building period of the Tertiary era. The horsts nearest the Alps underwent the greatest uplift, particularly the Massif Central and the Vosges, but the Armorican Massif was raised relatively little. All these horsts consist mainly of Palæozoic and earlier rocks, including a considerable proportion of granites, gneisses, and other hard rocks which provide thin infertile soils. The Hercynian massifs of France generally form dissected infertile highlands, with the exception of the Armorican Massif which, although dissected and infertile, is mainly below 600 ft in height.

Around the Massif Central lie three basins of sedimentation. The

Paris Basin and the Basin of Aquitaine form the principal lowlands of France, and are composed of strata of Secondary and Tertiary age. In the Paris Basin scarpland formations are well developed, particularly on the east, since the upthrust of the Vosges Massif caused a pronounced tilting of the strata and allowed erosion to emphasise the difference between the harder and softer rocks. The Saône–Rhône depression is largely an area of sedimentation, but some of the rocks became involved in the Alpine folding so that the area of lowland is now narrow and discontinuous.

The young folded mountains of the Alps and Pyrenees form the frontiers of France on the south-east and south-west. On the eastern frontier, France also includes portions of the Rhine rift valley and of the Belgian Basin of sedimentation.

## GEOGRAPHICAL REGIONS

**The Paris Basin.** *General.* This is the most important agricultural lowland of western Europe, both as regards size and productivity. It measures some 200 miles from the English Channel (Fr., La Manche) to the Massif Central, and some 300 miles from the Armorican Massif to the Vosges. The greater part of the area is under 600 ft high, except in the eastern part (Lorraine), which though geologically part of the basin structure, is often placed in a separate geographical region on account of its differences of physical, historical, and economic development.

Structurally the basin is formed of strata of Secondary and Tertiary rocks which were laid down on a gradually sinking floor. During the Tertiary period the outer edges were slightly tilted up like the rim of a saucer, and erosion has stripped off the upper and younger layers, especially from the higher outlying part of the basin. Accordingly the older strata are now exposed round the rim and progressively younger strata are met as one goes towards the centre. The oldest rocks belong to the Triassic system and are found bordering the Vosges in Lorraine, but as the basin was mainly land in this period the deposits were limited in extent and no other outcrops occur, though borings reveal rocks of this age on the southern and western borders. The Jurassic system is much more widely represented, and rocks of this age probably floor the greater part of the basin, and they appear at the surface in a horseshoe-shaped outcrop on the eastern, southern, and western sides. On the north this formation appears only in denuded anticlines. The Cretaceous formation outcrops in a great ring, somewhat irregularly shaped, round the Tertiary beds of the middle of the basin. These Tertiary beds have their longer axis from north-east to south-west and are transgressive over the Jurassics in the south of the basin.

The strata consist of very varied types of rock, and the effect of denudation and peneplanation has been to produce rapid alternations of outcrop. The formation of scarps was thus favoured, and these are particularly noticeable in the eastern part of the basin, partly due to the greater dip and partly because a greater number of formations are represented. The basin is also crossed from north-west to south-east by a number of shallow folds, but apart from the

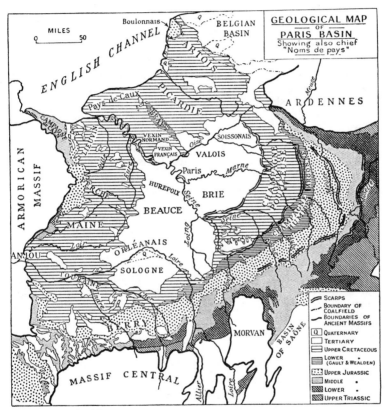

Fig. 31. GEOLOGICAL MAP OF THE PARIS BASIN

north-eastern region, these rarely have any effect on the relief. The rapid alternation of outcrops naturally causes rapid alterations of landscape, a fact which has long been appreciated by the inhabitants who have applied distinctive local names (*noms de pays*) to regions which possess distinctive individuality, though this individuality is not always very noticeable to the traveller at first sight and has become more blurred owing to the improvement of communications and the pull of the Paris market, with their subsequent economic effects upon agriculture.

The Paris Basin possesses in marked degree the type of variety which was needed before the Industrial Revolution when almost all the needs of man had to be supplied in a comparatively small area. There is land suited to wet crops and dry crops, to cereals and market gardens, to vine and to orchard; there are dry pastures and wet pastures, the first suited to sheep and the second to cattle; there are wooded areas for supplying timber for fuel and building; there is good building stone, markedly absent from the similar London Basin, as well as materials for bricks, cement, and plaster of Paris. There are also small bodies of iron on the borders of the basin which were useful before the vast Lorraine ironfield could be worked.   And to bring these commodities from one place to another was the useful, slow-moving Seine and its tributaries, which are still of considerable importance, in spite of the development of canals, railways, and roads.

The basin may be conveniently divided into five subdivisions as follows: (a) the central region with Paris; (b) the scarplands of Champagne and Burgundy; (c) the scarplands of Lorraine; (d) the south-west, or middle Loire region; (e) the coastal regions of Normandy and Picardy.

In addition, the region of the lower Loire may be conveniently treated here, although geologically it belongs to the Armorican Massif.

**The Paris Basin.** (1) *The Central Region, including Paris.* This region corresponds broadly to the outcrop of Tertiary deposits, but without their southern extension into the region of the middle Loire. These deposits constitute a complex alternation of limestones, sandstones, and clays, with a general predominance of limestone which forms the most widespread subsoil, a noteworthy and advantageous contrast to the London Basin, where in a similar position the clays predominate.   The limestone plains, usually about 300 to 600 ft high, are mainly covered with superficial deposits of loam (*limon*).   This is finely grained deposit, believed to consist of wind-blown material which was subsequently re-sorted by water. In fertility and appearance it is scarcely to be distinguished from *Löss* (cf. p. 359), and gives rise to very suitable soil for the cultivation of cereals and sugar-beet.   In parts, however, particularly south-east of Paris, the place of the *limon* is taken by the impermeable clay-with-flints, and dairy cattle become important on their heavier and moister soils.   Towards the centre of the basin, near Paris, the converging rivers have incised their valleys, cutting the level limestone plain or low plateau into isolated patches.   In doing so they have exposed small areas of sandstone and clay which are usually less fertile than the limestone, the sand in particular often being left under forest. The alluvium of the valleys contrasts rather markedly with the stretches of dry plateaus between them, and allows the cultivation of green vegetables and other market-garden produce needing a good deal of moisture.

Apart from Paris the whole central region is entirely agricultural, but many *noms de pays* indicate differences between one part and another. Of these, Beauce, situated midway between the Seine and the great bend of the Loire, and almost surrounded by areas of poorer soils that are forested, possesses the most marked individuality. The level limestone plain, covered with a great thickness of *limon*, is very fertile in spite of the absence of running water. With its lack of trees and hedges and its devotion to cereals and sugar-beet, Beauce recalls very strongly the *Löss*-covered regions of central and eastern Europe. It is one of the main granaries of France and farms are large by French standards. In Hurepoix, between Beauce and Paris, the limestone has been eroded by many small streams and the underlying sands and clays appear. When sufficiently fertile, these are devoted to market-gardening for Paris, but otherwise have been left under forest (as are the sands of Fontainebleau), and the district forms a 'playground' for the great city. East of the Seine, the different types of landscape alternate with each other to a greater extent. The clay and *limon* cover of Brie, between the Seine and Marne, gives a fertile but much damper soil than in Beauce. Here there is woodland, and the rural settlements are not as highly nucleated as in Beauce where the problem of water supply has discouraged dispersion. Apart from sugar-beet and cereals, fodder crops and dairying are important, the milk being either sent liquid to Paris, or, in the remoter areas, made into Brie cheese. Soissonais and Valois show an alternation of limestone plateaus and humid valleys. In 1958 petroleum production commenced in the Paris basin with wells near Meaux, Brie-Cartrettes, Chailly and elsewhere.

**Paris.** Paris grew up at a crossing-place of the Seine where a small island first gave protection and afterwards facilitated the building of bridges. Before the days of big ships, sea-going vessels could come up river as far as this bridge, and even today Paris is still a great port, though goods now come in barges. The large extent, the fertility and diversity of the surrounding country have already been emphasised, and the nodal position, with routes converging from all directions, has been suggested. The site was sufficiently favourable to attract settlers in pre-Roman times, but the city did not become the centre of administration of Gaul under the Romans, who preferred Lyons, since the latter was better situated from the point of view of external administrators, who were also concerned with communications leading to Rome and to the Rhine frontier. Paris, in fact, owes its supremacy among French cities largely to the Capet kings, who in the twelfth century chose the town as their capital. The city grew as their rule was extended from the region between Paris and Orleans over all the country which is now called France, but which took its name from the land in the immediate neighbourhood of Paris. The highly centralising policy of the French kings, especially from the seventeenth century onwards, added to the size and prestige of the city, and the large numbers of nobles and officials assembled there led to the development of a number of industries, of which the luxury trades became world famous.

Paris has witnessed a number of attempts at town planning, the walls of former city limits being successively replaced by boulevards. Traces can thus be found, for example, of the city extent in *c.* 1200, 1370, 1793 and the nineteenth century. The chief of these was the city planned by Haussmann for Napoleon III which brought into being the Champs Elysées and the ring of outer boulevards including Haussmann and the Parc Royal. Some of the most impressive buildings of central Paris stand on *buttes témoins*—residual hillocks of Tertiary limestone, e.g. those of Montmartre 380 ft on Beauce limestone and the Nôtre Dame 135 ft and Arc de Triomphe 190 ft on Brie limestone.

Like London, Paris has considerable traffic problems and currently plans are being put forward for three ring roads at 22 miles, 42 miles, and 65 miles from the centre, ten radial motorways and two express metros.

Paris is today not only the supreme administration centre of a highly centralised country, the chief commercial, intellectual, and artistic centre, but is also the largest industrial centre, with as many industrial workers as the coalfields of the 'Nord' and the silk-manufacturing region of Lyons combined. It has long been supreme in the design and manufacture of women's clothing and of all manner of luxury goods. In addition it has long been renowned for the elegance of its furniture and for interior decoration generally, though in this branch it has been rivalled and perhaps surpassed in the twentieth century by other countries. Many other kinds of consumer industries are also represented in Paris. It possesses a great variety of manufactures needing skilled labour and comparatively small amounts of raw material, such as scientific and musical instruments, jewellery, motor cars, airplanes, electrical and light metal industries, as well as rolling-stock and river craft. Lastly, there are many industries which were established to process the agricultural produce of the surrounding country for the dense population of the city, such as flour milling, sugar and jam manufacturing, brewing, the making of shoes, and so on. At present over 17 per cent of the population of France live in the three departments of Seine, Seine-et-Oise, and Seine-et-Marne which together occupy only 3 per cent of its area. Not only is population concentrated in and around Paris, but so also is industry, to the economic detriment of other parts of France. Paris has become overcrowded and is already one of the most highly concentrated cities in Europe with a much greater proportion of people as flat dwellers than in London. It lacks adequate open spaces: London has six times as much per head of population and Vienna eighteen times. To relieve the pressure the government has, over the last ten years, attempted to decentralise by legislation. Some success has been achieved but the magnet of Paris and its market still draws people and industry.

Paris still holds an important position as an educational centre. Throughout the later Middle Ages and almost down to modern times it was the leading university city of Europe, and attracted large numbers of foreign students, but the devotion to letters (arts) and the comparative neglect of natural philosophy (science), caused Paris to lose ground in favour of universities in England, Switzerland, and Germany.

Like the other great capital cities of Europe, Paris draws the gifted and ambitious from all over the country, but to an even greater degree, so that the provinces lack the active life to be found in, say, England and Germany. Even so, however, the city has been surpassed in size by London, Berlin, New York and Tokyo, its population being 2,753,000 at the census of 1962, though Greater Paris had a population of $7\frac{3}{4}$ million.

**The Paris Basin.** (2) *The Scarplands of Champagne and Burgundy.* The central basin terminates on the east in a well defined outward-facing scarp of Tertiary limestone, known as the Falaise de l'Île de France. This is pierced by a number of rivers, Oise, Aisne, Vesle, Marne, Seine, which afford easy routes converging towards Paris and which are now followed by the railways. From beneath the Tertiaries of the Falaise comes an outcrop of chalk which forms a stretch of dry country known in its central area as 'La Champagne Pouilleuse', meaning 'poor or barren Champagne', the word 'champagne' being applied to many dry, level, treeless areas in different parts of France. This rises gradually towards the east only to fall by means of a scarp to the clays of 'Le Champagne Humide', from beneath which permeable rocks again emerge to form the

Argonne Heights, formed of Lower Cretaceous sandstone, while farther south emerges the Côte des Bars, a scarp of Portland limestone of Jurassic age. To the east of the Argonne rise the plateaus and scarps of Lorraine, while to the south-east of the Côte des Bars rises the plateau of Burgundy, usually called the Plateau de Langres.

La Champagne Pouilleuse, with its extension northwards to the Pays de l'Aisne, extends for some 35 miles from east to west and twice that distance from north to south. The region has a marked individuality. In general, there is an absence of superficial deposits, and the chalk by itself provides a poor, thin soil, for centuries devoted to sheep rearing, but during the nineteenth century partly put under cereals or more recently afforested with pine trees. It corresponds to the English Salisbury Plain and is similarly used for army manœuvres. The open ground also provided a noted route from north to south in the pre-railway era, and was crossed by the east–west routes utilising river gaps in the scarps. Noted medieval fairs were held at Troyes and Rheims. The famous Champagne wine comes from the narrow Tertiary scarp of the Falaise. As Champagne is near the northern margin of wine production (c. 49° N), the vineyards need a warm soil and a southern exposure, but the excellence of the wine produced seems to be due not only to natural conditions, but also to the technique of manufacture. The wine is largely exported. Rheims (136,000)[1] is the great organising centre of the industry, followed by Epernay on the Marne. Both are gap towns. The only other town of any size is Troyes (67,500), an isolated textile manufacturing town, specialising in hosiery and knitted goods – an industry originally based on wool from local sheep – and now also on engineering.

The Plateau de Langres forms a threshold of rather high, scantily-peopled country between the lowlands of the Paris Basin and those of the Saône. In general the plateau is over 1,000 ft above sea-level. The Jurassic limestone here reaches a great thickness and there is little surface water except in the valleys, which deeply dissect the plateau and allow canals, roads, and railways to wind through the country. In some places the valleys cut down to the impermeable Liassic marls, and rich valley pastures result. The Oolitic limestone forms a scarp overlooking the Saône valley, particularly towards the west, where it rises to more than 2,000 ft above sea-level and is known as the Côte d'Or.

**The Paris Basin.** (3) *The Scarplands of Lorraine.* Structurally all the land west of the Vosges in Lorraine belongs to the Paris Basin, and consists of successive outcrops of Jurassic, Lias, and Triassic beds. Lorraine, however, differs in many ways from the rest of the

[1] Population figures are from the 1962 census.

basin. Apart from its rivers draining northward instead of westward, it is also higher, averaging between 900 and 1,000 ft, while the Côtes de Meuse reach over 1,300 ft. Consequently it is bleaker and wetter. Agriculturally this is one of the poorest areas of the Paris Basin. Soils are heavy and poor due to the absence of *limon* and are partly under woodland. Here are to be found some of the most extreme examples of strip cultivation contributing to the low returns from agriculture and encouraging rural depopulation, except on the better patches of soils or along the main transport arteries which enable the rural dweller to work in a factory and look upon his farm as a part-time source of income.

The two main outcrops and scarps of Jurassic limestone are the Côtes de Meuse (Corallian) to the east of the River Meuse and the Côtes de Moselle (Oolitic) to the west of the River Moselle. These outcrops are both infertile zones of scanty population, mainly under forest. Between the two is the clay vale of the Woëvre, with fertile but heavy soils, while east of, and overlooked by, the 800-ft-high Côtes de Moselle is the largest area of low-lying and relatively fertile land in Lorraine. This lowland extends for over 100 miles from the Luxembourg lowland in the north to the low Mts Faucilles in the south, and is developed on four types of rock, the Lias clay, the Keuper sandstones and marls, and the Muschelkalk, the latter being, as its name implies, a shelly limestone. Towards the south Muschelkalk forms the low hills of the Mts Faucilles where the Saône rises, but further north it does not form a perceptible scarp. This zone is succeeded eastward by the infertile and forested Bunter sandstone (*grès Vosgien*) which forms a hilly region bordering the crystalline Vosges and reaching to the Rhine rift itself farther north. Gaps through the scarp aided the construction of roads and railways from east to west, of which the route from Paris to Strasbourg via Toul and Nancy is the most important.

The main riches of Lorraine consist of great bodies of iron-ore which occur in the Lias and outcrop at the base of the Oolitic scarp of the Côtes de Moselle, from Nancy northwards to Longwy and across the Luxembourg–Belgium frontier. The deposits also extend under the Oolitic plateau, and are extensively mined in the region round Briey. This is one of the largest iron deposits in Europe.

The deposits extend over a long narrow strip some 70 miles long by about 12 miles wide, and the reserves are estimated to amount to 4,400 million tons in the French section alone, excluding those in Luxembourg. In spite of the vast quantities of ore, the deposits were almost entirely neglected until the last quarter of the nineteenth century, for the ore is phosphoric and produced a brittle iron of very poor quality.   It is also low grade with an iron content of 23–40 per cent, compared with Swedish ore of about 55–65 per cent.   The first great impetus was the invention of the Thomas and Gilchrist basic process of smelting in 1879, and the second was the discovery in 1884 of the vast Briey deposits underlying the Oolitic plateau. By this time, however, much of the eastern part of the Lorraine orefield had been lost to Germany after the Franco-Prussian War in 1871.

PRODUCTION OF IRON-ORE IN LORRAINE.   MILLION METRIC TONS

| Mining Area | 1930 | 1937 | 1953 | 1960 |
| --- | --- | --- | --- | --- |
| Metz–Thionville | 20·24 | 15·63 | 15·09 | 25·97 |
| Briey–Longwy | 24·35 | 18·79 | 22·60 | 34·08 |
| Nancy | 1·41 | 0·99 | 0·90 | 2·66 |
| Total Lorraine | 46·00 | 35·41 | 38·59 | 62·71 |

Most of the ore is obtained by adits and shallow shaft mines and the industry is highly mechanised.   The establishment of a large iron industry has been hindered by the absence of a large coalfield in the neighbourhood, the Moselle coalfield having an output of only about 15 million tons per annum.   The industrial development of the region has been hampered by lack of suitable coal for coking, coke being imported from the Nord and Ruhr.   Now new coking methods have been evolved which enable a much greater proportion of Lorraine coal to be used in making coke.   Proximity to the German frontier too, in the past, has discouraged the development of heavy industry.   Recently the European Coal and Steel Community (see p. 622) has done much to reduce barriers between Benelux, France, and Germany and the canalisation of the Moselle should further help the prosperity of the Lorraine heavy steel industry.   Nancy (130,900) has the advantages of being an old-established town with a nodal position, as well as being the commercial centre for the iron industry and possessing metallurgical works in the vicinity.   However, it produces only a small amount of iron and steel and is rather isolated from the major areas.   The principal steel producing area is the Moselle district with such centres as Thionville, Hayange, Joeuf and Seremange which have a number of recently expanded and modernised plants.

On the eastern border of Lorraine, cotton manufacturing is carried on in a number of small, scattered towns of which the chief is Epinal.   This cotton industry is an offshoot from the Alsatian and was originally dependent upon water-power provided by the streams from the Vosges.

**The Paris Basin.**   (4) *The South-West, or the Middle Loire Region.*
This region lacks the symmetry of the east of the Paris basin, mainly
on account of the widespread Tertiary deposits, patches of which lie
unconformably even on the Jurassic measures.   There are no well-
marked scarps and the region forms a great plain drained.by the
Loire and its tributaries, which flow between wide low terraces
in valleys slightly below the general level.   The actual floodplain
is usually sandy, but the old floodplain (which now forms the
accompanying terraces), and the valley sides, are regions of intensive
cultivation.   On the other hand, the interfluves are only of moderate
fertility and tend to be dry, either when they are developed on the
Tertiary and Cretaceous sands or on the Cretaceous and Jurassic
limestone.   The Tertiary sands, clays, and gravels of La Sologne
were probably deposited by a large river which in Miocene times
flowed northwards from the Massif Central.   They are among the
poorest and most thinly peopled lands of France.

The valley of the middle Loire itself (known under various local
names, such as the Val de Loire, Val d'Orléans, Val de Blois, Val
de Touraine, Val d'Anjou), the lower valleys of the Cher, Indre,
and Vienne on the south of the Loire, and the valley of the Sarthe
on the north, resemble each other in their rich agricultural development, with noted vineyards, orchards, and poultry rearing.
Touraine, in particular, with its concentration of converging valleys,
has long been celebrated as the 'Garden of France,' the chief
agricultural fair of France being held annually at Tours.   The
large number of fine old castles, particularly between Orléans and
Anjou, which have earned for the middle Loire region the name
of 'château country' and a certain popularity as a tourist resort,
are to some extent an indication of the long-continued agricultural
wealth of the region and also of its popularity with the kings of
France.

The intervening sandy plains retain considerable stretches of the
woodlands and heaths in which the kings of France delighted to
hunt, but they were mainly brought under cultivation in the eighteenth
and early nineteenth centuries.   Thanks to the railway and motor
cars, Parisians have built weekend cottages here.   On the Jurassic
limestones of Berry, however, the bare treeless plain of La Champagne
Berrichonne, between the Indre and Loire, resembles La Champagne
Pouilleuse, and for centuries was devoted to sheep, and later also
to cereals.   To the north of Berry, in the great bend of the Loire,
lies La Sologne, on whose flat surface water stagnated and produced
marshes and lakes, partially reclaimed in the nineteenth century,
though even today numerous small lakes remain as haunts of wild
fowl.

There are no large towns in the south-western part of the Paris Basin, though many of medium size and of historical and architectural interest, such as Orléans (86,600), Tours (94,600), Angers (119,900), Le Mans (133,000). The region is of considerable historical importance as its possession aided the Capet kings of France to expand into the basin of Aquitaine, the second great lowland of the country.

The threshold known as Le Seuil de Poitou is much lower than that leading from the Paris Basin to the upper Saône. In fact, it forms no break in the agricultural plain and has the same alternation of rich valleys (here reaching down to the Lias clay and providing good fattening pastures), with intervening stretches of drier lands, which though often only of medium fertility, contrast with the ungrateful lands of the old crystalline massifs to east and west.

**The Region of the Lower Loire.** In its lower course the River Loire flows across the old rocks at the southern end of the Armorican Massif. The region, known as La Vendée south of the river, is an old peneplain of low relief, and unlike the Paris Basin, its rocks are infertile, being composed of crystalline schists, granulites, and granites, which are quarried in places, and they are generally devoted to pasture, woods, and moorland. The valley of the River Loire forms a narrow ribbon of fertility across this area, and at its mouth is the considerable port of Nantes (241,000) and its outport of Saint Nazaire.

The position is not so advantageous as the site near the mouth of the longest river of France would suggest, for the purely agricultural character of the hinterland provides neither a large market for imports nor produces goods which are exported abroad. Nantes, however, imports 'colonial' products such as cocoa, sugar, palm oil; it has established factories to work them up, and also metallurgical works using imported coal, and oil refineries. A ship canal has been built, permitting vessels of 21-ft draught to reach the port. St Nazaire acts as an outport besides possessing the chief shipbuilding yards of France. Above Nantes the river is practically unnavigable as it suffers alternately from too little and too much water, for its upper basin and feeding area in the Massif Central consist mainly of impermeable rock, with a consequent quick run-off; moreover, the floods bring down large quantities of granitic sand which form troublesome sandbanks at low water.

**The Paris Basin.** (5) *The Coastal Regions of Normandy and Picardy.* This is the most thickly populated part of the basin apart from the central region immediately around Paris. The region is mainly developed on chalk, apart from the western section bordering the Armorican Massif where Jurassic limestone and marls appear, but both chalk and limestone are generally covered with superficial deposits of clay-with-flints (mainly to the west of the Seine), and *limon* (mainly to the east of the Seine). Moreover, the region benefits from its long sea border on the English Channel, for although the coast possesses only one great port, Le Havre, where the Seine estuary provides a good harbour, yet it has a number of smaller ports, fishing towns, and holiday resorts. Some of the towns, e.g. Dieppe and Boulogne, combine all three functions. The central part of the region also benefits from being crossed by the most useful river in France, and the north-eastern part from being near the main coalfield of the country.

East of the Cotentin Peninsula, which belongs to the Armorican Massif, the little-disturbed sedimentary rocks of the Paris Basin begin with the Jurassic measures, followed eastward by a narrow strip of Liassic marls. Both of these give rise to *bocage* country (see p. 257), similar to that of the adjacent Armorican Massif. The *limon*-covered limestones of the Campagne de Caen, whose dry soils offer one of the most favourable sites for cereals in Normandy, provide a quite exceptional stretch of hedgeless 'champagne' country. The port of Caen (93,000) itself is linked by the canalised River Orne to the sea and exports the agricultural products of Normandy (butter, eggs, vegetables) to England, and also iron-ore worked here in the Silurian measures. The annual output of ore is about 3 million tons.

Between the Campagne de Caen and the Seine are a number of *pays* which, though developed on chalk, have rich, humid soils, owing partly to superficial deposits of clay-with-flints, as in Lieuvin, and partly to the development of broad, alluvial valleys, as in the Pays d'Auge. The latter, with its valleys of the Touques, Dives, etc., is the richest producer of cider and cheese (e.g. Camembert) even in Normandy, which is famous for these commodities. In the Collines de Perche, on the south, an anticline of Cretaceous sandstone forms one of the few features of marked relief to be found in the western part of the Paris Basin. With a good deal of superficial clay, it is *bocage* country, with meadows devoted to the rearing of cattle and horses.

East of the Seine the deposits of *limon* covering the chalk in the Pays de Caux provides a good soil for wheat and sugar-beet, and agriculture approximates to that of Picardy (Fr., Picardie), but the Vexin Normand south-east of Rouen with less *limon* has more diverse farming.

The old historical name of Picardie is still often applied to the northern part of the Paris Basin on either side of the Somme. This region is traversed by a number of gentle anticlines and synclines running from north-west to south-east, of which the chief are the denuded anticline of Bray, which borders the region on the south-west, the syncline of the Somme–Avre Valley, and the anticline of Artois, which borders it on the north-east and which is denuded in the west to form the Boulonnais. The denuded anticlines disclose sands and clays below chalk and are moist lands suitable for cattle pasture, but the rest of the area is essentially an undulating lowland of *limon*-covered chalk. Patches of clay-with-flints and the presence of four wide, marshy valleys rescue the region from the monotony of, say, Beauce. As in Beauce, large, arable farms predominate, particularly for wheat and sugar beet: the by-products of the latter, supplemented by forage crops, are of value to the important cattle rearing industry which during the last sixty years has taken the place of the former sheep rearing. The valleys in general are waterless, as in all the chalk country, but a few rivers still maintain their way, in spite of the lowered water-table. Of these the most important is the Somme, whose marshes formerly served as a marked obstacle to movement from east to west, but have largely been reclaimed and devoted to market-gardening. The old town of Amiens (108,000) on the Somme and St Quentin farther east on the old route between Flanders and Paris, both have isolated textile industries, originally working the local wool, now mainly cotton, jute, and flax. Numerous sugar crushing and refining mills are to be found in the countryside.

**The Coast.** The English Channel was formed in geologically recent times, probably round about 5000 B.C. Previously its site had been occupied by the valley of a large river, which was fed by tributaries both from England and France, and which rose presumably in the Wealden-Artois anticline and flowed south-westwards. When the marine invasion started, cliffs began to form and the remains of truncated tributary valleys may be seen along them, for example between Tréport and Ault. Since then oscillations of level have occurred, but generally the coast is cliff-edged, with gaps where the rivers reach the sea. Along the Picardie coast, however, the change in direction from east–west to north–south allowed the buildings of sandspits (*cordons littoraux*) with material derived from the cliffs of La Caux, so that between the sandspits and the old cliff-edged coast lagoons were formed, which silted up and formed first marshes, and later with the aid of man were turned into dry land. The whole coast is thus generally inhospitable, apart from the estuaries, and these in their narrow chalk valleys are, with the exception of the Seine, too small for large vessels, even the small cross-Channel steamers having to be backed in to Boulogne as they cannot be turned in the narrow harbour. Boulogne (105,000) and Fécamp are the most important fishing ports, the former and Dieppe being noted packet stations. Numerous holiday resorts have developed owing to the proximity of Paris and of the dense population of the industrial north. Among these may be mentioned Deauville and Trouville to the west of the Seine estuary, and Le Touquet and Boulogne to the east.

Only the Seine estuary affords entry to large vessels and in addition offers a way far inland. Le Havre (182,000) is a modern port developed to meet the growing size of ships, and the Seine is here bordered by a sufficient breadth of alluvium for docks to be excavated. In addition to its cargo traffic it is also an important liner and passenger port, although challenged by the development of Cherbourg. It is second only to Marseilles in cargo tonnage, and has shipbuilding and various other industries including oil refining, and sends oil by pipeline to Paris. Rouen (121,000) is the old historic port of the Paris Basin, and is situated at the lowest bridging point, but although on tide-water it is about 90 miles up the tortuous, incised meanders of the river, and vessels drawing up to 30 ft can reach the port only at high tide. It is the chief coal importing port of France, and the place of transhipment to the Seine barges. It also imports raw materials for its own industries, particularly cotton textiles, shipbuilding, and heavy chemicals.

**The North-Eastern Industrial Region.** The low anticline of Artois, generally less than 600 ft high, forms no break between the Paris Basin and the similar Belgian Basin on the north-east. There is the same concentration on sugar-beet, wheat, and stall-fed cattle on the same *limon*-covered chalk, while farther north in Flanders are moister soils on which hops, flax, and other crops are added.

In the midst of this land of old-established, rich agriculture, the discovery of Coal Measures below the Cretaceous rocks led to the establishment in the nineteenth century of a large industrial district. The coalfield stretches from west to east in a narrow band, some 6 to 10 miles wide, on the north of the Collines d'Artois, and extends eastwards across the Belgian frontier. It is thickly built upon by small mining and manufacturing towns which form a great industrial conurbation, with occasional centres of importance, such as Douai and Valenciennes. A considerable iron and steel industry has grown up here (3 million tons of steel yearly); locomotive building and heavy engineering are important, but the principal industry is textiles, which are made just north of the coalfield. This industry is an ancient one, originally based on the wool from sheep on the neighbouring chalk lands and from the Ardennes, and on the local flax for whose preparation the waters of the Lys have been

famed since the Middle Ages.   The old towns took a new lease on
life with the discovery of the coalfield and new towns sprang up, so
that there is now a large conurbation of over 750,000 people, with
Lille (196,000), Roubaix (111,000), and Tourcoing (88,600) as nuclei,
all occupied in the woollen, linen, and cotton industries.   Armen-
tières on the Lys still specialises in linen.   In addition there are
important, though scattered, alimentary industries, preparing sugar,
beer, butter, cheese, and chicory.

The region possesses an intricate system of canals, still in great
use for carrying the bulky raw materials, coal, iron-ore, wool, and
cotton, to and from the coalfield, and linked to Paris and to the
coast at Calais (69,000), Gravelines, and Dunkirk (Fr., Dunkerque)
(28,000).   A steel works has been built on the coast at Dunkirk; for
transport it will use both the sea and improved canal connexions
with the Valenciennes area.   This new plant will produce over a
million tons annually.   The port of Dunkirk, although artificial, is
the chief one of the area, and its other industries include engineering,
oil refining, textiles, and brewing.

**The Armorican Massif.**   The Armorican Massif is a low dissected
peneplain never exceeding 1,400 ft in height and generally below
600 ft.   The region consists of Pre-Cambrian and Palæozoic rocks
which have undergone two periods of folding, the first of which
affected the Pre-Cambrian rocks and the second rocks of all ages up
to the late Palæozoic measures.   It seems that this area was never
a highly contorted mountain mass such as the Alps, but experienced
less intense folding, similar to that of the French and Swiss Jura.
Consequently metamorphism was less intense, and many rocks,
especially the shales, retain their original character.   These shales
form the lower ground, the higher ground generally being formed
of granites and of hard metamorphic rock such as gneisses and
quartzitic sandstones.   In general, the relief bears little relation to
the structure, and although the higher land follows the direction
of the strike, which is from east to west in the north and from south-
east to north-west in the south, yet it corresponds to the harder
rocks and not to one particular formation, or to either anticlines
or synclines.   There are two main areas of broad uplands, the
northern running eastwards from the Mts d'Arrée (1,283 ft) in
western Brittany to the hills of Alençon (1,368 ft) and a southerly
line running parallel with the south coast to the Gâtine Hills of
La Vendée, south of the Loire.   Both uplands have many gaps,
the southern line especially being discontinuous as well as seldom
reaching above 600 ft.   The land falls gently to the coastal and the
interior lowlands on either hand, except in the west of Brittany, where
the Montagnes Noires (1,069 ft) interpose a third zone of upland.

21 View in Puy de Dôme area. The volcanic soils of this area are utilised in the valleys for arable farming; and on the hill slopes for pasture. The steeper slopes are however forested.

FRANCE

22 Aerial view of the Tarn gorge at St Chely, Lozère. Note the shallowness of the river at the time of year when the photograph was taken and the sparse vegetation on the limestone. The massive nature of the limestone stands out well in the meander. The view also gives an indication of the problems of transport in parts of the Massif.

23   Fessenheim and the Rhine.   View of Ammerschwir, Haut Rhin.


FRANCE


24   Two contrasting views of Alsace.   The upper shows one of the new Rhine barrages and associated barge canals; and the lower the vine-covered Vosges slopes, nucleated settlement and flat Rhine plain beyond.

The Armorican Massif has often been compared to the south-western peninsula of England, although the latter is very much smaller, but in physiography, land utilisation, climate, distribution of the population, in fact both in landscape and mode of life there are strong resemblances between 'L'Ouest' of France and the West of England. Both show rocky coasts, drowned estuaries, incised valleys, and low but accidented relief. The explanation is the same in both cases. After peneplanation both were partially submerged, but re-elevation brought about rejuvenation of the river systems with the result that the valleys, especially near the coast, are deep and narrow. Later submergence gave a drowned coast-line. In climate also the two regions are similar. With their large number of rain days, and their mild winters, grass scarcely stops growing, cattle and horse rearing is favoured, while early spring vegetables and flowers do well near the coasts, though flowers are much more important in Devon and Cornwall. Like Devon and Cornwall, the Amorican Massif also has meadows, mixed cultivation, orchards, and woodland in the lower lands, and moors on the granites and on the higher regions generally. Both have worked deposits of granite and kaolin.

The French apply the term *bocage* to the interior of the Armorican Massif, e.g. the *Bocage Normand* east of the Breton basin of Rennes, and the Bocage Vendéen south of the Loire. The *bocage* type of country is not densely wooded, in spite of the term meaning wooded or shrubby. It actually carries little timber in solid stands, but rather it resembles a landscape in Devon or south-west Wales (e.g. Cardigan or Carmarthen) with scattered trees and many hedge-rows. The characteristic hedgerows are found nowhere else in France outside 'L'Ouest', but are exactly like those of Devon and parts of Wales, and consist of earthy banks, sometimes supported with stones, and overgrown with vegetation. The soils are generally impermeable, water is abundant, and the population is disseminated in small hamlets and isolated farms. There are few towns of any size.

The eastern edge of the Armorican Massif runs from Falaise (near Caen in Normandy) via Argentan, Alençon to Angers, and this edge is marked by a fertile depression forming an important line of communication, The *bocage* type or country, however, is continued eastward beyond this margin on to the western part of the Paris basin, where impermeable clay-with-flints often overlie Cretaceous and Jurassic strata.

The Armorican Massif falls into four sections, the western peninsula or Brittany, the northern Cotentin peninsula in the old province of Normandy, the Bocage Normand and Bas Maine east of the Rennes basin, and the lands round the mouth of the Loire which include La Vendée. Brittany in particular shows a well marked individuality, with its Celtic language, similar to Welsh, and its aloofness from the rest of France. The general poverty of the soil would suggest a scanty population, but, on the contrary, the density is above the average for France, though the coastlands (Ar Mor = 'the land of the sea') are much more thickly populated than the interior (Arcoet = 'the land of the woods') with 400 – 500 per square mile as against 100 – 150 per square mile in the *bocage*.

Until the middle of the nineteenth century, this was essentially a subsistence area producing cereals and potatoes, sending any surpluses to other parts of France. Towards the end of that century there came a marked revolution in land use, new crops were introduced, animals became of increasing importance and the development of railways together with the increasing standard of living stimulated the demand for fresh fruit and vegetables.

The coastlands have the benefit of a mild climate and early spring for the cultivation of 'primeurs' in the pockets of land around the numerous bays. Produce can reach the Paris markets ahead of that of the central Paris Basin, although later than that from the Mediterranean regions. Within the Brittany coastal belt there are local specialisations – onions at St Brieuc, asparagus in la Marais de Dol and cauliflowers in the vicinity of Paimpol and St Malo. As this industry has grown much in response to British demand it is more highly developed on the north than on the southern shore and produce is exported via St Malo (17,000).

As in the Channel Islands the coastal lands are fertilised by seaweed and crushed sea shells; and the rocky-bay-indented coast is a great tourist attraction, particularly the west and north shores.

The fisheries are mainly inshore on both coasts, but are otherwise different, the southern coast specialising in the sardine and tunny fishery, including the canning of the fish in numbers of factories along the coast. Here too fishing is on a larger scale and much more full-time than in the north where it is sometimes combined with agriculture. The waters of the northern coast are generally too cold for sardines and the catch is various (turbot, conger, ray, mullet), while the fisherman and his family, in addition, usually cultivate a small plot of land. Paimpol specialises in lobsters, and like Binic and St Malo sends ships to the Iceland and Newfoundland fishing grounds.

The interior of Brittany and also the southern coastlands have developed an important dairying industry, for which the interior basin of Châteaulin is especially noteworthy. Forage crops, to supplement the grass, are now being widely grown instead of the buckwheat and rye which were needed for human consumption in the pre-railway days, when Brittany was obliged to be economically self-contained. Farms are small and generally scattered.

There are few large towns in Brittany, Brest (139,000) is of national importance owing to its naval dockyards, but, although possessing a magnificent harbour, it has not developed as a commercial port for various reasons, including the lack of industrial concentration in the hinterland, and the slowness of the railway journey across the dissected Armorican Massif. Rennes (154,500), the former capital, in a fertile basin on the eastern edge of Brittany, is an important route centre, the crossing point of road and rail from Paris to Brest with those from St Malo to the mouth of the Loire; it is also the chief commercial and agricultural processing centre and the only university town. Lorient (62,000), once the base of the French East India Company, on the southern coast of Brittany, is ranked second or third among French fishing ports, though its naval station has declined in importance.

The Cotentin peninsula of Normandy resembles Brittany for the most part, but the neck of the peninsula round Carentan lies in a synclinal depression, which is flat and marshy, though dyking and drainage have reclaimed much of the land for cultivation. The change in the direction of the coast, from a generalised east–west line in northern Brittany to a north–south in the western Cotentin, has caused the partial silting of the bay of St Michel and the development of marshes along the west coast. These are absent from the short north coast, and there Cherbourg (39,000) has been developed largely as an artificial port behind a three-mile-long breakwater, Grande Rade, completed in 1853. It has however suffered as a transatlantic terminus from the expansion of Le Havre.

The Bocage Normand is typical *bocage* country developed on a dissected peneplain of old rocks, with flat-topped granitic uplands rising to over 1,000 ft. The typical occupation is the rearing of horses and cattle, the latter being sent away for fattening. Bas Maine, to the south, is rather similar country, but is lower and threaded by the Mayenne valley.

**The Basin of Aquitaine** (Le Bassin Aquitain). The basin of Aquitaine forms a great triangular plain, bordered by the Pyrenees on the south, the Massif Central on the north and east, and the sea on the west, but connected by means of broad lowland corridors to the Paris basin and the Mediterranean coast. It is almost entirely agricultural, and has less variety of climate, hydrography and soils than the Paris basin.

There is a much greater proportion of Tertiary deposits here than in the Paris Basin. They reach to the coast on the west and to the Pyrenean folds on the south and continue also through the gate of Carcassonne into the lowlands of Languedoc. On the east the Tertiaries abut on to the old Silurian and granitic rocks of the south-western part of the Massif Central, and it is only in the north-east of the basin that the Cretaceous measures are found, stretching from the coast (Ile d'Oléron) south-eastwards nearly to the River Lot north of Cahors, while the Jurassic measures lie still farther to the north-east in a band stretching from the coast (Ile de Ré) south-eastwards to the River Aveyron. The Cretaceous measures are mainly, and the Jurassic measures almost wholly, formed of lime-stone, but the Tertiaries, unlike those of the Paris basin, mainly consist of clays and marls. The Cretaceous and Jurassic outcrops together form a belt of dry land on the north-east of the basin, while the Tertiaries have plenty of water and are generally more productive and more thickly peopled.

There are two exceptions to the fertility of the Tertiary region, both occurring on the outer margins of the outcrop, namely the Lannemezan on the south and the Landes on the west bordering the Bay of Biscay. In the first case the Tertiary rocks have been covered by immense fan-shaped screes (*cônes de déjection*) brought down in the Ice Age by glacial torrents from the high central Pyrenees. These thick deposits of gravel extend for fifty miles from south to north and have now been divided into isolated plateaus by feeders of the Garonne and Adour. These valleys with their steep eastern (west-facing) and gentler western slopes, become flooded with the summer torrents, while the plateaus themselves are high (*c.* 2,000 ft), dry and bare, and afford only sheep pasture. Population is very scanty and mainly confined to the valley sides, where maize forms the staple crop. The Landes region is a low, flat plain which has been invaded by wind-blown sand from the coastal dunes. The real mischief, however, is the presence at some depth of a band of impermeable rock (*alios*), caused by the cementing of the band by an iron oxide, aided by humic acids produced by the decomposition of roots and plants. This prevented the water in the subsoil escaping and aggravated the lack of surface drainage, a lack which was caused by the level relief and by the blocking of surface drainage seawards by a line of dunes, except for the Gulf of Arcachon. These dunes developed from a *cordon littoral*, which substituted a straight coastline for a former uneven one, the earlier bays becoming lagoons. In their original state the Landes were covered by dry, sandy stretches alternating with swamp, the former giving pasture to a few sheep. Reclamation in the nineteenth century took the form of planting and fixing the coastal dunes, cutting drainage canals, and planting the interior with pine woods, which now cover half the total area. The pine trees utilise the water of the subsoil, help to lower the water-table, and provide some humus, in addition to their valuable immediate use for turpentine, timber and pasturage.

Petroleum was discovered at Parentis in 1952 and the oil is piped to refineries near Bordeaux. Other areas of production in Aquitaine are at St Marcet, Proupiary and Lacq in Basses Pyrénées. Production is about 2 million tons a year. Lacq is more important as the major centre of natural gas production and is linked by pipelines to Pau, Toulouse and Bordeaux (see Fig. 26). These finds have led to the development of refining and petrochemicals. The gas is so rich in sulphur, that France is now a sulphur exporter rather than importer. Brown coal is mined near Aujuzank some 35 miles south of Parentis (750,000 tons a year).

The central part of the basin, however, is a great zone of rich agriculture. This lowland is traversed by the main river of the basin, the Garonne, which almost monopolises the drainage, though the Adour drains the south-west corner. The whole of the Garonne plain is devoted to agriculture, noted as much for its variety as for its richness. Cereals, especially wheat and to a less extent maize, orchards, cattle rearing, and vineyards all flourish. Along the Garonne estuary, however, the cultivation of vines is almost a monoculture, the wines, particularly those of Médoc and Graves on the west of the river, being of good quality and widely exported through Bordeaux. Bordeaux also *imports* considerable quantities of good wine from Languedoc, Algeria and other places, and after suitable treatment these also acquire the name of 'Bordeaux'.

Bordeaux (249,000) is the largest town of the basin, standing on the left bank some 60 miles up the Garonne estuary. It was first used by the Phœnicians and Greeks and since Roman times has been the chief port of the south-west. During the time it was held by the English in the Middle Ages it flourished as a port for the export of claret. When the English left in 1453 it declined and did not regain its importance until the development of trade with France's overseas colonies, especially those in the Americas, in the eighteenth century. During that century its population trebled to over 125,000. Since then, while expanding, it has failed to become a really great port owing to the lack of an industrial hinterland, the loss of some overseas possessions and the poor quality of the Garonne for navigation in spite of the Midi and Garonne lateral canals. Today it is still concerned with colonial products, for example groundnuts and sugar and their processing. It also handles crude oil and raw materials for the chemical industry. Its exports are wine and spirits, pit props and other wood products and refined oil products.

Modern factories and refineries have been built on the hitherto neglected right bank. Owing to silting and the increasing size of vessels, outports have been built at Pauillac, where there is also a large oil refinery, and at Verdon. The latter was damaged by the Germans in 1944 and the decline in liner traffic has resulted in the port not being completely repaired. At present it is used mainly by pilgrims *en route* to Lourdes.

The basin of Aquitaine has no natural centre and its two most important towns are on the margins. Toulouse (324,000) is an ancient political and intellectual centre of southern France, and possesses a large university. It is also a very important route and market centre and the chief industrial town of the basin. Agricultural processing accounts for one large group of industries but explosives, textiles, engineering and chemicals are also important. Power is provided by the coalfields of the southern central Massif, hydro-electric power from the Pyrenees and natural gas pipeline from the St Marcet and the Pauillac fields.

To the north-east of the fertile Tertiary deposits are a number of 'pays' which are transitional to the Massif Central. Between the rivers Vezère and Aveyron on the Jurassic limestone are the karst-like plateaus, or Causses, of Quercy (1,300 – 2,000 ft). These plateaus are devoted almost exclusively to sheep rearing, Rocamadour cheese being made from the milk. But the deep, sheltered valleys with their alluvium form rich, if limited, agricultural land, devoted to maize, vines (for brandy in particular), and other fruits. Périgord, on the Cretaceous chalk, shows the same contrast, but the uplands are lower (*c.* 600 – 700 ft) and are partly cultivated, partly under sheep pasture and partly under oak forest, in which the famous truffles (a subterranean fungus) are found. Its prehistoric 'grottoes' of Cro-Magnon, La Madeleine, and Le Moustier along the River Vezère are caves and holes in the chalk.

North-west of Périgord the 'pays' of La Petite Champagne reveals its character in its name and is typical of the plains that accompany the River Charente from Angoulême westwards. The sides of the valley, however, produce excellent vines, which are made into brandy, named 'cognac' after a small town on the river.

**The Central Plateau** (Le Massif Central). This high, triangular-shaped horst is not as centrally placed as its name implies, and being entirely surrounded by lower lands it forms less of an obstacle to movement than one might think at first sight. It attains an average height of about 3,000 ft, with an extreme elevation of a little over 6,000 ft. But the massif, though rather scantily populated in parts, especially in the south, is by no means devoid of resources. It is deeply penetrated by the two tectonic depressions of the Allier and upper Loire in the north, it possesses some mineral resources in a number of small coal basins, and even the plateau itself was long ago cleared of forest to provide pasture, and in places, arable land.

The rocks of the massif were folded in early Carboniferous times, the strike being north-west to south-east in the western half and north-east to south-west in the eastern half. The whole region underwent denudation which resulted in its reduction to a peneplain. In this peneplain granites and crystalline schists predominated, and the Coal Measures, which had been deposited in lake-filled synclines after the folding had taken place, were in some cases preserved. It should be noted that the Coal Measures were never very extensive, and that they were subsequently often disturbed by volcanic intrusions, by lateral compression which threw them into folds, and by later faulting. Small wonder, then, that the coalfields of the Massif Central are small and the coal expensive to work, but the coal is of good quality. During the calm of the Mesozoic period limestones were formed in the sea surrounding the island-massif, but in mid-Tertiary times the earth movements connected with the building of the Alps made their influence felt, and the massif was raised to a great height, especially in the south-east, where the high Cévennes Mountains now form the main watershed of the plateau. Included in this uplift were certain areas of Jurassic limestone, whose unfolded strata were raised *en bloc* to form the high plateaus of the Causses in the south and south-west of the massif. Extensive faulting also occurred, particularly in the north, where large segments of the plateau foundered and were covered by fresh-water lakes in the valleys of the Allier and upper Loire,

An active vulcanism developed along these lines of weakness which continued into Quaternary times and raised up volcanoes and spread lava plateaus over the centre of the massif. The highest point of the massif today is formed by one of these volcanoes, the Puy de Sancy (6,188 ft), and though the Tertiary volcanoes are considerably weathered, those of the Chaine des Puys, of Quaternary date, are extraordinarily well preserved. The older lava plateaus have been weathered sufficiently long to cause extensive decomposition and now provide the most fertile soils of the massif. Apart from the volcanoes and the foundered zones, the plateau still retains its peneplain appearance, with rounded outlines and large areas of flat or undulating ground. The uplift naturally caused a rejuvenation of the river system, and, particularly in the south, where the uplift was greatest, the larger rivers have formed deep, narrow, and wild valleys (e.g. the Tarn and Lot), while short torrential streams have fretted the south-eastern edges of the plateau into mountainous forms. On the other hand, the north-western part, which was little uplifted, retains its senile shallow valleys.

It can be seen from the above brief summary of its physical history that the Massif is an area of considerable diversity, which is increased by differences in the relation of the various parts with the plains at their feet, and also by differences of climate, the southern border of the Massif coming under the Mediterranean régime, and the whole of the western part being more oceanic than the eastern.

The Massif can conveniently be divided into four sub-regions, (a) eastern, (b) central, (c) southern, (d) north-western.

(a) *The Eastern Part of the Massif*, bordering the great highway of the Rhône–Saône valley and lying east of the upper Loire, consists of an alternation of highlands and depressions, all oriented from north-east to south-west in the direction of the strike. This means that the area was open to penetration from both sides, and through routes, utilised by road, railways, and canal, traverse the depressions. The mountain masses from the Morvan in the north to the Vivarais in the south are generally composed of granite, possess rounded forms, and are regions of much bog and poor agriculture, though cattle rearing and some cultivation of hardy crops such as rye and buckwheat are carried on. Some patches of forest remain and the Vivarais still cultivates mulberry trees, though in decreasing quantities. The lower parts of the eastern slopes bordering the Saône–Rhône depression are devoted to vineyards, but north of Lyons these slopes are mainly formed of sediments belonging to the Saône basin, and do not strictly belong to the ancient massif. Population and activity are concentrated in the depressions of Le Creusot and St Etienne, though industry has also invaded the highlands round the latter town. Both these depressions possess small coal basins, the output from the former being *c*. $1\frac{1}{4}$ million tons a year, and from the latter $3\frac{1}{4}$ million tons. Le Creusot (33,000), now joined by an agglomeration of factories and housing to Montceau les Mines with a combined population of about 60,000, was actually the first place in France to use coke in smelting iron, the first blast-furnace of that kind being set up in 1782 by an Englishman. The Canal de Centre, built shortly afterwards between the Saône and Loire, was of great value to the industry before the railway era, but owing to the absence of iron and the shortage and expense of the coal, the industry only keeps going thanks to its historical momentum and to its safe position, remote from a frontier, for the manufacture of armaments. The same remarks are true for the St Etienne iron industry, and though there is a less acute shortage of coal, yet without the restrictions on imports foreign coal could undersell the local product, and Cardiff coal did so in 1913 on these central coalfields themselves. The industry survives by concentrating on products needing a small amount of raw materials but considerable skill and experience, such as cutlery, small arms, and special steels. St Etienne (199,500)[1] was once important mainly for textiles. It is still associated with silk, cotton and lace manufacture, being influenced by nearby Lyons, but is also deeply concerned in highgrade steel (using local coal) and associated armaments, aircraft, motor vehicle parts and machinery.

(b) *The Central Part of the Massif* includes the great tectonic depressions of the upper Loire and Allier, the associated volcanic areas, and parts of the old crystalline plateau on which the volcanic deposits rest. Along the upper Loire are three tectonic basins, but only the most southerly one, that of Le Puy, has really fertile soil, since this basin alone is surrounded by Tertiary volcanic outpourings. The remains of these deposits, which once filled the whole basin of Le Puy, form isolated stacks – often picturesquely crowned by old churches – and also the columnar basalt 'organ pipes' of Espaly (cf. Fingal's Cave, Staffa). The western part of the Allier depression also has fertile soil derived from the volcanic region of the Auvergne, but the eastern part, with soils from the crystalline Mts du Forez, is less productive. Vichy on the eastern border is noted for its thermal springs. The former feudal borough of Mont Ferrand stands on a small hill about half a mile to north-east of Clermont to which it was joined in 1731. The former remains today with a population of about 8,000 and is a 'fossil' city that has not shared at all in the industrial prosperity of its neighbour. Clermond-Ferrand (131,700) on the western border, the second largest town of the Massif, uses fruits of the plain and milk of the mountains to manufacture jams and chocolate. The initiative of its inhabitants has led to the establishment of rubber manufactures, particularly motor tires, the firm of Michelin employing some 70,000 people. Other industries include engineering, transport equipment and chemicals. The volcanic region of the Auvergne shows a great variety of volcanic forms in many stages of denudation. The Cantal and Mt Dore are gigantic volcanoes eaten into by erosion, and the parts left upstanding are the actual *puys* or peaks, of which the Puy de Sancy (6,188 ft) is the highest mountain of the whole Hercynian zone of Europe. North of Mt Dore and immediately west of Clermont-Ferrand is the extraordinary landscape of the Chaine des Puys, with sixty or more volcanoes stretching as far as the eye can see, mostly with beautifully preserved craters

[1] The 'conurbation' of St Etienne, stretching along the depression, numbers about 350,000 people.

and lava streams.   But it is the old lava plateaus, known as *planèzes*, round the older volcanoes, which offer the good soil of the district, and these, though bleak, carry excellent pastures devoted to dairy cattle.

(c) *The Southern Part of the Massif* presents an alternation of crystalline and high limestone plateaus, which very seldom assume a mountainous appearance, apart from the Montagne Noire and the Cévennes on the southern margin.   The limestone plateaus known as 'Causses' are renowned for the deep, cañon-like valleys cut by the rivers Lot, Tarn, and their tributaries.   Here, as in other parts of the Massif, tourism is becoming increasingly important,  The plateaus themselves exhibit all the usual karstic phenomena, including dolines, swallow holes, and underground streams.   Economically the Causses are poor, though grass with its high calcium content supports flocks of sheep.   Sheep's milk cheese (Roquefort) is made in the valleys and sheepskin clothing at Millau and similar towns.   Many transhumant sheep from the Mediterranean plain of Languedoc pass the summer here.   The similar but lower Causses of Quercy haze already been mentioned in connexion with the basin of Aquitaine, The Alès coalfield on the south-east of the Cévennes has an annual output of about 3 million tons, and the Carmaux-Albi coalfield, to the west of the massif, of 2 million tons.

(d) *The North-western Part of the Massif* presents the most uniform appearance.   The whole of this plateau of Limousin aad Marche is a crystalline peneplain with poor soils and few resources. The higher parts of the plateau carry heath and some forest; the valleys are barely scooped out, are encumbered with alluvium, and are mainly swampy.   Only sheep and store cattle can be reared and these with difficulty, but towards the borders, where the effect of the rejuvenation of the river system has been felt, the valleys have a greater slope and when drained give good pasture for cattle. Western Limousin, west of Limoges, is sufficiently low-lying and penetrated by wide valleys to be much warmer.   Sweet chestnuts flourish and long afforded the staple food crop of the region. Limoges (118,500), noted for its porcelain made from china clay weathered from the local granite, is on the main route from Paris to Bordeaux, which here takes a short cut across the low north-western portion of the Massif.   It is also an important leather-making centre.

The Massif Central is one of the regions from which emigration to the richer parts of France has long taken place.   A specialised form of this emigration was that of the famed companies of stone-masons who carried out work far afield in the Middle Ages; they built, for instance, the cathedral at Uppsala in Sweden in the twelfth century. At the present time there is some seasonal migration to the vineyards of the surrounding lowlands, but the spread of the railways in the nineteenth century allowed the people to abandon subsistence farming and to concentrate on cattle rearing, for which most of the region is best suited. In spite of these improvements migration still continues and indeed this region is still the major area of population decline in France, especially the departments of Creuse and Haute Loire.

**Alsace.** This is the western part of the Rhine rift valley from Basel northwards to the River Lauter. Bordered on the east by the Rhine and on the west by the Vosges, Alsace comprises essentially a lowland some 10–20 miles in width and 80 miles long from north to south. The Mesozoic limestone and sandstone foothills of the Vosges are dissected by deep river valleys. The sharp descent from the Lorraine plateau to the Rhine valley is very marked, as is also the improvement in climate. The fertile and sheltered valley sides support vineyards and orchards while the swift-flowing streams early provided industrial water-power sites. A series of terraces lead down to the actual floodplains of the Ill and Rhine. Much of the marshy plain (*Ried*) of the former has been reclaimed for agriculture and between this and the Rhine floodplain is a strip of *Löss*-covered higher ground which is used for settlement and routeways. The Rhine *Ried* has been gradually regularised, canalised and banked.

The Rhine itself is an important waterway but above Strasbourg barges of 1,000–1,500 tons can use the river only for some three months of the year owing to the small depth of water. Although the river is paralleled by the Rhine-Rhône canal this is of smaller capacity and for years engineers and politicians have been concerned with the improvement of the Rhine navigation; a complicated problem since the river here forms an international boundary.

At present a series of barrages, diversionary canals and power stations are in course of construction which will ultimately give continuous passage to barges to Basel as well as providing a considerable amount of electric power. Already much has been done and only two stretches remain to be completed (Fig. 28, p.268). The associated power stations are amongst the largest in the country.

Much of the actual Rhine valley is under crops of wheat, sugar-beet, tobacco, and chicory, and store and beef cattle are reared. Some pasture is provided by the reclaimed areas of *Ried*. In 1904 potash was discovered to the north of Mulhouse by the Germans. Now about 8 million tons of potash are produced annually and provide the basis for a considerable chemical industry. Nearly 40 per cent of the potash is exported.

France's first oil was discovered at Pechelbronn but production is now small compared with that of Aquitaine.  Industry is repre-

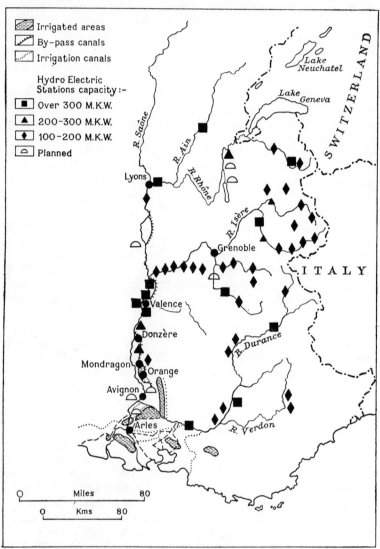

Fig. 32.  RHÔNE–SAÔNE VALLEY: POWER AND IRRIGATION
M.K.W. in the Key equals one thousand Kilowatts.

sented in the main by chemicals and the textile industry which is concentrated mainly in the Vosges foothills and the Vosges proper.

Strasbourg (230,000), however, possesses a more diversified industrial economy. This former Roman and Gallic stronghold, standing between the Ill and the Rhine (with its actual core on an island in the Ill), where both are bridgeable, lies astride the lowland routeway from the Paris basin through the Saverne gap in the Low Vosges and on into Germany by way of the lowland between the Black Forest and Odenwald. Owing to its position it has long been an important route centre and was a key position in the past struggles between France and Germany. It is an inland port of some importance handling over 8 million tons of freight yearly and has a wide variety of industries including barge building, paper, tobacco, and oil refining (being at the northern terminus of the pipelines from Lavéra, which lies at the mouth of the Etang du Berre). Strasbourg was chosen as the headquarters of the Council of Europe.

The other major town is in the south. Mulhouse (109,000) is another important route centre standing at the eastern end of the Belfort gap between the Vosges and the Jura. It was first incorporated with France in 1797 and is another fortress town. Its industries are principally concerned with textiles and chemicals (from the nearby potash deposits).

This eastern portion of France in many ways belongs to central rather than western Europe. For some years (1871-1918) it was under German jurisdiction and most of the inhabitants are German speaking.

**The Rhône–Saône Depression and the Mediterranean Coast.** This area of very varied relief consists of the Rhône–Saône corridor, the bordering mountains of the Alps and Jura on the east, and the Mediterranean coastlands of Provence to the east of the Rhône and of Languedoc to the west. The area may be looked upon as being mainly an elongated basin of sedimentation, with Tertiary deposits running from north to south down the long central axis, but the bordering Cretaceous and Jurassic measures on the east have been thrown into folds, while on the west their outcrop is not continuous, the Tertiaries in places coming directly against the old rocks of the Massif Central.

The Saône–Rhône corridor is particularly noted as a routeway from north to south and for the branch routes which strike off from it, though the waterway itself is neglected owing to the rapid flow of the Rhône, fed as it is from Alpine rivers, while the slow-moving Saône is used for local traffic only. Road and rail routes from the Paris Basin and Lorraine converge across the Plateau de Langres on the head of the Saône depression, where the route from the Rhine rift valley (via the Belfort gap between the Vosges and Jura) also comes in. Important routes, though more difficult ones, lead from the Saône valley across the Jura to the Swiss plateau and thence across the Alps to Italy, while farther south is the Lyons–Mt Cenis–Turin route directly across the Alps. The importance of these routes in connecting the busy well populated regions of north-west Europe with the Mediterranean lands has already been emphasised.

The Saône–Rhône corridor, in fact, is more than a mere routeway, for it has considerable agricultural importance and also contains the most important silk-manufacturing centre of Europe. Its agricultural importance however is limited by its narrowness. The Saône plain above Lyons is the widest part, the Tertiary lowlands extending here for some 40 miles from east to west and 130 miles from north to south, whereas the Tertiaries of the Rhône valley, between Lyons and the defile of Donzère (south of Montélimar), have undergone considerable uplift and the present lowland consists of small basins alternating with narrows. This narrow picturesque section between Lyons and Donzère, with its accompanying old castles and little towns, though some 80 miles long, varies in width from about 10 miles to practically nothing at all. Below the Donzère gorge the highlands recede from the river, leaving a triangular plain whose Mediterranean climate causes its agriculture to differ in some ways from that of the rest of the corridor. Throughout the region hot summers and early springs greatly favour plant growth and allow a rich and diverse agriculture in spite of the fact that the soils are by no means always fertile. The Tertiaries themselves are sandy in places, but the worst soil is probably produced by the morainic material brought down by the former glaciers of the Rhône and Isère which reached the Rhône valley just above and below Lyons during the Great Ice Age. The marshes and lakes of La Dombes in the angle between the Saône and Rhône are developed on impermeable glacial clays.

The main agricultural wealth of the corridor lies in its vineyards, the most famous being those of the Oolitic scarp of the Côte d'Or to the south-west of Dijon, where the renowned wines of Burgundy are produced, though indeed all the lower outer slopes of the Massif Central overlooking the river produce wines of good repute, and less esteemed wines come from the plain itself. Dijon (138,000), the old capital of Burgundy, is the organising centre of the industry and also possesses other industries including beer, biscuits, tobacco, chemicals and cement. Its importance as a route centre has already been noted.

At the other end of the Saône lowland, situated at the junction of Saône and Rhône, is the great city of Lyons (Fr., Lyon; 524,600), the third largest town in France. The city was made the capital of Gaul under the Romans owing to its nodal position at the convergence of the Rhône–Saône route with (*a*) the route between the Jura and the Alps leading to the Swiss plateau; and (*b*) the routes westward across the narrow eastern highlands of the Massif Central to the Loire.  Its modern importance is due to its silk industry and banking organisation, but a detailed study of the growth of both reveals how much they owe to artificial fostering on the part of the French kings from the fifteenth century onwards.  The raw material for the silk industry at first came from Italy, the Levant, and Spain, but the cultivation of the white mulberry, on whose leaves the silk-worms are nourished, gradually spread in southern France from the fourteenth century onwards, although raw silk continued to be imported.  In modern times the greater part of the raw silk has been imported from Japan (75 per cent) and Italy.  This highly organised industry maintains its world reputation largely owing to the experience, skill and initiative of the people engaged in it.  Most of the production is exported to the USA.  The area has also attracted a considerable portion of the synthetic fibre industry.

Lyons's nodal position has made it a very important road and rail centre and it will become an increasingly important inland port with the gradual improvement of the Rhône–Saône.  The good communications, abundant hydro-electric power, and coal from the fields to the west and south led to the development of a diversified industrial economy.  Industries include chemicals, electrical and mechanical engineering, leather, tin-plate, food processing and glass making, located in Lyons itself and its suburbs like Villeurbanne and the surrounding towns that together constitute the Lyons conurbation.  As already mentioned, the industry has spread into the neighbouring mountains, particularly those of the Massif Central.

Although the Rhône valley is a lowland routeway the river itself, which is unpredictable in depth and rate of flow and liable to flood, has been a menace to the large scale development of water transport.  This fact, together with the need to irrigate farmlands and to overcome the lack of fuel resources, has led to the development of the Rhône valley project.  For some time a Rhine–Rhône link suitable for large barges has been envisaged and this project will provide a vital part.  The Compagnie Nationale du Rhône was established in 1921 with the task of producing hydro-electric power and improving the means of navigation and irrigation between the Swiss border and the sea.  Amongst the parts already completed are the Genissiat, the Donzère–Mondragon and Montélimar projects.  By 1962 the power stations on the projects were already producing some 8 million kWh per annum and together with the Grère and other Alpine stations, account for some two-thirds of France's hydro-electric power; the scheme was also irrigating about 0·3 million acres; and already as a result of improved navigation water traffic has doubled in the last ten years. When the project is complete electricity production will be at least double that of 1962. By 1965 all the project north of Orange was finished and it is expected to complete the works here and at Avignon and Vallabrêgues so that the whole waterway will be open for barges of up to 1,500 tons by 1972, utilising twelve locks. At present a motorway is under construction through the valley.

Apart from greatly improving navigation the abundant electricity has led to the development of a number of industries particularly the electrochemical and metallurgical. On completion also another 0·25 million acres at least will be receiving direct irrigation from the river in the lower Rhône valley. The alternating constrictions and broadenings in the Rhône valley have helped the siting of dams.

**The French Jura.** Accompanying the Saône lowlands on the east is the highland region of the Jura, averaging some 3,000 ft and reaching to over 5,000 ft.

This region presents the classic example of a simple type of folding, where practically every anticline forms a ridge and every syncline a depression, though it is only the eastern side, partly in Switzerland, which shows this type of country (*Jura plissé*), and in the central and north-western parts the rocks are unfolded though faulted, and plateaus have resulted (*Jura tabulaire*). A markedly individual river system has arisen in the folded portion, with sluggish longitudinal courses in the synclines and short rapid stretches where the rivers break through the anticlines in gorges (*cluses*). The alternation of ridges and valleys lends itself to a complicated system of river capture; the 'incredible' course of the River Doubs with its abrupt hairpin bends presents one of the best examples of a river of this kind. Some of the longitudinal valleys have no apparent outlet, but drain away through the Jurassic limestone which forms the greater part of the mountain system. The synclines often retain Cretaceous deposits, sometimes even Tertiaries, which are usually clayey and retentive of moisture, while bands of clays in the Jurassic series cause the occurrence of powerful springs. The Keuper marls of the Triassic system, sometimes brought to light in the denuded anticlines, and always present at depth, are also little permeable.

The Jura Mountains have a heavy precipitation and were originally mainly forested. Clearing has taken place whenever good pasture would result and the whole area has become an important dairying country, the cattle being turned on to the higher pastures in summer and stall-fed from the rich produce of the valley meadows in the winter. A good deal of forest still remains in the higher parts, and on the lower slopes, below 1,000 ft, vines are cultivated. Settlement is agglomerated in large villages and small towns, principally at the entrance of *cluses*, e.g. Pontarlier and Nantua, both on main international railway lines which insinuate themselves through the mountains along the synclines or cut in short tunnels through the anticlines. Besançon (99,500), an old frontier town on the Doubs, near its entrance to the Saône plain, is the main market town of the French Jura, and the main centre of the watch and clock industry, which is widely scattered in many small workshops in the Jura villages.

**The French Alps of Savoy and Dauphiné.** The Alps border the Rhône valley closely from Lyons southwards. Their outer folds (Préalpes), formed mainly of limestone, are known as autochthonous, in contrast to the transported material of the *nappes*, and have a north–south strike. (See Chapter 23.) They reach a height of over 6,000 ft. but are deeply penetrated by two great valleys, the upper Rhône and the Isère. A good deal of river capture has taken place here, and before the Ice Age the upper Rhône flowed northwards to Lake Geneva and along the depression between that lake and Lake Neuchâtel. Also the Isère, by cutting a deep longitudinal furrow in a band of soft Liassic rock, has beheaded the transverse valleys of the Lac du Bourget and the Lac d'Annecy, though the through routes remain, the former being used by the Paris–Mâcon–Mt Cenis railway line. The Isère and Arc valleys provide narrow but fertile ribbons of agriculture almost into the heart of the Alps, and contain also a considerable industrial development especially for the manufacture of paper, aluminium, steel and ferro-alloys, and calcium carbide, using hydro-electricity. Grenoble (159,500), at the junction of the Drac and Isère, is a route centre and a university town noted for its researches on hydro-electricity, and has considerable manufactures such as silk, gloves, paper.

The high inner French Alps which include the high crystalline massifs of Mont Blanc, Pelvoux, and Mercantour are little productive, but water-power is being further developed, and the fine scenery attracts large numbers of tourists.

The most widespread occupation of the Alps of Savoy (Fr., Savoie) and Dauphiné is the rearing of dairy cattle. There is also some forestry.

**The Mediterranean Lands of France.** South of the Montélimar gorge begins the Mediterranean coastal region. The Rhône itself forms a delta owing to the tidelessness of the Mediterranean Sea, and there is no suitable site for a great port actually at the entrance of the great Rhône–Saône corridor. Marseilles is 25 miles to the east of the delta, away from the river silt which is carried westward by a coastal current.

The region of Mediterranean France has a unity of climate, but in relief and structure the area shows many contrasts, there being marked differences between Provence on the east of the Rhône and Bas Languedoc on the west. The latter is mainly a lowland, but the former is a complex region of folded mountains and old massifs, together with basins and valleys. In the Alps of Provence two sets of folds have come in conflict with one another. The main strike, especially in the west, is from west to east, i.e., the same as that of the Pyrenees, and it is considered that these folds are older than the Alpine folds, which here are from north to south, and that they interfered with the development of the latter. Peneplanation seems to have been carried to an advanced stage, and the subsequent re-elevation has produced a great development of plateau forms in the limestones of which the mountains are largely composed.

These east–west folds are also visible to the west of the mountain zone though they form only low ridges standing a few hundred feet above the surrounding Tertiary plains, as Les Alpilles, northeast of Arles. Everywhere, however, the dry climate and the permeability of the rock produce only a thin growth of thorny or resinous plants, so that the southern Alps, unlike the northern, are good for sheep pasture only, and even in the low ridges the bare white limestone gleams through the scanty vegetation. The consequent heavy weathering has given these hills a singularly rugged and mountainous appearance in spite of the low altitude.

The basins and plains to the east of the Rhône and north of the delta are highly cultivated, and often irrigated, mainly from the Durance. The cultures are extremely varied, but early vegetables have a considerable place, and are usually grown on the sunny side of thick cypress hedges, which are reinforced by bamboo fences, as a protection against the Mistral, a cold northerly wind which blows in winter and spring. This wind, whose name means 'The Masterful', is merely the usual cold north-east wind which blows at the back of a cyclone, but its coldness is here intensified by the contrast between the warmth of the Mediterranean coasts and the cold of the mountains, and the wind is especially strong because the narrow Rhône valley acts as a flue or funnel. The expression is often used locally for any rather strong wind regardless of its direction. Almonds, peaches, and other fruit trees are common, as well as vines. Avignon with its textiles and canneries is now mainly a centre for tourists who come for the sunshine and for the fine Roman and medieval buildings of the lower Rhône valley. East of the main distributary of the Rhône is the region of La Crau, whose surface is covered with pebbles and boulders brought down by a former course of the Durance. According to the old saying: 'Parlement, Mistral et Durance sont les trois fléaux de Provence'. The dry surface is still largely devoted to winter pasture for sheep which in summer are taken up to the Alps, but it has been partly reclaimed for olive growing and other cultivation.

Immediately east of La Crau rises the low chain of the Estaque, at the western end of the rocky coast of Provence. West of Toulon and east of Nice the limestone Alps reach to the coast, but between these are the two crystalline masses of the Maures and the Estérel, separated and bordered on the landward side by depressions of softer (Permian and Triassic) rocks, which afford opportunities for cultivation and movement. The valley of the River Arc with its Tertiary sediments continues the line of the Argens depression. The coast is rich in harbours, but Marseilles is the only commercial port, Toulon (168,800) being a naval base and shipbuilding centre. The main resources of the Provençal coast are its sunshine and scenery and more particularly its accessibility to the people of north-western Europe, many parts of the Mediterranean coasts being equally endowed but suffering from remoteness. Cannes, Nice (290,700), Monte Carlo, Mentone, and many smaller centres are too well known to need comment.

West of the main distributary of the Rhône is the silt-formed delta known as the Camargue, a salty and marshy area devoted mainly to cattle pasture with some sheep, The more northerly drier parts are being reclaimed for vineyards, market-gardening and other cultivations, including rice (*c.* 60,000 acres). The plain of Low Languedoc consists of an alternation of Tertiary lowlands with low limestone hills known as *garrigues*, the former being chiefly devoted to vineyards, partly irrigated, and the latter to olives and winter pasture for sheep. Over half the French output of wine is produced here, mainly *vin ordinaire*. Nîmes (103,000) and Montpellier (121,000) are old centres near the junction of *garrigues* and plain. The coast is an entire contrast to that of Provence as it is edged by a dune-crowned *cordon littoral* behind which are lagoons, some of which have been drained for cultivation. Sète (36,000) is a small artificial port, with a large export of wine.

At present new irrigation canals are being built from the Rhône westwards into eastern Languedoc and are bringing considerable areas of land under more intensive agricultural use and making farming a much more profitable enterprise. The project is due to be completed by 1980 when 0·75 million acres will have been added.

Further west along the coast salt extraction by atmospheric evaporation of sea water is an important industry. Perpignan

(84,500) is the chief town of the Roussillon plain. As a whole Roussillon is not very fertile but on some of the gravel terraces almonds, olives, apricots, and cherries are grown. Perpignan itself is an old fortress and is the chief market centre controlling the eastern lowland route into Spain.

Marseilles (Fr., Marseille; 773,000) is the leading passenger port of France, closely followed by Calais, and the leading port by value of merchandise in tonnage. Founded by the ancient Greeks, the city long played an important rôle in Mediterranean trade, but its modern prosperity dates from the last quarter of the nineteenth century. The imports are of raw materials, largely from the Orient via the Suez Canal, from North and West Africa and South America, and include vegetable oil, fruits, cereals, wool, silk, cotton, rubber, sugar, coffee, and mineral oil. The exports are mainly of manufactured goods, including cotton and silk tissues, metal objects, vegetable oils, sugar, rubber goods. Considerable manufactures have grown up in the neighbourhood, including soap, originally made from local olive oil, silk tissues, flour, sugar, and other products manufactured from the imported raw material.

A canal ($10\frac{1}{2}$ ft deep) connects Marseilles to the Rhône via the Etang de Berre. It pierces the Estaque in a tunnel $4\frac{3}{4}$ miles long, which was completed in 1927, and is part of a great scheme to improve the Rhône as a waterway. The sheltered waters of the Etang de Berre are bordered by a number of small ports, mainly developed since 1914, which handle a large tonnage of mineral oil, amounting to some 10 million. These ports, with plenty of level ground available, are complementary to the old port of Marseilles and are under the jurisdiction of the latter. Their industries include oil refining and associated petrochemicals, the manufacture of explosives, cement, chemicals, shipbuilding, and aircraft. The importance of crude oil imports has increased with the opening in 1962 of the South European Pipeline ($33\frac{3}{4}$ in) from Lavéra via Besançon to Strasbourg. In due course it will be linked with the Rotterdam–Cologne pipeline (see Fig. 26, p, 155).

**Economic Summary.** Unlike many countries of western and central Europe France has aimed at economic self-sufficiency as far as possible. Until recently agriculture has been the main employer but since the war industry has taken the lead and now accounts for one-third of the employment followed by agriculture with about one-quarter. The number of agricultural workers has declined rapidly, 1·3 million leaving agriculture between 1954 and 1962.

Although a relatively early start in the Industrial Revolution was initially a great help, France has been outstripped by the Federal German Republic. One hindrance has been that coal is both expensive to mine and of only mediocre quality. The production in 1960 was 58 million tons and was distributed amongst the principal coalfields as follows:

PRODUCTION OF MAIN FRENCH COALFIELDS (MILLION METRIC TONS)

|  | 1936 | 1960 |
|---|---|---|
| Nord and Pas de Calais | 28·4 | 30·9 |
| Moselle | 5·4 | 14·7 |
| St Etienne (Loire) | 3·2 | 2·9 |
| Le Creusot (Cévenne) | 2·4 | 2·7 |
| Alès | 2·1 | 2·6 |
| Others | 3·7 | 4·2 |
| Total | 45·2 | 58·0 |

France's relative fuel position is now somewhat brighter as the dependence of her industries directly on coal as a source of power has declined over the last half century. Much coal is now used in generating electricity; also France possesses a great hydro-electric potential of which a considerable proportion has now been harnessed and some 45 per cent of her electricity supply is water-generated. Small amounts of oil also are now produced in France (2·3 million tons in 1962) and the recent developments have turned Algeria into a major producer. Important natural gas resources have been discovered and are linked by a system of pipelines to Lyons, Bordeaux and Paris. Most recent of all is the development of atomic power, based on rich uranium deposits obtained near Rennes and Limousin.

Although France still has to import part of her coal needs (about 16 million tons a year), she exports considerable amounts of iron ore. Iron ore production in 1962 was 66 million tons, the largest production in Europe west of the USSR, although of low grade compared with the ores of Sweden and Lake Superior. This ore provides the basis of the French metallurgical industry, which is mainly located on the coal and ore fields, but supplies also the ports and the electro-metallurgical industries of the Alps and the Pyrenees.

Nearly two-thirds of the French output of iron and steel is produced in Lorraine and about one-quarter in the north-eastern industrial zone which is more important than Lorraine for engineering. Le Creusot and St Etienne have specialised in high-grade special steels and associated engineering products. Finally, in the Alps and Pyrenees there are numerous electric furnaces producing steel and ferro-alloys. It is in Lorraine and the north-east that more of the recent expansion in the steel industry has taken place, these being areas near to the 'hub' of the European Iron and Steel Community's production.

Apart from iron-ore France possesses important deposits of bauxite in the south Alpine department of Var (over 2 million tons a year), which provides the basis of the French aluminium industry. The large deposits of potash in Alsace are second only to those of Germany. On the Mediterranean and Aquitaine coasts and in Alsace some 4 million tons of salt are produced yearly.

The variety and importance of industry have increased greatly over the last twenty-five years. On the basis of numbers employed engineering is the chief industry with 1·4 million employees in 1962. Among the principal branches are automobiles (France being the third largest producer and exporter in the world, the chief firms being Renault, Citroen, Simca and Peugeot), aircraft and electrical engineering. As in other west European countries the textile and clothing industries are now less important. Textiles employ only about half a million, as against 1 million in 1931, and clothing workers have declined from 1 million to 200,000 in 1962. The woollen industry is largely concentrated in Nord (Roubaix and Tourcoing) and also in the Vosges. The cotton industry is principally located in Alsace, Nord and Normandy, and France ranks second as a European cotton manufacturer with considerable exports to the franc zone. France is particularly famed for the silk industry and Lyons is still the main centre with St Etienne as an important subsidiary. The recent development of artificial fibres has been particularly marked in the towns of the Rhône valley and the Paris region and France closely follows the Federal German Republic, United Kingdom, and Italy in European production.

The chemical industry is of increasing importance and complexity employing a labour force of over 0·25 million. The heavy chemical industry is located chiefly (a) on the coalfields of the north-east; (b) in the Alps, Pyrenees and along the Rhône where hydro-electric power permits the manufactures of calcium carbide and other electro-chemicals; (c) in the ports where petroleum is refined and fertilisers are manufactured; and (d) in Alsace-Lorraine where salt, coal and potash are available. Paris is the main centre of the pharmaceutical and cosmetic industries.

The alimentary industries are widely scattered, and chiefly concerned with wine, spirits, cheese, sugar refining, brewing, flour milling and confectionery. France is the most important wine producing country of the world, for although Italy has a greater acreage under vineyards the total yield is greater in France and the quality and variety of French wines remain unsurpassed.

Agriculturally, France is almost self-sufficient in temperate foodstuffs and, with the help of a protected home market, is one of Europe's chief wheat producers providing soft wheats for the export market. It is interesting to note that although France is nearly twice the size of the British Isles (215,000 v. 122,000 square miles), yet the population is smaller in numbers, and this in spite of the lower latitude and larger proportion of tillable land. One of the curses of French agriculture is the fragmentation of holdings and scattering of strips within holdings leading to uneconomic units which are unsuitable for modern farming techniques. However, as a result of an Act of 1941 a policy of *rémembrement* (consolidation) is being gradually carried out. The aim of this policy is to make the number of parcels smaller, the holdings larger, more easily accessible, and mechanised; although considerable strides have already been made in this direction in certain areas, a very considerable amount still remains to be done. Taken as a whole farms tend to be small, those over 50 acres being the exception. About one-third of the farms are worked by tenants and one-sixth by the practice of *metayage* by which the owner supplies the capital, the farmer the labour, and both share the produce in varying proportions. Of the total land area 35 per cent is cultivated, 23 per cent is under permanent pasture, 8 per cent rough pasture, 22 per cent is forested, 2 per cent is in vineyards and 2 per cent in orchards and market gardens. As a result of the Common Market France is expanding her market for agricultural products to the detriment of the agriculture of the Federal German Republic.

Owing to her large agricultural output, France is less vitally dependent on foreign trade than either the United Kingdom or the Low Countries, yet in volume of trade she ranks fourth in the world, only USA, the United Kingdom and the Federal German Republic having a larger share. Her main exports are agricultural products, particularly wine, manufactured goods like automobiles, chemicals and electrical equipment, and raw materials such as iron-ore, bauxite and wood products. Imports are principally non-temperate food products, coal, oil, cotton and certain engineering products. France has a considerable mercantile marine and in 1961, with a tonnage of 5·1 million tons, held fourth place in Europe and eighth in the world.

**The Status of France in Present-Day Europe.** At the time of the Napoleonic Wars, France was, after Russia, the most populous country of Europe. About 1801, her population numbered some 27 million as against 11 million in Great Britain, 18 million in the Italian states, and 25 million in the German states. Moreover, the Germans and Italians could not make their numbers felt because of their political disunity. The French superiority in numbers *vis-à-vis* her neighbours was maintained until the middle of the nineteenth century, but from 1870 to 1936 the total population increase in France was only 5 million, against 16 million in Italy, 20 million in the United Kingdom, and 28 million in Germany. The total population declined from 41,907,000 in 1936 to 40,519,000 in 1946, but rose to 46,300,000 in 1962.

The decline in the birth rate during the late nineteenth and twentieth · centuries was felt throughout north-western and west-central Europe, and was thus not confined to France, but it started earlier in that country and its results were felt more acutely there than elsewhere. The low French birth rate was partly offset by the immigration of foreigners, chiefly Poles and Belgians in the industrial districts of the north-east, Italians in the south-east, and Spaniards in the south-west. About 1½ million people of foreign extraction were living in France in 1962. Now the population of France is rising, as is the country's status, after the low ebb reached by 1945. The stature of France in Europe and in the world has grown with the expansion of her economy, membership of the Common Market, and the leadership of General de Gaulle.

## REFERENCES

*La France* (3 vols), by E. de Martonne and A. Demangeon, Paris, 1942, 1946, and 1948, Tome VI of the *Géographie Universelle*, is an authoritative study. P. Vidal de la Blache's *Tableau de la Géographie de la France*, Paris, 1908 and later editions, remains a classic. work. *France*, by H. Ormsby, London, 1950, gives a very detailed regional account. Among smaller works are *France, An Introductory Geography*, by E. Estyn Evans, New York, 1966, *Géographie de la France*, by L. Gallouédec and F. Maurette, and *The Geographical Regions of France*, by E. de Martonne, translated by H. C. Brentnall.

The great *Atlas de la France*, published in separate sheets from 1933 onwards, should be consulted; as well as the *Atlas Classique de la France*, by Schrader and Gallouédec, Librairie Hachette.

*The France Yearbook* contains much up-to-date statistical information.

Reference may also be made to the series of regional monographs, one of which is *Géographie de la Bretagne*, by M. Le Lannou, Rennes, 1952.

For a comprehensive series of photographs with explanatory texts the most valuable source is the five-volume *Atlas Aérien*, Paris, Gallimard, 1956–63, with its numerous oblique and vertical air photographs.

A recent series of regional monographs has been published under the general title of *France du Demain*. Paris, Presses Universitaires de France, 1959–62. In all there are eight volumes.

A good regional atlas is *Atlas de France de L'Est*, Nancy, Université de Strasbourg, 1959. The most up-to-date account of the country in English is provided by F. J. Monkhouse in *A Regional Geography of Western Europe*, New York, Praeger, 1967.

Two books on agriculture are worthy of mention – J. Klatzmann, *La localisation des cultures et des productiones animales en France*, Paris, Institut National de la Statistique et des Etudes Economiques, 1955, is very detailed and B. Oury, *L'Agriculture au Seuil du Marché Commun*, Paris, Presses Universitaires de France, 1959, deals with the other members of the Common Market as well.

Numerous articles appear in the geographical journals and there are recent ones in *Geography* on the oil industry (1957), iron and steel in Lorraine (1961), and 'Le Rémembrement en France' (1961).

### CHAPTER 13

# THE LOW COUNTRIES (BELGIUM, THE NETHERLANDS, AND LUXEMBOURG – THE BENELUX GROUP)

BELGIUM and the Netherlands have an interest and importance out of all proportion to their small size. The former, in the Middle Ages, showed the most precocious development of city life north of the Mediterranean zone, the earliest development of a great medieval textile industry outside Mediterranean Europe, and later led the way in the Agricultural Revolution which spread over the Continent. It was the first country to follow England in the Industrial Revolution and today has great manufactures and the most intensive agriculture of the continent. The Netherlands has long attracted interest by its unrelenting struggle with the sea, a quarter of its surface being actually below sea-level. This effort to create land where none existed before is still going on, and the great project of reclaiming the Zuider Zee has been partially carried out (see p. 293). The Netherlands' former possessions in the East Indies are an important witness to the country's long-continued overseas enterprise, though Belgium's former possessions in Africa were obtained only in the latter part of the nineteenth century. The position of both states at the junction of the Rhineland and the sea has given them commercial advantages of the greatest value. The Netherlands and Belgium, in this order, are today the most densely populated countries in Europe. The integration of the economies of Belgium, the Netherlands, and Luxembourg in the 'Benelux' Union is to some extent a resumption of former historical trends.

A word regarding nomenclature. The low-lying regions which we now know as part of the Netherlands and Belgium were formerly appropriately known as the 'Low Countries'. Nowadays only the northern section retains its title of the 'Netherlands' (Nederland) which perhaps is just as well, since the Belgian state, created in 1839, mainly out of fragments of ancient Flanders, Hainault, Brabant, and Luxembourg, includes a southern mountainous strip. The term Holland (=hollow land), however, properly applies only to one part of the Nederland, namely the part between the Maas (Meuse) estuary on the south and the Helder on the north, where

281

the land is mainly below sea-level, with the North Sea on the west
and the Zuider Zee (='South Sea') on the east.

The countries are transitional between central and western

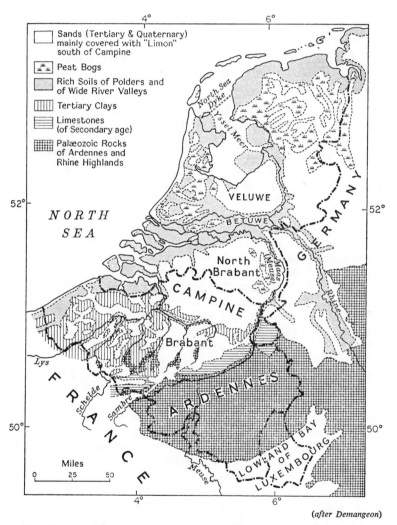

(*after Demangeon*)

Fig. 33.   GEOLOGICAL MAP OF THE NETHERLANDS AND BELGIUM

Europe. Culturally and climatically they belong to the west,
structurally they relate to central Europe.

# BELGIUM

With the exception of the Campine or Kempenland in the north-east, the natural regions of Belgium are symmetrically arranged in parallel strips, running from west-south-west to east-north-east, parallel with the North Sea Coast.

**The Ardennes.** Most of the southern portion of Belgium is occupied by the horst, or dissected plateau, of the Ardennes, a western continuation of the Rhine Highlands, which stretch from east-north-east to west-south-west following the direction of the strike. The highest part of the Ardennes lies near the south-eastern frontier of Belgium, and reaches nearly 2,000 ft. This, combined with the westerly position, gives the Ardennes a very heavy rainfall, and as the slates and greywacke, of which they are mainly composed, do not produce a fertile soil, the region is one of forests, moors, and pastures, with the emphasis on butter, pig raising and the rearing of store cattle. Settlement is found mainly in the valleys. The Ardennes are thinly populated, though there are a number of small tourist resorts.

Separating the High Ardennes from the Low or Sub-Ardennes to the north is the Famenne depression, developed in soft Devonian shales, and occupied in its eastern section by the River Ourthe. Here oats and fodder crops are grown and there are also some orchards.

In the region of the Low or Sub-Ardennes the old peneplain has been less elevated than in the High Ardennes, and heights do not often exceed 1,000 ft. The climate is less severe, and the region possesses bands of limestone, usually covered with loam (*limon*), which provide wide stretches of arable country amidst the forests. The Meuse cuts a rather deep valley from south to north through both these zones to join the Sambre at Namur, whence it continues in the direction of the upper Sambre and flows parallel with the strike.

**The Sambre-Meuse Depression and the Belgian Coalfield.** On the northern side of the old massif, and still partaking of its folded character, are the Coal Measures containing what is still the more important, but declining, coalfield of Belgium. The output averages about 13 million tons per annum (cf. 23 million tons in 1954) out of a total of 22 million tons for the whole country. The Coal Measures are a continuation of those across the frontier in France and they stretch eastwards from the coalfield of Mons to reach the Sambre valley near Charleroi, where they first outcrop on the surface. Thence the Coal Measures continue eastward, though only as a very narrow unproductive band along the east-west stretch of the Meuse valley, until they broaden out and once more become productive in the Liège district. From Mons to Liège, for a distance of some 80 miles, there is a great concentration of industrial development, the great iron, glass, zinc, and chemical industries of Belgium being situated on these coalfields. Even between the Charleroi and Liège fields, where hardly any coal is worked, it is brought on the canalised river to supply a considerable number of factories. The Belgian coalfield, like its continuation in France, suffers from contorted seams which make the coal difficult to work and therefore expensive; the average output per man being less than the corresponding output in Britain and a ninth of that in the USA, though the hours of work in Belgium are longer. Industry here, however, got an early start and has a good deal of historic momentum behind it, the first Belgian blast furnace to use coke being started as early as 1823, on the Liège coalfield at Seraing, by an Englishman, John Cockerill, whose firm grew until it is now one of the largest in Belgium. At first local iron-ore was used from the Carboniferous and Devonian limestones of the Low Ardennes, but practically all iron-ore now has to be imported. In the same way the zinc, formerly obtained near Moresnet, is now almost exhausted, but the refining industry remains.

The industrial region is composed of a large number of towns and villages of small and medium size, though Liège with its suburbs numbers about 250,000 and Charleroi with its satellites is about the same size.

An isolated but important industrial region is situated to the east of Liège round Verviers in the valley of the Vesdre. This region already manufactured textiles before the days of power looms, the principal geographic factor being the pure streams for washing the wool and for supplying power for fulling. The first mechanical spinning frame and power-loom for wool set up on the Continent were erected here about 1798, again by an Englishman, William Cockerill, father of the more famous John.

The Sambre-Meuse depression offers a route skirting the Ardennes and is used by the Paris–Cologne express. The valley itself, particularly below Namur, is about a mile wide and highly cultivated. Namur (33,000[1], with suburbs 50,000), an old route centre at the confluence of the Sambre and Meuse, has a certain amount of industrial development.

**The Belgian Plain.** North of the industrial region of the Sambre–Meuse depression begins the Belgian plain of unfolded Secondary, Tertiary, and later deposits. It is drained principally by the River Schelde, which flows across Belgium in a north-easterly direction from its source in France towards its mouth in the Netherlands. The plain can be divided into three parts, first the *limon*-covered

[1] Population figures are from 1962 census.

plain of middle Belgium centred on Brussels and comprising the old provinces of Brabant, Hainault, and Hesbaye, secondly the clayey and sandy plains of Flanders bordering the sea, and thirdly the sandy Campine which stretches to the north-east bordering the Dutch frontier.

*The Plain of Middle Belgium.* This slopes down gently northwards from a height of some 200 ft, near the Sambre-Meuse depression towards the wide low-lying valley of the Schelde. It is traversed by a number of the Schelde's right-bank tributaries which flow in rather deep valleys cutting down to the Hercynian core in the south, though they become shallower farther north. It consists largely of Tertiary sands in Brabant, has considerable stretches of chalk in the south-east in Hesbaye and of clays in the south-west in Hainaut, but almost everywhere the solid deposits are masked by a thick covering of *limon*, which gives the region a great uniformity. As in France, the *limon* is the special domain of sugar beet and cereals, especially wheat, but the agriculture is very varied and includes orchards and market gardens, and so intensive that the country is divided into minute, hedgeless fields, with a great deal of hand-labour bestowed upon them. There are practically no trees. In spite of the high density of population there is only one really large town, Brussels (1,453,600 in 1962, including suburbs), the capital of the whole country and once the seat of the princes of Brabant, whose choice was the deciding factor in the city's growth at the expense of neighbouring centres, such as Louvain. The city is the chief commercial and intellectual centre of the country and also carries on a very varied industry, the necessary coal being brought by way of the Cherleroi–Brussels canal, along whose banks many factories form an industrial link between the two conurbations.

*Flanders.* Flanders is an historical entity rather than a geographical one, since it comprises two distinct regions of different soils and relief, first, the flat maritime plain formed of clays deposited by a post-glacial invasion of the sea, and secondly the undulating, mainly sandy, plain which stretches south-east to include the valley of the Schelde. South of Ghent, however, the Schelde valley is crossed and the country partakes of the character of Brabant with stretches of *limon*. It is man, however, who has imposed a unity on this little area, principally by so improving the sandy soils of the interior that they are as productive as the naturally fertile clays of the maritime plain. The Flemings were able to do this owing to their discovery of the value of heavy manuring. This arose out of their desire to abolish the wasteful system of fallowing, in order to feed the large numbers of people in the medieval industrial cities, who, in the days of difficult transport, had to be supplied with food from the immediate neighbourhood. This leads back to the early development of city life in Flanders, which is one of the unique features of the country. Bruges, Ypres, and Ghent, for instance, are known throughout the world for their medieval monuments to civic pride. There is no wholly satisfactory explanation for this burgeoning of city life, though geographically the country had the advantage of being situated where three important river routes, along the Schelde, Meuse, and Rhine, make their way to the sea, whereas the Dutch were too preoccupied in early days in fighting the sea to be able to take advantage of the commercial opportunities offered by a somewhat similar position. The great, but in medieval times backward, land of England also provided a fine market just across the narrow seas for Flemish textiles and other goods, England afterwards supplying the raw material (wool), much in the same way that Africa now provides raw materials in exchange for England's manufactured goods. Of the historical aspect, including the enlightened legislation of certain of its rulers, this is not the appropriate place to speak, but when all the favourable factors have been displayed the fact remains that it was the quickness of the Flemings in seizing their opportunity that really counted, an opportunity which unfortunately for them soon passed. The great development of city life began in the twelfth century and decay set in at the beginning of the fifteenth century, owing partly to the silting up of the harbours and partly to political troubles.

The contribution to agriculture remained, and though the Flemings were not the only people in the world who discovered how to abolish the wasteful method of fallowing, yet it was from Flanders that the method spread to England and to other parts of Europe. The abolition of the fallow was combined with the growing of root crops as a winter feed for cattle, and the latter provided the manure necessary to restore the fertility to the soil, though sewage from the dense urban population and estuarine silt were also used. At the present day, manures of all kinds are employed, holdings are generally very tiny, many not exceeding half an acre, and cultivation is so intensive that the spade is commonly used instead of the plough.

The variety of crops grown is great, for example cattle food, including root crops, clover, and other forage crops, industrial cultivations such as sugar-beet, chicory, and flax, and cereals for cattle fodder and human consumption, though the area under cereals decreased considerably. Dairy cattle and pigs are common in both areas. The two regions, however, have a totally different appearance, the flat maritime plain being quite treeless owing to the force of the sea winds, while the undulating interior plain is a country of trees, each field being surrounded by a row of trees useful for timber.   It was on the basis of the home-grown flax that the Belgian linen industry grew up along the Lys tributary of the Schelde, the waters of the former river being renowned for their excellence for the, retting process, which consists of steeping the flax stalks until the fibres separate.   This textile fibre replaced wool in the sixteenth century when England had established a woollen textile industry of her own.   At the present day it has been partly superseded by cotton and artificial fibres, the earliest spinning jenny on the Continent for cotton being set up here in 1798.   The requirements of linen industry, however, are greater than can be supplied in the country itself, and flax is also imported.   The textile region of Flanders is centred in Ghent (156,000, with suburbs 460,000) at the junction of the Schelde and the Lys, and is spread through the Lys and Schelde lowlands in many smaller towns including Courtrai or Kortrijk (43,900), Lockeren (26,000), Alost or Aalst (45,200), St Nicholas-Waes (48,000), and Roeslare or Rouleurs (35,600).

The coast of Flanders offers no site for a large port; its ancient *cordon littoral*, which once contained useful gaps, now being a practically continuous line of sand-dunes, bordering the maritime plain.   Ostend (56,800) is a packet station, the chief fishing port of Belgium, and a seaside resort. The old town of Bruges or Brugge (52,500) is now connected by a ship canal, 26 ft deep, to Zeebrugge. A whole row of bathing resorts is found along the dune coast, which in all is only 40 miles long.

*The Campine* (*or Kempenland*).   This plain is an expanse of coarse sands and gravels brought down by the Meuse during the Quaternary Ice Age.   It extends across the frontier into Holland and is a barren windswept area of heath and marsh in process of reclamation. Sand-dunes often occur, in places fixed by the planting of pine trees. In certain areas the region resembles the Landes of Aquitaine with the same impermeable *alios* of ferruginous tufa at depth.   The area is being reclaimed by the planting of pine trees (*Pinus sylvestris*), by the bringing of water in canals from the Meuse to irrigate the dry soil, by heavy manuring, and the cultivation of nitrogenous crops. Root and forage crops, rye and oats are now widely grown, and the dairying industry is well established, but the most highly culti-vated region is around Antwerp and supplies this city with market-garden produce.

The discovery of the Campine coalfield, first worked in 1917, is having the effect of introducing manufactures, e.g. zinc, glass, pottery, rolling-mills, chemicals, electrical engineering and foodstuffs. Although the coalfield is at great depth, some 1,500 to 3,000 ft, the seams are more productive than those of the Charleroi-Liège fields, and the reserves are estimated at nearly three times the amount of the old Belgian coalfield—about 8,000 million tons as against 3,000 million tons. In 1960 the output was 8·8 million tons.

**Antwerp.**[1] This city of 251,000 people, or 878,000 with the suburbs, is the great port not only of Belgium but to some extent of the Rhineland and north-eastern France also. It is situated 55 miles up the Schelde but is accessible even at low tide to large ocean-going vessels drawing 35 ft of water. It is one of the three leading ports of the continent of Europe, vying in tonnage with Rotterdam and Hamburg, and handling some 46 million tons of goods annually. Serving, as it does, one of the most populous regions of Europe, it imports, as one would expect, foodstuffs and raw materials, and exports manufactured goods. It has become the centre of varied industries, such as the chemical, metal, engineering (including motor cars and ship-repairing and building), sugar refining and tobacco. Its diamond industry now exceeds that of Amsterdam. The Albert Canal linking Antwerp to Liège has helped not only development of Antwerp and industry in the Sambre–Meuse valley but also the industrial development of the Campine. Agreement was reached in 1963 for a canal link from Antwerp via the Eendracht and Volkerak to the Rhine, utilising in part the new Centre of the Delta Scheme.

**Economic Summary.** Belgium is, after the Netherlands, the most densely populated country of Europe with an average density of 782 per square mile, in spite of the fact that the thinly populated regions of the Ardennes and the Campine reduce the average. In Brabant the density reaches 1,400 per square mile (Fig. 34, p. 289).

The country depends to a very great extent on the export of manufactured goods and the import of raw materials. Thus *ca.* 1960, 90 per cent of the total production of glass was exported, 60 per cent of the textiles, and a high percentage of the chemical and engineering output. In spite of its size and a total population of only 9·25 millions (in 1960), Belgium is able to compete on the world market owing to a comparative abundance of coal, an established tradition of industrial skill, an unsurpassed system of internal communications by water, rail and road, and the possession of small holdings by large numbers of industrial workers which serve to supplement their income and to tide them over spells of unemployment. Indeed, the extent of ownership of small holdings by workers is probably unique in Europe. In the past the Belgian Congo, with its supplies of radium, copper, and diamonds, was an immensely valuable asset.

The exports consist of manufactured goods, particularly of metal

[1] Total population of the region is 2·3 million.

goods and engineering products, textiles, chemicals, and glass. The imports are headed by raw materials for the textile and metal-lurgical industries, followed by foodstuffs.

The business language and that of the educated classes is French to which Walloon, the language of the southern part of Belgium, has been assimilated.   North of a line joining, roughly, Courtrai and Brussels, Flemish is widely spoken, and after a good deal of agitation it has been placed recently on a parity with French in Flanders.

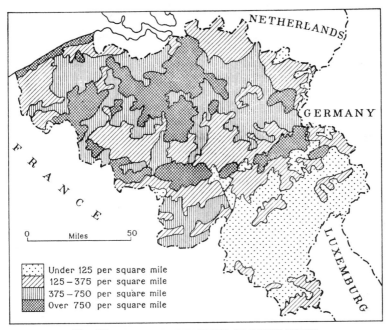

Fig. 34.  BELGIUM: DENSITIES OF POPULATION

Belgium is among the most thickly populated countries of Europe, with specially high densities (*a*) on the northern plains around Brussels, Ghent, and Antwerp, and (*b*) on the coalfield from the French frontier eastward along the Sambre–Meuse depression. Population, however, remains scanty on the infertile Ardennes.

Friction between the Flemish and Walloon elements in the population has grown serious.   In the past the south has been much more industrialised than the Flemish north, which resents the fact that many of the senior posts in industry and commerce are held by French-speaking people.   Then the rather higher population increase in the Flemish areas,[1] together with the industrialisation of

[1] In 1910 the Flemish area had 47 per cent of the population; in 1960 – 51 per cent.   In 1960 the bilingual Brussels area had 15 per cent of the population.

the north after the development of the Campine area and the Albert Canal, coupled with the decline of the textile and coal industries of the south (the latter losing some 60,000 jobs in five years), led to increased animosity. However the south has been able to weather the storms over employment problems caused by the development of new industries and the fact that many of the miners were Italian, Greek and of other nationalities. Within the next ten years it is hoped that the differences between the areas will be much reduced and this language problem will become less severe. The developing Common Market and the completion of the Moselle canalisations should do much to help the southern coalfield which in the need to export by sea was unfavourably placed. The 'Benelux' economic union (Belgium, Netherlands, Luxembourg) came into being in 1950 and has since been superseded by the Common Market (see p. 622).

**Luxembourg.** The little state, known as the Grand-Duchy of Luxembourg, has since 1947 been a member of the Benelux customs union. It lies partly on the Ardennes Massif, but mainly on the scarplands which continue from France to form the lowland bay of Luxembourg, part of which actually lies in the extreme south of Belgium. The Triassic and Lias series are here represented, the minette iron-ore of the latter being present in considerable quantities. During the last twenty years the output of iron-ore has fluctuated between 2 and 8 million tons and was 7·5 million tons in 1961. With the aid of home and imported ore and imported coke, the output of steel was 3·2 million tons in 1962, the highest rate per head of total population in the world. Luxembourg was linked in a customs union with Belgium as early as 1931. It has a population of 314,890 (1960).

## THE NETHERLANDS

The low-lying country of the Netherlands represents the western continuation of the Germano-Polish glaciated plain, although its southern province of South Limburg escaped glaciation. It shows an alternation of reclaimed marsh with high fen and poor sandy heaths, the marshland lying along the sea coast and river valleys, and the high fens and heathlands generally farther inland. Three large rivers have their mouths in the Netherlands, the Schelde, the Maas, and, most important of all, the Rhine, which also sends a distributary towards the Zuider Zee (now the Yssel Meer), and it is the presence of these great natural highways inland which gave and still gives the country its importance.

The same sequence of glacial and post-glacial oscillations of level took place here as in the German lowlands west of the Elbe and produced the same type of landscape and the same problems for man. (See Chapter 21.) The glacial sands and gravels extend as far as the Rhine and even beyond, and, south of this river, sand was widely spread by the swollen rivers of the Ice Age. Later the rivers cut broad shallow valleys, leaving the sandy tracts standing between them as low terraces, which exceed 300 ft high only in Veluwe north of Arnhem and generally range from sea-level to about 100 ft high.

At the end of Glacial times a considerable rise in the level of the sea led to the formation of the Straits of Dover, and this allowed marine currents from the south-west to sweep a sandbank or sandbar, afterwards crowned with dunes, in front of the coast. Marine clays were deposited at first behind this *cordon littoral,* but a slight relative gain of the land, and the rise in height of the protective rampart of sand-dunes allowed fresh-water lagoons to take the place of salt-water marshes, and in these the formation of peat began a natural process of land reclamation. During the first century A.D. the land probably stood slightly higher than it does at present, and the protective line of sand-dunes was less broken, though it was apparently never continuous at the mouths of the Rhine and Maas in Zeeland ( = 'sea land'). The Roman historian Pliny records that the native inhabitants took refuge during times of flood on large artificial mounds, the *terpen* or *werden* which are still to be seen especially in Zeeland and Friesland.

Unfortunately the level of the sea in respect to the land continued to oscillate, and on more than one occasion, for example in late Roman times, the sea breached the sand-dunes and again flooded widely, while much land was lost in the late Middle Ages by the transformation of the fresh-water Lake Flevo into the much larger salt-water Zuider Zee. Protective dyking had certainly begun before the year A.D. 1000, possibly as early as the seventh or eighth century, and were it not for man's success as a geological agent, all the western part of the Netherlands would now be under the sea.

Man also had to protect himself against the rivers, whose high-water level is above that of the surrounding land. Although the lower courses of the Rhine and Maas are so valuable for navigation, yet they have in reality semi-deltaic mouths, a unique phenomenon in the tidal North Sea. The explanation lies in the fact that the high tide advancing southward along the North Sea almost coincides with the low tide advancing up the English Channel, with the result that the piece of coast from the mouth of the Elbe to the mouth of the Schelde has only a very small tidal range, about 5 ft at Den Helder, increasing to 12 ft at the mouth of the Schelde. The main distributaries of the Rhine used to flow to the north via the Yssel river into the Zuider Zee (Yssel Meer) and to the west via the Oude

Rijn (= 'Old Rhine') past Utrecht and Leiden.  The latter river was the frontier of the Roman Empire, and though of negligible importance today, it is the only distributary which still bears the name of Rhine.  The present main distributary is the Waal, which near the sea becomes inextricably mingled with the distributaries of the Maas, and indeed takes the name of the latter river in the Brielle Maas or New Maas, the Oude Maas or Old Maas, etc.

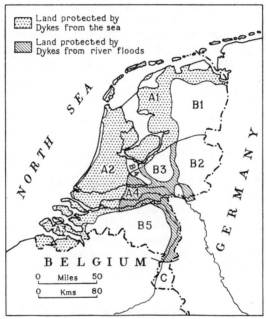

Fig. 35. THE GEOGRAPHICAL REGIONS AND DYKED LANDS OF THE NETHERLANDS

A = Polder Lands: (1) of parts of Friesland and Groningen.  (2) of North and South Holland.  (3) of Zealand.  (4) along alluvial valleys.

B = The Sandy Lands: (1) of Drenthe and interior Friesland and Groningen. (2) of eastern Gelderland and Overyssel.  (3) of Veluwe. (4) of the Utrecht–Gelderland ridge.  (5) of North Brabant and North Limburg.

C = The *limon*-covered plateau of South Limburg.

**Geographical Regions.**  The Netherlands fall naturally into two main types of country (see Fig. 35): (*a*) the low-lying fertile lands along the coast and along the main rivers, which require dyking; (*b*) the higher regions of the east and south, which are mainly sandy and infertile, except for the 'appendix' of South Limburg which is covered with fertile *limon*.  The dyked lands, which are below high-tide level or below the level of 'normal' river floods are the main historic lands of the Netherlands, whereas the higher, sandy tracts carried few people and were relatively unimportant until modern times.

**The Historic Dyked Lands.**    There are four main areas of *polders*, that is of drained and dyked lowlands, in the Netherlands.    First, the marine clays and peaty fens of Friesland and Groningen in the north, bordering the Wadden Sea, and partially protected by the 'breakwater' of the dune-covered Frisian Islands,    Secondly, the peaty fens of north and south Holland which lie east of the dune rampart stretching from the Helder to the Hook.    Thirdly, the marine clays of the Zeeland Islands and adjacent islands of south Holland.    Fourthly, the dyked riverine lands along the Rhine–Waal–Maas.    The reclaimed land has not only to be protected by dykes against tide and flood, but in many cases the water accumulated in the hollows has to be pumped up from the canals intersecting the polders to a sufficiently high level for it to be drained off to the sea or rivers, hence the many windmills in Holland, now almost entirely replaced by power pumps.    The more recently created polders, such as those on the sites of the interior lakes in Holland, the Haarlemmermeer and others, which were drained in the nineteenth century, are considerably below the level of low tide, and so also are the polders of the Zuider Zee, where it is hoped in time to reclaim an area of 552,000 acres (see Fig. 35).

By means of a great sea wall 18 miles long, the Zuider Zee has been made into a fresh-water lake, the Yssel Meer.    The first polder (50,000 acres) in the north-west, on the site of the Wieringermeer, was completed about 1930 and brought under full cultivation in the next few years; the north-east polder so-called (119,000 acres) was completed in 1942.    Eastern Flevoland (133,000 acres) was enclosed in 1957 and is completely settled with its main town at Lelystad.    Owing to change in farming economics and techniques and social developments, eastern Flevoland has a larger average size of farm than the north-east polder (75 acres as against 50 acres) and fewer villages.    The Maerkerwaard (150,000 acres) is now under construction and should be finished by 1968.    The whole project should be completed by 1980 when it will have added some 10 per cent to the arable land of the country.    The rich polder soil is ideal both for pasture and arable land, though dairying is becoming increasingly the dominating interest.    However, cereals, sugar-beet, tobacco, flax, vegetables, and other crops are grown, especially in Groningen and Zeeland.    The bulbs of the Haarlem district of Holland are world famous.    Along the inner side of the sand-dunes, where peat, silt, etc., could be added to the light soil of the older dunes, there is a belt of country devoted to intensive horticulture, including glasshouse culture, where a rural density of population of over 2,000 per square mile is attained in places. Like Denmark, the Netherlands has exceedingly good methods of marketing its dairy and vegetable products abroad.

South of the New Waterway the coastal region is fragmented into a series of islands by the Rhine distributaries. Here over 3,000 polders are protected by dunes and dykes. For over one hundred years these had not been seriously affected by flooding; then came the disastrous floods of 1953. In order to prevent such a recurrence the 450 miles of dykes would have had to be raised 6 ft, a long and expensive task. A cheaper solution with many other advantages is

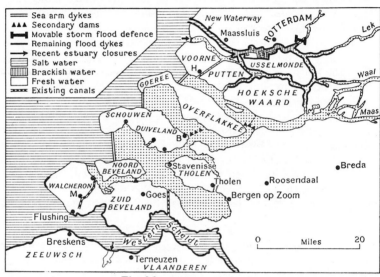

Fig. 36. THE DELTA PLAN

the $480 million Delta Plan (see Fig. 36). This involves joining the islands together by a new series of dykes some 10 miles in length, thus making most existing dykes a second line of defence. Other advantages include the making of fresh-water lakes which could be used for irrigation, the prevention of salt water damaging farm land in the minor distributaries whose water volume would have been decreased by dredging proposals for the Rhine and Lek, and the provision of much-needed facilities for recreation. The provision of a much more direct road link to the south-western areas which are relatively less developed, will also be provided, thus stimulating population, industry and agriculture in these areas. The chief difficulty is that the project cannot be completed fully since the amount of traffic using Rotterdam and Antwerp makes it impractical to construct lock gates on their approaches. The first dyke, between Walcheren and North Beveland was completed in 1961 and the whole project is due for completion by 1978.

**The Towns of the Dyked Lands.**    It is impossible to understand the urban life of the historic dyked lands without taking into account the fact that the towns are not dependent merely on the little Netherlands of some 13,500 square miles, but that their inhabitants derived their wealth also from centuries of sea trading, until recently from an empire of 50 million people, and from the land transit trade to Germany.    Hence the large size of the ports of Amsterdam and Rotterdam, the number of towns of medium size, and the number and importance of the university towns.    Urban development is concentrated mainly in Holland itself, where a double sea frontage and the Rhine distributaries provided unique opportunities for the establishment of trading ports, even though the actual sites left much to be desired.    Amsterdam (867,000[1]) on an inlet of the shallow but sheltered Zuider Zee, was already a great port at the end of the fourteenth century, but with the growth in the size of vessels a route had to be sought direct to the open sea.    The North Holland Canal was used from 1815 to 1876, and the North Sea Canal from 1876 onwards.    The latter, with a depth of 46 ft, reaches the sea at Ymuiden.    The suburbs of Amsterdam, including Zaandam, have a large and very varied manufacturing industry, with flour milling, brewing, sugar refining, margarine manufacture, and many others, and a total population of over a million.    In addition Amsterdam is the great commercial and intellectual centre of the Netherlands and the 'official' capital.    A number of towns lie on the eastward side of the line of sand-dunes, including Haarlem (170,000) and The Hague (Dutch, s'Gravenhage; 605,000), which is the royal residence and the seat of government, reputed the wealthiest town of the country owing mainly to the large numbers of business men who have settled there on retirement.

Most of the other towns are placed on the distributaries of the Rhine and some have decayed as the water channels have silted up.  Thus Utrecht (258,000) and Leiden (97,500), both university towns on the Old Rhine, were formerly of greater relative importance, but the northern distributaries of the Rhine have been abandoned progressively in favour of an ever more southerly channel, because of the increasing amplitude of the tides from north to south and the consequent increase in scouring action southwards. Although canals usually follow the old courses, the number of distributaries is now reduced to three: the Yssel, which flows past

[1] Population figures are, except where stated, estimates for 1962.

Deventer to the Yssel Meer, officially being allowed 11 per cent of
the total water; the Neder Rijn or Lek, which flows past Arnhem
(126,000) and Rotterdam, 22 per cent; and the present main
distributary, the Waal, flowing past Nijmegen (134,000) 66 per
cent.   Arnhem and Nijmegen owe their positions to the narrowing
of the flooded alluvial belt between two spurs of higher and drier
glacial ridges, which here come close down to the rivers and offer
firm, defensive sites.

The largest port in Europe is Rotterdam (730,000), handling
well over half of Dutch trade, reached its position of dominance
only in the nineteenth century.   It stands at the confluence of the
Rotte and the New Maas.   In the Middle Ages it suffered much from
the competition of Dordrecht but by the eighteenth century had
reached sufficient importance to establish outports downstreams
such as at Schiedam.   The increasing size of vessels and the gradual
silting of the Maas led to serious problems that were solved only by
the construction of the New Waterway, opened in 1884.   At the
western end of this canal stands the Hook of Holland, one of
the two main packet stations in the Netherlands (the other being
Flushing).   Opposite the Hook a vast new industrial and port complex known as Europort is being built.   Increasing trade, increasing
ship size and the continual demand for more land for building led
first to the construction of new facilities at Botlek, completed in
1959, and then to Europort.   Here channels and berths are being
dredged and the material used for reclaiming the marshland for
docks, industrial sites and railways.   The project is planned to take
oil tankers of over 65,000 tons, and has bulk ore and coal handling
plants; industries will include oil refining, iron and steel (with an
ultimate capacity of $2\frac{1}{2}$–3 million tons) and chemical plant. Facilities
will also be provided for rail, canal and road transhipment.   Although not finally due for completion till 1980 part is already open
and the availability of work has done much to increase the population of villages and towns in Voorne.   At present Rotterdam
handles 90 million tons of goods per annum and Amsterdam 11
million.   The Hook of Holland (Dutch, Hoek van Holland), at the
western end of the 'New Waterway', is a packet station towards
England, and so is Flushing (Dutch, Vlissingen) on the island of
Walcheren in Zeeland.

Except in Holland and the Rhine–Meuse delta, towns are not
well developed, Groningen (148,000) being the only large town of
the north-east, and Leeuwarden, the capital and largest town of
Friesland, having only 84,000 people.   Zeeland has many small late-
medieval towns, but the silting of the channels has hampered their
growth.

25 View in Ardennes, south of Semois. Note the dissection of the general plateau surface, the wooded slopes and the concentration of farming in the valley floor.

BELGIUM

26 Industrial view of Liège. Note the concentration of factories near the river, the tip heaps on the hill slopes, and the close proximity of the housing to the factories.

27 Aerial view of the centre of Amsterdam. In the centre background stands the Central Railway Station, built on concrete piles driven into the river marshland and behind it the port of Amsterdam. In the foreground is the old core of the city still clearly marked by the lines of the canals. The Damrak running down from the centre and then to the left the Singel, Heerengracht, Keisersgracht, and Prinsengracht. The very narrow nature of some of the intervening strips of land is obvious and along the tree-lined banks of the canals some of the medieval houses can still be seen. The canals are still much used for local goods traffic.

## HOLLAND

28 View of Burgh, Duiveland. Old medieval form of the town still preserved in the ring road, site on a slight mound above general level of the surrounding land; such mound sites are quite typical of older Netherlands settlements.

**The Sandy Areas.** The regions to the north of the Maas, lying in the provinces of Friesland, Groningen, Drente, Overyssel, Gelderland, and eastern Utrecht, consist of a complex of outwash sands, clayey ground-moraine, and morainic ridges, while the regions to the south of the Maas, in North Brabant and North Limburg, consist almost solely of outwash sands. The ice-sheet at its maximum reached a line running approximately from Nijmegen via Utrecht to Haarlem; but the ground-moraine, deposited beneath it, was later almost covered by outwash sands. South of the Yssel Meer are ridges of terminal moraines, consisting of sand and gravel, which actually form hills of some altitude, especially in the Veluwe (='bad land') which reaches 327 ft and in the Utrecht–Gelderland ridge (see Fig. 33, p. 282). These two heights almost surround the Geldersche Vallei, or valley of the River Ems, which marks the site of a former glacial 'tongue-basin'.

The sandy and gravelly soils are very poor in plant food. In many places the loose, white sand looks as unproductive as the sand of the seashore, and at best was a natural heathland and at worst, in Veluwe, was often piled into unstable sand-dunes, now planted with pine trees. In places, however, owing to the haphazard deposition of the glacial material and the consequent lack of drainage system, sphagnum peat bogs were formed, especially north-east of the Zuider Zee in east Friesland, Drente, and Groningen. Exploitation of the bogs for peat has long been carried on, but their reclamation began only in the seventeenth century, when the city of Groningen undertook an ambitious project of reclaiming a large area of 'High Fen' which lies to the south-east. Drainage canals were cut; the peat was dug out, the top layer being preserved and mixed with the underlying sand; finally the soil was heavily manured. This method, pioneered by Groningen, was later adopted elsewhere in the Netherlands, and in many other parts of Europe. The resultant soil gives excellent crops of potatoes, oats, and rye, and many kinds of vegetables. This type of reclamation, involving the creation of a complex drainage system, was a large scale enterprise needing considerable capital and organisation, and was sponsored by the large towns, special societies, etc. On the other hand, the heathlands have been partly reclaimed in the course of centuries by peasant farmers, who kept a few sheep, a few beehives, and cultivated a little patch of rye or buckwheat. Nowadays modern methods of agriculture, including the growing of root-crops which do well in this light soil, enable cattle to be kept, though these are mainly stall-fed, and the manure is used to improve the land. Cattle and pigs, the latter partly fed on skim-milk, and poultry now dominate farming on the heathlands.

There is a very considerable industrial development in the sandy areas, partly old-established and partly modern.   Domestic industry

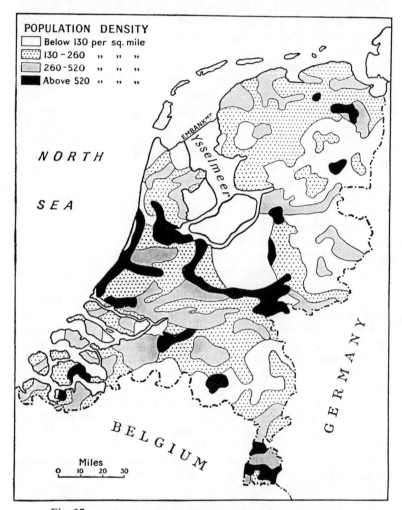

Fig. 37.   THE NETHERLANDS: DENSITIES OF POPULATION

Very high densities in the polders, the alluvial valleys, and the reclaimed highfens contrast with very low densities on the sandy areas of Veluwe, parts of North Brabant, and of the north-eastern provinces.

was started in order to supplement the meagre returns from agriculture, especially in the Twente region of eastern Overyssel and in North Brabant.   The Twente region is mainly devoted to cotton

textiles, the main centre being Enschede, but there are varied engineering and chemical industries; Overyssel actually possesses a
higher percentage (49 per cent) of its population engaged in industry
than any other province, though it is followed closely by North
Brabant and Limburg, each with 44 per cent. North Brabant
originally concentrated on the woollen textile industry, which
is still carried on at Tilburg (129,000), though the rayon industry
is of growing importance, but all kinds of secondary industries have
recently been added, especially the manufacture of electric lamps,
radio apparatus, etc., at Eindhoven (173,500). Just west of
's Hertogenbosch (74,000), the capital of North Brabant, stretches
the Langstraat, an almost continuous line of villages, containing
about 90,000 people, which concentrates the boot and shoe industry
of the Netherlands.

The Plateau of South Limburg. This small area is very unlike the
rest of the Netherlands. It consists of a dissected plateau of
dissected rocks, covered with deposits of fertile *limon*; it is generally
over 300 ft in height and in the extreme south-east reaches over
1,000 ft. Its soils are highly cultivated, particularly for wheat
and sugar-beet, but the region has acquired especial importance
during the present century as it contains the only workable coalfield.
The chief mining centres are Heerlen (74,000) and Kerkrade (50,000),
the output averaging 12½ million tons a year during 1960-62.

The old town of Maastricht (92,500) stands anomalously on an
enclave on the west side of the Maas, and was already important
in Roman times as the crossing point of the river.

Economic Summary. A number of historical circumstances combined in the fifteenth and sixteenth centuries to render the Dutch
conscious of the advantages of their geographical position, and having thrown off the Spanish yoke in the sixteenth century, they turned
their attention to overseas trading, and in the seventeenth century
were the leading maritime people in the world, though later eclipsed
by England. All that remains of the former Dutch colonies are
Surinam and the Netherlands Antilles; but the large size of the
country's trade was due mainly to the development of the Ruhr coalfield in Germany in the nineteenth century and to the transit trade
with the Rhinelands generally. The value per head of Dutch commerce was the highest in the world. The merchant fleet also revived
during and after the war of 1914–18, took eighth place among the
world's mercantile marine before 1940, and in 1962 figures as eighth
in the list. It may here be noted that the Netherlands have never
possessed the raw material for building ships, neither timber in the
old days nor iron-ore at the present day, but they were in a good
position for importing timber from Germany via the Rhine and

iron-ore from Sweden, and a large amount of shipbuilding is normally carried on between Rotterdam and Dordrecht, inclusive. During the present century there has been a great development of secondary industries, especially of the lighter types of engineering, and of the working up of colonial produce from the Dutch colonies, e.g. margarine, cocoa. The well known and old-established diamond cutting industry of Amsterdam is a comment on the wealth of the Netherlands as a result of its overseas trading ventures.

Agriculturally the Netherlands are characterised by high quality livestock and market-garden produce, with a well developed and highly efficient system of marketing, packing and grading. The chief contrast lies between the polder areas of the west and the sandier areas of the east. In the former there is little woodland (2 per cent as against 12 per cent in the east and arable is slightly more important than pasture (51 : 49 per cent), whereas in the east grassland accounts for 64 per cent of the farm land. Market-gardening predominates in the west while livestock are concentrated in the east. The farms of the polderlands tend to be larger than those of the heath areas. With free movement of goods the Dutch farmer would be able to compete on very favourable terms with his Common Market colleagues.

The Netherlands have only very limited resources of minerals. The chief is coal but it was not worked till early this century. The pits are highly mechanised and the largest pit in western Europe is in South Limburg. Annual production is about $12\frac{1}{2}$ million tons. In Drenthe and south Holland petroleum is produced ($2\cdot0$ million tons a year) and recent discoveries of large amounts of natural gas (reserves are estimated at 1,000 million cubic metres) in Groningen will do much to help industrial development in the country. Apart from these fuels the other important raw material is salt ($1\cdot1$ million tons 1961).

Until recently the Dutch have relied upon trade and the processing of materials before re-export. They lacked iron-ore, an essential ingredient for the early Industrial Revolution and it was not until the 1870s that industrial development on any scale began. Iron and steel production is concentrated at Ijmuiden at the sea end of the North Sea Canal where production commenced in 1918 and at the new works at Europort, where production will begin soon. Current production of steel is about 2 million tons. Shipbuilding is concentrated between Schiedam and Dordrecht with important specialised centres at Amsterdam, Flushing, and Groningen. The most famous branch of engineering is electrical engineering epitomised by the vast Phillips complex centred on Eindhoven. Other important industries are textiles, chemicals and especially food processing.

The Netherlands possess an excellent system of waterways totalling in all some 4,505 miles of which 1,062 miles are suitable for vessels of over 1,000 tons. In 1961 some 155 million metric tons of goods were handled by the waterways of which 60 per cent are international traffic. About 45 million tons of goods were transported up the Rhine and 25 million down the river.

Apart from the transit trade, exports are mainly agricultural, and consist chiefly of dairy produce, vegetables, and flowers, but the specialised agriculture means that large quantities of cereals, especially wheat and maize, must be imported. Among other imports, timber, petroleum, coal, textiles, and iron and steel goods take a high place.

## REFERENCES

The most up-to-date work in English is F. J. Monkhouse, *Regional Geography of Western Europe*, New York, Praeger, 1967. An interesting book is G. L. Burke, *The Making of Dutch Towns*, London, Cleaver-Hume Press, 1956.

The *Atlas of the Netherlands*, The Hague, 1963, should prove of very great value. For Belgium the best modern atlas is *Atlas de Belgique*, Brussels, 1949; another useful one is *Atlas Classique*, Namur, Wesmael-Charlier, 1962, with its numerous maps of Belgium.

A periodical of special value is the July 1960 issue of *Tijdschrift voor Economische en Sociale Geografie*, which contains a number of very useful articles on the Netherlands in English. A very detailed geography of the Netherlands is provided by the six volume *Handboek der Geografie van Nederland*, Zwolle, 1949–58. The soils of the country are best covered in C. H. Edelman, *Soils of the Netherlands*, Amsterdam, North Holland Publishing Co., 1950.

A number of articles have appeared in journals of recent years including F. J. Monkhouse, 'South Limburg Coalfield', *Economic Geography*, 31, 1955, 126–137; A. Lambert, 'Farm Consolidation and Improvement in the Netherlands', *Economic Geography*, 37, 1961; and G. Bull, 'The Netherlands Delta Plan', *Geography*, 47, 1962. H. D. de Uries Reilingh *et al.*, The Changing Human Geographical Aspect of the Netherlands' (5 articles), *Tijdschrift voor Economische en Sociale Geografie*, 54, 1963, 30–59.

# SECTION III – NORTHERN EUROPE

### CHAPTER 14

# GENERAL INTRODUCTION TO NORTHERN EUROPE

THE three Scandinavian countries of Denmark, Norway and Sweden, together with Finland and Iceland, are conveniently grouped under their own title of 'Norden' or that of Northern Europe. Although the region is probably more favourable to human habitation than any other area in the same latitudes (54° 30' to 71° 10'), the traveller cannot but be impressed by the vast stretches of forest and *fjeld* (moorland) and the constant assertiveness of bare rock. A scanty human settlement is the natural consequence of the northern climate, high relief, and much infertile soil north of 60° N. Hence, although Norway's area equals that of the British Isles, its population is only 3·3 million, as against 56 million for the British Isles; while Finland, although slightly larger, has only 4½ million people. Even Sweden, with an area 50 per cent greater than that of the British Isles, has a population below 8 million.

These figures indicate not only a small amount of farm land, but also an absence of any widespread industrial development such as could lead to the growth of densely populated manufacturing districts, for Scandinavian industries, which largely consist of small or specialised goods of high value and low bulk, depend on the use of electric power. Hence industry is widely spaced, independent of local resources, and located near to transport, to power sources, or to a labour supply.

The outlook of Denmark, Norway, Sweden, and Finland is to the west and south, though Finland has the closest ties with the USSR in a politico-economic sense, and is as democratic and as divergent in trading interests as her three partners in Norden. The four countries have been in fairly close touch with the civilised life of the more southerly lands since their conversion to Christianity in the tenth, eleventh, and twelfth centuries. In many respects Norway, Sweden, and Finland appear to lead Europe, especially in education and general culture and such material matters as the widespread application of modern electrical and heating devices.

In addition there are changes of emphasis in their alignments with international organisations. Sweden, by dint of its position, strength of resources, and conviction, is a prominent neutral state and member of UNO; Denmark and Norway, along with Iceland, belong to NATO and have made approaches to join EEC; while Finland occupies a buffer position between the free world and the east.

It may be said, however, that to English eyes large areas of Fennoscandia bear a colonial 'backwoods', or pioneer aspect, reminiscent, say, of Canada, and to a large extent this aspect is due to the same causes. There is, in particular, a strong likeness between Fennoscandia and the eastern part of Canada, a likeness based on a fundamental similarity of structure and to a less extent on climate. Up to the Industrial Revolution, only the southern and coastal regions of Fennoscandia were developed to any extent, and even in Skåne, which was for long controlled by Denmark, the population which the soil could support was small. With the coming of a world demand for timber in the nineteenth century, however, Sweden and Finland discovered a use for their vast forested hinterlands, roughly north of 61° N, which they had been trying, with scant success, to colonise for the previous three centuries.

The absence of coal kept the Norden countries aloof from the Industrial Revolution in the nineteenth century though much was achieved by the use of water-power and charcoal, but the development of hydro-electricity, since 1882, has led to an increase in industrialisation, and is also helping to conquer the 'colonial' handicaps of great distances and small population.

Although the countries of Fennoscandia are broadly similar, yet there are certain divergencies in their dominant outlook. These differences may be explained to a large extent by differences in position, as well as by certain contrasts in resources and relief which will be dealt with later on. The differences in position involve contrasts of climate and different contacts with other lands and peoples. For instance, the position of Norway with regard to the open ocean and to rich fishing grounds has given that country better opportunities for developing maritime activities than are possessed by Sweden or Finland, since the Baltic is poor in fish and hampered by ice in winter, though Sweden's west coast on the Kattegat gives her better opportunities than Finland in this respect and supports a tourist industry. On the other hand, position combined with relief has given Sweden better opportunities for agricultural life than Norway, since in addition to wide lowlands the climate is more favourable, being warmer in summer and always drier. Finland is less fortunately placed than either. In latitude she corresponds to the northern, less productive half of Sweden and has no ice-free coast, for her short stretch of ice-free coast on the Arctic Ocean was annexed by the USSR in 1944. Moreover, Finland was historically more backward than Norway or Sweden, being

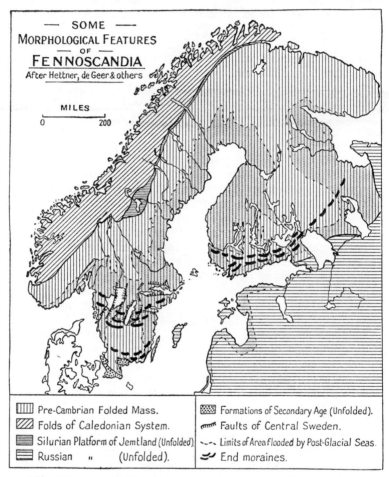

Fig. 38. SOME MORPHOLOGICAL FEATURES OF FENNOSCANDIA
The fine stipple represents the area flooded by post-Glacial seas.

remote from the early cultural centres. Her close connexions with Russia in the nineteenth century did not help to promote cultural development, although this connexion in recent decades has served to stimulate industrial growth.

**Structure.** Fennoscandia consists fundamentally of an extremely ancient 'shield' of Archæan or pre-Cambrian rock representing the stumps of mountain systems that had already been peneplained before Palæozoic times. This formation now appears at the surface in the whole of Finland, most of Sweden, in most of Norway south of 61° N, and underlies the rest of the area. On top of this ancient peneplain sediments of later Cambrian and Silurian age were spread, which in the north-west of the region were folded in late Silurian times into another ancient, though relatively much younger, mountain system, the Caledonian system of folding. This second mountain system stretches from south-west to north-east and forms the Scandes, the highest land of the present Scandinavian peninsula, though nearer to the west than the east coast. Farther east the sediments remained unfolded and were denuded from Finland, eastern and southern Sweden, and southern Norway during the long period of subaerial erosion which ensued. Where folded, the sediments were piled so thickly in a kind of trough in the Archæan .platform that even the prolonged denudation, from Devonian times to the present day, failed to remove them, though in places the Palæozoic deposits have been worn so thin that the underlying Archæan rocks are revealed through 'windows'. It is clear also that overthrust masses of the Caledonian system extended somewhat farther eastward than at the present day, as evidenced by outliers in north-west Sweden.

The Caledonian mountain range in its turn was reduced to a peneplain, and the present great elevation of the chain is due to epeirogenic uplift, that is uplift *en masse*, at the end of the Tertiary period, as is proved by uplifted erosion surfaces in the Hardangervidda. Other diversification came earlier with Permian volcanic activity in the Oslo area.

Between the end of the Devonian period and the Tertiary rejuvenation, Fennoscandia was probably a land mass, and at some time during this long interval there occurred the complicated system of faulting which forms a characteristic feature of the geology of the area, though the precise age is uncertain. This faulting has left little to show on the surface, though it is largely through downfaulting that vestiges of the former unfolded sedimentary Palæozoic cover of the eastern and southern parts of Fennoscandia have been preserved. Similarly only the southerly areas of Skåne, Denmark and Jaederen were covered by Cretaceous and Tertiary seas.

The Tertiary uplift gave the rivers new erosive power, but though the ancient peneplained surfaces now stand at greater heights than formerly, the general evenness of the skyline betrays their essential nature. In the highest parts of the Norwegian *fjeld*, or high moors, the rivers still flow in wide open valleys, and this feature, combined with the gently undulating character of these plateaus, shows that the rivers have not yet had time to attack the central mass of the peneplain. The great valleys of Scandinavia, especially those of Sweden, seem obviously consequent to the strike of the Caledonian foldings, and this may be either an ancient inheritance from the time when the mountain chain still existed, or may have been developed after the Tertiary uplift, or may be related to the direction of melt-water flow.

The Quaternary Ice Age is responsible for much of the detail of the present-day topography, and the disappearance of the icesheet is so recent – since 8000 B.C. from Oslo and Stockholm – that the glacial morphology is still very little touched by subaerial weathering. There seem to have been at least three glacial periods, since at least two long interglacial periods can be proved. Scandinavia was one of the centres of dispersion of the northern ice-caps, and while almost all the phenomena connected with extensive ice action can be seen on the topographic map, the main result on the area, as far as human exploitation is concerned, was the removal of soil. It is true that thin and patchy deposits of morainic material were left behind as the glacial cap retreated, and in the lower levels there are patches of ground-moraine seamed with eskers. Yet the morainic material is only suitable for forest growth, not for agriculture. Almost all the fertile land is composed of postglacial marine and lacustrine sediments, mainly clays, which were spread over the lowlands as a result of an extension of the proto-Baltic in geologically recent times (see Fig. 39b).

At the close of the Ice Age a fall of the land level relative to the sea caused the coastlands of Finland, Sweden, and southern Norway to disappear under the waves. (The southern shoreline of the Baltic was but little affected.) The enlarged Baltic, called by geologists the Yoldia Sea, from the fossils of a mollusc *Yoldia arctica*, extended also right across central Sweden, in the region of the present lakes Väner, Vätter, and Mälar, thus communicating with the Skagerrak and North Sea. The central part of southern Sweden, however, now known as Småland, remained above water as an island. A slight positive movement, particularly in the region of central Sweden, put an end to the broad channel mentioned above, which communicated with the Skagerrak, and turned the Baltic into a fresh-water lake, known as the Ancylus Lake, after the mollusc *Ancylus fluviatilis*. This lake, though smaller than the Yoldia Sea, was larger than the present Baltic and still covered the coastlands of Finland and Sweden, but only overflow channels allowed the drainage of water to the Skagerrak. This stage was followed by the opening of the Danish Straits which caused the sea once more to become salt. There was a gradual recovery of land to present conditions, with the flooding of the southern North Sea,

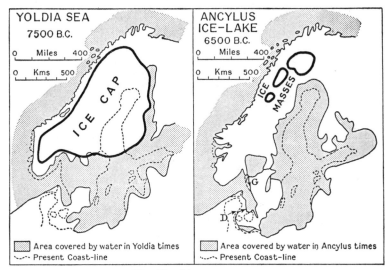

Fig. 39. (*a*) YOLDIA SEA
The southern North Sea is dry land and the ice is building the stadial moraine of Oslo, Uppsala, and Central Finland.

(*b*) ANCYLUS ICE-LAKE
With its extension on to land areas in Sweden and Finland and an outflow through the Göta and later the 'Dana' rivers.

the creation of the marshes of south-west Denmark, and the stabilisation of the Norwegian strandflat.

## REFERENCES

The student is well served with textbooks on the countries of Northern Europe.

The most direct, authoritative, and systematically arranged text, both by country and by topic, is A. C. Z. Sømme (Ed.), *The Geography of Norden*, London, Heinemann, 1961. Others are W. R. Mead, *The Economic Geography of the Scandinavian States and Finland*, London, Univ. of London Press, 1958; and A. C. O'Dell, *The Scandinavian World*, London, Longmans, 1957. The two volumes in the Orbis series from Paris, 1958, are also original in their approach: A. Guilcher and J. Beaujeu-Garnier, *L'Europe du Nord et du Nord-Ouest*, Tome I, *Généralités Physiques et Humaines*, and Tome II, G. Chabot, *Finlande et les pays Scandinaves*.

Cultural developments are dealt with in G. R. Nelson (Ed.), *Freedom and Welfare, Social Patterns in the Northern Countries of Europe*, Copenhagen, Munksgaard, 1953.

The agriculture of the Nordic countries is studied in Sir E. J. Russell, *World Population and World Food Supplies*, London, Allen and Unwin, 1954, Chapter

IV.   The national atlases of the four countries are a mine of information as well as providing examples of advanced yet clear cartography: *Atlas över Sverige* has over 100 sheets and long summaries in English; the Atlas of Finland (*Suomen Kartasta*) has recently appeared in a new edition, Helsinki, 1961, while two volumes of the *Atlas over Danmark*, Ed. N. Neilsen, have appeared – on *Landforms* 1949 and on *Population* 1961.   *Norway in Maps* by T. Sund and A. Sømme, Bergen, 1947, is an examination of the geography of representative Norwegian otpographic maps.

### CHAPTER 15

# FINLAND

A POPULATION map of Finland, such as that given in the *Atlas of Finland*, shows a striking concentration of people on the coastal regions, particularly those bordering the Gulf of Finland. Indeed, the land north of 64° N away from the coast may be looked upon as unpopulated, while even the southern half, Mikkeli province, in the interior, carries only a scanty settlement. It may be noted here that Finland lies in the latitudes of Alaska and southern Greenland, and that Helsinki, situated just north of latitude 60° N, is the most northerly capital city in the world, apart from Reykjavik in Iceland. The scanty population, then, is largely explicable on climatic grounds, but the nature of the soil adds to the inhospitable nature of the country.

Finland lies entirely on the Archæan Baltic Shield, and consists of a peneplain of highly folded and faulted rocks of metamorphic crystalline character, together with intrusive igneous rocks, mainly granites. The ancient folds have little influence on the landforms, and the system of faults only partially controls the drainage lines. Yet the more resistant rocks, such as the gneisses, form the low, broad swellings which give the sole diversification of relief, apart from the superficial phenomena, notably the Salpausselkä. The Quaternary ice-cap in its advance swept the rocks bare of soil, and the material deposited by the retreating glaciers, consisting mainly of gravel and boulders scattered sporadically, is unsuitable for agriculture. In consequence there is very little land suitable for cultivation, except in the western coastal belt with its postglacial sandy marine sediments and the silts and clays of the south.

Although the whole country has a low relief, there is a certain amount of contrast between the morphology of the northern section of Finland in eastern Oulu and Lappi provinces, say north of 64° N, and of the land to the south. South of that line we find the typical Finnish landscape, a labyrinth of lakes and islands, and a chaotic river system. North of 64° N the river system is well defined and the land rises eastward from the Gulf of Bothnia up to a line of hills, known as the Man Selka, which reaches a height of over 2,000 ft in places. The forested wastes of this range pass into the tundra of Finnish Lapland by Lake Inari. The broad forested coastal lowlands carry only enough people to bring the density up to 30 per square mile. A motor road was constructed during the 1920s through northern Finland to Petsamo (now Pechenga in the USSR) on the Arctic Ocean, and both the Man Selka and southern Lapland are connected by rail to the coast at Kemi. The northern part has road outlets to Porsanger fjord and Skibotn in Norway.

**The Lake Plateau** is bordered on the east by the low heights of Karelia which branch southwards from the Man Selka. On the south is a rampart of a different nature. Instead of a low swelling of the Baltic Shield, there are the steep, though not very high, walls of one of the best defined end-moraines in the world, known as the Salpausselkä. This end-moraine, dating from about 8800–8200 B.C. and the Baltic Ice Lake times, in places forms a double wall, running in a great arc parallel with the coast, at a distance of some 40 miles inland. To the north of these low walls occurs the type of landscape which gave Finland its name Suomi, meaning 'Lakeland' or 'Swampland', for lakes cover about an eighth of the total surface of Finland and there are said to be 60,000 of them. These lake hollows have been gouged out of the solid rock by the Pleistocene glaciations, though their island-studded, branching character betrays the presence of eskers and heaps of morainic material. In many places the lakes have been transformed into swamps, and occasionally the process has gone still further, so that the soil has been sufficiently drained for agriculture, mainly for pasture. Indeed, the neutral low moor or fen peats are far more productive than the podzolised stony soils on moraine. This hummocky, lake- and forest-covered surface, interspersed with patches of bare rock and occasional clearings, characterises the Finnish landscape. Seen from a slight eminence which enables the spectator to look over the tree-tops, the skyline has the long even lines that betray the peneplain character of the area, further smoothed by glacial and periglacial action, which the accidented detail of the country tends to make one forget.

The water of the Finnish lake zone escapes by means of a few large rivers through the Salpausselkä, generally by means of rapids, such as the Imatra rapids on the Vuoksi river draining to Lake Ladoga, or the 'force' at Tampere (127,000) in the west, which, along with that at Lahti (65,000), in the east, have provided power for industries such as timber and furniture making. These towns are the only two nodal towns of any size in the interior of Finland, almost all the others being on the coast. The development of Lahti has been hastened by the influx of refugees from Karelia.

**The Coastal Belt of Finland,** especially in the south, has the advantages of more productive soil, milder climate, and easier access to the sea than the rest of the country. Originally covered with mixed forest, its marine clays provide reasonably good soils, though even here the stony heritage of glaciation is much in evidence. Climate and the cheapness of imported foodstuffs cause agricultural concentration on fodder crops, such as roots, hay, and oats. The dairy industry is important here as in other Baltic countries. The shortness of the growing season is the greatest climatic handicap to agriculture, even in southern Finland. As late as early June the country still has a wintry aspect and crocuses are in flower. By the middle of July everything is in full bloom, and the meadow grass, abounding with scabious and other sweet-scented flowers, is ready for cutting. August is the season for collecting wild berries, such as raspberries, which owing to the severity of the winter are the only cheap fruit. Summer ends in early September and rain resumes until November, when the snow comes. Winter is the visiting season, and the time for cutting the timber and dragging it over the snow to the frozen rivers, ready to be transported on the spring floods.

The coastal towns, Helsinki (464,000), Turku (165,000), and Oulu (60,000) handle the great timber exports and manufacture timber products, such as wood-pulp and paper, using hydro-electric power, but Viipuri (now Vyborg; 51,000), together with the land around it, became part of the USSR in 1940. As this port was the main outlet for timber by river and canal from the forest belt round Lake Saima, Finland's timber industry has been reoriented towards Kotka-Karhula and more westerly ports. Other manufactures are developing; textiles also in Helsinki and Tampere. Most Finnish towns are modern in appearance and originate mainly from the seventeenth century. Helsinki is the capital city and has a university.

**Historical and Economic Summary.** Finland was conquered by, and integrated with, Sweden during the later Middle Ages. The Swedes brought Christianity and may be looked upon as the chief civilising influence here, and many Swedes settled in the coastal belt, Åbo (Finnish Turk-u) being the capital under the Swedish régime. With the decline of Sweden as a great power Finland came under the rule of the Russian crown in 1809, but eventually lost the autonomy that it was allowed. After the war of 1914–18 it obtained its independence, but in 1939–40 lost certain areas on the north, east, and south-east to the USSR, besides being forced to lease to that country a piece of coast west of Helsinki for the construction of a naval base, now returned to Finland. Territorial losses, however, were accompanied by an inflow of Finnish population from ceded areas.

Almost the whole wealth of modern Finland is yielded by its forests, which increase in importance away from the agricultural coast plains. Mainly of pine and spruce, the latter dominant in the south, the coniferous forest covers about three-quarters of the land surface. About 80 per cent of the exports consist of forestry products, pulp, paper, timber, and furniture in that order of importance; the remaining 20 per cent consisting chiefly of ships and electro-technical equipment (7 per cent of each) and dairy produce – butter and cheese.

Most of the wood processing was originally sited on waterfalls, and is now the main consumer of hydro-electric power. The main site is the Kymi river area, with rapid development too, in the north at Oulu and Kemi, the latter town also a rapidly expanding timber centre. Finland is not devoid of mineral wealth, with iron in the north at Kolari, and copper at Outokumpu on Lake Juo. Metal manufacture and machinery now employ the largest number of workers of any industrial group in Finland.

The country has a favourable balance of trade in normal times, in spite of the need of importing fuel and foodstuffs and many kinds of manufactured goods, such as textiles and machinery. Despite her necessarily close trade relations with the USSR, Finland has 60 per cent of her trade with western Europe and is an associate member of EFTA.

### REFERENCES

Apart from the chapters on Finland in the regional works on the Nordic countries so far cited, and the works on the regional geography of Europe, especially S. van Valkenberg and C. C. Held, *Europe*, New York, Wiley, 1952, the following works may be consulted: W. R. Mead, *Farming in Finland*, London, Athlone Press, 1953; *Suomi, A General Handbook on the Geography of Finland*, published by the Geographical Society of·Finland, in 1952; and R. G. Platt (Ed.), *Finland and its Geography*, New York, American Geographical Society, 1954. See also L. Aario, 'Die Räumliche Gliederung Finnlands', *Die Erde*, 94, 2, 1963, 98–114.

**29** General view of north-east Polder. Notice the rectangular pattern of the fields, the rectangular spacing of the farms, and the complete lack of trees except for the wind-breaks around each farm.

**30** View of north-east Polder. Notice the general geometric pattern of the fields, the rectangular road pattern, and also the irregular shape in the foreground. This is an old island that since reclamation stands out as a slight rise and also is in the area of poorer land. In the background stands one of the main villages of the Polder.

HOLLAND

**31** Intensive horticultural district south of Amsterdam. This aerial view shows clearly the great concentration of glasshouses in this area and also the complex intermingling of waterways and roads.

32  Rühivuori Sawmill, one of the smaller mills belonging to the Rauma-Repola concern.  It has an annual production of 10,000 standards.  The rafts, the lake, and wooded, rocky, undulating terrain evoke the Finnish scene.

FINLAND

33  Outokumpu copper mine, the largest in Europe lies in eastern Finland, and yields 35,000 tons of copper annually.

### CHAPTER 16

# SWEDEN

SWEDEN has four main settlement areas. To the north of the Dal valleys lies the new 'colonial' area of Sweden, though a few of its settlements date back to the fifteenth century. To the south is the old settled countryside, which falls into three main parts: the central lowland of *Mellansverige*, between Göteborg, Örebro and Nörr-köping–Gävle, containing the lakes of Väner, Hjälmaren, and Mälar, as well as Stockholm and the industrialised valleys of Bergslagen; second is the plateau of Småland, and third, in the south, are the lowlands of south-west Skåne and of Blekinge. The twofold contrast of north and south is based on difference of climate, relief, and soils, the southern parts being more favourable to human habitation. Lying mainly to the north of latitude 61° N, northern Sweden may be looked upon as a land of forests, mines, and electric power sources, a producer of raw materials; while southern Sweden is a land of farms and towns, of commerce and industry, with an integrated transport network.

**Northern Sweden** corresponds in latitude to Finland north of the southern coast zone, and lies therefore north of the belt of mixed forest whose boundary runs just to the north of the Dal valleys. The severity of the climate, particularly the absence of light in the long dark winter, is a great handicap to development. It is difficult to get workers to stay very long in the iron workings of Gällivare and Kiruna, though, at work and at home, they evade the outdoor climate.

Structure and relief are both unfavourable to settlement except in very restricted areas. From the Kjöllen mountains of the Norwegian border the land slopes down to the Baltic sea, usually in a series of steps. The mountains of the frontier region belong to the Caledonian system of folds and raise their wastes of *fjeld*, rock, snow, and dry tundra above the tree line. The overthrust masses of folded rocks here often overlie unfolded Silurian measures on the east and usually form an eastward-facing scarp. From the foot of the Caledonian system, roughly at a height of 1,500 ft, the old peneplain surface, mainly developed on Archæan rocks, slopes down towards the south-east. Periodic isostatic uplift has caused the rivers to deepen their beds, thus dividing the old peneplain into a number of isolated blocks or ridges. The presence of a long lake in the course

313

of each river, roughly at the junction of the Caledonian mountain system with the Baltic Shield, produces a 'glint line' which has a remarkable extent from the Stor Lake at Östersund at 63° 20′ N to the Törne lake at 68° 20′ N (by the railway line to Narvik). The lakes are of importance in the human geography of northern Sweden, as their drained portions and terraces offer settlement sites and better soil for cultivation than the surrounding land, especially Storsjön.

Most of the dissected peneplain is covered only with an uneven deposit of coarse morainic material, unsuited to cultivation and mainly covered with a dense growth of coniferous forest, spruce and pine, the latter dominant in the higher more northern areas. Many lakes exist besides those already mentioned, some being small rock basins, some being dammed by morainic material.

To the south-east of this forest belt lie the alluvial sediments deposited in the Yoldia Sea and its successors, especially the Ancylus Lake. This strip is naturally of uneven width, extending deeply up the valleys and being rather more restricted elsewhere. The rivers have already begun to cut into these sediments owing to the lowering of the base-level, and have left broad, flat terraces of fertile soil. These are suitable for settlement and cultivation, and enjoy the further advantages of freedom from cold air drainage and of proximity to the sea. Conditions here are thus broadly similar to those in the Finnish coastal belt bordering the Gulf of Bothnia, and there is the same concentration of population, though the density is nowhere high. The population maps in the *Atlas of Sweden* give an excellent picture of the density and distribution of population.

A 'fall-line' at or near the junction of the crystalline rock with the overlying recent sediments provides a useful source of motive power for the saw mills of the coastal belt up to 1,900 ft, though some mills use sawdust as a source of motive power.

The main prosperity of northern Sweden at the present day is based on the exploitation of its forests. The Baltic timber industry assumed large dimensions only after the Napoleonic Wars, although the trade in 'naval stores' goes back much farther. At first the saw mills were at the fall-line and used crude water-power, but with the development of steam engines, English coal was imported and the mills moved down nearer the coast and could be enlarged. The more recent development of hydro-electricity has restored the falls to importance, and decentralisation of the Sundsvall–Kramfors wood industry centre has taken place; the mills have moved inland, as they are not dependent on the floatways for their supply of unhewn logs, but on the ease of transmission of electricity. The two towns mentioned have now become important for the production of pulp.

The coastal region gets the benefit from its agriculture and transport routes as well as the products of its hinterland which are either exported or manufactured, though now manufacture is more important than export.

The iron-ore resources of northern Sweden are as restricted in area -as those of the forest are dispersed. These ores occur in Norrbotten, north of the Arctic Circle. The best known deposits are Malmberget (Gällivare), and Kiruna, farther to the north, with reserves of 1,000 million tons of ore of over 60 per cent iron content. Present production is less than 12 million tons per annum. Other considerable deposits exist near by in the leptites of the valleys of the Torne and Kalix rivers and at Kolari in Finland. As a rule the ore bodies are more or less intimately connected with the rocks, which are eruptive, and are now generally looked upon as magmatic segregations. The most important deposits are found in hill ranges (the crests of which sometimes consist of very high-grade ore), owing to the fact that these masses of dense magnetite resist atmospheric disintegration better than the surrounding rock. The ore, mainly phosphoric, was therefore of little use before the invention of the Thomas and Gilchrist method of smelting in 1878. The iron content varies, but in the ores now being worked it is above 60 per cent and they must therefore be classed among the richest in the world. The mines provide up to 10 per cent of the annual world production.

Owing to the unfavourable position of these mines and the expense of maintaining workers in such an isolated northern region, the ore is exported to other parts of Sweden or to other countries to be smelted. Export was begun as recently as 1892, but was handicapped until the completion in 1902 of the railway to the Norwegian port of Narvik, which gave the ore an ice-free harbour. A state-owned steelworks is in operation at Luleå, opened in 1940, along with an exporting port of Svartö, operative in summer, exporting ore and steel to Gävle and Oxelösund. Other important ore resources are the copper deposit at Boliden and the lead of Laisvall, with a smelting works at Rönnskär, near Skellefteå.

Apart from the coastal belt and the Lapland mining area, one other region of northern Sweden deserves special mention: Jämtland in the upper and middle basins of the Indals Älv (=river). Here a wide band of unfolded Silurian material has been preserved through faulting, and gives relatively fertile soil. Its importance is enhanced by a through-route, followed by a railway, connecting Sundsvall to Östersund in the valley and via the Storlien col to the fertile Tröndelag depression round the Trondheim Fjord.

**Central and Southern Sweden.** The heart of Sweden is the low-lying lakeland that stretches between the Baltic and the Skagerrak. The navigable waters of the lakes and the partially connecting rivers were useful in providing easy links between the two coasts, especially before the days of railways. The importance of this area is emphasised by the through rail routes from Göteborg to Örebro, thence to Bergslagen and Gävle, or to Stockholm, as well as by the presence, at either end of the lowland, of the two largest towns of Sweden, namely Greater Stockholm with over one million inhabitants, and Göteborg, with a population of half a million.

In southern Sweden the population is densest along the coasts, as is characteristic of Fennoscandia, though the coastal belt here is broader than usual. In the centre of this southern peninsula is the rocky plateau of Småland or Götaland, which stood above the waters of the Yoldia Sea, and which reproduces to a less severe extent the conditions of the Archæan slope of northern Sweden. In the extreme south-west is the region of Skåne, which belongs morphologically to the Würm till plains of north-central Europe and which, agriculturally, is the most productive lowland of Fennoscandia.

Transitional between northern Sweden and the central lakeland is the basin of the Dal river, which has two important branches, the west and the east, as well as the large Siljan lake, and the uplands surrounding it. This area belongs physically to northern Sweden in many respects, yet its lower altitude and lower latitude, the Silurian measures round Lake Siljan, and the presence of minerals in the bordering uplands of Svealand, early attracted settlers. The mining belt lies mainly in the uplands separating the Dal river system from the central lakeland, but has an extension north of the Dal also, namely at Falun. The only mineral mined in important quantities at the present day is iron, and, although a variety of other metalliferous ores exist in small quantities, even the famous copper mines near Falun have been abandoned. The iron-ores are both phosphoric and non-phosphoric and pyrites were also available, but are now obtained from Norrland. The non-phosphoric ores are associated mainly with Dannemora, and are mainly obtained from small deep mines, providing the material for much of the world's finest steel work. It is used in the country and also exported, especially to Sheffield. It was the high quality of this ore that laid the foundations of Sweden's medieval fame as an iron workshop. The phosphoric or apatitic ores, associated mainly with Grängesberg and with much larger concerns, are present in greater quantity, but were of no consequence until the early years of this century.

The central Swedish lakeland presents a landscape rich in variation, in spite of the absence of great heights. The area is a mosaic

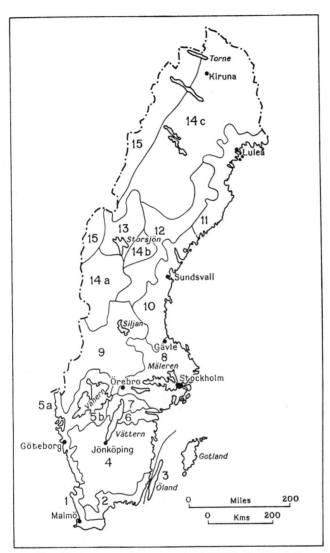

Fig. 40. THE AGRICULTURAL REGIONS OF SWEDEN

1. The plain of W. Skåne. 2. Foothills of S. Sweden—E. Skåne, Blekinge, Kalmar. 3. Öland and Gotland. 4. Småland Plateau (above marine limit). 5a. Bohus–Göta—Halland plains. 5b–8. Central Swedish Lowlands. 5b. Västergötland clay plains. 6. Östergötland plains. 7. South Bergslagen. 8. Eastern Mellansverige. 9. N. Bergslagen—Värmland. 10. Lower Norrland. 11. Upper Norrland. 12. Mid-Norrland Plateau. 13. Jämtland-Siljan Lowland. 14. Inner Norrland. a. Dalarna. b. E. Jämtland Plateau. c. Väster-and Norrbotten. 15. Scandes.

(after K. Anderson, in 'Svalof, 1886–1946', Lund, 1948, pp. 35–45) of faulted basins, now mainly filled with marine clays or morainic material, where they are still not covered by water and swamp. There remain low horsts of the ancient crystalline rock which stand up above the surrounding landscape, and as these are useless for cultivation they have been allowed to remain covered with coniferous forests. Eskers are also numerous and are also forest-covered though they serve as settlement sites, routeways and reservoirs; and coarse morainic deposits are also widespread.

Even in this favoured part of Sweden it was not an easy matter to bring the land under cultivation, since swamps had to be drained, forests cleared, and in many cases stones removed from the ground. The resulting landscape of lake and forest, meadow and moorland, arable land and orchard, is one of great diversification and charm.

Lake Mälar may be looked upon as the historic core of Sweden. The old royal residences of Sigtuna and Uppsala have given place to Stockholm as the modern capital, sometimes called 'The Venice of the North'. Situated on islands and on both banks of the narrows connecting Lake Mälar with the Baltic, Stockholm was a bridge town controlling the most important north–south routes of Sweden, as well as being the eastern terminal of the east–west water route of Mälar. Its position near the branching of the Baltic into the gulfs of Finland and Bothnia made it a good base from which to control the whole of the Baltic lands.

The second largest town of Sweden, Göteborg, has surpassed Stockholm as a seaport, partly because it faces the open North Sea instead of the enclosed and ice-hampered Baltic, and partly because it is accessible to large ocean-going ships, which are unable to reach Stockholm. Situated at the mouth of the River Göta, it lies at the western end of the water-route by River, lake and canal to Motala and Norrköping, thence by sea to Stockholm, and though this route is of little importance today, except for tourism, yet it indicates the extensive hinterland of the port. The famous falls of Trollhättan, on the Göta river, are caused by a resistant block of gneiss. They operate a great hydro-electric power station and modern metallurgical industries are sited near them, extending along the Göta valley toward Göteborg.

The manufactures of the country are scattered throughout central Sweden, though southern Sweden also has a share. Yet there is no great concentration of urban manufacturing areas in central Sweden, such as is found in countries possessing large coalfields, with the possible exceptions of the mining and smelting centres in the valleys of Bergslagen, the Göta Alv, and Öster Götland (Linköping–Motala) and Karlskoga–Örebro. The modern industries were mainly developed from local handicrafts which grew up where there was water-power and a local demand. The use of imported coal as motive power in the nineteenth century led to the coastal situation of the newer industries, such as cotton. This is mainly manufactured in and around Göteborg at Mölndal and Borås, where also the raw material was imported. Yet the development of a hydro-electric grid as the chief source of power based on the large power stations of Porjus and Harsprånget on the Luleälv and of Kilforsen, Krångede and Storfinnforsen in central Norrland, as well as others in south Sweden with a complementary oceanic regime, means that industry can be dispersed and that there will be no 'Black Country'.

As a result of the dispersion of manufactures it is somewhat difficult to associate them with the names of towns, though Eskilstuna (59,000) is noted as the cutlery centre of Sweden and Norrköping (91,000), founded over two hundred years ago by Gustavus Adolphus, for its woollen industry. Jönköping–Huskvarna, within the wooded uplands of Småland at the southern end of Lake Vätter, has large engineering works but no longer derives iron-ore from Paberg. Jönköping is the centre of the Swedish match industry, and its clothing industry employs much female labour.

Southern Sweden presents a different structure from central Sweden. The middle of the peninsula is occupied by the barren uplands of Småland, with granitic and gneissic rocks appearing at the surface. The picture presented is similar to that of Norrland, with moorland and forest predominating, but owing to the more favourable latitude some agriculture is carried on and the population is denser. Surrounding this upland lies the totally different landscape of the coastlands, with their fertile lowlands covered by marine clays, and with a correspondingly denser population. On the North Sea coast the population is notably denser than on the Baltic coast, owing to the addition of fishing as a means of livelihood, resultant from the nearness to rich fishing grounds. Tourism is also important here. In the much drier eastern Kalmar coast, agriculture is hampered by the dry conditions, though various industries are located here, such as the famous Örrefors glass and the furniture of Nassjö.

The densest population of all, about 270 per square mile, occurs in the south-western part of the peninsula of Skåne. The rock formations here include strata ranging from the Archæan to the Cretaceous, which are brought into juxtaposition with each other by means of a series of faulted horst and graben striking from north-west to south-east. Little indication of the solid geology appears on the surface, however, apart from the low swellings of gneiss in the horsts rising above the surrounding plain. This region is covered with a mantle of boulder-clay and is intensely cultivated.

The fertile soil and southerly latitude allow wheat and sugar-beet to be grown successfully, and it is here that the internationally famous crop research stations of Svalöf and Weibullsholm (Landskrona) are sited. The string of towns along the coast includes Malmö (230,000), a considerable port and shipbuilding centre at the Swedish end of the train ferry from Copenhagen, while Trälleborg holds the corresponding position in regard to the train ferry from Germany (Sassnitz) and is the centre of an important rubber industry, controlled by a German concern. Lund (41,000) is an inland centre and university town. Other industrial centres are Limhamn, where cement is made, and the towns on the Swedish side of the Sound, together with Hälsingborg and Landskrona and the Danish towns of north-east Sjaelland, chief among them Copenhagen, form an urban complex, linked by ferries and soon by a bridge, already termed Øresundstat.

**Economic Summary.** Fifty-five per cent of the total land surface of Sweden is forest-covered, so that forest products naturally occupy a high place both among the manufactures and the exports—in the latter case 40 per cent by value. The trees are mainly conifers, and are very largely utilised for pulp and paper. Careful forestry management aims at keeping the annual cut below the annual replacement rate. Only 9 per cent of the land is arable, and the country is not quite self-sufficing in temperate foodstuffs, especially cereals, though there is some export of dairy produce. The large iron resources not only supply the home market but give a large surplus for export; the greater part of the 18–19 million tons mined annually is usually exported. Sweden comes second in Europe as an exporter of iron-ore, France being first, the chief importer of Swedish iron-ore being the Ruhr.

The development of manufacturing for export is very recent, apart from the timber trade, and is partly based on the wood and steel industries, partly on the production of foodstuffs. It was not until 1912 that the exports of iron and steel goods surpassed the imports of those commodities in value. Sweden is now almost completely self-supporting in textiles. Owing to the high level of wages and the restricted home market, Sweden can compete on the world market only in 'speciality' produce, with the great exceptions of iron ore and timber and its products. In addition to wood-pulp, paper, furniture, joinery, matches, and prefabricated houses, Sweden exports such specialised products as those of the electrochemical and electrotechnical industries, ball-bearings and labour-saving devices such as cream separators and telephones. Other important exports are cement, dairy produce, machinery, and clothing, as well as cars, and equipment for forestry and roadmaking. Well-known consumer goods are Ryvita (Filipstat) and Findus frozen foods, based on Bjuv, west Skåne. Most exports of Sweden come to western Europe (70 per cent) and very little to her Scandinavian neighbours. Her standard of living is third highest in the world, measured in national income per head. Imports consist chiefly of petroleum, colonial produce, cereals, heavy machinery, and metal goods.

## REFERENCES

The most up-to-date sources on Sweden are the various excursion handbooks published in Stockholm for the International Geographical Congress in Stockholm, 1960. Other works are A. Ångström, *Sveriges Klimat*, Stockholm, G. L. A. Forläg, 1960; O. Tamm, *Northern Coniferous Forest Soils*, Oxford, Scrivener, 1950; P. Hannerberg, *Migration in Sweden*, Lund Studies in Human Geography, B. 13, 1957; and E. F. Heckscher, *An Economic History of Sweden*, Harvard Univ. Press, 1954. One of the best studies of the contribution of agricultural research to the prosperity of modern Scandinavia is *Svalöf 1886–1946*, Ed. Å. Åkerman and R. O. Whyte, Lund, 1948. On Swedish industry see L. Jörberg, *Growth and Fluctuations of Swedish Industry, 1869–1912*, Stockholm, Almqvist, 1961; M. W. Childs, *Sweden, the Middle Way*, Yale Univ. Press, 1961; A. Elshult, *Economic Life of Sweden*, Swedish Institute of Cultural Relations, 1957. In addition, the general regional geographies, listed in the References to Chapter 14, may be consulted.

### CHAPTER 17

# NORWAY

NORWAY is at a disadvantage compared with Sweden, both as regards latitude and relief. Whereas the southern tip of Sweden is in the latitude of Alnwick (55° 20′ N), the southern tip of Norway is in the latitude of Lairg (58° N). In addition, the broad southern part of Sweden is occupied mainly by a wide, productive lowland; whereas the broad southern part of Norway is occupied by a high, barren plateau, and the narrow northern 'tail', apart from the most northerly province of Finnmark, is almost wholly mountainous. The average density of population of 28 per square mile is lower even than in Finland and is actually the lowest in Europe, apart from Iceland. The interior of Norway is generally so mountainous that the population is almost entirely coastal, especially from the North Cape, 71° 11′ N, to Stavanger, 59° N. Only on the more gentle south-eastward drainage slope of Norway, from Stavanger north-eastwards to the Swedish frontier near to the Faemund Lake, does the population spread inland in a belt of any considerable width and then only confined to the valleys. It is here, in the south-east, that the bulk of the population is to be found.

As far north as the latitude of Trondheim the drainage of Norway is in two opposed directions from the great plateau-like *fjelds*. On the southern side the rivers flow to the Skagerrak or to the Glommen river, or to Oslo fjord, while on the northern and western sides they flow in a west-north-west direction to the Atlantic, some-times into the larger Hardanger, Sogne, Nord or Trondheim fjords.

North of latitude 65° N Norway consists of only a narrow strip of land draining to the Atlantic, the watershed forming the frontier with Sweden. Although this narrow northern strip can be subdivided still further into the Provinces of Nordland, Troms and Finnmark, as well as the Lofoten–Ålen island groups, yet in a work on Europe as a whole it will suffice to consider it as a single region. The broad peninsular head of southern Norway, on the other hand, is sufficiently important and varied to demand subdivision. Four main physical regions may be recognised: the interior *fjelds* and *vidde*, the south-eastern slope, the Glommen–Lågen valleys to the east, and the western coast of the great fjords and strandflat.

In common speech, Norway is popularly divided into five cultural regions – Østlandet, Sørlandet, Vestlandet, Trøndelag, and Nord-Norge.

**The Interior Fjelds.** These great *fjelds* consist morphologically of peneplained surfaces uplifted in late Tertiary times and since attacked with renewed vigour by river erosion in a cool oceanic climate and re-emphasised by glacial overdeepening and scour. The western *fjelds* of Jöstedalsbraeen are developed mainly on the rocks of the Caledonian foldings, but in the centre and east the Hardanger is based on the Archæan system, so that it is evident that the age of the formations has little relevance to the present topography. In places mountains rise above the general peneplain level, and these owe their existence either to the great resistance to weathering of the rocks which compose them or else they are remains of an older and higher peneplain surface (cf. the peneplain surfaces in the Carpathians, Chapter 30). For instance, the Snöhette Peak (7,359 ft) of the Dovrefjeld is developed in hard Archæan gneiss, while Glittertind and Galdhöppigen (the highest mountains of Scandinavia both just over 8,000 ft) on the Jotunfjeld are developed in gabbro, a coarse basic intrusive rock of great resistance and of an age contemporary with the Caledonian folding. These great peaks show Alpine features, for during the Ice Age they stood above the ice sheet (cf. the *nunataks* of Greenland at the present day), and they accordingly developed cirques, sharp ridges, and the angular forms characteristic of such mountains. Alpine types are, however, quite exceptional, and most of the mountains form rounded bosses, similar to those of other high, denuded peneplains, such as the Highlands of Scotland.

The present cycle of erosion is still so youthful that there remain considerable areas of upraised peneplain scarcely attacked by the deepening of the river beds which has taken place in their lower and middle courses. Accordingly the high *fjelds* still retain the shallow valleys and meandering streams which date back to the days before the Tertiary uplift. The western margins of the *fjelds*, on the contrary, have been intricately dissected by U-shaped valleys, and as in the case of the Highlands of Scotland or the mountains of Wales, it is often difficult to recognise the existence of the former peneplain surface, though it is betrayed by the even skyline and uniform heights of the mountains.

The *fjelds* rise above the tree limit, which is here at a height of about 2,000 ft, and although there is a good deal of grazing for cattle in the short summer, yet the highest *fjelds* carry only a tundra-like vegetation, which was useless until the recent introduction of the reindeer industry from Lapland. Considerable ice fields are present in the highest *fjelds* in the north-west, but great valley glaciers are few.

**The South-Eastern Slope.** The south-eastern slope of Norway is drained to the Skagerrak from the Hardanger Fjeld by the Hallingdal, from the Jotunfjeld by the Lågen, and from the Dovrefjeld by the Glommen, and it bears a close resemblance to Swedish southern Norrland. These flow in the same direction from the heights of the Caledonian fold system, over the Baltic Shield to the coastal sediments deposited by the sea in postglacial times. Similar rivers in their trough valleys of glacial origin, are accompanied by lakes of similar origin, and there is a similar sporadic covering of morainic material. The south-eastern slope of Norway is more favourable to settlement than the similar slope north of the Dal river in Sweden, owing partly to the more southerly latitude, partly to the extensive down-faulted area in the Oslo region, and partly to the fact that it drains to ice-free ports and to a sea rich in fish. The population is therefore considerably greater than in the morphologically similar strip in Sweden, even though the altitude is often higher in Norway.

Even in this favoured part of Norway conditions are distinctly adverse to agriculture. Woods or forests form the background to every scene and many farmers engage in forestry in the winter months. Indeed, the mass of Norway's forest wealth of spruce and pine comes from the slopes between the *fjelds* and the lowlands of the south-east coast, for the west coast is usually too steep and wind-swept for much timber, though trees occur on the slopes of the inner fjords. Much of the mixed forest of south-west Norway was cleared in the eighteenth and nineteenth centuries for shipbuilding.

The Oslo lowland, especially Vestfold, Akershus, and Östfold, roughly coterminous with Østlandet, is the most favourable part of Norway for agriculture. This area has a rift valley structure and is separated from the Archæan region on the east by a marked fault escarpment and from the Archæan rocks on the west by heights formed of igneous rocks, associated with faulting. The Oslo region is also largely block-faulted within itself, and in such a manner that there is no large area of fertile ground even here, for patches of agricultural land alternate with forested or unproductive areas. Much of the land is hummocky moraine, or fluvio-glacial sand, with intermingled peat and moraine clay. Owing to the damp climate and short summer the arable land is mainly devoted to hay, though oats, barley, and potatoes are of some importance. Dairying and market-gardening are the leading forms of agriculture.

Oslo (465,000), the capital, lies at the head of the sea-filled rift of the Oslo fjord and is situated not only in the best agricultural region of Norway, but also in the only area of Norway that has any degree of nodality. The great through valleys of Gudbrandsdal and the Glommen focus here and give the only easy through routes from Trondheim and the north. The great rivers of these valleys both rise in flat indeterminate watersheds which give easy saddles across the *fjelds* and lead down to the short valleys which descend to the fjords of the western coast. It is reasonable to suppose that the through valleys were formed by heavy ice erosion during Pleistocene times. The lie of the Scandinavian relief was against the path of ice currents from the Bothnian centre of dispersal, which lay north-east of the present watershed, so that ice streams from this direction were diverted by the stronger ice flows from the *fjeld* which moved across the Skagerrak into northern Jutland. Some useful cols were created, which now give access to Swedish Värmland. Oslo is also the focus of routes from Bergen, over the Hardanger fjeld via Voss and Gol; and the coastal railway from Stavanger via Kristiansand and Bö, as well as a third from Göteborg.

The chief development of manufacturing industries has taken place in the lowlands bordering the Oslo fjord and the Skagerrak. The older established industries are chiefly concerned with the working-up of timber, food and dairy products and with the canning of fish, especially brisling, carried on extensively at Stavanger (53,000), though Haugesund (20,000) is the chief centre of the south coast herring fishery. The pulp and paper industries are located in the south in Østlandet, mainly on the chief rivers and harbours.

The modern electrochemical and electrosmelting industries are primarily dependent upon the very large resources of water-power (see Fig. 41). Over half of Norway's hydro-electricity is developed in the valleys of the south-eastern slope, where there are numerous large power stations on the southern Glommen river, and farther west in Numedal and in Skien's catchment area, especially Rjukan. A wide range of electrochemical products is obtained from the primary process of extracting pure nitrogen from the air, at Glomfjord, and from the manufacture of calcium carbide which needs limestone and carbon as raw materials. A few products which may be mentioned are cyanamide (used for fertilisers and plastics), calcium nitrate, nitric acid, liquid ammonia, sulphate of ammonia, caustic soda, etc. Most of the nitrogenous derivatives are used either for agricultural fertilisers or for explosives. The two most important centres are Notodden and Rjukan, both in Telemark county. A few factories manufacture aluminium, as near Mosjøen, and a new plant is to be established at Husnes. Others are concerned with electrolytic copper, nickel, steel, and ferrosilicon, etc., but there is less electrosmelting here than on the west coast, though more general industries. In fact the chief 'industrial belt' of Norway lies mainly in

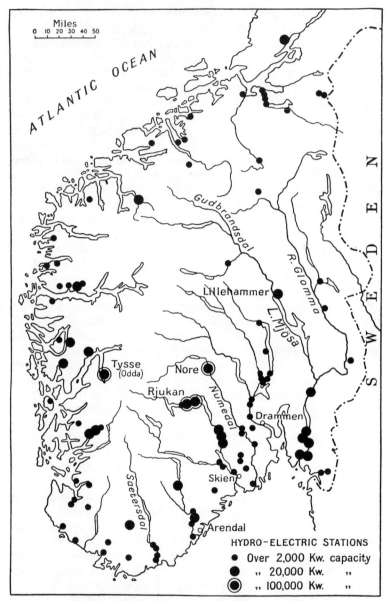

Fig. 41. NORWAY: HYDRO-ELECTRIC STATIONS

There is little development of hydro-electricity north of the Trondheim fjord, but large State installations are nearing completion on the Glom fjord and at Rôssåga, in the Arctic Nordland.

the Oslo depression, with sporadic extensions along the south coast, westward to Stavanger, and in Hordaland (Bergen) and Møre.

**The Great Fjords.** Controversy has raged over the origin of the Norwegian fjords and skerry-guard. It may be mentioned here that in Norwegian the word 'fjord' has no precise structural significance, but has much the same meaning as the Scottish word 'loch', and the name is applied somewhat loosely to any kind of sea inlet whether the banks are low or high. It has, however, become the custom among geologists and geographers to restrict the word 'fjord' to long, branching sea inlets with steep, high walls and submarine rock-sills at their entrance, such as are found on west coasts in high latitudes, as in Norway, Scotland, British Columbia, Chile, and New Zealand. It is generally held at the present time that fjords originated as river valleys which were over-deepened by glacial action and subsequently drowned. Some geographers, particularly D. W. Johnson, deny that drowning occurred, for ice could work below sea-level before being floated off as icebergs, and they therefore attribute the great depth of the inner part of the fjords to the abrasive action of the great glaciers alone. Recent slight elevation has produced raised beaches, which provide some of the scanty sites for settlement. Accompanying the fjord coast of Norway is a somewhat discontinuous shelf of land reaching to about 100 ft high and of rounded and dissected form. The explanation of this comparatively low-lying land, the so-called 'strand-flat', is also highly controversial, and equally so is the origin of the fringe of islands known as skerries. The skerries, which are low, hummocky islands sometimes strewn with morainic material, are not to be confused with the lofty islands which have only been separated from the mainland by glacier-filled tributary valleys of the fjord system. Many writers consider that the skerries and the strand-flats are remnants of a plain of marine denudation, but as the strand-flats are to be seen in places even inside the fjords, where the action of waves would be negligible, recent writers have doubted this.

Fjord life is highly distinctive. The scarcity of lowland has concentrated attention on the sea, especially behind the sheltering skerries and in the fjords. There are good fishing-grounds inshore, particularly for herring, cod, salmon, and brisling, and there is practically no trouble from ice, in spite of the high latitude, owing to the warming influence of the Gulf Stream Drift. Up to recent years, however, there were few people engaged solely in fishing. The fjord economy south of Trondheim was essentially threefold. Its essential basis was the small area of pasture or arable land near the coast on which was situated the homestead; this was supplemented by the harvest of the sea, while an important contributor was the summer pasture centred round the *sæter* (mountain hut) on the *fjeld*, whither cattle and sheep were driven when the snow had melted (cf. the similar system of transhumance in the Alps and Carpathians). Transhumance declines in the south, but is still prevalent in the mountains of Vestlandet. Increased yields of fodder have largely led to the abandonment of many sæters.

Bergen (115,000) is the only large town of this area, apart from Trondheim, which is not quite typical. In fact, there is little opportunity for urban development on a fjord coast, owing to the difficulty of access by land, and the consequent absence of nodal points. Bergen itself had no hinterland at all until the construction of the marvellously engineered Voss railway via the Hallingdal, and this remains a tourist rather than a goods line. Bergen is the main centre of the fishing and shipbuilding industries. The textile (clothing) industry is also important. Trondheim (60,000) on the Trondheim fjord has the great advantage of lying in a fertile depression. It is the centre of a small but productive agricultural region and is the oldest cultural centre of Norway. It also lies at the west end of a through valley connecting it with Jämtland in Sweden, as well as at the north end of the Glommen route leading to Oslo. Both these routes are followed by a railway. Elsewhere, apart from a few small market towns and fishing centres and an occasional factory manufacturing electrochemical or electrometallurgical products, the population is very scattered, the single homestead being the normal unit of settlement. This extreme dissemination of population was very adverse to political unity, and together with the low density of population may explain long domination of Norway by her richer and better organised neighbours between the fourteenth century and 1905. Even the great factories (e.g. at Tysse and Odda on the Hardfangerfjord, which produce aluminium, zinc, and chromium), employ very few people, in spite of their large output.

**The Northern Strip.** North of the Trondheim lowland, which lies about 64° N, there stretches for 1,000 miles the northern strip or 'tail' of Norway. Only 6 miles wide at its narrowest part east of Narvik where it adjoins Swedish Norbotten, it is nearly 100 miles wide in Finnmark at the head of Ofot fjord but its mountainous interior is almost entirely an unpopulated waste, apart from a few Lapps (called Finns in Norway), who pasture their reindeer in the scanty vegetation. The population is otherwise entirely coastal and largely in the islands, the mail-steamers providing the only regular means of communication for the small scattered communities, which are almost entirely dependent on the sea for their livelihood. Narvik (12,000) is the Norwegian railhead and port for the Swedish iron-ore field of Norrbotten: the Kirkenes area and Nordland

34 The Scandes, near Tärne. The Norra Storfjällen (66° N) in the fjällzone has much bare rock, hummocky, glacially-infilled valley floors and periglacially-smoothed centre slopes.

35 Kiruna, founded in 1899, lies at 1,600 ft (500 metres) at 68° N between the iron-ore mountains of Luossavaara and Kirunavaara. Open-cut mining is being replaced by shaft mining in the world's largest underground mine. Beyond the lake the office building of LKAB, the separation plant, the old terraces, and the deep shaft (left), are seen in this view under the midnight sun.

36 The plains of western Skåne, strongly reminiscent of Danish, indeed all, lowlands based on recent glacial till. Much of the land is given over to barley for stock feed, to fodder roots, and to ley pasture. Isolated patches of trees and orchard shelter the courtyard-farms.

37  The Heröya Electrochemical Plant, belonging to Norsk Hydro, sited at Porsgrunn. The plant is sited away from the power-supply source on flat land near to the coast.

NORWAY

38  The Borregård woodpulp factory at Sarpsborg, adjacent to its power source – the lower Glommen, which is also the main floatway for logs.

produce most of Norway's own iron-ore, with mines at Bodö and Mo in operation. The total production of concentrated iron-ore (*slick*, 65 per cent Fe content) is 2 million tons, with three-quarters exported, though this is declining due to the demand of the state-owned Mo-i-Rana steel works which produces nearly a quarter of a million tons of crude iron and a slightly larger amount of steel per annum. Tromsö (11,000) is the base for the sealing industry. Hammerfest, 70° 35′ N, was the most northerly town in the world until the development of the Siberian Arctic posts. It was utterly destroyed by the Germans in 1945, when the whole northern strip was devastated, but rebuilding is now complete, the chief industry being the modern one of fish-freezing.

**Historical Summary.** One of the most interesting aspects of the history of Norway concerns the exploits and migrations of the Vikings or Norsemen. Although the Norsemen came from Sweden and Denmark as well as from Norway, those Vikings who changed the history of western Europe came mainly from the *vik* or 'calm waters' of the fjords.

Between the Saga Age and the twentieth century Norway suffered a long period of political eclipse. From 1319 to 1814 Norway was politically dependent on Denmark, from the Napoleonic period onward was united to Sweden, and achieved independence only in 1905; a separation, it may be added, which was accomplished with the consent of the Swedes and without bloodshed.

**Occupations and Industries.** Owing to the great amount of emigration in the nineteenth century, it is reckoned that there are as many people of direct Norwegian extraction living outside Norway, mainly in North America, as inside it, the present population being 3·6 million (1960 census). There is a good deal of rural depopulation, and derelict farms may be seen in the poorer valleys, such as Saetersdal, where barren rocks and sandy soil alternate with bogs. As in Denmark, industrialisation and the complexities of urban employment make up for the loss of farming land.

About 18 per cent of the population live mainly off the land, from farming and lumbering, 41 per cent are engaged in manufactures and mining, 22 per cent in commerce and land transport, 4 per cent in fishing, and 4 per cent in shipping. The numbers engaged in fishing appear small in comparison with the importance of this industry to the country and to the publicity it has enjoyed, but the percentage given applies only to men who are engaged in fishing as their sole means of support, and these are much less numerous than those who engage in fishing as a part-time occupation. In fact, it is only since about 1890 that this new class of fisherman came into being, with the changeover from the old open boat to the decked boat, now mainly motor-driven. The fish (chiefly cod, herring, and brisling) come principally from inshore waters and little part is taken in the North Sea fisheries; but more than half the world's whaling industry is in the hands of Norwegians and is now carried on mainly in Antarctic waters. The base is at Sandefjord and Narvik and much of the production of oil and fat is used in margarine and soap manufacture. As regards the merchant fleet, which amounted in October 1963 to 13·7 million gross tons, the tonnage per head of population is the highest in the world and the part played in the national economy by the carrying trade is of great importance. Owing to the poverty of Norway's natural resources the ships are chiefly engaged in carrying goods between foreign countries, only about one-tenth being engaged in the Norwegian coastal trade and another tenth between foreign countries and the home country. The foreign currency earnings of the fleet exceed $780 million. Contrary to what one might expect, the Norwegian carrying trade is not of great antiquity, but dates back only to the seventeenth century, and is much younger, for instance, than the Dutch.

Nowadays, with the replacement of wooden vessels and sail by diesel engine-driven ships of steel, Norway is not in a good position for shipbuilding, mainly relying on Swedish shipyards. Yet, despite grievous wartime losses, and aided by reparations and insurances, the fleet has been replaced by modern vessels. In total tonnage, the Norwegian mercantile marine ranked fourth in size in the 1950s though only two fleets, those of Great Britain and the United States of America, were really much larger. The development of hydro-electricity (Fig. 41), is the prime cause of the establishment in the country of electrochemical and electrometallurgical industries particularly in the manufacture of aluminium (though the raw material must be imported), of calcium carbide (though here again the necessary anthracite and coke employed must be obtained from foreign sources), and of nitrates from the atmosphere. The timber, pulp, and cellulose industries also employ large quantities of hydro-electricity. Apart from these two main branches of electro-engineering, Norwegian industry is mainly concerned with the preparation of canned fish and fish products, such as cod-liver oil, and with the manufactures of machinery used in the above industries and of cans for the preserving industries. Almost all the metals used in these industries must be imported, as only pyrites (at Grong), and iron-ore, are mined in any considerable quantities in the country. About 850,000 tons of pyrites are produced annually, with an S content of 42 per cent, chiefly from the Lökken mines, near Röros, about thirty miles south-west of Trondheim. The sulphur is mainly exported to Sweden and Finland. Small deposits of copper exist and are mined chiefly at Röros on the Glommen railway line, and both copper and pyrites at Sulitjelma, which lies east of Bodö. Iron-ore is worked at Kirkenes in the extreme north, 1·3 million tons being produced in this region in 1963. An iron and steel plant is sited at Mo-i-Rana, in Nordland, based on local ore and on hydro-electric power from the new generating plant at Rössåga. Norway is also the only European source of molybdenum, mined at Knaben in Setesdal, and is also a leading producer of titanium. There has been a marked expansion of Norwegian mining and industry since 1950; it is often on a large scale and is partly state-owned. Investment in fixed capital is proportionately greater than in most western European countries at present.

## THE SPITZBERGEN ARCHIPELAGO (SVALBARD)

Norwegian sovereignty over these islands was officially recognised in 1920. The islands lie between 76° 30′ N and 80° 50′ N, that is, in the latitude of northern Greenland, but they lie on the edge of the Winter Gulf of Warmth and feel the influence of the North Atlantic Drift, so that although the subsoil is permanently frozen, the harbours of the west coast of Spitzbergen are accessible to shipping for six months of the year. (Svalbard means cold coast.) The landscape is one of tundra, and considerable ice-caps exist on North Island and Edge Island. Rocks range in age from Pre-Cambrian to Tertiary. The value of the islands lies mainly in the large deposits of good quality coal, of which on average one-third of a million tons are exported annually. The deposits are worked on the west coast of the main island, chiefly at two concessions south of Ice Fjord, one called Longyearbyen – the name of a former owner. Another is leased to the USSR. Mining is carried on even in winter and production is perhaps 300,000 tons per year.

### REFERENCES

'Geomorphological Studies in Norway', by H. W. Ahlmann, in the *Geografiska Annaler*, 1919, may be profitably consulted, though it gives more detail than will be wanted by most students of geography. See also K. M. Strøm, 'The Geomorphology of Norway'. *Geog. Journal*, CXII, 1948; A. Sømme, 'The Physical Background of Norwegian Agriculture', *Geog.* 1950; together with *Jordbrukets Geografi i Norge* (Geography of Norwegian Agriculture), Bergen, 1949. *The Norway Year Book* (in English), last issue, is a mine of information.

Two articles on the human geography of the country are well worth consulting: W. R. Mead, 'Sogne and Fjordane in the Fiord Economy of Western Norway', *Economic Geography*, 1947; and S. Heiden, 'Odda and Rjuken: Two Industrial Areas in Norway', *Annals of the Association of American Geographers*, 1952. *Norway in Maps*, by T. Sund and A. Sømme, Bergen, 1947, should be mentioned; it contains an English description of each of 19 selected topographic maps of the country.

More recent works are: O. Holtedahl (Ed.), *Geology of Norway*, Oslo, Asche-houg, 1960; Norges Geologiske Undersøkelse Nr. 208. Ø. Vorren, (Ed.), *Norway North of 65° N*, London, Allen & Unwin, 1961. There are several works on the Vikings, notably P. H. Sawyer, *The Age of the Vikings*, London, Arnold, 1962, and H. Arkman, *The Vikings*, London, Thames & Hudson, 1961; also J. Brønsted, *The Vikings*, Harmondsworth, Pelican, 1960.

### CHAPTER 18

# DENMARK

DENMARK, although the oldest of the independent Norden nations, has the peculiarity of resembling central Europe geomorphologically; having a climatic regime which is transitional from oceanic to continental; yet in almost every other respect the country is similar to northern Europe, especially in economic and cultural matters. Often aspects of modern geography have first appeared in Denmark to be passed on to the other Norden and Baltic nations.

The whole country is lowland, though the Baltic end-moraine of the Weichsel period reaches a height of 500 ft and more, and runs northward through the peninsula of Jylland (or Jutland) as far as Viborg, where it meets the west–east trending end-moraine of the Norwegian ice. North of this is the ante-morainal depression of Limfjord, the productive till-lands of Thy, and the drumlins of Salling. The western side of Jutland is partly covered by the sandy outwash plain from the end-moraine, of extremely coarse sand near to the former ice margin, but finer westwards nearer to the coast. This outwash material occupies lowland straths of sandy material, sometimes terraced and dry, but peaty and wet near the rivers. It did not entirely cover the pre-existing plain of older boulder clay of the Saale glaciation, much of which stands up as broad, low 'hill-islands', much smoothed by periglacial solifluction. On both landforms the soils are strongly podzolised, with conifer plantations and twentieth-century farmsteads, spread out in a distinctive cultural landscape, with occasional 'station towns' as market centres. The north-western province of Harsyssel is confined to the largest hill-island.

The eastern side of the peninsula of Jutland and all the islands are covered by the boulder clay of the Weichsel ground-moraine, or more correctly, of the Baltic Sea ice-streams of the Pomeranian phases. There are, too, several stadial end-moraines and some patches of fluvioglacial sand, as well as drumlins, dead-ice landscapes and morainic flats smoothed by active ice. The glacial material reaches a thickness of 600 ft in parts of the end-moraine, but is usually much thinner. In places the solid rock appears at the surface, in the form of chalk on the coasts of Møn and Stevns, near Aalborg and on the north-west coast of Jutland; as Eocene plastic clay near Aarhus; while granite outcrops in spectacular cliffs on the northern coast of Bornholm, which, geologically, belongs to the Scandinavian Massif – continuing the trend of the horsts of central Skåne.

The western coast of Jutland is bordered by dunes similar to those of the Friesian islands, forming an almost continuous rampart along the coast to the north of Esbjerg in an area of isostatic uplift, but being breached by the sea to the south in an area of subsidence. Behind these dunes, lagoons (fjords), or marine marshes have formed, which have always had a distinctive life of their own, with cattle and sheep rearing for the Hamburg and British markets, as well as sea-faring – now, however, almost completely integrated into the modern Danish dairying industry, though supplemented by inshore fishing. After 1864, when Denmark suffered defeat and loss of Slesvig, a movement of land reclamation, led by Dalgas and the Danish Heath Society, improved and reclaimed the western heathland by marling, ploughing, draining, and the planting of shelter belts with the result that, though the geographic landscape is very different to that of the east, the method of agricultural production is very similar. The port of Esbjerg (55,000) was created in 1863 in consequence of the increasing livestock trade with England, and later became the focus of dairy export to Britain for much of the western part of Denmark, though much is still shipped from Odense, Aalborg and Copenhagen. Thus, and as a paradox, in a physical sense and from the point of view of population density, Denmark turns her back on Britain, yet economically she looks to Britain as her chief market, though increasingly related to Germany for trade purposes.

The morainic hills of the Würm (Pomeranian) terminal moraine of eastern Jutland have sandy or gravelly tree-clad hummocks, peaty hollows, and steep slopes, and lie westward of the clay-rich limey ground-moraine on the coastal plain, made doubly fertile by its favoured climate with a longer frost-free period, and less intense frosts. This coast plain or low plateau at about 150 ft altitude is split up by the fjords and tunnel valleys, which are poorly drained and form meadow land and sites for routeways. The highest point of Denmark, the Yding Skovhøj (568 ft) lies to the south of the Danish Lake District, just north of Horsens. Thus there are three distinct relief elements in the landscape of eastern Jutland: the tunnel valleys, the low plateau, and the terminal ridges. The fjords and their continuing tunnel valleys were formed by melt water under the ice and have steep, though low, sides and have fjord-head settlements at the lowest crossing points, such as Randers (55,000), Vejle and Kolding. The larger towns of Aalborg (120,000) and Aarhus (180,000) the latter the second largest town in Denmark, have less restricted sites and more important hinterlands.  Aarhus, its name derived from Å-ros, 'the mouth of the river' (cf. Nidaros, the old name for Trondheim), was located at a ford: a meeting place of routes from inland and along the coast in Viking times, and the oldest crossing-point to Sjaelland.  By 948 the town was a bishop's seat, a mill town and port.  Today it has large industrial and port functions, as well as being a university and medical centre.

The northern part of Jutland, largely consisting of Vendsyssel, is made up of varied materials: the morainic Jyske Aas in the east, yet largely of marine clays of post-glacial (Yoldia) age, deposited when this part of Denmark was depressed beneath the sea.  The lower-lying Litorina *Marine Foreland* is largely formed by muds or beach ridges and partly covered by peatlands – the Great Wild Moor, or *Store Vildmose*, reclaimed in 1890.  Sand and dunes form the northern tip of Denmark, called *Skagen* or The Skaw, while each headland in the north-western coastline marks a resistant bed in the underlying chalk.

The Danish islands, Zealand (Sjælland), Fünen (Fyn), Laaland, Falster, Møn, Langeland and Aerø, and many other smaller islands, at the shallow entrance to the Baltic Sea, represent the remains of a plain which was continuous between Jutland and southern Sweden as late as post-glacial (*Ancylus*) times (see Fig. 42), but which has since been partially drowned.  The straits of the Sound, the Great Belt, and the Little Belt represent drowned river valleys, and all of them present difficulties to large modern ships.  The Little Belt is very shallow, the Great Belt has a very winding and narrow deep-water channel, partly fault-guided; and the Sound, which is most frequently used, has a depth insufficient for the largest of modern vessels.  It is, however, deep enough for all except the ocean giants, and since it connects the North Sea and Baltic by the shortest route it has long been the most important and, consequently, was an important factor in the growth of Copenhagen (Dan., København).

The Baltic islands of Denmark may be looked upon as forming the heart of the country.  They mostly carry very fertile brown earths developed on the ground-moraine, with only occasional morainic ridges of coarser material, or peaty depressions, now drained and reclaimed.  The islands are supremely well cultivated and thickly populated, the main branches of farming being the production of dairy produce, bacon, poultry and eggs.  The basis of this livestock farming is essentially the intensive eight- or nine-year rotation, including winter wheat in coastal areas in the east on limey brown earths; perhaps two or three courses of barley, clover ley or grass, some oats and one or two root crops.  Sugar-beet production, in decline, is largely related to factories on Lolland-Falster, and in south-west Fyn or near Odense.  A number of large farms specialise in cash grain crops, seed production, or practise a looser rotation (*fridrift*), geared to changing economic circumstances.

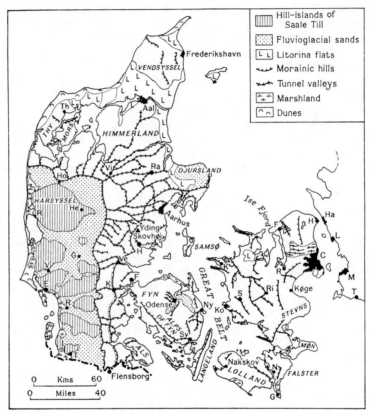

Fig. 42. THE REGIONAL UNITS, GEOMORPHOLOGY, AND TOWN SITES OF DENMARK

The large areas left unshaded in north and east Jutland, and in the eastern islands, including the largest, Zealand or Sjaelland, are largely of drifts dating from the last glaciation.

Towns: Jutland: E. Esbjerg, G. Grindsted, H. Horsens, He. Herning, Ho. Hobro, K. Kolding, R. Ribe, R. Ringkjøbing, Ra. Randers, T. Tønder, Th. Thisted, V. Varde, Ve. Vejle, Vi. Viborg, Aal. Aalborg.  Eastern Denmark: C. Copenhagen, F. Frederiksvaerk, G. Gedser, H. Helsingør, K. Korsør, N. Nykøbing, Ny. Nyborg, R. Roskilde, Ri. Ringsted, S. Slagelse, Sv. Svendborg. Sweden: Ha. Hälsingborg, L. Landskrona, M. Malmö, T. Trälleborg.

Market-gardening is common near to towns and fruit production is a speciality of southern Fyn.

The city of Copenhagen has a large proportion of the total population of the country, numbering 1·4 million in a total of 4·6 million. It has been called the key to the Baltic and Denmark was once able to block the entrances of the Baltic in times of war and to impose tolls in times of peace at Helsingør. It possessed a protected harbour on the narrow strait between Copenhagen and the island of Amager, close to which large oil storage and other industrial complexes are now being developed to the south of the city, close to the international airport of Kastrup and the proposed take-off point for the bridge to Sweden via Saltholm. The Mølle valley to the north is also intensively industrialised. The main channel of the Sound swings close to the western side of the Sound near to Copenhagen, which originated as a harbour and fishing settlement, while later defensive fortifications can be traced in the present urban mosaic.

At the present day the city concentrates the intellectual and commercial activities of the whole country and has shipbuilding, brewing, clothing, and porcelain industries as well as the usual functions of a capital. Copenhagen too is a focus of routes and the fulcrum of north-west Europe. Routes pass from Esbjerg to Sweden; from Hamburg via Gedser to Göteborg, and one may add the sea and air routes from the North to the Baltic Seas and from the Polar and Atlantic areas to eastern Europe and Russia respectively.

The chief contribution of Denmark to modern Europe is the development of the cooperative movement within agriculture, especially to the preparation and marketing of dairy products, and the purchase of farming requirements. Up to the 1860s Denmark was a country of mixed farming, producing cereals for export up to about 1820 and, increasingly after that date, concentrating on the export of livestock by ship or on the hoof, or by rail after 1870.

The competition of the great prairies of eastern Europe and America made cereal growing unprofitable in this country of small farms and after 1870 cereal production was increasingly oriented to stock feed. The change in the agricultural system from livestock farming and export to cooperative dairy farming was initiated in western Jutland in 1882, and the founding of cooperative dairies in many villages was rapid and was widespread by 1900. It was then followed by other forms of cooperative organisation and was coupled with a great improvement in the rural and vocational educational system which had been initiated earlier.

Danish agriculture now produces a number of highly standardised articles which are exported abroad, and also increasingly supplies an expanding home market, for population and urbanisation increase rapidly and the non-rural population has a high purchasing power. The cooperative system of marketing is especially helpful in this country of small holdings, most of them established with state support by way of loans and appropriation of parts of large estates; and the commodities of butter, bacon, eggs, cheese, and poultry are all products which can be fairly easily graded and which keep fresh for some period of time, given adequate storage. Yet one must also note that many private firms produce and export commodities based on farm produce – processed cheese, preserved meat, fruit, confectionery, and insulin, among others.

The stability and success of the cooperative system, both in marketing and in distribution of some imports such as seed, machinery and fertiliser, depend on the capacity and willingness of foreign countries with a large industrial population to continue importing foreign dairy produce. Great Britain and Germany, which are the main markets for Danish dairy and meat products, could hardly satisfy all their needs. Only the former can rely on the distant agricultural lands of the Commonwealth, while the latter can, in part, rely on Holland.

If Denmark has sought to diversify both her agricultural export and her markets, seeking outlets in South America and southern Europe for canned milk and butter, she also has become world renowned for the production of beer. Since 1950 Denmark has launched some large-scale manufacturing industries based on imported ores and fuel, other than the traditional industries based on agriculture, or those on native mineral matter: cement, porcelain, and various clays. The lack of coal and water-power is held to have hindered industrial development, but textile industry and ship-building have a long history. Yet such deficiencies no longer hinder development for oil is readily imported. Danish industry now, and since 1959, dominates the national economy in terms of number of people employed and in value of exports, though some of the industrial export is derived from farm produce. In 1962, the total value of manufacturing exports was 6 billion kroner and of farm exports only 4·6 billion kroner. Imported electricity and oil are more efficient, cleaner, and more readily transported sources of power than coal. Scrap iron, Swedish iron, and modern power sources support the largest and most rapidly expanding industry – metal working – which includes marine engineering, engineering for constructional purposes and farm, dairy, and transport machinery. A steel mill is established at Frederiksvaerk in north Sjaelland by the Isefjord. Oil refineries operate at Kalundborg (Gulfhavn), Skaelskor (both on the eastern shore of the Great Belt), and near to Fredericia; this last at the hub of Denmark's international transport system, east–west from Esbjerg to Malmö; south–north from Hamburg to Oslo and Göteborg. The large building materials and foodstuffs industries have both home and overseas markets.

In Copenhagen a considerable number of small industries work for the home market, as well as well-known large concerns, while the distinct Herning district in mid-Jutland has a woollen industry of some standing.

This modern movement of industrialisation has implied great increases in the imports of raw materials, foodstuffs, machinery and fertilisers, cars and tractors, though a potentially large deficit of trade is counterbalanced by the high quality and cost of many of Denmark's exports. The United Kingdom, taking two-fifths of the exports by value, mainly pork, bacon, butter and consumer goods, is the chief market and is also the chief source of imports, followed by Western Germany and Sweden.

Internationally the country is a member of EFTA. If Britain were to join the Common Market, it would mean that 75 per cent of Denmark's foreign trade would then be with EEC and she too would need to join. Inspection of an atlas-map shows too, that her communication system provides a link between Scandinavia and the EEC countries.

## THE FAEROES

The Faeroe Islands lie 180 miles north of the Shetland Islands on the Wyville-Thomson Ridge at 62° N. They are heavily glaciated basaltic lands, up to 2,900 ft high in the north-west, lower in the south, where the capital Torshavn (6,000) is sited. The climate is ameliorated by the North Atlantic Drift. They were part of Norway until the seventeenth century, and became part of Denmark only in 1814 and a strong movement for independence exists. The population approaches 35,000, with a density of 70 per square mile. Sheep are the dominant form of livestock, half the flock being slaughtered annually; otherwise there is little farming. Fishing is the vital industry, supporting one-third of the population directly, but the native boats use Greenland and Iceland waters, exporting salted and dried cod to Mediterranean countries and to Brazil, and fresh and frozen fish to Britain. Herring fishing is increasing also. There is a small hydro-electric station on Strømø by the Fosså.

## GREENLAND (ARCTIC DENMARK)

Stretching from Kap Farvel at 59° 46′ N to Kap Morris Jessup at 83° 39′ N this is a vast island, with a width from 11° 39′ W to 73° W. Ice-free land, amounting to 132,000 square miles occurs in coastal strips in the moist south-west, while that in the north-east is dry arctic desert. Mountain ranges occur in the north, west, and east, with Gunnbjørns Fjeld the highest at 12,000 ft. The internal ice field is over 12,000 ft deep and large glaciers move to the west and east. Greenland occupies a vital strategic situation; it is the centre of Polar air routes and a key in NATO's defensive system. The physical geography is complex and fascinating, the human geography a contrast of early medieval Norse settlement, indigenous Eskimo life, and the modern Danish colonisation, which began in 1721. The present population is 31,000, of whom 2,500 are administrators, the rest native-born. Fishing based on Godthåb and Frederikshåb is the main activity of the indigenous people supporting 3,000 of them fulltime, mainly in cod and shrimp fishing. This is followed by hunting of seal in the north at Umanak and Upernavik. Sheep rearing is the main form of farming in the south at Julianehåb. Cryolite is mined near Ivigtut, but former galena production at Mestersvig is now closed.

## ICELAND

Iceland has been an independent republic since 1944, but formerly owed allegiance to the King of Denmark. It is situated between $63\frac{1}{2}°$ N and $66\frac{1}{2}°$ N, and covers an area of 40,000 square miles. It lies within the Winter Gulf of Warmth and its southern coasts are rarely frozen. The main island consists of a plateau covered with recent volcanic material cementing together older Eocene basalt masses. From this plateau rise active volcanoes, e.g. Hekla (5,107 ft). Both latitude and altitude are adverse to cultivation and tree-growth, indeed ice-sheets such as Vatnajökull cover the higher parts of the plateau, and only one-tenth of the suitable land is productive. Only one-quarter per cent is actually under cultivation, which is confined to hay, potatoes, and turnips, though the basaltic-loessal soils are potentially productive. The dominant element in the farming is dairying which has become more important than sheep rearing. Farming, now mechanised, occupies 18 per cent of the working population. It supplies hay for livestock and meets the domestic requirements of meat, dairy products, potatoes and, in part, those of some other vegetables. Glasshouse cultivation is increasing, use being made of geothermal heat—hot springs—which also serve to heat the factories, public buildings and houses in the capital, Reykjavik.

Iceland is an excellent example of the way in which a small community can live well despite certain physical difficulties. It occupies a marginal location—in the extreme north-west of Europe and under a marginal climate (cold temperate-oceanic), yet has so applied modern techniques that it maintains a high standard of living for almost all of its inhabitants who, though increasing steadily, numbered only about 190,000 in 1964. Actually one-third of the working population is engaged in industrial production, especially in that related to fish (and whales), dairying, textiles, leather, and building construction. Iceland has an enormous potential of water power, a little of which is already used to provide electricity for farms as well as for other settled places. So also its geysers are numerous and increasingly useful: 'Geysir', which gives its name to hot springs, lies in south-west Iceland. Fish remain the chief source of wealth: located at a confluence of warm and cold ocean currents, Iceland has rich spawning grounds (for cod and herring) and her fishermen—10 per cent of her workers—operate as far afield as Greenland and the Newfoundland Banks. Fish and fish products make up 80-90 per cent of the exports, being sent to the U.S.A. ('lobster tails'), to Africa (dried cod), to Mediterranean countries and elsewhere.

Icelanders speak the oldest form of the Germanic language and clearly, as a result of history, culture and inclination, form part of Norden. Iceland is well placed on the air routes between North America and Europe, is a member of NATO, and has an American defence force. Reykjavik (80,000) has grown remarkably since World War II; there, and in the country around, live about 70 per cent of the whole population.

## REFERENCES

Unbiassed studies of the development of Danish agriculture may be found in E. Jensen, *Danish Agriculture Its Economic Development, 1870–1930*, Copenhagen, Schultz, 1937, and F. Skrubbeltrang, *Agricultural Development and Rural Reform in Denmark*, FAO Agricultural Studies, 22, 1953. A vivid and fascinating account of earlier times is given in H. Rider Haggard, *Rural Denmark and its Lessons*, Longmans, 1911.

The generous proportions of *Denmark*, published in 1961 by the Royal Danish Ministry of Foreign Affairs, provide a wealth of authoritative information on all aspects of the Danish life and scene.

Studies mainly in English are contained in *Geografisk Tidskrift* and in the *Folia Geographica Danica*, especially on marshlands, coasts, village forms, agricultural distributions, and urban and transport problems.

Aage H. Kampp provides a full study of farming organisation in *Agricultural-Geography Studies of Denmark*, Kulturgeografiske Skrifter 6, 1959, and in 'The Agricultural Geography of Møn', *Erdkunde*, 16, 3, 1962. He is the leading authority on the geography of the Faeroes and his *Faerøerne, Folk og Ervherv*, Danske Forlag, 1951, is well illustrated. The geology of the Faeroes is dealt with by Arne Noe-Nygaard in the *Quarterly Journal of the Geological Society*, 118, 1962, 375–383.

On Iceland, the soils and agriculture are studied in B. Johannesson, *Soils of Iceland*, Department of Agriculture Bulletin, B. 13, 1960, Reykjavik; and more general studies are in V. H. Malmström, *Iceland: A Regional Geography*, Nat. Research Council, Washington, Pub. 584, Washington, 1958.

The journal *Meddelelser om Grønland* contains many studies on the physical geography, biogeography, and history of Greenland.

# SECTION IV – CENTRAL EUROPE

### CHAPTER 19

## GENERAL INTRODUCTION TO CENTRAL EUROPE

THE concept of central Europe is a familiar one, not only to geographers but also to the general public. The region, however, cannot be said to possess any structural unity, since it is composed of three main morphological units; in the north, a glaciated lowland; in the middle, worn-down relics of the Hercynian fold mountain system, separated by basins containing sediments produced by the denudation of that system; in the south, a young folded mountain system, heavily glaciated, with associated plains of glacial deposition. Climatically, it is true, there is a general similarity, since the whole region has cold winters with a mean January temperature below freezing, warm summers (*c.* 64°F 17·7°C, to 75°F 23·8°C for July), and a fairly well distributed precipitation with a maximum in summer. Consequently there is a general similarity of natural vegetation and cultivated crops, but only very generally, since crops needing summer warmth, such as maize and the vine, which flourish in the southern parts of central Europe, are unable to reach maturity in the north. Also, in contrast to the forest-covered lowlands of north Germany and Poland, those of south-central Europe are mainly prairie-like grasslands. In culture and language, also, there are wide divergences, since central Europe is divided between two main language groups, the Germanic and Slavonic, with certain smaller additional elements such as Hungarian, Turkish, and Rumanian. As regards the stage of development, there is a great contrast between the modern up-to-date social and economic life of, say, Germany and Switzerland and the more primitive social organisation and economic life of, say, Rumania and Bulgaria. This remains true, despite the great efforts toward economic development in eastern Europe since 1945.

The interior position of this kernel or core of Europe is the key to the matter. Central Europe is, indeed, transitional between east and west, north and south, and is therefore more varied within itself than any of the other main regions of Europe. For instance, in relief it lies open to eastern Europe both in the Germano–Polish and the Rumanian lowlands.    Structurally, it has less of the monotony of Russia, but not the extreme diversity of western and southern Europe.    Climatically, it covers the marginal zone where the maritime cyclonic elements, which so powerfully influence the climate of western Europe, begin to weaken; and so it is transitional between the wet changeable weather of western Europe and the more stable dry and extreme climate of eastern Europe.    Historically, it came later into the civilised world than southern Europe, but earlier than eastern Europe and parts of western Europe.

In this great region there may be distinguished two main sub-regions of somewhat different climate and of considerable differences of outlook.    The first, which may be called north-central Europe, is an area which by either latitude or altitude has generally cooler summers than the south-east, and where the precipitation is generally sufficient to produce a natural vegetation of forest. Here are the German-speaking lands of Germany, Austria, and most of Switzerland, which culturally may be considered as practically West-European, and have a long tradition of culture, deriving in part from Greece and Rome.    To these may be added the Slavonic-speaking Czechs of Bohemia and Moravia and the Poles, who have both been intimately concerned in the history of western Europe, though economically their countries have developed later, and are still slightly behind the more advanced countries of the west.    Opposed to north-central Europe is south-central Europe[1] which historically has been bound up with eastern Europe.    With its dry steppe-covered plains surrounded by mountains, but open to repeated invasions from the east, its development has been delayed in almost every respect.    Both regions may be looked upon as essentially non-maritime, with the conspicuous exception of the North Sea and for Baltic Sea margins of Germany and Poland.

**North-Central Europe.**    There are three structural units in the make-up of north-central Europe.    Of these the most widespread and continuous is the Germano-Polish lowland which stretches right across the north of the region and even across the frontiers of Germany into Holland on the west and Denmark on the north.    On the east the Pripyat (Pripet) marshes in the borderlands of the USSR may be taken as the margin of this lowland, and on the south it extends to the uplands of central Germany and central Poland.    The northern margin of these central uplands runs from the Weser Hills, along the Harz Mountains, Erzgebirge, and Sudety, and thence along the Polish Jura, the Łysogóry, and Lublin Hills; but the higher land is interrupted by many bays of *Löss*-covered lowlands.    The

---

[1] South Central Europe is dealt with in Section V, pp. 458–527.

whole lowland is covered with unconsolidated deposits resulting from the ice-sheets of Quaternary times.

The central uplands of ·Germany and Poland belong to the Hercynian zone, where the structure is dominated by the extensive stumps of the former vast Hercynian chains, which were originally

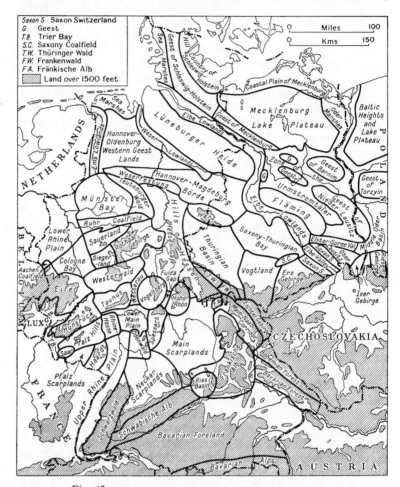

Fig. 43. NATURAL REGIONS OF CENTRAL EUROPE

folded in late Carboniferous times. These stumps underwent elevation in the great positive movement of the Tertiary era, and at the same time the overlying sediments were often warped upwards, so that even where old rocks do not actually appear on the surface,

39 Bergen. The city has an extensive water frontage, with distinct passenger, freight and industrial docks. Bergen is ideally situated for export, and for labour supply from the rural population nearby.

40 Sandefjord, Vestfold. The whale-catching fleet, the town and the coastal lowlands. Beyond, the forested hills on basic intrusive and volcanic lands, backed in the distance by the higher, harder, Archaean rocks of the Shield.

41 Melöy Kirke, Glomfjord, sited on the uplifted sea-floor.

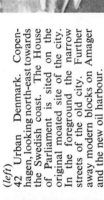

*(left)*
42 Urban Denmark. Copenhagen, looking north-east towards the Swedish coast. The House of Parliament is sited on the original moated site of the city. In the foreground the narrow streets of the old city. Further away modern blocks on Amager and the new oil harbour.

*(right)*
43 Industrial Denmark. Rørdal Cement Works near Aalborg. The watercourse in the distance is the Limfjord.

*(left)*
44 Rural Denmark. Knudstrup, mid-Jutland. Heathland on fluvioglacial sand, first cultivated in 1925, with young shelter belts and scattered farms. In the distance the slopes of a hill island.

*(right)*
45 Arctic Denmark. The harbour of Angmagssalik, east Greenland.

DENMARK

the relief is affected by the Hercynian formation. The name is derived from the *Hercynia silva* or Hercynian forest of the Romans, a term applied vaguely to the forested mountains in the north of Bohemia, whence the name has been extended to apply to all similar massifs of the same age and origin. The Polish uplands belong structurally to this region, but were sufficiently low for the maximum advance of the ice-sheet to over ride them – at least, for a short period. The highest point reached in this zone of the central highlands and uplands is about 5,000 ft, but even the highest land usually shows the rounded landforms which characterise the so-called block mountains of Europe. The central Rhinelands will be included here on structural grounds, although Alsace is politically French. Among the relics of the Hercynian mountains occur basins of various sizes, containing the sedimentary rocks laid down in the Mesozoic and Tertiary eras of geological time, as a result of the denudation of the Hercynian mountains. These rocks, of Triassic, Jurassic, Cretaceous and Tertiary age, commonly occur in the form of gently dipping slopes and steep scarps. In the Jura area of Switzerland they are more intensely folded.

In contrast, the third region, that of the Alps, consists of great chains whose mighty peaks, covered with ice and snow, rise to a height of over 15,000 ft. The Alpine Foreland of Switzerland, Germany, and Austria may be included in this zone, since it is built up of waste from the Alpine denudation, first in mid and late-Tertiary times, then during the Quaternary glaciation.

### REFERENCES

The standard textbook in English on the area is A. F. A. Mutton, *Central Europe*, New York, Praeger, 1968. A very full account, well illustrated by diagrams and photographs, is given in E. de Martonne, *Europe Centrale*, Part 1, Generalités, Allemagne, and Part 2, Suisse, Autriche, Hongrie, Tchecoslovaquie, Pologne, Roumanie, Paris, Colin, 1930, 1931. P. George and J. Tricart, *L'Europe Centrale*, 2 Vols., Paris, Presses Universitaires de France, 1954, is also indispensable. R. E. Dickinson, *The German Lebensraum*, Harmondsworth, Penguin Special, 1943, deals with many aspects of the historical and economic geography of central Europe. F. Machatschek, *Länderkunde von Mitteleuropa*, Vienna, Deuticke, 1925, gives a good short account dealing chiefly with the physical aspect and contains an exhaustive bibliography. J. F. M. Partsch, *Central Europe*, London, Heinemann, 1903, though much out of date, contains some useful material.

See also, O. S. Morgan (Ed.), *Agricultural Systems of Middle Europe* New York, Macmillan, 1933, and J. Ancel, *Manuel Géographique de Politique Européenne*, Tome I, L'Europe Centrale, Paris, Delagrave, 1936; R. E. Dickinson, *The West European City*, London, Routledge, 1951; K. A. Sinnhuber, 'Central Europe – Mitteleuropa – Europe Central: An analysis of a geographical term', *Transactions of the Institute of British Geographers*, 1954.

### CHAPTER 20

# GERMANY

**Germany and the Germans.** A unified German nation (*Deutsches Reich*) existed for less than three-quarters of a century, from 1871 to 1945. But Germany, and the Germanic peoples, have had a common cultural and social history since earliest times. The first great formative influence was the colonisation of western Germany by tribes speaking Germanic tongues, between the time of the Roman Empire and the ninth century A.D. These tribes appear to have originated in the north around the Baltic coasts, and to have moved southwards from the early centuries A.D. They included the Alemanns (who settled south-west Germany), the Bavarians and the Saxons (who settled the areas bearing their name), and most important, the Franks, a section of whom occupied the lands along the Rhine and then progressively conquered the other groups to establish a Germanic kingdom – the kingdom of Charles the Great – by the late eighth century. By this time, the eastern parts of Germany and the present area of Poland had been occupied by people speaking Slav languages, who appear to have originated in the Pripet marshes and the middle Dnieper basin, and to have moved west. In the ninth century the boundary between Germans and Slavs was roughly along the line of the middle and lower Elbe. During the centuries that followed, the German peoples advanced over the Slav territories, subjecting the Slavs (who managed to survive) and establishing their own distinctive colonisation forms on the landscape. Between about 800 and 1100 A.D. the main advances were in the south, in what is now Austria, but between about 1100 and 1350 the Germans overran the Germano-Polish lowland, east from the Elbe as far as East Prussia.

**East and West.** The result of this evolution is a fundamental division in Germany between the 'older-settled' lands of the west and the 'colonisation lands' of the east. The western area shares many features of the cultural landscape with other lands of western Europe which were occupied by Germanic tribes in these early centuries (northern and middle France, southern Britain): here are the characteristically irregular nucleated villages; here also survives, in many cases, the landscape of irregular open fields. Only on the remoter lands of the western part of the northern plain of Germany does this pattern give way to a different one of small hamlets and isolated farms – a change which must in part be ascribed to the influence of the physical environment, for these are lands ideally suited to stock farming. In the east, on the other hand, the settlement forms are characteristically those of planned colonisation: the lowlands are dominated by the 'street village' (*Strassendorf*) and 'green village' (*Angerdorf*) with their large, rectangular, planned open fields; in the highlands to the south these are replaced by the looser linear village (*Waldhufendorf, Kettendorf*) with their long individual landholdings at right angles to the main street of the village. Characteristic of the border zone between east and west – in the eastern part of the Lüneburger Heide south-east of Hamburg, for instance – is the small round village or *Rundling*, long thought to be a relic of the Slav occupation, but now believed to be a defensive form evolved by Slavs and Germans alike in an area of political instability.

In later centuries the contrast between east and west appeared, if anything, more marked. During the era of the French Revolution the west moved in the direction of liberal agrarian reform: the great feudal estates were broken up and distributed among the peasants, and a society of small landowners has resulted. But in the east the feudal lords (the so-called Junker class) rapidly evolved into progressive capitalist farmers, and managed to reduce the peasants to a condition of almost completely landless subjection. The balance sheet was not without its credit side, for east German farming took the lead in technical advance in the nineteenth century, making extensive use of the new discoveries in agricultural chemistry, and producing ever-increased surpluses of grain and other basic foods and materials to serve the growing industrial population of the west. But the end-result was that (with the exception of some important industrial areas like those of Saxony and Silesia) large parts of the east were reduced more and more to the status of a primary production area for the more advanced west. By a curious irony of history, the division of Germany in 1945 left the resolution of the problems of the east to a communist régime. It has tried to deal with it by sequestration of the big estates, by distribution of the land among the peasants, and (more recently) by a programme of collectivisation. On the industrial side the communist powers have sought to make the east independent of western supplies by developing a wide range of industries, at first without much apparent regard for the limitations imposed by lack of resources.

Other fundamental lines of cultural division have appeared in the course of German history. In particular, the end of the Middle Ages saw a split between north and south. The north, in general, went Protestant at the Reformation, but kept its old spoken language (Low German) which has affinities with Dutch; the south as a whole remained Catholic, but its language evolved into High German, which is also the basis of the written language of today. But the geographical implications of the east–west division – implications economic, social, cultural and finally political – are incomparably the more important.

**Modern Germany.** Even after the losses imposed by the Treaty of Versailles in 1919, Germany was the most populous of the purely European countries, being second only to the USSR among European powers, though in area she ranked fourth, being considerably smaller than France and slightly smaller than Spain.

In spite of further territorial losses in 1945 and a high number of fatal casualties, the German people[1] are still numerically (after the Russians) the second largest group in Europe, owing to the accession of German-speaking refugees from the territory east of the Oder, and from lands previously outside the political limits of the country, for example, Czechoslovakia, northern Italy, and the formerly independent east Baltic republics of Estonia, Latvia, and Lithuania. Moreover, the fact remains that Germany is still an exceptionally well-endowed piece of the earth's surface, especially as regards the main requirements of industry: namely, abundant sources of mechanical power, a stimulating climate, and an excellent world position, to which may be added the presence of large numbers of intelligent and industrious people.

The phenomenal development of German agriculture, industry, and commerce, in the forty-four years between 1871, when the German 'Reich' or Empire came into being, and 1914, when she became involved in the first world war, were achievements which won the admiration of all civilised lands, and contributed greatly to the wealth and prestige of Europe as a whole. Germany had been slow to adopt the methods of the Industrial Revolution, and before the middle of the nineteenth century was lagging behind both the United Kingdom and France in the development of her resources, partly because the German-speaking lands were split up into a number of small independent states, each with a restricted economic field and divided from the others by customs-barriers. The early years of the nineteenth century showed the first steps towards the establishment of a great modern state, with the ending of the old feudal restrictions, and the establishment of a customs union or *Zollverein*. By 1841 the *Zollverein* included all the German lands, except some small north German provinces, the free Hanse cities (Bremen, Hamburg,

---

[1] Taking into account the population of the two Germanies, i.e. the Federal German Republic in the west and the German Democratic Republic in the east.

and Lübeck), and Austria. The middle years of the nineteenth century also coincided with the active development of railways, which facilitated movement over long distances, and helped to remedy the handicap of the inland position.

Germany was the last of the great European powers to achieve unity, and the extreme political subdivisions of the early years of the modern era prevented the Germans from reaping the economic and political benefits to which their numbers and skill might otherwise have entitled them. Once unity was achieved in 1871, with only Austria standing outside the new Reich, the way was open to the full industrialisation of the country and to the utilisation of its large and varied resources. In spite of a late start in the Industrial Revolution, Germany fully caught up with the industrialised western countries; indeed, in many ways, thanks to the late start, she surpassed them, especially in the application of scientific and technical knowledge to the development of her resources, for example in the chemical industries, where progress is more dependent on research and powers of organisation than on natural endowment. Moreover, the state and higher educational establishments played more active parts in the development of industry than they did in France and England.

Between the middle of the nineteenth century and 1914, Germany experienced profound changes in its economic, political, and social life, which had repercussions on the whole of Europe and much of the rest of the world. The phenomenal development of industry was accompanied by a great natural increase in population, from 41 million in 1871 to 65 million in 1913. Thanks to improved methods of cultivation, these increased numbers were fed largely on home-produced food, only 20 per cent of the necessary foodstuffs being imported from abroad. The country, however, became dependent on foreign lands for imports of many industrial materials, such as cotton, copper, and tin, and became increasingly dependent on foreign countries for marketing her manufactured goods.

As a result of the war of 1914–18, Germany lost the few overseas possessions she had gained in the colonial era in Africa and elsewhere, as well as most of her reserves of iron-ore (in Lorraine), and a certain amount of her coal (in Silesia). She was therefore in a worse position between the two wars than she had been in 1913, but by the vigorous exploitation of her existing resources and her continuing tradition of technological advance, she made a wonderful recovery. Unfortunately, the whole world was swept by a wave of economic nationalism, or autarchy, which hit all the European exporters of manufactured goods very hard. Whether Germany could have weathered the economic storm by legitimate means it is difficult to say, but instead she chose to find a cure for her troubles in territorial expansion. The *Lebensraum* concept had been evolved by German exponents of *Geopolitik*, a pseudo-scientific study, which sought to find plausible geographic reasons for the aggressive policy of the state, and was enthusiastically taken up as official policy by the Nazi régime after the accession of Adolf Hitler to power in 1933. In March 1936 Germany reoccupied the Rhineland, which she had lost under the Versailles treaty of 1919; in March 1938, under the guise of political union (*Anschluss*) she took over Austria; in September 1938, under the Munich agreement with Britain and France, she occupied the Sudetenland area of Czechoslovakia; in March 1939 she occupied the Bohemian and Moravian areas of Czechoslovakia; and in September 1939 she occupied the Free City of Danzig and marched into Poland, plunging Europe into the second world war.

At her capitulation on 8 May 1945, Germany suffered the *de facto* loss of 44,000 square miles of territory in Pomerania, Brandenburg and Silesia to Poland, including that of the territory of East Prussia (an 'outlier' of German territory from 1919 to 1939) which was shared between Poland and the Soviet Union. Thus she has lost extensive tracts of first-class agricultural land – the *Löss* soils of the Silesian Bay – and the valuable mineral and industrial resources of Silesia, as well as the regional capital of Silesia, Breslau (Polish Wrocław), with a population of 629,600 in 1939 (442,700 in 1961) and the Baltic ports of Stettin (Szczecin, 383,000; 279,100), Danzig (Gdansk, 250,000; 296,700) and Königsberg (Russian, Kaliningrad, 372,200; 202,000 at the 1959 census). 8·8 million Germans were displaced and had to find new homes within the restricted boundaries of post-1945 Germany.

The Potsdam Agreement of July 1945 between the Allied Powers (USA, USSR, Britain, France) postponed a final decision on boundaries until a peace treaty was signed, but this treaty has failed to materialise. In consequence, the post-1945 boundaries between Germany, Poland and Soviet Russia are still formally under dispute.

Under a declaration of 5 June 1945, Germany was divided into four military zones of occupation, one for each of the Allied powers. In view of its special status Berlin was similarly divided. After increasing conflict between the three western powers and the Soviet Union in 1949, the west set up the Federal Republic of Germany and the USSR set up the satellite German Democratic Republic. The Federal Republic has consistently refused to recognise the communist régime and officially refers to the area as the 'Soviet Zone of Occupation'. The frontier between the two states became increasingly difficult to cross in the years that followed and is today one of the most impenetrable parts of the 'Iron Curtain' which divides western from communist eastern Europe.

| | AREA (thousand *square miles/km*) | POPULATION (*million*) | |
| --- | --- | --- | --- |
| | | 1939 | 1961 |
| German *Reich* (1937) | 181·6 (470·3) | 69·3 | 81·1 |
| Federal Republic | 95·7 (247·9) | 40·2 | 54·0 |
| Democratic Republic | 41·5 (107·5) | 15·1 | 16·1[1] |
| Berlin, West | 0·2 ( 0·5) | 2·8 | 2·2 |
| East | 0·1 ( 0·26) | 1·6 | 1·1 |
| 'Eastern Territories' (to Poland and USSR) | 44·0 (114·0) | 9·6 | 7·7[2] approx. |

[1] *Excluding* East Berlin which is part of the Republic.
[2] Of which 6·4 million are Poles, 0·6 million Russians (1960).

**Modern Germany: Economic Summary.** *Agriculture.* The soils of Germany vary greatly in quality. Against the rich *Löss* soils of Westphalia, Saxony and the 'corn chambers' of the south German scarplands must be reckoned the large areas of poor glacial sands and gravels in the northern plain and the marginal lands of the higher levels of the Hercynian *Mittelgebirge*. Of the total area of Germany in 1939, no less than 28 per cent was forest, and another 18 per cent under grass; arable land accounted for only 42 per cent of the total area, and the arable percentage was lower in the west than in the east. By 1960–61 the combined figures for the Federal and Democratic Republics gave almost exactly the same proportions, though there were important differences between east and west:

| | FEDERAL REPUBLIC 1961[1] | DEMOCRATIC REPUBLIC 1960 | BOTH[1] |
| --- | --- | --- | --- |
| Arable | 34 | 47 | 38 |
| Meadow, pasture | 23 | 13 | 20 |
| Forest | 29 | 27 | 28 |
| Other uses | 14 | 13 | 14 |
| Total | 100 | 100 | 100 |

[1] excluding West Berlin.

Up to 1871 Germany was still self-sufficient in foodstuffs. From then on there was a progressively increasing deficiency, caused by the rapid growth of the industrial population and the fall in the farm population, and aggravated by territorial losses of agricultural land in 1919 and 1945. In addition the division of Germany after 1945 had profound effects; for the great estates of the east (which had formerly produced large surpluses of foodstuffs for the industrial west) were lost to Poland or passed under communist control (where they were collectivised), while the Federal Republic inherited a small-scale tradition of peasant agriculture, a legacy of the agrarian reforms of the Napoleonic period. In an effort to improve the productivity and living standards of its small farmers, the Federal Republic in 1955 introduced its 'Green Plan', which made available considerable sums of government money for the improvement of the structure of agricultural production – in particular, the consolidation of scattered holdings, together with the construction of new farms and roads – for raising agricultural yields and quality of products, for reduction of costs and for research and education. The central aim was to raise productivity per acre in order to make the most efficient possible use of a limited area of farm land. The success of the policy may be judged by the fact that, despite a big drop in the agricultural labour force in the late 1950s, each acre of the Federal Republic fed eight people in 1960, as compared with five for the whole of Germany in 1937; and that despite the tremendous upsurge in urban population since 1950, Federal Germany still manages to provide three-quarters of its needs for basic foodstuffs. But German peasant agriculture, especially on the small farms of the south, still suffer from problems of under-use of labour and equipment, and high costs; in the discussions on Common Market agricultural policy, Germany has been concerned to give some measure of protection to its small producers, who are ill-fitted to withstand strong competition from imports.

*Industry*. The changes in Germany's industrial patterns as a result of the 1939-45 war and the subsequent division of the country, were profound. Germany in 1939 was the most heavily industrialised nation in Europe, with the exception of Britain. 57 per cent of the population were engaged in industry and commerce, only 18 per cent in agriculture. The postwar Federal Republic is even more markedly an industrial state, for it lacks the great farmlands of the eastern parts of the former German *Reich*, while it has inherited a disproportionate part of the industrial tradition. In 1961 only 13 per cent of the occupied population were engaged in agriculture and forestry, 49 per cent in mining and industry, 20 per cent in trade, transport and government service and 18 per cent in services.

This industrial development is based on large resources of many of the most important industrial raw materials. Germany's reserves of hard (bituminous) coal in 1955–56 were estimated at 220,000 million tons (down to 6,500 ft) out of total European reserves (excluding European USSR) of 650,000 million tons. In addition, out of total European reserves of 110,000 million tons of brown coal, Germany has some 45,000 million tons. As a result

46 The North Sea marshes. A view near Emden in the extreme north-west corner of Germany. The large unit farmhouse, with all the functions under one roof is usual in this area – the historic province of Friesland.

47 Lüneburger Heide. A characteristic landscape of the sandy *Geest* country of the North German Lowland. Sheep farming is a traditional activity, but since 1875 large areas of the Geest have been afforested.

GERMANY

48 West Berlin. After war-time devastation, West Berlin has been almost completely rebuilt in a modern and imaginative style. Special attention has been paid to road planning, and it is intended that eventually an urban motorway will completely circle the city centre.

49  Cologne.  A view of the city centre from the opposite (east) bank of the Rhine where much of the heavy industry is concentrated.  The Cathedral towers mark the position of the ancient Roman High Street which runs parallel to the river and is still the major shopping street of the city.  The ring of more open ground in the background marks the limit of the medieval city, with latest urban growth behind.  Note the extensive area given over to railways – a mark of Cologne's importance as a major junction.

### GERMANY

50  Landscape in the Ruhr.  The Rhine front at Duisburg.  Heavy metal industry has monopolised the water-front – here a copper-smelting works.  Residential areas behind.

Germany is a leading producer of both types of fuel; but the division of Germany has given the west most of the hard coal, while the east has more (but by no means all) of the brown coal. In 1960 Germany produced some 145 million tons of hard coal, or 7 per cent of the world output (Britain produced 11 per cent), nearly all from the Federal Republic; it produced some 330 million tons of brown coal, no less than 50 per cent of the world output (75 per cent in 1938), of which 35 per cent was in the east and 15 per cent in the west. This lack of balance in the communist régime's resource structure has forced them to ingenious technical expedients for the use of brown coal for unusual purposes – e.g. for the production of coke.

Hydro-electricity has been greatly developed since 1918, but it still accounts for only about 10 per cent of all electric power generated, a reflection of the huge resources of brown coal suitable for generation.

The most revolutionary change in Germany's fuel position since 1945 has been the exploitation of the oil resources beneath the north German lowland. Production increased from 450,000 tons in 1936 to 6,200,000 tons (Federal Republic, 1961), nearly all of it from the western part of the lowlands between Elbe and Ems. Even this production however meets only some 19 per cent of the Federal Republic's current needs. Production in the Democratic Republic is negligible.

Almost as revolutionary is the exploitation of home supplies of iron-ore. Up to 1918 Germany possessed large resources of ore in Lorraine, but these passed to France under the Versailles Treaty. By 1938, despite Nazi efforts to develop home production in the northern plain and in the Siegerland, this amounted to only 11 million tons against 28 million tons in 1913 (including Lorraine's). Yet by 1961 the Federal Republic was producing 18·9 million tons – over half of it from the Harz Foreland field around Salzgitter near Braunschweig – and the Democratic Republic 1·6 million tons. The newly developed Salzgitter reserves are of low grade, however; the iron content of the Federal Republic's production for 1961 was only 5·0 million tons. So Federal Germany must rely on ore imports to cover over three-quarters of its total iron needs; in 1961 it imported 32·7 million tons of about 17 million tons iron content. Sweden supplies about one-third of the imports.

Germany's salt deposits have also been of great value in the development of modern manufacture, particularly to the chemical industry, in which before 1914 she occupied first world position, since challenged by the USA, USSR and Britain. Before 1914 she had a complete world monopoly of potash salts due to the supplies in Alsace and at Stassfurt.    After the first world war this monopoly was broken by the loss of the Alsace deposits and by discoveries in the USSR.   The division of Germany after 1945 meant that the valuable Stassfurt deposits of potash and common salt passed to the communist régime.   Despite this advantage to the east the Federal Republic's production of the most important basic chemicals is three to five times that of the Democratic Republic.   An important historical advantage to the west was the heritage of the vast IG Farben chemical combine, which was broken up by the Allied military authorities after 1945, but important parts of which are situated in the west, especially at Leverkusen near Cologne, Hoechst near Frankfurt and at Ludwigshafen.   The sites indicate that because of their dependence on a variety of heavy raw materials, often imported, chemical plants tend to seek locations on navigable water.   This tendency has been fortified by the growth in recent years of the petrochemical industry, in close association with the refining of imported oil.   The complex at Wesseling, near Cologne, is especially important here.   From the basic chemicals are produced a wide range of products, including dyestuffs, artificial fertilisers, synthetic rubber, plastics, artificial fibres, pharmaceuticals, and photographic chemicals.

The German heavy iron and steel industry is by far the biggest in Europe, west of the USSR.   The Federal Republic produced 25·4 million tons of pig-iron and 33·5 million tons of raw steel in 1961, nearly half the total production of the European Economic Community in each case.   The industry is heavily concentrated on the Ruhr coalfield, where it enjoys the advantages of large supplies of excellent coking coal and cheap import by water of iron-ore (especially from Sweden), chiefly via the Rhine.   The Ruhr produces about two-thirds of the Federal Republic's iron and steel; the Saar about one-sixth.   The smaller production of the Democratic Republic mainly stems from plants developed by the communist régime since 1945, notably at Eisenhüttenstadt (Iron Works Town; formerly Stalinstadt), on the Oder, which uses Ukrainian ore, Silesian coal and coke made from indigenous brown coal.   From it stems a second main tradition of manufacturing industry, the metallurgical.   Two main strands may be distinguished here.   One is the complex of heavy metallurgical and engineering industries.   Mining equipment, iron and steel smelting equipment, heavy machine tools, and constructional engineering often tend to stay close to their supplies of semi-finished materials on the coalfields, especially if their natural markets are also found there.   In contrast is a variety of lighter products which are not material-oriented, but which prove to be subject to very different factors of location.   Agricultural machinery is produced close to its main markets in centres like Mannheim, Hanover and Cologne, while electrical engineering has historically been associated with Berlin, though the tradition has weakened somewhat in West Berlin since the division of the city. Precision and optical trades have evolved out of a local craft tradition in the small towns of central and south-west Germany; machine tools are manufactured in every size of city and in every type of location, though there is a higher degree of concentration in the south. The tendency to extreme specialisation in the lighter metal industries is well seen in the concentration of the German ball-bearings industry at Schweinfurt, a small town on the River Main east of Würzburg, of cutlery at Solingen-Remscheid, and of locks and keys at Velbert, south of Essen.

Transport equipment is a special branch of the engineering trades. The manufacture of railway locomotives and rolling-stock has tended to concentrate at major junctions like Berlin, Kassel and Munich. The motor car industry developed slowly in Germany before 1939, despite an early lead in technical development (Daimler). By 1961 however the Federal Republic had become by far the largest producer of motor cars in Europe, with a production nearly twice that of Britain, its nearest rival; though in goods vehicle production it still stood second to Britain. Leading centres of the industry today are widely spread: they include Wolfsburg near Braunschweig (Volkswagen), Stuttgart (Daimler), Sindelfingen near Stuttgart (Mercedes) and Rüsselsheim near Mainz (Opel). Production of vehicles, both of private cars and goods vehicles, was still very retarded in the Democratic Republic in 1961. The Federal German shipbuilding industry stood third in world production in 1961 after Japan and Britain. It was naturally concentrated in the major seaports, particularly Hamburg and Bremen.

In textiles Germany has never held such a dominating position as in the metal industries, but nevertheless ranks high among European producers. The Federal Republic is (the USSR apart) the largest European producer of cotton goods (followed by France and Britain); in woollens she stands behind Britain, France and Italy; she occupies a high place in the manufacture of artificial fibres. In contrast to Britain, Germany never concentrated her textile industries in particular industrial areas; they are widely spread. Outstanding in the Federal Republic are the city of Wuppertal, on the southern edge of the Ruhr industrial area, and the small towns of the Schwäbische Alb and the Alb scarpfoot zone in south-west Germany. Saxony and Lausitz are the main textile centres of what is now the Democratic Republic.

*Internal Transport.* Internal water transport is more important to the German economy – at least to that of the Federal Republic – than to most of the industrial nations of Europe.   This is a reflection partly of the splendid natural endowment of great navigable rivers in western Germany, in particular the Rhine, which as a result of nineteenth-century improvements is navigable for small sea-going vessels and for barges of 1,500 tons to Basel on the Swiss frontier; and partly of the tradition of constructing high-capacity canals in the late nineteenth and early twentieth centuries: for example, the Rhine–Herne (1914) and the Dortmund–Ems (1899) canals, which together provide a continuous waterway from the Rhine at Duisburg to the North Sea at Emden, and the Mittelland Canal (completed 1938), which connects the Ruhr with Berlin.   30 per cent of goods traffic in the Federal Republic (measured in ton-kilometres) travels by inland water; the corresponding percentage in Britain is negligible. As compared with Britain, a larger percentage of goods transport is by rail (especially in the Democratic Republic); but the growth of goods transport by road, together with the increasing number of private cars (5·4 million in 1961), has caused the Federal Republic to embark on an ambitious programme of major road works, including the completion and extension of the *Autobahn* (motorway) network, planned and partly constructed under the Nazi régime in the 1930s. A special feature of the new extensions are the international links to motorways in the Netherlands, Belgium, Switzerland and Austria, to form eventually an integrated European motorway network.   In the Democratic Republic the growth of road transport has been much slower and the *Autobahn* network has not been extended, although a link from Berlin to the seaport of Rostock is to be constructed.

*Trade.*  Germany's trading pattern, both pre- and postwar, is dominated by the export of semi-manufactured and manufactured goods, though the division of Germany, coming while a shattered economy was in course of reconstruction, has altered the whole orientation of the economies of the two Germanies, and has emphasised a distinction between a manufacturing west and a primary producing east.   In 1960 no less than 83 per cent of the exports of the Federal Republic (by value) consisted of fully manufactured goods; but 90 per cent of the exports of the Democratic Republic consisted of raw materials and semi-finished products.   The economy of the Federal Republic has become much more like Britain's than was prewar Germany's; it is involved predominantly, and increasingly, in the exchange of manufactured goods with the other highly industrialised nations of western Europe; nearly two-thirds of its total trade is with other European nations.   In the circumstances it was logical that Federal Germany should have been, one of the six signatories to the Rome Treaty of 25 March 1957 which established the European Economic Community. On the other side, three-quarters of the much smaller total trade of the Democratic Republic is with the communist states of eastern Europe and China. Trade between the two Germanies, relative to their total economic activity, has been reduced to negligible quantities.

## REFERENCES

The standard work on the geography of Germany in English is R. E. Dickinson, *Germany*, 2nd ed., revised, London, Methuen, 1961. Smaller but extremely useful texts are T.H. Elkins, *Germany*, New York, Praeger, 1968; and K.A. Sinnhuber, *Germany: Its Geography and Growth*, London, Murray, 1961. K. A. Sinnhuber's book contains a useful reference guide to the available periodical literature in English, to which should be added: H. Uhlig, 'Old Hamlets with Infield and Outfield Systems in Western and Central Europe', *Geografiska Annaler*, 43, 1961, 285–312; T. H. Elkins, 'The Economic Background to Berlin', *Geography*, 47, 1962, 92–95; and R. E. H. Mellor, 'The German Democratic Republic's Falling Population', *ibid.*, 409–12; and T. H. Elkins and E. M. Yates, 'The South German Scarplands in the Vicinity of Tübingen', *Geography*, 48 (1963), 372–392. On a particular region see N. J. G. Pounds, *The Ruhr*, London, Faber, 1951. The *Diercke Atlas*, Braunschweig, Westermann, regularly revised, is an indispensable companion to the study of the geography of Germany; it is soon understood by someone with no knowledge of German. The standard work in German is G. Braun, *Deutschland*, 2nd ed., Berlin, Borntraeger, 1936, long since out of print. A useful modern standard textbook, though presenting a highly nationalistic view of German political geography, is *Harms Erdkunde*, Band I, *Deutschland*, 23rd ed., Munich, List, 1962. The same firm is now producing a regional series, of which one has appeared: *Harms Landeskunde*, Band I: J. Wagner, *Hessen*, Munich, List, 1961. An indispensable regional work of reference edited by E. Meynen and others is *Handbuch der naturräumlichen Gliederung Deutschlands*, Remagen and Bad Godesberg, Bundesanstalt für Landeskunde, 1958–62.

### CHAPTER 21

# NORTHERN GERMANY AND THE
# GERMANO-POLISH LOWLAND

**The Northern Lowland.** This region includes the whole of Germany north of the Hercynian *Mittelgebirge*; it extends eastwards across Poland to the border of the USSR. The area is here treated as a single physical unit, which it is; but the description of the human geography is limited by the Oder–Neisse line, representing the eastern boundary of post-1945 Germany. The human geography of the Polish section of the plain is described in Chapter 23.

**Effects of the Quaternary Glaciation on Physical Features.** This lowland is covered with unconsolidated, superficial deposits laid down by great ice-sheets which spread out from Scandinavia in Quaternary times. These deposits consist of various kinds of glacial materials, such as boulder-clay, morainic material, gravel, sand, and wind-blown *Löss*, (a German word, meaning 'loose, uncompacted material'), either deposited *in situ* or reworked by wind and water; their thickness has been proved by borings to vary from about 40 ft to more than 600 ft. Only very occasionally can the solid geology be seen through the covering mantle, as, for instance, in the gypsum outcrop of Sperenberg, or the *Muschelkalk* of Rüdersdorf near Berlin, though the islands of Rügen and Heligoland both reveal the underlying rock in their cliffs of chalk and Bunter sandstone respectively. The deposits were evidently laid down on a pre-existing lowland surface composed mainly of Tertiary material, a fact which is of economic significance in connection with the deposits of brown coal in the southern part of the German lowland, e.g. in Niederlausitz, and near Leipzig and Cologne.

The lowland surface offered no obstacle to the successive advances of the great ice-sheet, whose greatest extension was stopped only by the mountains of central Germany and southern Poland: e.g. the Harz, Erzgebirge, Sudety, and Carpathians. The later advance or advances, however, had evidently less momentum behind them and petered out in the plain itself.

Over the greater part of the Germano-Polish lowland east of the Lüneburger Heide (Lüneburg Heath) the glacial material is arranged in a number of concentric bands, which are extended in an east–west direction, or more correctly, parallel with the generalised line of

the southern shore of the Baltic.   The plain immediately bordering
the Baltic rises quickly to the Baltic Heights, which reach over
1,000 ft in places.   South of these is a zone consisting of great
shallow valleys alternating with bands of rather higher ground, and
south of these again comes a *Löss*-covered zone bordering the
mountains.   The lowland is not wholly devoid of relief, though
there are large areas of flat land, both in and between the great
valleys.   West of the lower Elbe this concentric arrangement is
not found and there is practically no break in the flatness of the
plain.

There are three main types of deposits associated directly with
those parts of an ice-sheet which are far from the centre of dispersion and which have reached low ground (Fig. 44, p. 360).   First
there is the finely pulverised material of the ground-moraine beneath
the ice.   This is known as glacial till.   The older name, boulder
clay, implies clay mixed with coarser material dropped from the body
of the ice-sheet as it melts *in situ*.   In the Germano-Polish lowland
there is a higher proportion of sandy material in the ground-moraine
areas than is usual (for instance) in the glaciated lowland areas of
Britain.   Second, where conditions were favourable for its formation, there is the end-moraine, which consists of very mixed material,
including fragments of rock of all sizes, from grains of sand to large
boulders, which have been carried in and above the ice-sheet, rather
than under it, so that there is a lower proportion of finely abraded
material than in the boulder clay.   A terminal moraine is not, of
course, a necessary accompaniment to an ice-sheet; in fact, it can be
formed only when the rate of growth and the rate of melting are so
nicely balanced that the edge of the sheet stays in one place for a
prolonged period of time.   When an end-moraine occurs, it is usually
backed by a transitional zone between it and the ground-moraine
deposits consisting of hummocky, ill-sorted material (often forming
the 'basket-of-eggs' topography characteristic of *drumlins*) separated
by ill-drained depressions which may contain lakes.   Thirdly, there
is the outwash material (*Sander*) which the waters of the melting
glaciers carry away with them, and which consist mainly of the finer
particles from the end-moraine, particularly sand.   A fourth type
of deposit may be added, namely, the *Löss*, but this is a product
not so much of the glacial period as of the inter-glacial and post-
glacial periods.   These latter periods were dry, so that steppe-like
conditions prevailed over the unconsolidated material of the newly
exposed surface.   The loose, dry particles could easily be picked up
by the wind, which carried them, no doubt, in different directions,
but a large number of particles were arrested on the wetter southern
margins, which here were along the northern foot of the mountains

of central Germany and southern Poland.   These *Löss* deposits consist of very finely powdered yellowish material, on which fertile dark brown soils have usually developed.   These, in turn, have allowed

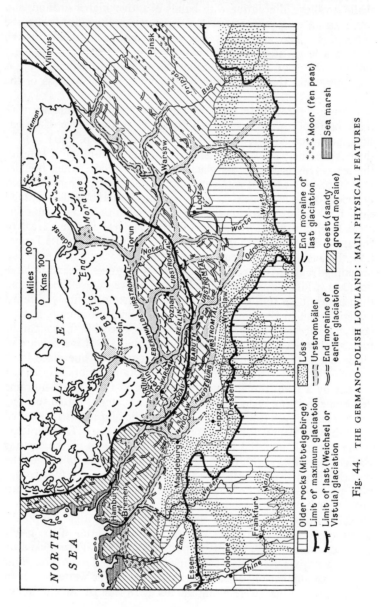

Fig. 44.   THE GERMANO-POLISH LOWLAND: MAIN PHYSICAL FEATURES

the development of very productive agriculture which contrasts remarkably with that over many other parts of the plain.

Although four periods of advance of the Quaternary ice have been established for the Alps, in the Germano-Polish lowland only three advances (and two corresponding periods of retreat, in the last of which we are now living) can be distinguished for certain. They correspond to the three last advances of the Alpine ice, as follows:

(No. 1 is first chronologically, and therefore stands lowest in the lithological series).

| | GERMANO-POLISH LOWLAND | ALPS (SOUTH GERMANY) | CORRESPONDING BRITISH GLACIAL PERIOD |
|---|---|---|---|
| 4 | Weichsel (Vistula) | Würm | North British York; Main Irish Sea |
| | Interglacial between 'Older' and 'Newer' Drifts | | |
| 3 | Saale | Riss | Gipping Till; 'Older Drift' of Vale of York |
| | Main Interglacial | | |
| 2 | Elster | Mindel | Scandinavian Ice (Lowestoft Till) |
| 1 | 'Cromerian' | Günz | Cromer Till |

These advances were of decreasing order of magnitude. The first advance, although it reached further south than the others, has left little impress on the present topography, either because time and weather have obliterated the marks of its terminal moraines or because no extensive terminal moraines were formed. The last glaciation was so recent, geologically speaking, that subaerial erosion has not yet had time to blur the work of the ice.

**Zonal Topography East of the Elbe.** It is only east of the Elbe that the Germano-Polish lowland was affected by the last (Vistula) glaciation, which produces a characteristically immature topography. South of the immediate coasts of the Baltic is the ground-moraine zone consisting of a belt of lowland covered with glacial till, or till similar in character to that of East Anglia (though formed by a different advance of the ice), and similarly formed under the ice-sheet. The soil here is heavy and tenacious and generally fertile, but difficult to work. It was covered originally with deciduous forest, mainly beech. Southwards the land rises to the Baltic Lake Plateau. Here, sand and gravel alternate with loams in a hummocky area, dotted with lakes, and traversed by typical end-moraines of coarse angular material. The most prominent of these is the northernmost

and latest produced during the last (Pomeranian) stage of advance of
the ice during the Vistula period; it reaches a maximum height of
550 ft at its eastern end, and is known as the *Baltic End-Moraine*,
forming the Baltic Heights.   These heights are generally unsuitable
for cultivation and are retained under forest, consisting mainly of
coniferous trees.   The accumulation of morainic material in these
Baltic Heights bears witness to the length of time during which the
end of the ice-sheet must have rested here.   This, however, was

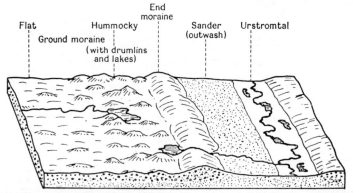

Fig. 45.   SCHEMATIC DIAGRAM OF THE MAIN FEATURES OF A LOW-
LAND OF GLACIAL DEPOSITION

but the last period of pause in the spasmodic retreat of the most
recent ice-sheet, and there are a number of other end-moraines
parallel to and south of, the Baltic Heights, though the more southerly
ones are lower and more discontinuous.   In front, that is, south of
each of these end-moraines, one would expect to find an outwash
plain of sand, but matters were here somewhat complicated because,
from the southern border of the glacier, the ground sloped slightly upward, so that the melt-water could not flow directly away from the
ice face, but had to flow along its front for a long distance, until a
lateral way of escape could be found.   Moreover, the amount of
water hemmed in between the ice and the mountains was augmented
by the drainage from the mountains themselves.   In consequence
of the spasmodic retreat of the ice-sheet northwards, a number of
great east–west depressions were formed, and these great
*Urstromtäler* (sing. *Urstromtal*; 'ancient river valleys'), as they
are called in Germany, form a characteristic feature of the landscape
of the greater part of the north German lowland.   They are most
important between the Elbe and the Oder, where they form a belt
about 60 miles wide, in the centre of which lies Berlin.   This area
is known as 'the zone of the *Urstromtäler*'.

In the Polish plain, where the east–west depressions are called *pradoliny*, they are far fewer in number and farther apart than between the Elbe and Oder. This seems to have been due to the different configuration of the country, with lines of higher ground running from south to north, and so preventing the easy lateral escape of water and leading to the formation of great ice-dammed lakes. Also there are fewer end-moraines in the Polish section of the lowland, particularly east of the Vistula and south of the Bug, which seems to indicate a more continuous melting or a smaller amount of debris.

Most of the *Urstromtäler* of Germany and Poland do not contain any considerable quantity of water at the present day, for the supply of water from a melting ice-sheet is no longer available. Nor, as can be seen from the map, do they form the main arteries of any water system. On the contrary, the general direction of drainage is now generally from south to north. This diversion of the drainage evidently took place after the disappearance of the ice-sheet. Active erosion began on the part of short streams flowing to the Baltic Sea from the Baltic Heights. These evidently cut back their heads, and captured streams flowing in a generally west or north-westerly direction along the *Urstromtäler*. In general therefore the present courses of the most important rivers of the lowland and of their tributaries, show abrupt alternations between north–south and WNW–ESE (*Urstromtal*) orientations; and tributaries along the *Urstromtäler* often make straight lines with their main river, which enters the confluence at a sharp angle: e.g., the entry of the Aller into the Weser above Bremen, of the Havel and Schwarze Elster into the Elbe near Havelberg and Wittenberg respectively, and that of the Baryez into the upper Oder. Borings reveal marked valleys below the glacial deposits in the lower courses of the Weser and Elbe, as well as of the Oder and Vistula, and also in the upper (Silesian) course of the Oder, so that it seems possible that the development of the main streams of the present river system is guided in part by the preglacial topography.

The *Urstromtäler*, though most of them are no longer occupied by major rivers, yet afford admirable opportunities for the construction of canals. The floors of the depressions are usually marshy, though often partly choked by sand-dunes which were accumulated by the wind in postglacial times. The particles are coarser than those of the *Löss*, which were carried much farther. Owing to the present damp climate these dunes are generally no longer active, but are mainly covered with vegetation, particularly pine forest and heath, and the marshy tracts have mainly been drained, as they provide the most fertile soil apart from that on the *Löss*. For long, however, the great marshy *Urstromtäler* proved great barriers and offered great difficulties to settlers. Dutch and Flemish workmen carried out much of the reclamation in the *Urstromtäler* both in Germany and Poland, using techniques of drainage and reclamation they had evolved in their homelands, and Frederick the Great is said to have 'subdued a province in time of peace' by drainage of the Oderbruch. The land between the *Urstromtäler* offered even less promising material, since it consists mainly of the sandy outwash material and of the end-moraine itself. Unfortunately the retreat of the ice-sheet usually resulted in the fertile ground-moraine being covered up by the infertile material of the end-moraine and outwash sand, and only in a few places, presumably, where the ice-sheet was not carrying a heavy load of course material, does the boulder clay remain on the surface, though deep borings have reached two and sometimes three layers of boulder clay at increasing depths. The discovery that the potash salts (*Kalisalz*) of Stassfurt could turn this 'sand-box' (*Streusandbüchse*) into quite moderately good land created a revolution in the husbandry of the North German Plain in the nineteenth century, and largely contributed to the wealth and strength of the kingdom of Brandenburg–Prussia, which was the main political unit of the plain.

**The Baltic Coast.** The actual coastline of the Baltic is largely a result of changes in the relative level of land and sea, rather than a direct consequence of glacial modelling, though some glacial features are discernible. East of the Oder, the Baltic coast is noted for its smooth outlines which are associated with the development of great dune-crowned sand-spits, formerly known as *Nehrungen* (cf. French *cordons littoraux*) which were built up in front of a formerly indented coastline by the action of longshore drift and the prevailing south-west wind. The Frische Nehrung (Mierzeja Wiślana) and the Kurische Nehrung (Kurskaya Kosá) are outstanding examples, and between these and the old shore lie great lagoons—the Frisches Haff (Zalew Wiślany)—see p. 372—and the Kuriches Haff (Kurskiy Zaliv) and, though in Pomerania the lagoons are smaller, yet most of these latter appear completely devoid of direct access to the sea (cf. the Landes coast of France). The coast east of the Oder, therefore, has comparatively few harbours, and no good ones by modern standards, with the possible exception of Gdynia (see p. 410). Glacial modelling is seen chiefly in the mouths of the Oder and Vistula, both of which appear to occupy the sites of former glacial 'tongue-basins', which are depressions formed by lobes of the retreating ice-sheet.

West of the Oder, the coastline becomes progressively more articulated, and the *Nehrungen* diminish in length and continuity until

they finally disappear. The maintenance of the old indented coastline is presumably the result of the feebler strength of winds and
currents, and of the smaller quantity of available material, owing
to the presence of the Jutland peninsula. Two types of coast are
distinguished here, the *Bodden* and the *Förden*. The *Bodden* coast
includes the Oder mouth, and extends westwards along the Mecklenburg coast to Lübeck Bay, while the *Förden* coast lies on the eastern
coast of Schleswig-Holstein between Lübeck Bay and the Danish
frontier. Both are drowned coasts, but the *Bodden* are irregularly
shaped inlets in contrast to the long, straight-sided *Förden*. The
*Bodden* are formed behind an irregular breakwater of islands
partially linked together by sand-spits, with the core of the islands
varying from the chalk of Rügen to the glacial material of those at
the Oder mouth. The *Förden* (e.g. Flensburger Förde, Kieler
Förde, Eckernförder Bucht) are shallow drowned valleys, formed
originally by rivers flowing beneath the ice-sheet (cf. the *fiords* of
Danish Jutland). They provided very good harbours until the days
of really big ships.

**Topography West of the Elbe.** Here the same infertile sandy
and gravelly deposits are found, but they were laid down in earlier
advances of the ice; the last (Vistula) glaciation did not extend
south and west of the lower Elbe. The dominant glaciation here
is the second (Saale) advance; the deposits have suffered extensive
postglacial denudation, so that relief is much more subdued. Wide,
infertile, dry, sandy regions called *Geest* (p. 368) are intersected by
the fenlands of the lower-lying areas and fringed by the marshes of
the coast. Between the Elbe and the lower Weser lie the extensive
heathlands of the Lüneburger Heide; westwards again, between the
Weser and Ems, is the Geest platform of Cloppenburg and the
sandy Hümmling. These latter areas in particular contain extensive
areas of low-lying fen peat or *Flachmoor*, which remained unre-
claimed until recent centuries. Along the coast these fens pass into
sea marshes, just as in the East Anglian fenlands on the other side
of the North Sea. The region evidently underwent subsidence at the
close of the Ice Age, when the North Sea came into being and
the English Channel was opened. The sea even invaded part of
the present coastlands both in western Germany and Holland and
penetrated the lower courses of the existing river valleys. It is
possible that a slight uplift followed, but it is not necessary to
postulate this to explain the present topography. Sandbanks were
formed by the currents sweeping parallel to the coast and later
developed into lines of dunes. Between the dunes and the shore
were shallow lagoons, which gradually became largely transformed
into marshes by being filled up with silt and by the growth of

halophitic plants.  Further sinking took place, since the protecting line of dunes was later pierced by the sea and in the east was reduced to a string of islands, known as the West, East, and North Frisian Islands, the first of these being Dutch, the second German, and the last mainly Danish.  Much of the marshland was again converted into shallow lagoons, known as *Watten*, which are uncovered at low tide, and even the low-lying mainland was invaded by the sea to create the Jadebusen (eleventh century), the Zuider Zee (thirteenth century), and the Dollart (fourteenth century), which were all afterwards enlarged by further flooding.  It is the tidal flats along the coasts and up the river estuaries which have been worth the trouble of reclamation by prodigious efforts of dyking and pumping, since they are covered with fertile silt, whereas the sandy soils of the mainland, though available without any such trouble, are so sterile as to be practically worthless.

**Political Frontiers on the Germano-Polish Lowland.**  The lack of well-defined natural frontiers in the Germano–Polish lowland is no doubt one of the chief reasons for the historical tug-of-war across the plain between the Teutonic- and Slavonic-speaking peoples. Within historic times there have been extraordinary fluctuations of this frontier between the two types of speech.  While it seems clear that Teutonic-speaking people occupied the plain during the later Folk-Wanderings (having replaced Celtic-speaking people), yet they migrated westwards and southwards, leaving the lowland free for the expansion of the Slavonic-speaking peoples whose homeland appears to have lain east of the Vistula.  Until the early part of the twelfth century[1], the effective eastern frontier of the Germans was the River Elbe, but then began 'that great eastward movement of conquest, colonisation and Christianisation, which under the ægis of bishop, monk, noble, and merchant, continued steadily for 200 years' (Dickinson).  The German colonists set about clearing the forest between the Elbe and the Oder, and even beyond, to make room for agriculture, and they virtually introduced urban life, but save in the *Löss* belt at the southern edge of the plain, these northern lowlands were not rich, fertile, smiling areas similar to the Paris and London basins.  On the contrary, the poverty of the soil prevented the establishment of a political unit rich enough in natural resources and man-power to attract and dominate the other German political units, until (in the course of the late eighteenth and early nineteenth centuries) the *Urstromtäler* were

---

[1] The earlier conquests of Charlemagne, Henry the Fowler, and Otto I were followed by recessions, and in any case were conquests over the Slavs rather than large-scale German settlements. (See *Agrarian Life in the Middle Ages*, Vol. I of Cambridge Economic History of Europe, Cambridge, 1941).

drained and fertilisers applied to the sandy soil of the interfluves. Thus the ease of communication, which seemed to render this northern lowland an appropriate place for the early growth of a powerful state, was largely negatived by the presence of sterile soils, while the lack of a nodal or focusing point no doubt also proved an important negative factor. Indeed, the best focusing point of routes, which lay in the Brandenburg–Berlin area, was cursed with particularly sterile sands.

The partitioning of Poland in the late eighteenth century between Prussia, Russia, and Austria was to some degree, at least, a corollary of the lack of well-defined frontiers on the Germano–Polish lowland. The resuscitation of Poland in 1919–20 meant loss of territory both to Germany and Russia, but was more serious to Germany. as she possessed no extra-European area, whereas Russia had her vast Asiatic lands which were admittedly capable of enormous development. The 1939 advance of the USSR westwards to the 'Curzon' line of Brest-Litovsk (now Brest) followed by the advance of Poland's western frontier to the Oder in 1945 is a Slav advance at the expense of Germany of much significance, especially when taken in conjunction with the partition of East Prussia between the USSR and Poland. Comparing her 1939 and 1945 territories, Poland has lost an eastern third but gained a more valuable western third; the country has been shifted bodily westward. Germany has been as dramatically shifted since 1919: she has lost one-third of her 1919 area, by far the greater part of this loss being in the east.

**The North German Lowlands: Regional Description.** The German section of the northern plain, in spite of having relatively small areas over 600 ft, contains more variety than might be imagined at first sight. The lowlands fall into three main subdivisions (see Fig. 44), A, the area west of the Elbe, containing large areas of low sandy *Geest*, fen peat and sea marsh, with its rivers flowing to the North Sea; B, a large area east of the Elbe, with its physical features arranged in concentric arcs parallel to the Baltic coast, and lending itself to subdivision into (i) the Baltic coastal zone and Baltic Heights in the north, and (ii) the zone of *Urstromtäler* farther south; C, a transitional southern strip or border with 'tongues' of lowland extending southward into the mountainous zone of central Germany. These tongues have been termed the Cologne, Münster, and Leipzig 'bays of lowland'. In contrast to (A) and (B), this last division is mainly covered with fertile soils, largely developed on *Löss*, and is a region of ancient settlements with a high density of population.

**A. West of the River Elbe.** This area lies almost wholly within the Federal Republic. The lowland is here at its narrowest, the distance between the Jadebusen (west of the Weser estuary) and the Weser uplands south of Minden being about 75 miles. In this generally featureless area variety is provided chiefly by differences in land utilisation, which are based mainly on differences of soil. There are three types of landscape in this area, (i) the reclaimed sea marshes (*Marschen*) along the North Sea coast and river estuaries, (ii) the bogs developed on extremely flat parts of the mainland owing to impeded drainage and called *Moore* ('moors' or 'bogs'), and (iii) the heath lands of the higher and drier sandy stretches called *Geest* ('infertile'). Human activities are mainly concentrated in the first of these regions, especially on the river estuaries of the North Sea coast.

*The Geest.* The *Geest* is divided into two parts, the larger and higher section, the Lüneburger Heide (Lüneburg Heath), lying between the Elbe on the east and the Weser–Aller *Urstromtal* on the south-west, and the smaller and lower western section lying between the Weser and the Ems. The Lüneburger Heide seldom exceeds about 350 ft and its surface is often quite flat and rarely more than undulating, though its sides are rather steep where it descends to the valleys of the Elbe and Weser. The Heath is crossed by end-moraine ridges representing retreat stages of the second (Saale) glaciation, which run N–S or NW–SE. One of these rises to 570 ft in the Wilserder Berg, in an area which has been set aside as a national nature park. Such an area of light soil was attractive to prehistoric man, but became culturally and economically backward as more difficult environments were colonised elsewhere. The traditional economy combines rather poor arable farming and sheep rearing, but since 1850 one-third of the area has been afforested, mainly with conifers – a development which probably represents the most suitable use for most of the area. Rather better soil is found in the infrequent valleys. The section west of the Aller is similar, but smaller and less continuous, being encroached upon by bogs and by the alluvium of the river valleys.

*The 'Moore' or Bogs.* These peat bogs have an appearance very similar to those of Ireland. They are similarly caused by lack of drainage. Two types are distinguished: those at an elevation above base-level, where the peat appears dry on top but in reality is sodden with water, and secondly those at lower levels, which are often partly water-covered. From the seventeenth century onwards the bogs have been slowly reclaimed by drainage, clearance of the peat, and improvement of the underlying sand. Settlement has taken place in planned linear settlements along canals – the 'fen colonies' or *Fehnkolonien* – of which the oldest and largest, Papenburg, contains over 15,000 inhabitants. The farmers cultivate potatoes, green vegetables, some cereals, and are engaged in cattle rearing. The peat itself is burnt for domestic use or converted into electric power.

*The North Sea Coast of Germany.* The sea coast and lower courses of the Elbe, Weser, and Ems are bordered by reclaimed lands which have been gained from the flood by means of dyking and drainage. A few feet above the level of the marsh stand the part natural, part artificial mounds called *Wurten* (the *terpen* of the Netherlands) which provided the original settlement sites from prehistoric times onwards. Systematic drainage of the marshes took place from the early twelfth century, and resulted in long planned villages (*Marschhufendorf* type) along dykes. These *Marschen* carry chiefly meadowland for cattle and horses, but also grow sugar-beet and vegetables in the parts quite free from salt, Hamburg in particular making a large demand for market-garden produce. The rich soil of the *Marschen* supports a large farming population, in spite of the danger of living below the level of high tide.

Between the coast and the dune-covered islands, with their sandy beaches and holiday resorts, are the tidal flats or *Watten*, which are dry at low water except for channels of greater or less depth where rivers, great and small, cut across them to the sea. It is obvious that the only means of entry for shipping is up the estuaries, which fortunately are numerous in relation to the length, or rather the shortness, of the coast.

Although the North Sea coast of Federal Germany is less than 100 miles long (as the crow flies), yet it was much more important than her erstwhile Baltic coast, mainly because it has direct access to the open ocean and is very little troubled by ice in winter. No port on the Baltic coast could compete with Hamburg, which has a population of 1,832,400[1] and was the leading port of the mainland of Europe in pre-war days, and the third largest port in the world. (It has now been supplanted in first European place by Rotterdam.)

Hamburg was a self-governing city and a member of the old 'Hanse' or league of free German cities that dominated the trade of central and northern Europe in the later Middle Ages. The town grew up on the Alster, a right-bank tributary of the Elbe, where the firm ground of the *Geest* offered a dry site. It profited, like Liverpool, from the discovery of the New World of America, especially after that continent was opened up to international trade in the late eighteenth and early nineteenth centuries; but its most rapid growth came later with the extension of the power of Prussia and the unification of Germany under the Empire. Naturally, also, the increased agricultural productivity and the accompanying

[1] Population figures are 1961 census figures of resident population for the Federal Republic and Democratic Republic unless otherwise stated.

increase of population in the North German lowland greatly enhanced the importance of its hinterland.

Hamburg entered the German *Zollverein* as late as 1888, seventeen years after becoming part of the German *Reich* (Empire), but retained many privileges right down to the 1930s, including its free port, whose freedom from customs duties enabled it to become a great entrepôt like London.

At the present day the city not only extends to the Elbe, but also has its newer quays on the farther, i.e. southern, side of the more northerly channel, in the islands of the estuary, at Wilhelmsburg, and on the southern bank of the more southerly channel at Harburg. Here the soft alluvial *Marschen* made excavation easy, whereas the firmer sand on the high right bank made harbour construction difficult. Owing to the small amplitude between high and low tide, averaging only 6 ft 6 in, there is no necessity for lock gates to the basins, so that no time is lost on arrival or departure for this reason. The port is actually about 85 miles from the first Elbe lightship, which is taken as the mouth of the estuary, but dredging has given a channel deep enough for the largest vessels afloat and some of the basins have a depth of 36 ft. Its outport of Cuxhaven, however, was built for passenger traffic, since the slow 85-mile journey up the river wastes half a day.

The hinterland of Hamburg before 1939 comprised all the land drained by the Elbe and its tributaries, including the Bohemian section of Czechoslovakia and the canal system between the Elbe and Oder. The River Elbe was the main highway for the movement of goods to and from the port until the network of railways became fully organised. Nearly half the goods traffic was river-borne in 1938, and inland navigation was considered sufficiently important to warrant the construction of the new *Mittelland* Canal connecting the Elbe westward with the Weser–Ems–Rhine system, and so to link up the two main inland water systems of Germany, which were formerly isolated from each other. Since 1945 the division of Germany, and the very tight limitation on trade between the two German states, have greatly reduced Hamburg's natural hinterland; for the 'Iron Curtain' bars the Elbe only 20 miles upstream from the city. In particular the valuable Czech trade has been diverted to ports in the Democratic Republic. Hamburg has had to reorient itself westwards towards the Federal Republic and the European Economic Community, to both of which it is peripherally placed. For this reason the Federal Government has speeded the improvement of overland communications from Hamburg, notably through the completion of the 500-mile 'Hafraba' (Hanse cities–Frankfurt–Basel) motorway, in 1962. By such means Hamburg has managed to remain by far the most important port of Federal Germany, with an overseas trading turnover of nearly 30 million tons in 1960, compared with 20½ million tons in 1938.

Besides being a port, Hamburg was also a manufacturing centre, especially concerned with shipbuilding and engineering. Various other industries are carried on, particularly in Altona, Harburg, Wilhelmsburg, and Wandsbek, which form part of the Hamburg conurbation, and since 1949 have formed part of the provincial (*Land*) Government of Hamburg. These industries are mainly concerned with processing imported raw materials, such as mineral and vegetable oil, rubber, grain and the agricultural produce of the surrounding countryside.

The other two North Sea Ports of Germany are Bremen (564,000) on the Weser and Emden on the Ems. The former is an older port than Hamburg, but its growth was hampered through its being on a smaller river, having a smaller hinterland, and also because its estuary is shallower and narrower than that of Hamburg. With its outport of Bremerhaven, which is accessible to the largest liners, Bremen was the second largest port in Germany, and, like Hamburg, was a free (Hanse) city; since 1949 it has (again like Hamburg) been an independent *Land* of the Federal Republic. Its commerce is rather more specialised than that of Hamburg and it is the chief Continental cotton market and importer. The turnover of the port (including Bremerhaven) in 1961 was nearly 15 million tons, about half that of Hamburg. Bremerhaven, together with Wesermünde, is the leading fishing port of Germany. The port of Emden was created with the object of capturing some of Rotterdam's traffic for Germany. It has the advantage of being connected with the great coalfield and industrial area of Westphalia by means of the Dortmund–Ems Canal (built 1892–98), and attracted to itself a large traffic, particularly in iron-ore and timber from Scandinavia, besides its exports of coal from the Ruhr. It is predominantly a port for bulk transfers of heavy raw materials.

**B. East of the Elbe.** The parallel arrangement of the main lines of relief has already been mentioned, and an explanation given of the main features of the topography (see pp. 361–364).

*The Baltic Ports.* West of the Oder, along the *Förden* and *Bodden* coasts (see p. 365), there are many inlets associated with famous old ports, but the coast as a whole is less important than the North Sea coast, owing to its position off the main lines of commerce and to its relatively severe winters. The necessity of making a detour round the 250-mile-long Jutland peninsula, or alternatively of paying the heavy dues through the Kiel Canal, has handicapped the Baltic ports in recent centuries as compared with those of the

North Sea coast. Moreover, physical conditions in the Baltic conspire to render its ports more liable to freeze. Not only does the more easterly position produce more Continental, i.e. colder, winters, but the Baltic Sea is so cut off from the open ocean by the shallow sill on which the Danish Archipelago stands that it receives very little salt ocean water and has practically no tide. On the other hand, it receives large quantities of fresh water from the many rivers which flow into it, so that the coastal inlets, on which most of the harbours stand, contain almost fresh water and therefore freeze more easily than if they were salt (cf. Frisches Haff=fresh-water haven). While the North Sea ports seldom have any trouble with ice, Stralsund is subject to freezing for 27 days per annum on an average, with wide fluctuations from year to year; navigation actually came to a standstill for over a month in the three consecutive years of 1940-1-2, while in 1947 the period of severe freezing was even longer. Despite the reduction of Hamburg's hinterland, the total trade of Germany's Baltic ports (both in the Federal and Democratic Republics) was less than one-third that of Hamburg in 1960.

*The Förden Coast of Schleswig-Holstein.*[1] Along the Baltic coast of Schleswig–Holstein are numerous ports, situated at the head of long inlets or *Förden* (see p. 365). The most important are Flensburg (98,500), Lübeck (234,600) and Kiel (273,300). Kiel is the only one which possesses deep water. It was Germany's main Baltic naval base, and stands near the entrance of the Kiel Canal, whose depth of 36 ft enables it to take the largest battleships. It was built by Germany mainly for strategic purposes to connect the North Sea and Baltic through German territory, and so avoid the channels through the Danish islands. Traffic through the canal amounted to about 44,900,000 tons in 1960. Kiel itself had graving-yards and a fishing industry.

Lübeck, on the River Trave, was formerly the leading member of the Hanse. Its shallow harbour, and in modern days its unfavourable position as compared with the North Sea ports, have caused its decline, though it trades with the Baltic countries through its industrial suburbs, which led to its devastation during the war. After the war, however, trade with Scandinavia grew, and in 1961 the turnover of the port was some 3 million tons. Since 1963 the ferry traffic to Scandinavia has been concentrated in the new harbour of Puttgarden on the island of Fehmarn some 50 miles north of Lübeck.

*The Bodden Coast.* This is the coast of the historic province of Mecklenburg, which now includes the western part of Pomerania (the

[1] In the Federal German Republic.

rest of Pomerania having passed under Polish control in 1945). It has two important ports which both flourished under the Hanseatic League in the Middle Ages, then declined, but which have experienced a renaissance since 1945 due to the division of Germany. The communist régime of the Democratic Republic has developed them to replace outlets now in the west (especially Hamburg). Stralsund (66,100) has become a shipbuilding town while Rostock (161,800) is being developed as the main port and shipbuilding centre of the country. But in 1960 it had a total turnover of only 1·4 million tons compared with Hamburg's 30·8 million tons. From Warnemünde, the outport of Rostock, a train ferry service operates to Gedser in Denmark. The most important port of this coast has been incorporated in Poland since 1945; it is Szczecin (formerly Stettin) (279,100 in 1961) at the head of the Oder estuary.

*The Immediate Hinterland of the Baltic Coast and the Baltic Heights.* A strip of fertile lowlands covered with boulder clay (the ground moraine zone of northern Mecklenburg) margins the Baltic coast and extends inland for some 10 to 20 miles, attaining a maximum width of about 50 miles on the borders of Mecklenburg and west Pomerania. With strong resemblances to East Anglia it has similar farming; most of the land is under the plough, with sugarbeet on the best soils, though rye is more important than wheat, and potatoes cover a large area; green fodder crops are extensively cultivated, and livestock (cattle, pigs, horses and some sheep) are important. The region was one of the chief food suppliers to the Ruhr industrial area, but has reoriented itself since 1945.

The ground moraine zone rises southwards to the Baltic Lake Plateau. To north and south this hummocky plateau is bounded by terminal moraines of course material, deposited during the last (Vistula) glaciation. The innumerable lakes are of all shapes, the largest being the Müritz-See, the largest lake completely within German territory. The soils vary from boulder clay to sands and gravels, but at least 70 per cent is under cultivation, though many woods of pine and beech still remain. On the southern margin the plateau falls to a sandy outwash plain which merges into the zone of *Urstromtäler*.

The population density is rather low in the whole of this area, and the towns are few and small, apart from the ports already mentioned. The Baltic Lake Plateau was a traditional stronghold of large estates, which justified themselves by evolving and maintaining very high standards of scientific farming. Since 1945 these have been turned into collective farms by the communist régime. Holstein, on the other hand, was a province of small holdings, and this it has remained.

*The Zone of Great Valleys.* This low-lying region, which is also part of the Democratic Republic (save for the enclave of West Berlin), presents a series of broad, swampy valleys (*Urstromtäler*), running from east to west, and alternating with slightly higher *Geest* land composed of dry, generally sandy soils. The present river system has developed valleys which partly run at right-angles to the old *Urstromtäler*, though in some cases the old Ice Age valleys are still utilised by streams, as, for instance, by the lower Havel and Spree. The soil is prevailingly sandy and gravelly, though occasional patches of ground-moraine are found between the *Urstromtäler*, and in the valleys there is a considerable amount of alluvium, since the post-glacial sinking of the Baltic coast raised the base-level of erosion and so reduced the gradient of the rivers and increased their liability to flooding. The alluvium itself, however, is often sandy, since it is derived to a large extent from the zone of recent glaciation; so there are large areas of 'valley sand'. The whole region was originally forested and was colonised by the Germans at a relatively late date, mainly from the twelfth century onwards, principally through their efforts at draining the swampy valleys. The *Urstromtäler* with their alternation of peat swamp and heath-covered or wooded sand-dunes must have presented a discouraging picture, but once drained they offered more fertile soil than the sandy stretches between, in whose forests lay the scattered clearing of the original Slavonic-speaking peoples. The names *Altmark*, *Mittelmark*, and *Neumark* indicate the stages of advance of the 'march' or border county of Branden-burg, since the old *Mark* (cf. the English phrase 'the Welsh Marches') lay west of the Elbe, the middle *Mark* between the Elbe and Oder, and the new *Mark* east of the Oder. The *Urstromtäler* therefore show the characteristic planned settlement forms of the German advance eastwards in the later Middle Ages. Although cumbered by old sand-dunes and by later postglacial alluvial cones which were deposited by the new north–south or south–north flowing rivers, the *Urstromtäler* yet lent themselves to utilisation for canals, which have the great advantage of being almost entirely free from locks, such is the lack of gradient from east to west. Not only were these canals important before the railway era, but they were still able up to 1945 to compete with the railways for heavy bulk goods such as coal, timber, building stone, cement, and so on, which were needed to supply the city of Berlin.

Apart from Berlin there are no large cities in this region, nor is there any considerable industrial development. Berlin (4,338,800 in 1939; West Berlin 2,187,600, East Berlin 1,055,300 in 1961) is the great exception. When the capital of the county of Brandenburg was moved from Brandenburg town eastwards to Berlin at the end of the fifteenth century, only a small settlement existed at this crossing-place over the Spree, where the river could be fairly easily bridged owing to the presence of an island. From that time onwards the town grew with the power of the Elector of Brandenburg, who became king of Prussia in 1701 and emperor of Germany in 1871. It had only about 100,000 people at the end of the eighteenth century, whereas London had 959,000 in 1801 and Paris 547,000. As in the case of London and Paris, the railway system was made to focus upon the capital city. Its population reached the million mark just after the achievement of German unity in 1871, and from then on, as capital of the most populous country in Europe after Russia, its future was assured. It was not only the centre of government but of the other activities that are naturally drawn to a capital city – finance, headquarters office, distributive trade, and the types of manufacturing which flourish in a metropolis. Although excentric to Germany as a whole (and even more so after the losses of 1918), Berlin had excellent communications by rail and water which helped to foster the growth of a great variety of manu-facturing industries, and it was, in fact, like London and Paris, the most important isolated manufacturing centre of its country. Among the multitudinous variety of manufactures, electrical apparatus took first place, while there was also a great development of the clothing, building, printing, and publishing industries, and miscellaneous light engineering. Half the working population of prewar Berlin was engaged in government, commerce and other services; the other half in manufacturing industry. In 1945 the devastated capital was put under four-power military government. This broke down completely in 1948, since when East Berlin (the former Russian zone) has in practice been integrated into the communist Democratic Republic, of which the seat of government is in the suburb of Pankow, while West Berlin has been an independ-ent administrative entity, associated with (but not part of) the Federal Republic. The two halves were virtually severed from each other, and this severance became complete on 13 August 1961, when the communist authorities built a wall across the city to prevent uncontrolled movement between the two halves. Even before this, West Berlin had developed an extraordinarily separate economy as an 'exclave' surrounded by hostile territory. Virtually all its trade links, both for raw material and food supplies and for markets for its manufactured goods, are in the Federal Republic and in western Europe, from which it is separated by over 100 miles of communist territory, crossed by only three authorised road routes, three author-ised railway, three air lanes and the *Mittelland* Canal. Despite these handicaps, though not without considerable help from the government and people of the Federal Republic, West Berlin has made an extraordinary recovery; in 1961 its population stood at 2·2 million, against 2·8 million in 1939.

Brandenburg (86,700) and Frankfurt an-der Oder (57,000) both lie in the same *Urstromtal* as Berlin. The latter, an old Hanse town, was built at a crossing-place over the Oder, its commercial fairs being of considerable importance. It now stands on the Germano-Polish frontier.

The zone of great valleys virtually terminates on the south with the infertile, upland zones of the Fläming and the much dissected Lusatian Hills, though there are some traces of *Urstromtäler* to the south. These ridges continue the line of the Lüneburger Heide. The last ice-sheet was halted just south of Berlin, probably by the increased elevation, for beneath a relatively thin cover of glacial material are Tertiary sands and clays, together with beds of brown coal. The Fläming partakes of the character of the Lüneburger Heide, with heath and forest covering its dry, unproductive sands, and so to a less extent do the Lusatian Heights, which in any case do not exceed 723 ft and would hardly be distinguished as 'heights' if the surrounding country were not so flat. The Lusatian brown coal is used to provide briquettes and electricity for East Berlin, and fuel for the local glass industry, while the woollen industry of Cottbus (67,700) and other towns of Niederlausitz, which arose out of a desire to supplement farm-incomes in an unproductive area, was one of the main suppliers of the Berlin clothing industry up to 1945, when much of the latter industry was redeveloped in the west.

**C. The Southern Transitional Borderlands.** Festooned along the southern edge of the glaciated plain of northern Germany is a strip of fertile lowland which closely follows the wavy northern edge of the *Mittelgebirge* or Central Uplands. Here are no great thicknesses of morainic material; instead, the solid rock is usually near the surface, though often concealed by a mantle of *Löss*, or by similar loams, which perhaps represent *Löss* reworked by water action. This transitional strip, known in Germany as the *Börde* zone (dialectal German = 'border'), becomes very attenuated and practically disappears near Osnabrück, where the Weser Hills project like a great bastion into the plain; it broadens out in great embayments in three main areas, particularly round Leipzig, in Upper Silesia, and on a smaller scale round Cologne. The fourth great embayment – the Münsterland, south-west of the Weser Hills – has only a narrow strip of *Löss* along its southern edge; but this strip is of great historical importance in carrying the ancient east–west route of the Westphalian *Hellweg* (literally 'light, easy route'), on which a line of cities developed which later became the centres of the industrial Ruhr coalfield.

The soils of this zone are mainly degraded chernozems and brown forest soils of great fertility, and their significance lies in their occurrence between the ungrateful morainic deposits farther north and the thin soils of the rugged mountain country to the south. The *Löss* belt is one of those 'regions of increment' which amply reward human effort, and it has been assiduously cultivated from the beginnings of agriculture in Neolithic times. It is still perhaps the best farming land of Germany, especially for cereals. Even where patches of soil fall below the general level of fertility, heavy manuring and skilful rotation of crops have rendered them as productive as the rest. The land carries a high density of rural population (between 400 and 500 per square mile), and is so costly that none can be wasted; the variegated cultivation strips succeed one another without hedges or fences. Wheat, sugar-beet, barley and stall-fed cattle are the chief preoccupations of its rich agriculture.

Numerous ancient towns lie in this belt, such as Aachen, Cologne, Essen, Dortmund, Soest, Paderborn, Hanover, Braunschweig, Halberstadt, Magdeburg, Halle, Leipzig, Karl-Marx-Stadt (Chemnitz), and Dresden. Most of these are situated at nodal points, where valleys from the mountain zone debouch on the plain, for the *Löss* strip seems to have been cleared of its light woodlands in prehistoric times, and thus offered an east–west line of movement. The cities became great during the Middle Ages through commercial activities and manufacturing crafts; in many cases they were also administrative centres of secular and ecclesiastical authority, the three main functions obviously being closely bound up with each other.

To this wealth of agricultural and commercial prosperity was added in the nineteenth and twentieth centuries the exploitation of vast deposits of coal and brown coal, and the large-scale development of factory industries. Small wonder, therefore, that this belt at the foot of the Central Uplands is one of the most densely populated zones of Germany, and, indeed, of Europe. It forms part of the great axial belt of dense population which runs from the Straits of Dover eastwards and south-eastwards to the Ukraine.

These transitional borderlands may conveniently be treated in three main divisions: (*a*) to the west of the Weser Hills are the lower German Rhinelands including the Westphalian (Ruhr) industrial area; (*b*) adjacent to it, the Münster bay of lowland; (*c*) farther east, the Saxon bay of lowland, centred on Leipzig, with extensions to Hanover on the north-west and Dresden on the south-east. Farther east still, yet another projection has passed out of German hands;

the great lowland embayment of Schlesien (Silesia), long a bone of contention between German- and Polish-speaking people, has been Polish since 1945, the *de facto* boundary having been pushed westwards to the valley of the western Neisse river, close against the projection of the central uplands.

The names Ruhr and Silesia at once suggest great coalfields, and, in fact, practically the whole of the coal output of Germany comes from this 'belt; in addition to the bituminous coal of the abovementioned fields, there are vast deposits of brown coal in three main areas: a western mining area between Cologne and Bonn, a central mining area round Halle and Leipzig, and an eastern area in the Lusatian (Niederlausitz) Hills, which lie between the *Urstromtäler* and the *Löss* belt. The annual German production of bituminous coal from this transitional belt amounts to about 150 million tons (over 80 per cent from the Ruhr), together with over 300 million tons of brown coal of which some 30 per cent comes from the Cologne–Bonn field (Federal Republic), another 30 per cent from Halle-Leipzig and 40 per cent from Niederlausitz (both Democratic Republic). The industrial character of the belt is perhaps its main feature in modern times. It should be noted, however, that industry grew up amidst a cultural landscape of smiling agriculture and ancient settlements, unlike much of that in the main industrial belt of England. A good deal of formerly fertile land has been sacrified to open-face mining of brown coal and to industry; there is fierce competition for land and none is wasted, so that industrial cities end abruptly against intensively cultivated fields.

The transitional belt is closely linked with the Central Uplands on the south, as many of its industries were originally sited in the uplands, but moved downhill to the coalfields in the nineteenth century.

(*a*) *The Lower German Rhinelands.* The rich agriculture of the North Rhenish Plain and of the Münster area tends to be overshadowed by the industrial developments connected with the great Westphalian (Ruhr) coalfield, the small Aachen coalfield, and the important Cologne–Bonn deposits of brown coal.

In spite of much twentieth-century industrial expansion in other parts of Germany, the Ruhr coalfield is still the mainstay of German industry, particularly of heavy industry, such as coke production, pig-iron and steel manufacture, heavy engineering, and heavy chemicals. Nor could these be moved, as they depend primarily on the presence of coking coal, and secondly on the position which gives ease of transport by rail, road, and the great artery of the Rhine and its feeder canals.

The Ruhr coalfield lies east of the Rhine on the northern border of the Rhine Highlands (see pp. 392–395). It has a greater output than any other in Europe and probably greater reserves even than the Silesian and Donets coalfields, its only rivals on the Continent. Its exploitation is more recent than that of the great coalfields of the British Isles, which stand next to it in output, since it produced only about $2\frac{1}{2}$ million tons in 1850 and less than 12 million tons in 1870, whereas the Yorks, Derby, and Notts coalfield was producing 10·8 million tons even by 1855. It had therefore the advantage of being able to profit by the experiments of others in regard to technique, not only in the actual mining, but in the development of industries dependent upon coal.

For some years before 1914 the annual production of the Ruhr coalfield averaged about 100 million tons, or about 60 per cent of the total German output. In 1937 the output was 129 million tons out of a total of 185 million tons, i.e. 70 per cent. With the loss of the Silesian mines the Ruhr is Germany's sole bituminous field of importance, producing, in 1960, 120 million tons out of a West German total of 142 million tons, the Aachen coalfields producing only 6 million tons. (In comparison the Silesian field, including those parts lost in both 1919 and 1945 produced 100 million tons in 1960.)

Like the mines of Great Britain, and in contrast to those of France and Belgium, the Coal Measures are little disturbed except by occasional faults and gentle warping, and are fairly easy to work. The Coal Measures were apparently slightly tilted by the Tertiary uplift of the Rhine plateau, and the upper measures, as well as the covering mantle of later material, were denuded from the southern part of the field, so that here the coal actually outcrops in the valleys. It was therefore easily worked in the early days by means of adits and shallow mines, but this coal is not of such good quality as that obtained north of the Ruhr river. The Coal Measures gradually sink northward under a mantle of Secondary, Tertiary, and recent material, and the northern limits of the coalfield have not yet been ascertained, though mines are worked at a depth of more than 4,900 ft. near Münster. As the Coal Measures sink northward, the depth of the overlying rocks becomes greater, but at the same time the Coal Measures themselves increase in thickness, and coals of ever richer quality are added to the stratigraphical sequence, having escaped the denudation which removed them farther south, so that on top of the poor coals of the Sauerland border come coking coals along the Ruhr valley, on top of these farther north come gas coals, and lastly north of the Emscher come long-flame coals (see Fig. 46, p. 380). Two-thirds of the total coal output is suitable for coking.

The working of this coalfield has given rise to a great industrial belt some 45 miles long from east to west by 15 miles wide from north to south, which is ever extending northwards and devouring

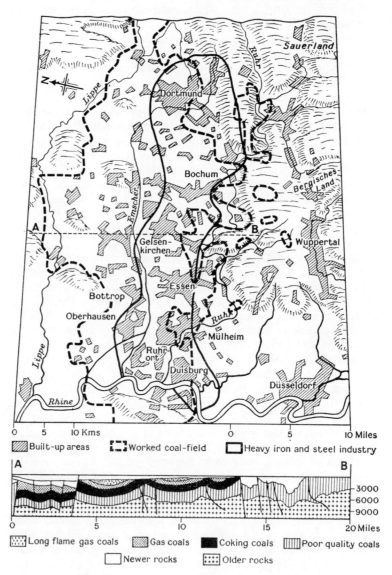

Built-up areas    Worked coal-field    Heavy iron and steel industry

Long flame gas coals    Gas coals    Coking coals    Poor quality coals

Newer rocks    Older rocks

Fig. 46. THE RUHR: PERSPECTIVE DIAGRAM

more of the agricultural countryside as newer and deeper mines are opened. The main industrial area, which lies north of the River Ruhr and stretches from Duisburg (503,000) to Dortmund (641,500), contains about 5 million people and forms in reality a single conurbation, there being practically no break in the continuity of houses and factories, though the names of Essen (726,600), and Gelsenkirchen (382,700), Bochum (361,400) and Oberhausen (256,800) may be mentioned among the more important urban centres. South of the industrial belt, however, even along the River Ruhr itself, the thinly populated, hilly and wooded country of the Sauerland forms a natural 'playground' for the workers, while on the north of the industrial belt, north of the Emscher, the coal mines and mining settlements are scattered among farms, woods, and heathland.

Apart from the actual mining, the chief forms of industry are the manufacture of heavy iron and steel goods of all kinds, and the essential preliminary manufacture of coke and pig-iron. The iron-ore now has to be imported, as Germany's own resources in this raw material are limited. Even before the loss of the Lorraine ores in 1919, millions of tons of iron had to be imported; today about one-quarter of requirements are met by home output. Formerly the most important home source was in the Siegerland, south of the Ruhr, but in recent years the low-grade Jurassic and Cretaceous ores, north of the Harz mountains around Braunschweig, have been developed, and now make up over half of home ore production. Swedish ore accounted for over half the imports (see 'Economic Summary', page 353). Needless to say, the position on the plain renders the transport of this heavy raw material a relatively easy matter, and river, canal, and rail supplement each other in the supply and distribution of raw materials and manufactured goods. Heavy goods travelling in bulk, such as imported iron-ore and imported grain, move principally by water. The exception in the past was provided by the Lorraine ores which had to go by train, as the meanders of the Mosel made navigation prohibitively tedious. In any case the Ruhr now uses relatively little Lorraine ore, and the scheme for the canalisation of the Mosel (to which Germany agreed as a condition of the return of the Saar to her in 1957, and which was completed in 1963) will mainly benefit Lorraine users of Ruhr coal. The large amounts of coal and coke sent away from the Ruhr also utilise the waterways, particularly the canalised Ruhr and Emscher, which penetrate the heart of the coalfield, and the Rhine itself, both downstream towards Holland and upstream to the middle Rhine valley and the adjacent lands. The twin port of Duisburg–Ruhrort on the Rhine forms not only the most important river port of Germany, but also of Europe; its total trade stands just behind that of Hamburg if for the latter both internal and overseas trade are reckoned.  It is concerned with the transhipment of coal outwards, and iron-ore, grain, and petroleum inwards, either on to the Rhine–Herne canal and River Ruhr or on to the railways and vice versa.

South and west of the Ruhr coalfield are a number of other manufacturing districts which form part of the industrial complex of the Lower Rhinelands; they draw their supplies of fuel mainly from the Ruhr coalfield, and of electric power from a grid system fed by the Ruhr coalfield and the Cologne–Bonn brown coal.  They might be looked upon as satellites of the Ruhr industrial area, except that many of them were established long before the coalfield was opened up.  The chief of these districts are, first the Bergisches Land with the Wuppertal textile towns and the cutlery towns of Remscheid and Solingen; secondly, the textile towns of the Krefeld-Mönchengladbach area; thirdly, the Cologne–Düsseldorf district; and fourthly, the Aachen district.

The Wuppertal towns of Elberfeld and Barmen, which make one conurbation of 420,700 people hemmed in along the narrow incised valley of the Wupper in the Sauerland plateau, were noted for their textiles long before the exploitation of the coalfield began, for the clear soft waters of this stream provided both power and the necessary water for washing and dyeing.  Cotton, silk, rayon, haberdashery, and carpets are among the chief manufactures, together with machinery and chemicals needed for the various manufacturing processes involved.

Solingen (169,900) and Remscheid (126,900) farther south, on the Sauerland plateau, form jointly the Sheffield of Germany and have long been noted for their cutlery and fine steels, but in recent years have added all kinds of hardware and domestic metalware.  Formerly they exploited small local iron-ores which were smelted by charcoal, but they now derive their pig-iron or bar-steel from the Ruhr area.  Light metal wares are a characteristic product of the surrounding Bergisches Land; they developed out of an old tradition of home industry in this agriculturally poor plateau area.  Thus the small town of Velbert, on the edge of the plateau between the Wupper and Ruhr valleys, has become the centre of the German lock and key industry.

Krefeld (213,100) is a fairly old textile centre chiefly noted for its silk, but now, like its neighbours, Mönchengladbach (152,200) and Rheydt (94,000), it also manufactures cotton and rayon.

Standing somewhat aloof from the industrial area dependent on the Ruhr coalfield is the frontier town and woollen manufacturing centre of Aachen (Aix-la-Chapelle, 169,800) on a little coalfield of its own, which is situated, like the Ruhr coalfield, at the foot of the Middle Rhine Plateau. One of the oldest towns north of the Alps, its mineral springs were known to the Romans, and the city was the capital of the Carolingian Empire. It stands on the important European motorway (E 5), which will eventually connect the English Channel and Vienna.

For all this region the commercial capital was the old Roman foundation of Cologne (Köln); the name is a corruption of the Roman *Colonia*. Its nodal position, where the Rhine river route crossed an east–west land route, skirting the Rhine Plateau, was obviously an important factor in its rise and development, but although it flourished in Roman times and still more in medieval times, with the overland trade in eastern and Mediterranean commodities, its modern growth dates from the development of the Ruhr coalfield, for in 1871 it was still a comparatively small city of 80,000 people. A good deal of the capital for the early mines and industries of the Ruhr district was supplied by Cologne, which thereby added to the field of its commerce. Of recent years the fuel wealth of the northern Rhinelands has been increased by the large-scale working of Tertiary brown coal at the very doors of Cologne itself, in the Ville mining area which extends as far as Bonn. The brown coal is practically on the surface and therefore easy to work, and it forms a cheap source of electrical power, thereby freeing the Ruhr coal for other purposes. It now produces about nine-tenths of Western Germany's brown coal.

Despite tremendous destruction in the second world war, Cologne has made a rapid recovery and is now again the unquestioned administrative, commercial and cultural capital of the region around it. It has exceeded its prewar population (1961, 809,200; 1939, 772,200). The industrial area of Cologne spread in prewar years to the right bank of the Rhine (Mülheim, Deutz), where engineering industries are mainly located. Farther downstream, the modern town of Leverkusen (94,600) noted for the great Bayer chemical plant, belongs to the Cologne industrial complex. Upstream from Cologne, an important complex of oil refineries and petrochemical works has developed since 1945 on the left bank of the Rhine at Wesseling, which now receives oil by pipeline direct from Rotterdam and Wilhelmshaven.

Still further down stream on the right (east) bank of the Rhine is Düsseldorf (702,600), long renowned as one of the most elegant of German cities, a former provincial capital, and since 1949 capital of the *Land* of Nordrhein-Westfalen (North Rhine-Westphalia), most populous and highly industrialised of the provinces of postwar Federal Germany. It is a leading administrative centre for industrial firms – the modern skyline is dominated by the impressive sky-scraper buildings of the Phönix–Rheinrohr steel complex – and it is a big engineering, electrical, vehicle, and chemical centre.

At the south apex of the triangular Cologne embayment, where the Rhine emerges from its dramatic passage through the Rhine gorge, stands the capital of the Federal Republic, Bonn. Of Roman origin, Bonn became successively a local capital of a small principality, a university town, and then in the nineteenth century (thanks to its splendid position opposite the volcanic hills of the Siebengebirge) a residential town for people with private means. Since it became Federal capital in 1949, the influx of officials and foreign diplomats has helped to swell the population from 100,800 (1939) to 143,900 (1961).

(*b*) *The Lowland of Münster.* This may be looked upon as an Hercynian basin covered in parts by glacial deposits, and it is therefore transitional between the Hercynian region of middle Germany and the northern plain. On its eastern and southern borders the chalk outcrops in the middle of the basin are Tertiary deposits, mainly marls, while on the northern edge are glacial sands. The landscape of the Münsterland affords a classic example of the settlement pattern of isolated farms (*Einzelhöfe*), surrounded by hedged fields; characteristic of the western part of the north German lowland, it stands in sharp contrast to the nucleated village and open field landscape of the Westphalian *Börde* only a few miles to the south. The region was almost wholly agricultural until the discovery of the underlying Coal Measures, but industry is gradually creeping into it along the Dortmund–Ems canal, partly owing to the sinking of mine shafts in the south. The ancient town of Münster (182,700), which is the regional capital, is an important railway junction, with some agricultural industries.

(*c*) *The Leipzig Lowland and Adjacent Areas.* Some 250 miles east of the Münsterland, this great embayment is now part of the communist Democratic Republic. The core of the area is the lowland bay which pushes southward into the Hercynian uplands between the Harz and the Thüringer Wald on the west and the Erzgebirge (Ore Mountains) on the south-east. *Löss* deposits are especially extensive round Leipzig and Halle, while Magdeburg on the Elbe may be looked upon as the extreme northern limit. A great new industrial complex developed in this lowland in modern times, particularly during the present century. A narrow extension of the *Löss* lowland continues to the north-west into the Federal Republic as far as Hanover, in a *Börde* zone at the foot of the Harz and Weser Hills. On the south-east, the old industrial complex of the Zwickau–Karl-Marx-Stadt–Dresden area (the Saxon Uplands, see

51 Schwäbische Alb. A view from the summit of the steep scarp slope, looking north-wards into the lowlands of the Neckar basin. This is a typical south German landscape with large nucleated villages enclosed by open fields cultivated in strips; small residual areas of woodland separate the fields of one village from the next.

GERMANY

52 The Alpine Foreland of Bavaria. A landscape of glacial deposition, formed by valley glaciers from the Alps, which form the background. Moraine-dammed lakes are frequent: this is the Chiemsee, the largest in Bavaria. There are considerable tracks of woodland; the cleared land is mainly in pasture.

**53** Eifel. One of the *Maare* (explosion crater lakes) in this remote uplands region, part of the Rhine plateau block. Although the altitude here averages about 1,500 ft and the climate is fairly bleak, most of the land is in open-field cultivation.

GERMANY

**54** Rhine Gorge at Kaub. Extensive vineyards cover the valley sides, but where they are absent the land reverts to scrub – a reminder that exposure to the sun, not quality of soil, is responsible for the cultivation of the vine here. Railways and main roads crowd together on the narrow belt of flat land alongside the river. The stream is intensively used both by freight barges and pleasure steamers.

p. 402), has some features in common with the Leipzig area, though it is a dissected plateau rather than a plain.

The Leipzig bay of lowland, while still important agriculturally and containing many ancient cities with old-established industries, has been chiefly significant in modern times for its heavy chemical industries, based on the exploitation of vast deposits of brown coal and salt. Brown coal was first used here, on a considerable scale, about the middle of the nineteenth century, as the region possessed the strategic advantage of remoteness from Germany's frontiers, unlike the Ruhr and Silesian industrial areas. The large-scale and ingenious exploitation of brown coal may be said to amount to a minor industrial revolution, while the amount produced was greater than in any other area of the world.

Since 1945 the division of Germany has led to further exploitation of the middle German brown coal deposits, for the Democratic Republic lacks any major source of bituminous coal. In Niederlausitz a large plant (the Lauchhammer works) produces brown coal coke to be used in the giant iron and steel complex of Eisenhüttenstadt (formerly Stalinstadt; 33,000) on the Oder. But considerable imports of bituminous coal and coke from the other countries of the Eastern bloc are still necessary.

In addition to the heavy chemical industries already mentioned, agricultural industries are scattered throughout the countryside, while the making of machinery and the working up of metals, e.g. aluminium from imported bauxite, are important.

Three large historic cities lie in this area. Magdeburg (262,400), though not the largest, has become the chief commercial centre, dealing especially in brown coal, potash, and sugar-beet. It also has considerable manufactures, including foodstuffs (sugar, chocolate), machinery, and chemicals. It benefited during the nineteenth century from improvements in navigation on the Elbe. The presence of two large towns so near together as Leipzig (585,300) and Halle (276,200) was the result of the political subdivision of Germany before 1871, a boundary formerly running between them. The more central position of Leipzig favoured its growth, and so also did its famous twice-yearly industrial fairs, which date from the thirteenth century. Before the postwar division of Germany, Leipzig was noted as the leading German printing and publishing centre, and, in addition, made machinery, textiles, pianos, etc. Although many publishing firms migrated west after 1945, it remains an important centre with a strong tradition of quality printing. Halle's medieval importance lay in its salt mines, but in the nineteenth century it became an industrial town with varied manufactures, including machinery for the sugar-growing and sugar-manufacturing industries, printing and paper, brewing, and chemicals. It has an important grain market.

The north-western extension of this area, which is part of the Federal Republic, is less industrialised but manufactures have grown up during the last eighty to ninety years on the basis of good communications, surplus agricultural production, and mineral wealth (salt, brown coal, iron-ore, petroleum). Agricultural industries are scattered throughout the countryside and also concentrated in the old market and administrative centres of Hanover (Ger., Hannover; 573,100) and Brunswick (Ger., Braunschweig; 246,200). Both these towns manufacture rolling-stock, road vehicles, and machinery of various kinds. Hanover is also the chief German manufacturer of rubber tires. It also refines mineral oil from the nearby Nienhagen oil field, which was originally developed under the Nazi policy of autarchy, but which has experienced a dramatic increase of production in the years since 1945. This field produced 430,000 tons out of a total German production of 450,000 tons in 1936: by 1960 it was producing 2 million tons out of a total (for the Federal Republic) of 5·5 million tons. The exploitation of the new resources of mineral oil and iron-ore has made the Hanover–Brunswick region one of the fastest-developing industrial areas in the Federal Republic. Symbolic of the rapid change is the 'New Town' of Wolfsburg (64,000), created in 1938 by the Nazi régime round the Volkswagen works. After the war the plant lay 75 per cent destroyed, and the division of Germany meant that it was only a few miles from the zonal border. Yet production mushroomed, and by 1961 the Volkswagen plant was the biggest vehicle factory in Europe, with an annual production of over 1 million vehicles.

### CHAPTER 22

# SOUTHERN GERMANY

## THE HERCYNIAN LANDS

IN contrast to the monotonous and often dreary lowlands of northern Germany, one enters in southern Germany into a region of great diversity. Here smiling plains are backed by wooded hills and mountains; agriculture is more varied, and orchards, vineyards, hops, and tobacco enter into the scene; holdings are small and population dense; old, comfortable-looking farmhouses are met with at every turn; and though manufactures are added to agriculture, as a rule there is no disfigurement of the landscape. In short, this is the old Germany of legend and song, of Holbein and Dürer, Beethoven and Goethe. With its picturesque old towns and villages and the well-cared-for appearance of its countryside, it is perhaps more reminiscent of south-east England than of any other part of Europe, though to English eyes everything appears exaggerated: the hills are higher and more wooded, the scarps steeper, the plains more fertile, the summers hotter, the winters more snowy, and finally the buildings are more fantastic in style, the Gothic more betimbered and begabled and the Renaissance style definitely Baroque.

This region of Hercynian horsts with the included scarplands and plains is often called by German geographers *Die Mittelgebirge*, which may be rendered into English as the Central Uplands.

**The Rhinelands.** (1) *The Rift Valley and Bordering Mountains.* Immediately below Basle (German-Swiss, Basel) the Rhine enters a great rift valley, 180 miles long and about 20 miles wide, which is flanked on either side by mountains. Though the French frontier now reaches to the Rhine in Alsace, yet the structure on either side of the river is so similar and the region such an obvious physical unit that it will be treated here as a whole.

The bordering mountains, Vosges (Ger., Vogesen) and Hardt on the west, Schwarzwald ('Black Forest') and Odenwald on the east, represent the flanks of an Hercynian massif of which the middle section has dropped, like the keystone of an arch, to form the plain of the rift valley. The massif, which represented the stumps of part of the Hercynian system, was raised up in mid-Tertiary times, together with the hitherto undisturbed sedimentary rocks of Meso-zoic age which had been deposited on top. The collapse of the middle portion between lines of faults running from north to south took place in late Tertiary times. Evidently the southern part of the massif had been raised to a greater height than the northern portion; consequently erosion was greater in the south, and the Mesozoic sediments were removed from the regions of greatest elevation, particularly in the southern Vosges and southern Schwarzwald, where granites and gneiss were exposed. The greatest heights, however, are still to be found there, the Ballon d'Alsace in the Vosges reaching 4,101 ft and the Feldberg in the Schwarzwald 4,898 ft. Farther north, and on the outer flanks of these mountains, are found great expanses of Lower Triassic sandstone, known as Bunter sandstone (Ger., *bunt* = variegated). The same type of rock is called *grès vosgien* in France. In both areas it dominates the scenery of the flanks of the hill masses, giving huge expanses of sombre forest, as along the Black Forest High Road (Schwarzwaldhochstrasse) which leads south from Baden-Baden to the Feldberg.

Both the Schwarzwald and Vosges are in places deeply dissected by rejuvenated valleys, without losing the generally rounded forms of the old Tertiary peneplain which existed before the massif was raised. Originally densely forested, much of the land has been cleared, mainly for pasture, though the timber industry remains important. In the Schwarzwald the carving of wooden articles is a considerable home industry in winter, while in the valleys of the Vosges an important cotton industry has grown up.

North of the Schwarzwald is the depression of the Kraichgau, or Neckar–Bergland, which, though higher than the rift valley, contrasts with the forested mountains to north and south, because the Bunter sandstone is here overlain by a Keuper (Triassic) limestone, not found in the corresponding succession in England — the mussel limestone or *Muschelkalk*. It gives a good agricultural soil here because of an extensive *Löss* cover. Like the similar low-lying Saverne col north of the Vosges, this break in the mountains is utilised by an express railway line (Paris–Constantinople) and by a major trunk road, the Frankfurt–Munich *Autobahn*.

The Odenwald and the Hardt face each other across the northern part of the rift valley. The Odenwald repeats the features of the Black Forest on a smaller scale, with old crystalline rocks on the west and Bunter sandstone on the east, but in the Hardt mountains the old crystalline core is completely covered by the Bunter sandstone, while farther north and west in the Palatinate (Ger., Pfalz) appear Permian and Carboniferous strata, including the coal measures of the Saar (Sarre) district. These have been preserved in a geosyncline following the direction of the strike, which is here from south-west to north-east.

The Saar region, administered by the League of Nations from 1919 to 1935, returned to Germany in 1935, to France in 1945 and back to Germany in 1957. Coal mines, producing about 16 million tons of coal per annum in 1960, were opened up in the midst of a partly forested, partly agricultural countryside and have been greatly developed since 1880, when the value of the Lorraine iron-ores became apparent. The marked tectonic depression of Landstuhl facilitates access between the Saar region and the Rhine Valley, by leading part of the way through the Bunter sandstone region via Kaiserslautern. The Saar is now the tenth province (*Land*) of the German Federal Republic; its 'capital' is Saarbrücken (130,700).

The Rhine rift valley itself was depressed between a series of step faults, by means of which strata of the Mesozoic epoch have been preserved in the fertile foothill zone. It is by no means a simple floodplain, but has a somewhat long and complicated geological history behind it, which accounts for the variety of deposits to be found at the surface. During early Tertiary times the rift valley, which opened to the south and had no outlet to the north, was covered by an arm of the sea. This sea gradually became a brackish lake and finally was drained by a river flowing towards the south-west through the present gap of Belfort. In the Pliocene period further earth movement followed, which reversed the drainage, and sent the Rhine northwards across the Rhine plateau, which was then presumably at a relatively lower level than at present. The lowering of the base-level of erosion, i.e., the increase in the gradient, following this change, caused much of the Mesozoic sediments to be eroded, but dissected Mesozoic and Tertiary material is to be found in the hills of Hesse in the north-west and in smaller patches elsewhere on the borders of the plain. The Ice Age caused much of the valley to be covered with infertile gravel and sand brought by torrents from the mountainous borders (as, for instance, between the Ill and the Rhine in Alsace), though the accumulation of *Löss* on and near the foothills perhaps more than compensated. The word *Löss* itself is apparently of Alsatian origin. Finally, alluvium was spread over the middle and lower part of the valley as the rivers ceased to have erosive power and swung in wide meanders from side to side of the floodplain. The alluvium is especially thick near the confluence of the River Main at the northern end of the rift valley and the neighbouring lower part of the Main valley; in this area sinking appears to be still in progress.

The rift valley presents, therefore, a surface where dry gravels alternate with swampy alluvium, between a border of *Löss* and other fertile deposits. Even volcanic rock (Tertiary) is represented in places, as in the isolated eminence of the Kaiserstuhl north-west of

Freiburg.   The gravels generally remain useless and have only a thin
covering of poor forest, but the swampy regions have been drained,
and these together with the *Löss* and foothill zones provide some of
the richest agricultural land of Europe.   The relatively low latitude
(about 47½° to 50° N) and altitude (mostly below 600 ft) combine
to give the rift valley lands of Baden, Hessen and Pfalz the best
climate to be found in the whole of Germany, mainly because the
spring comes earlier and the summers are longer than elsewhere.
Nor, in spite of its cold winters, is Alsace surpassed in agriculural
richness, even by the greater plains of France.   The typical cultures
are wheat, hops, and tobacco, Baden, for instance, being the
principal tobacco-manufacturing state of Germany.   Sugar-beet
is also of considerable importance, and along the foothills orchards
flourish, especially on the eastern side along the so-called Berg-
strasse, while vineyards are numerous, especially on the western side
in Alsace, Pfalz and Hessen where the slopes have a southerly as
well as an easterly aspect.   The wines of the Rhine-front villages of
Hessen, between the ancient cities of Mainz and Worms (e.g.
Oppenheim, Nierstein, Forst) have a particularly high reputation in
international circles, though many of them are marketed under the
generic and meaningless label of *Liebfraumilch.*

Although the Rhine has been regulated and a straight channel
cut through its meanders, yet its former uncertain banks prevented
any important settlements from growing up on the river south of
Speyer, and even at the present day a deserted swampy zone separates
Baden from Alsace.   The larger settlements in the southern part of
the plain are mainly near the junction with the foothills, for example,
Freiburg (145,000), Karlsruhe (241,800), and Heidelberg (125,300).
Even Strasbourg (226,700 in 1962, the capital of the French
Département of Bas-Rhin since 1919) the apparent exception, was
built away from the Rhine, actually on the River Ill, and has only
reached the main river in modern times.   Nowadays it stands at
the virtual head of navigation on the Rhine, a position formerly
held by Mannheim (313,900), which at the junction of the Rhine
with the Neckar is still one of the busiest river ports and manufacturing towns on the Rhine rift.   The northern part of the Rhine rift
has a surprisingly large number of big towns, probably too many
under present conditions.   Their growth was no doubt favoured by
the excellent nodal position of this region, as well as by the richness
of the soil, but they grew up under different political conditions
from those of the present day, at a time when Germany was much
divided into different sovereign states, each of which had its own
independent capital.   At present some of these towns, such as
Worms, seem to be stagnating, but others have been revivified by

the introduction of modern manufactures, particularly metallurgical, electrotechnical, and light engineering with motor cars and bicycles figuring prominently. Cheapness of transport on the Rhine has played its part, as in the development of the great heavy chemical works at Ludwigshafen opposite Mannheim, but the excellent rail and road networks are more important for most of the industries, which resemble those of the Coventry district of England. The division of Germany has meant that the road and rail networks of the Federal Republic are effectively focused on the Rhine–Main Plain (Fig. 48 p. 393), which has further enhanced the importance of its cities as industrial centres since 1945. Frankfurt-am-Main (683,100) originated on a crossing point of the Main, some 10 miles above its confluence with the Rhine (the name means 'the ford of the Franks'). In the Middle Ages its focal position on the main overland routes between the Mediterranean and north-west Europe made it a leading commercial and financial centre. It remains very important as a banking town, but is also the centre of a great industrial conurbation of over a million people. The city specialises in engineering, precision instruments, and electrical goods; it contains the headquarters of the great Hoechst chemical works, which

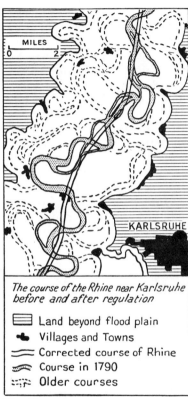

The course of the Rhine near Karlsruhe before and after regulation

▭ Land beyond flood plain
⚓ Villages and Towns
〰 Corrected course of Rhine
〰 Course in 1790
〰 Older courses

Fig. 47. THE COURSE OF THE RHINE NEAR KARLSRUHE, BEFORE AND AFTER REGULATION

are situated in the town of that name some five miles west of Frankfurt. Between Frankfurt and Mainz lies Rüsselheim with the great Opel works, while there are many other small industrial towns. The old Roman foundation of Mainz is a busy river port and has varied manufactures. In this area only the inland spa of Wiesbaden (253,300) seems to have held aloof; the very nature of its chief source of livelihood precluding its industrialisation. Farther afield, even

Heidelberg, the oldest university town of Germany, has added a manufacturing quarter on the Rhine plain to the west of the old town, while Karlsruhe, the princely seat of the former rulers of Baden, makes machinery.

North of the Odenwald the line of the eastern bordering highlands breaks down and a continuation of the rift valley takes its place, though the direction of the valley changes and runs here from south-west to north-east. This depression, known as the Frankfurt basin, is occupied by the lower course of the River Main, and it was no doubt once prolonged even farther north until the Tertiary volcano of the Vogelsberg blocked up almost the whole width of the depression, leaving only a narrow strip of lowland to the west. This narrow lowland is known as the Wetterau, and forms a route from the Rhine rift valley towards the Weser lowlands and the great northern plain (see Fig. 48, p. 393).

(2) *The Rhine Plateau.* Below Mainz the Rhine is confronted by the steep edge of the Rhine Highlands, more properly called a plateau, which lie athwart its valley, Initially the Rhine is diverted westwards to skirt the edge of the plateau for twelve miles or so in the region known as the Rheingau, but then it abruptly turns from Bingen onwards, to flow northwards through the plateau by means of a gorge some 80 miles long, until just above Bonn it emerges once more on to a plain. The river has here performed the apparently impossible task of carving its way through a mass of hard, resistant rock whose surface lies at an average height of 1,600 ft above that of the rift valley. Obviously, physical conditions must have been different when the river started to flow across this plateau, and the evidence suggests that we have here an old peneplain which began to rise in late Tertiary times, after the middle Rhine drainage had been reversed from a southerly to its present northly direction. As the Rhine rift valley sank and the peneplain was uplifted, the river was forced to cut its bed deeper in order to maintain its way (cf. the passage of the Meuse through the Ardennes, the Elbe through the Erzgebirge). This process of cutting is marked by a whole series of high-level surfaces and terraces, dating from the Tertiary and Quaternary eras of geological time.

The maximum uplift took place in the south, where some of the greatest heights, reaching nearly 3,000 ft are now found, namely in the Taunus and Hunsrück, just north of the great fault line which marks the southern edge of the massif. Broadly speaking, the massif sinks down towards the north, but it is crossed midway by an old down-warping running from south-west to north-east and marked by the lower course of the Mosel (Fr., Moselle) and Lahn, and north of this depression it rises again in the Eifel, Westerwald,

and still more in the Rothaargebirge. The Mosel and Lahn, like
the Rhine, have been obliged to incise their valleys in order to
maintain their way, and as their lower courses were originally very
meandering, the result is a very remarkable series of snake-like
twists and turns, especially in the Mosel gorge below Trier (Fr.,

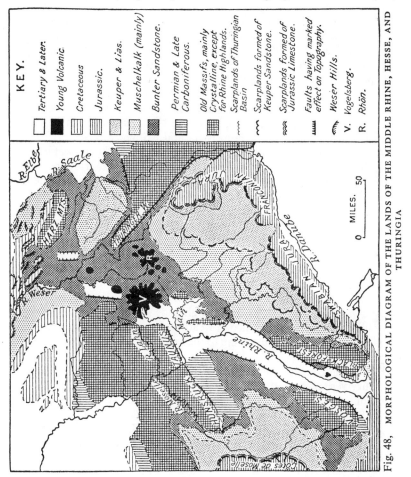

**KEY.**

Tertiary & Later.
Young Volcanic.
Cretaceous.
Jurassic.
Keuper & Lias.
Muschelkalk (mainly).
Bunter Sandstone.
Permian & Late Carboniferous.
Old Massifs, mainly Crystalline, except for Rhine Highlands.
Scarplands of Thuringian Basin.
Scarplands formed of Keuper Sandstone.
Scarplands formed of Jurassic Limestone.
Faults having marked effect on Topography.
Weser Hills.
V. Vogelsberg.
R. Rhön.

MILES.
0 50

Fig. 48, MORPHOLOGICAL DIAGRAM OF THE LANDS OF THE MIDDLE RHINE, HESSE, AND THURINGIA

Trèves). Parts of the valleys of the smaller rivers show similar
incised meanders, as in the case of the Ahr and Urft, but generally
speaking, the old peneplain character has been fairly well preserved
over wide stretches of the present plateau, though it is a fossil
peneplain, since the Mesozoic and Tertiary material has been almost
wholly removed by denudation. Most of the Mesozoic covering

had evidently been stripped off by Tertiary times and is preserved only in the Mosel depression round Trier, and the once complete Tertiary covering is preserved only where protected by young volcanic deposits. The latter accompanied the dislocation associated with the rising peneplain. The Eifel district is one of the few districts of Europe outside the Mediterranean zone in which craters and crater lakes can be seen, the volcanic activity here continuing from Tertiary into geologically recent times. (Cf. the Massif Central of France.) The quarrying of hard lavas, and of the pumice (*Bims*) formed from volcanic dust blown from explosion craters, is a flourishing industry along the Rhine border. Over the greater part of the plateau the old Palæozoic rocks have been exposed once more and consist mainly of slates and shales (Ger., *Schiefer*), though the upstanding ridges are usually formed of quartzites, as in the higher parts of the Taunus, Hunsrück, and Rothaargebirge.

An important distinction can be made within the plateau between the different types of structure. The high quartzite ridges (e.g. Taunus, Hunsrück, Rothaargebirge) have generally remained forested. The plateau surfaces, which range from about 500 ft to 2,000 ft have been partly cleared and devoted to agriculture, though on the higher bleaker surfaces (the High Eifel, for instance) this has proved so little remunerative that large tracts have gone out of cultivation and returned to moorland, as in the case of the similar 'intake' lands of the Pennines. The Hohe Venn (=fen) or foreland of the Eifel is a continuation of the Ardennes and is a moorland area with poor pasture and cattle rearing. Of the plateau areas, only the Westerwald region of the Rhine Highlands is of any considerable agricultural value, the presence of weathered young volcanic deposits providing a fertile soil, but owing to the raw climate it is used mainly for pasture.

Further north the old-established iron industry of the Siegerland still survives, though the increasing depth and difficulty of mining the iron-ore make its production a costly business. Beyond the River Sieg the plateau sinks down to the Sauerland, which, however, is still forested and of little use for agriculture. Like the Siegerland, it has some old industries, which have been mainly transformed under the influence of the Ruhr coalfield (see section on the Lower German Rhinelands, p. 378).

The general character of the plateau surfaces then is transitional. The small hamlets were established only late in the Middle Ages, as their place-name endings (-roth, -scheid, -berg) testify. They are surrounded by their characteristic block fields, which end against the large still uncleared forest areas. Lower down the settlements become larger and the block field gives way to the familiar big open field. These predominate in the few sizeable lowland basins within the area, for example, the Middle Rhine Basin around Koblenz and the area around Limburg or the Middle Lahn. The narrow valleys which are incised into the plateau, offer a completely different picture. They are intensely settled, and as the floors of these valleys are very narrow indeed, both along the Rhine gorge and along the lower parts of the Mosel and Lahn, the steep sides have been terraced wherever a sunny aspect could be obtained, and devoted to vineyards. The most famous German wines come from the southern slopes of the Taunus overlooking the Rheingau. Here is a line of small vintners' towns, with their characteristically close-set, multi-storeyed houses, each with its prominent cellar entrance: Rüdesheim, Oestrich, Johannisberg, Eltville.

The Rhine gorge, in spite of its narrowness, is normally one of the busiest highways of movement in Europe. Railways follow the banks, while great barge-trains dragged by powerful tugs animate the river. The Rhine gorge from Bonn to Bingen presents a piquant contrast with its romantic castle-crowned crags frowning down upon the bustling modern world at their feet. Between Bonn and Koblenz, the confluence town, where the Mosel joins the Rhine, factories of various kinds are rarely out of sight and villages succeed each other almost without a break. Even in the more unspoilt stretch between Koblenz and Bingen a modern Lorelei would find the sirens and smoke of passing tugs a sad hindrance to her singing. No river in Europe can compete in the amount of traffic carried, although the Rhine has by no means the longest navigable course, being far behind the Volga and Danube in that respect. The Rhine valley performs a uniquely important function in the economy of Western Germany because it supplies a means of cheap bulk transport, for heavy raw materials and finished products, between the two major industrial regions of the Federal Republic: the Ruhr–Cologne Bay region to the north and the Frankfurt–Wiesbaden–Mannheim triangle to the south, which are separated by the upland mass of the plateau block. Traffic through the gorge is dominated by the exchange between these areas. Main rail traffic between these regions also travels through the gorge, via lines on both banks of the river. The steadily increasing road traffic takes the straighter course through the wall of the High Taunus ridge and then across the high plateau surface; this applies to both the old high road (Federal Highway 8) from Frankfurt to Cologne, and to the modern *Autobahn* which parallels it.

**The Mittelgebirge between the Rhinelands and Bohemia.** (*a*) *The Scarplands of Schwaben and Franken.* This region is the largest of the basins of sedimentary deposition which were produced by the denudation of the Hercynian mountains in Mesozoic and Tertiary times. It occupies the historic provinces of Schwaben (Swabia), named after a branch of the Alemannic tribes which occupied the south-west corner of Germany in later Roman times, and Franken (Franconia), named after the Franks who overran the north-eastern part of the region (which was not occupied by the Romans) several centuries later. Today Schwaben is part of the province (*Land*) of Baden-Württemberg, while Franken is part of Bavaria (Bayern). This region, which is drained mainly by the Neckar and Main tributaries of the Rhine, has in broad outline a simple structure closely resembling that of the scarplands of south-eastern England. Strata of Triassic and Jurassic age have been tilted up towards the north-west so that they dip off the Hercynian 'Oldlands' of the Schwarzwald, Odenwald, and Spessart, and were then exposed to denudation, so that the younger rocks have been stripped off and progressively older layers have been exposed, the younger rocks remaining in the south-east. The edges of the more resistant rocks stand out as scarps which face westwards or north-westwards (Fig. 49, p. 397).

The geological formations thus form great areas of concentric circles centred upon the Odenwald in the north-west. But towards the south-west they become progressively compressed by the Alpine folding, so that in the south-eastern Schwarzwald it is possible to traverse within a few hundred yards a range of formations which extends over many miles in the north, along the Main valley. Starting from the north-west, the Bunter sandstone of the Lower Triassic has already been mentioned as covering the infertile forested eastern slopes of the Schwarzwald, Odenwald and Spessart. This is succeeded by the Middle Triassic measures, mainly represented here by the *Muschelkalk*, a shelly limestone, which together with the Keuper marls (Upper Triassic) on its eastern flank form the highly cultivated *Gäue*[1] country, though the fertility is largely to be attributed to the *Löss* and *Löss*-loam cover which overlies large areas of these formations: without benefit of this cover the *Muschelkalk* gives dry, infertile, thinly populated land. Bordering these plains eastward is the scarp-line formed by the edge of the Upper Triassic sandstones, the most notable of which, the massive *Stubensandstein*, gives rise to a marked scarp. In Schwaben the sandstone outcrop is only a few miles wide, though it may give rise to a notable scarp, as at Stuttgart where the city has been built in a great hollow in the sandstone ridge. In Franken the sandstone outcrops over a wide area to give the distinctive regions of the Frankenhöhe and Steigerwald, with sterile soils mainly under pine trees. Even here, though the

[1] *Gau*, plural Gäue; name often given in south Germany to a tract of exceptionally fertile, highly cultivated land.

scarp may reach 600 ft above the marl country to the west, it is so
discontinuous and uneven that it is often difficult to trace the ground,
revealing itself rather as a number of forested sandstone outliers
far out in the plain itself.    To the east and south the sandstone dips
under Liassic marls which in Swabia give a fertile belt below the
scarp of the Jurassic limestone, but which in middle Franken
are covered with masses of glacial outwash sand, giving the infertile,
forested soils of the Rednitz basin around Nuremberg.    Above the

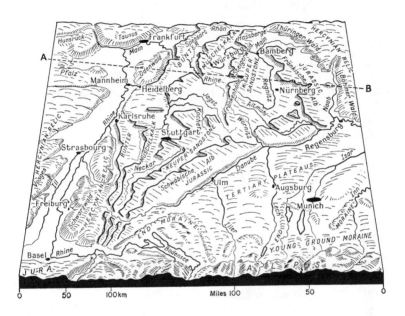

Fig. 49.   THE SCARPLANDS OF SOUTH GERMANY AND THE ALPINE FORELAND

Lias beds rises the very considerable scarp of the Schwäbische and
Fränkische Alb or Jura, formed principally of hard, white Jurassic
limestones, but even this scarp is not continuous, being interrupted,
for example, by the volcanic depression of the Ries, centred upon the
small town of Nördlingen, between the Schwäbische and the Fränkische Alb sections; and although the edge sometimes attains a height
of 1,000 ft or so above the plain, yet it is considerably frayed by
erosion.   Outliers often stand in front of the main scarp and are

often crowned by castles, e.g. the castle of Hohenzollern. The limestone of the Jura forms a plateau of considerable elevation, the true *Alb*. Especially where pockets of superficial deposits give a 'suspended water table' locally, the Alb is extensively cultivated in wide open fields around big villages. But in some areas water supply is a real problem, and the Alb gives true karst scenery, as in the Fränkische Schweiz (Franken-Switzerland) of the dolomite area north of Nuremberg. Owing to a fracture the limestone plateau sinks rather rapidly on the southern side under the Tertiary and glacial accumulations of the Alpine Foreland.

The river system of the scarplands is particularly complex, owing to the fact that there has been a major reversal of drainage. The rivers in early Tertiary times apparently flowed down the dip-slope towards the Danube, but the development of the Rhine rift attracted drainage in that direction, as the floor of the rift is several hundred feet lower than the upper Danube valley. Accordingly a complicated series of river captures took place, which accounts for the numerous elbows of capture, for instance the notable series along the middle Main valley. Naturally, also, the introduction of a lower base-level of erosion led to the incising of the rivers in their valleys, the steep sides of which, often devoted to vineyards, recall the Mosel valley in miniature. The earlier Tertiary peneplain surfaces, however, have not as yet been greatly affected by erosion, hence the generally level appearance of the uplands and the survival of old river alluvium.

The scarpland region is not very low-lying; even the *Gäue* plains are at a height of nearly 1,000 ft above sea-level, and the *Alb* reaches over 3,000 ft in the south-west, though it is under 2,000 ft in the north. The relatively southerly latitude, however, from 48° N to 50° N, together with the protection offered to the plains by the Schwarzwald, Odenwald and Spessart, give the lower lands a favourable climate in which wheat, orchards and tobacco all flourish, and the vines and maize succeed in favoured places. Even the *Alb* plateau, despite its water supply problems and its raw climate (cf. *Rauhe Alb* of the Schwäbische Alb), is mainly arable.

Minerals are scarce in the scarplands, but the lithographic stone or Solnhofer slate of the Franconian Jura may be mentioned, as it is still used to some extent. Small deposits of iron-ore are found in the Dogger sandstone of the Jurassic system, but are no longer of importance, and salt and gypsum are found in the Keuper series (cf. Cheshire salt mines).

The old towns of this region are numerous and beautiful. In the Middle Ages they were partly local market towns, but also active participators in the trade that crossed Europe from the Mediterranean to the North Sea lands. Hand industries were important, especially the metal industry, and also textiles, working chiefly flax.

Many of the smaller centres have stagnated since the end of the Middle Ages, though latterly they have gained a new lease of life through the tourist trade: the towns of the 'Romantic Road' – Nördlingen, Dinkelsbühl and Rothenburg ob der Tauber – are perhaps the best examples. But the coming of the railways brought modern industries to many towns, in spite of the absence of coal and raw material, but naturally the heavy industries are not represented. Some local agricultural produce is manufactured, and still more, such articles as need little raw material but are of high value when finished, such as textiles, leather goods, machinery, watches, optical and musical instruments. The industrial centres have generally remained rather small and are localised chiefly in Schwaben (modern Württemberg), along the middle Neckar valley, and along the nearby foot of the Schwäbische Alb. Stuttgart is the centre of the Neckar industrial region, which extends principally between Heilbronn and Plochingen, and the line is continued up the Fils valley from Göppingen to Geislingen. Stuttgart (637,500) is the only large town, and though it owed its foundation by the rulers of Württemberg to its pleasant site on the *Stubensandstein* scarp, yet with the advent of the railway it became the main seat of industry in the south-western scarplands, its Mercedes–Benz motor cars and 'Bosch' magnetos being especially well known. Today it has regained its historic importance as a provincial capital, for it is the seat of the *Land* (Government) of Baden-Württemberg.

In Franken, or the north-eastern section of the scarplands, Nuremberg (Ger., Nürnberg; 454,500) together with its suburb Fürth, concentrate most of the industrial development, though Würzburg and Schweinfurt have engineering industries, the last named town being noted for ball-bearings. Nuremberg's manufactures are very varied, but metallurgical products take first place, and include machinery, motor cars, bicycles and toys. In spite of its large size the city managed to retain, until the war of 1939-45, much of its picturesque medieval appearance, which recalled the fame of the city through its medieval trade with Venice and through its remarkable sixteenth-century metalwork. The central area of the town was devastated in the war, though a great deal of it has been rebuilt in the old style.

Owing to the smaller industrial development and the wider out-crop of the poor *Stubensandstein*, Franken has fewer people per square mile than Schwaben. The loam-covered lands of Schwaben seem to have had a light 'steppe-heath' (*Steppenheide*) vegetation, rather than dense forest, in Neolithic times, and in consequence to have early attracted a settled population.

(b) *The Uplands and Plains of Hessen and Thüringen.* This region of forested uplands and narrow but fertile plains seems at first sight a patternless mosaic of small land forms. It does, however, represent the continuation both of the Rhinelands and of the scarplands, but the symmetry is disturbed by Tertiary volcanic outpourings, by complicated faulting, and in the north even by considerable folding (see Fig. 48, p. 393).

*The 'Corridor' Lands of Hessen.* In the west these lands are bordered by the Rhine Massif, east of which lies the continuation of the Rhine rift valley known as the Wetterau (see section on Rhine Rift Valley, p. 387). Though interrupted by the dissected volcano of the Vogelsberg, the rift is continued still farther northwards towards Kassel (207,500), an important route centre on the Fulda tributary of the Weser. A much used corridor skirting the Vogelsberg is afforded by this rift, which like that of the middle Rhine is filled with Tertiary deposits, generally of considerable fertility. Today it is followed by the middle section of the 'Hafraba' (Hamburg–Frankfurt–Basel) motorway.

East of the rift the main floor of this region is formed by Bunter sandstone, thereby continuing the line of the Odenwald and Spessart. The sandstone, as usual, provides but a poor soil and has been left under dense forests. Sporadic cappings of Keuper marl remain, as for instance, to north and south of the volcanic Rhön (3,117 ft) and north-east of the Teutoburger Wald, and these afford better soil. The river valleys are also fertile, besides offering routeways, e.g. the river Fulda with the town of Fulda between the Vogelsberg and Rhön.

*Thuringia* (Ger., *Thüringen*). The salient of the Thuringian Forest (Ger., Thüringer Wald) acts as a separating wall to some extent between the uplands and 'corridors' of Hessen and the rather lower and more fertile lands of the Thuringian basin to the east, the latter having some unity through being drained by the River Saale and its tributaries. It therefore provides to some extent a natural frontier between the Federal and Democratic Republics, though the actual boundary runs to the west, across the Rhön: the whole of Thuringia is under the communist régime. The Forest itself is a typical horst and is bounded to north-east and south-west by fault-lines. It reaches a height of just over 3,000 ft and, as its name implies, is heavily forested. In spite of this apparently unfavourable environment it supports a considerable population, which is engaged mainly in manufactures demanding much skill and patience, such as fine metallurgical work, glass-work and porcelain for medical use (thermometers, etc.), and toys, e.g. dolls' heads. The population was formerly dependent upon local iron and copper mining and working, and turned to other forms of industry as these deposits became exhausted.

North-east of the Thüringer Wald lies the structural basin of Thuringia, a smaller analogue of the scarpland basin of Franken and Schwaben. Here are preserved the *Muschelkalk* and Keuper beds of the Triassic system, and in places also even Jurassic and Cretaceous rocks. The *Muschelkalk* forms a low and much interrupted scarp, facing outwards almost all round the edges of the basin, but the structural harmony of the basin itself has been disturbed by dislocations and flexures caused by the pressure of the adjacent horsts. The basin, with its fertile degraded *chernozems*, provides rich agricultural land and possesses several cities of fair size. Erfurt (186,400), the largest, is a commercial and industrial city, with somewhat the same industries as those of the Thüringer Wald; Weimar (63,700) (associated with Goethe and Schiller) and Gotha, the home of the famous Justus Perthes geographical institute, which remains just under 50,000. Jena (81,400) is famed for its optical instruments (Zeiss) and its university. Like many other famous German firms, Zeiss split in two after the war, one part migrating west, the other continuing as a nationalised undertaking in its old location.

The rest of the country between the Thüringer Wald and the Harz Mountains is mainly covered by the infertile Bunter sandstone, but the Goldene Aue is a little rift valley in which fertile Tertiary deposits are preserved and which is renowned for its rich agriculture.

The isolated Hercynian horst of the Harz Mountains still largely retains its peneplain character. About half the area remains under forest, the rest of its mainly undulating surface being cultivated for hardy crops, such as hay and potatoes. A considerable number of small towns on the margins carry on industries somewhat similar to those of the Thüringer Wald and present a somewhat similar history of a population formerly engaged in mining, here mainly for silver, who turned to manufacturing as the mines failed. Copper is still worked near Eisleben on the eastern side of the Harz. Today the heavily fortified Iron Curtain runs across the Harz.

Bordering the Hessen–Thüringen uplands on the north and west are a number of short, low chains, which represent earth ripples connected with the re-elevation of the Hercynian horsts. Little denuded anticlines are frequent, like those of our own Weald, and are of similar late Secondary or early Tertiary date, with the *Muschelkalk*, Jurassic or Cretaceous limestones standing up above the clays and marls exposed at their feet. A double line of such folding forms the highland wall of the Weserfestung which projects for

60 miles north-west into the north German lowland, shutting off the lowland bay of the Münsterland to its south-west. The towns of Osnabrück (138,800) and Bielefeld (174,600) guard gaps in these hills, while the Weser cuts through the northern folding at the Porta Westfalica near the town of Minden.

(c) *The Western Borders of the Bohemian Massif.* The frontier of the Federal Republic on the south-east, against Czechoslovakia, runs along the mountains bordering the Böhmer basin. The Bohemian forest (Ger., Böhmer Wald) on the south-west of that basin presents its steep side to the Regen valley and is a scantily peopled forested region of rounded mountains composed of granites and gneisses. The gap of Fürth, traversed by rail, separates it from the Forest of the Upper Palatinate (Ger., Oberpfälzerwald) which is somewhat lower and less desolate. Between these mountains and the Fränkische Alb lies the hilly basin of the Oberpfalz, drained by the River Naab. The basin is a denuded anticline, whose considerable elevation (mainly over 1,300 ft), heavy rainfall and heavy soils (derived mainly from Keuper marls and Lower Cretaceous clays), conspire to produce a pastoral country with considerable forest.

(d) *The Saxon Uplands.* The northern border of the Bohemian massif – the Erzgebirge and their German foreland which formed the old kingdom of Sachsen (Saxony) and are now part of the Democratic Republic – present a contrasting picture to the above. The main fault-lines and the abrupt descent are on the Bohemian side and the ascent from Germany is relatively gradual. The name Erzgebirge ('Ore Mountains') indicates the considerable metallic wealth of silver, copper, and lead which formerly attracted a German population on to the heights, and though these ores are no longer profitable to work, there is some uranium mined. The lower slopes, which represent a dissected plateau, merging northwards into a plain, were cleared for agriculture, but the main riches of this area at the present day lie in its industrial development.

The manufactures of this region show the influence of historic momentum, since they grew out of home industries and small concerns using crude water-power, and predate the development of the small coalfields near Zwickau and Dresden, and, of course, the more recent development of electric power derived from brown coal. The main industry was textiles, which developed out of an old hand industry; this in turn seems to have been adopted as a supplementary means of livelihood in a somewhat overpopulated district. Wool was the principal textile originally, and the merino sheep of Sachsen, introduced from Spain in the eighteenth century, were among the ancestors of the present flocks in Australia. Karl-Marx-Stadt, or Chemnitz (286,100) often called the 'Manchester' of Germany, was the great centre of the industry, which included the spinning, weaving, and dyeing of cotton, linen, jute, and artificial silk, and the manufacture of knitwear, but the industry was also widely diffused throughout the countryside of the Erzgebirge and Vogtland, and in the angle between them, factories being found in many small towns and villages. A large number of home looms persisted, though in recent years they were driven by electricity, as in the textile region of the French Massif Central round St Etienne. Plauen (78,900) and the Vogtland district generally specialise in net, lace, and other similar products. Metallurgical work of the finer kind, particularly the manufacture of machinery, including textile machinery, takes second place.

In some respects this industrial region of the former kingdom of Sachsen may be looked upon as forming part of a greater region, which includes the Leipzig bay of lowland lying mainly in the old Prussian province of Saxony, though the genesis of their industrial development was different. Agriculturally the northern and lower parts of the 'kingdom' of Sachsen continue to the wheat and sugar-beet lands on the *Löss* belt already mentioned as bordering the North German Plain.

The city of Dresden on the Elbe owed a good deal to the kings of Sachsen, who made it their royal residence. It is famous for its great royal palaces and art collections, which have been slowly rebuilt and restored after the terrible damage of the last weeks of the second world war. It reached its large size (491,700) through its commercial activities, and as the political and cultural centre of a densely populated industrial area. Its industries include machine tools, precision instruments and other metallurgical work, optical and electrical goods, and a wide variety of consumer goods.

The River Elbe breaks through the mountain border of Böhmen into Germany via a zone of structural weakness, where the old crystalline core had been downfaulted before Cretaceous times, and the depression filled up by a great thickness of Cretaceous clays and sandstones, which have here been preserved. The upper layer of sandstones has often weathered into fantastic forms, particularly into stacks or pillars of rock, which have given rise to the exaggerated and misleading title of Sächsische Schweiz ('Saxon Switzerland').

## THE ALPINE FORELAND IN GERMANY

This is a continuation on a larger scale of the Alpine Foreland in Switzerland and Austria. The geosyncline to the north of the Alps has been filled in by masses of sandstone known as *Molasse*, which were weathered from the great chain during Tertiary times, and by the products of later erosion, especially during the great Ice Age. The Foreland generally forms a plateau of little relief, which though about 1,000 to 3,000 ft above sea-level, has often the appearance of a plain, though it is dissected into hills in the north-east.

West of the river Lech the plateau is narrow and the *Molasse* has been completely covered by glacial material, mainly gravels. In the southern part, the impress of the most recent glaciation (here known as the Würm glaciation) is still very clear, and tongue-basins with morainic walls and outwash plains are common.    The

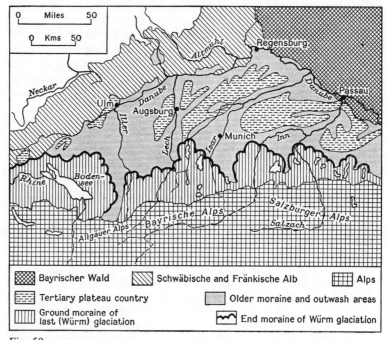

Fig. 50. MAIN FEATURES OF THE GEOLOGY OF THE ALPINE FORELAND

soils are generally poor, and the climate owing to the elevation and northward slope is cold and wet, so that agriculture is confined to hardy crops and pasture, and considerable areas are forest-covered. The southern edge of the region stands in sharp contrast; it faces south towards the Bodensee (Lake Constance), has a sheltered climate, and produces specialised crops, including even wine.

East of the Lech young glacial material and glacial landforms, including tongue-basins and glacial lakes, are found in the south, older glacial materials together with outwash gravels from the Würm glaciation appear in the middle, and the *Molasse* at the surface farther north. The *Molasse* has been slightly dissected by the rivers into low plateaus, and its fairly fertile, though heavy, soils give rise to considerable agriculture. The middle zone of gravels bear large stretches of dry forests and heathlands, while to the north, against the border of the *Molasse* plateaus, are extensive areas of ill-drained bog (*Moos*) land. It is in this unfavourable zone, that Munich (Ger., München; 1,084,500) is found. Like so many major German cities, it owed its growth to princely caprice, being chosen as capital and royal residence by the rulers of the kingdom of Bavaria (Ger., Bayern; note its repute as a musical and artistic centre), but its present size is mainly due to its industrial and commercial development. It is the largest city of southern Germany, and apart from Augsburg it is also the only great city of this extensive natural region of the German Alpine Foreland, a region generally lacking in raw materials and labour, and also in motive power, apart from water. Such industries as exist are concentrated in the towns, particularly in Munich, which to an old brewing industry have been added electrical, textile, and mechanical industries. Munich is also well known as a centre for technical education. It is capital of the *Land* of Bavaria.

Augsburg (208,700) at the confluence of the Lech and the Wertach, was a well-established town dating from Roman times when Munich was a mere crossing-place on the Isar for the salt route from Salzburg. It enjoyed great prosperity in medieval times as a trading city connected with the forwarding of eastern goods from the Mediterranean via the Brenner and Fern passes from Venice and via the Bündner passes from Genoa, but it has suffered in modern times from the attraction of its rival and neighbour.

### CHAPTER 23

# POLAND

**Historical Foreword.** It is impossible to understand the geography of Poland without knowing something of the main events in its history. Between the years 1795 and 1919 there was no independent state of Poland, except for the Grand Duchy of Warsaw (1807–15) and the small republic of Cracow (1815–46), and the land was divided between Russia, Germany, and Austria. Before the partitions of 1772, 1793, and 1795, the kingdom of Poland had had a long tradition behind it, dating from the tenth century, and had acted for centuries as one of the bulwarks of western Europe against invasions of Mongol-Tatars, Turks, and other such intruders from the south-eastern steppes. Even as late as 1683 a king of Poland (John Sobieski) came to the rescue of Austria and Christendom when the city of Vienna was closely besieged by the Turks and seemed doomed to capitulate. The traditional rôle of Poland, however, was not only defensive. It shared in the general forward movement towards the east on the part of all the great nations of the plains north of the Alps. The French aimed at reaching the Rhine, the Germans (Austrians, Prussians, and others) pushed forward among the Slavonic-speaking peoples, and in turn the Poles advanced still farther east into territory which was inhabited by Russians. A word of explanation is necessary to show how this came about.

It happened that from the fourteenth century onwards Poland was dynastically linked with Lithuania, its heiress having married the ruler of its eastern neighbour, the Grand Duchy of Lithuania. The latter State had previously extended its rule south-eastwards over large numbers of people who were not Lithuanians, but who spoke Russian dialects and were known as White Russians and Ruthenians, the latter sometimes called Ukrainians. In the former Grand Duchy the Poles had a favoured position, partly on account of Poland being the dominant partner and partly on account of their superior culture, and Polish nobles became overlords over large tracts of land, Polish traders became numerous in the towns, and Polish became the language of the educated. To a less extent, Poland proper had also expanded towards the south-east to include the Ruthenians of East Galicia.

From the beginning of its history Poland represented ideas – later crystallised into tradition – which were neither German nor Russian. Although the Poles and Russians both speak Slavonic languages, yet the two people derived their civilisation from the Mediterranean by different roads, Russia via Constantinople and Poland from Italy, and this gave the two countries a different bias from the start. Poland, on the other hand, though welcoming German settlers at one time, was thrown on the defensive against German ideas owing to the aggressiveness of Prussia, which, moreover, was a Protestant state from the sixteenth century onwards, while Poland remained Roman Catholic.

With the collapse of Russia and the Central Powers towards the end of the war of 1914–18, it became possible for Poland to be reconstituted, but the hundred years and more of partition had left their mark and accentuated the differences already existing between eastern and western Poland. This hundred years had been one of great change in western Europe, but by far the greater part of the former kingdom of Poland was under Russian rule during that period and shared in the relative stagnation of the latter country. Even in the west, in Poznań and Upper Silesia, though great economic progress was made, the large landowners were mainly German and there was a lack of Polish leadership which alone could have brought about a vigorous improvement in education and in the general standard of living.

The boundaries of Poland as reconstituted in 1920 reached to the Baltic Heights on the north and the Carpathians on the south. To east and west, the absence of definite limits, either physical or ethnic, made the determination of satisfactory boundaries extremely difficult. On the west and north-west some 740,000 Germans were included in the new Poland (1931 figures), while some 148,000 Poles remained in Germany. On the east there was the difficulty of balancing historical against ethnic claims in an area where national feeling among the peasants appeared to be little developed. The Curzon line, a suggested boundary planned to run from north to south through Brest Litovsk (now Brest in the USSR), would have excluded from Poland the Pripyat marshes with their majority population of White Russians as well as East Galicia with its Ukrainian-speaking people, but this proved unacceptable to Poland on various grounds, partly historical, partly strategic, and partly because the landowners and townsfolk were largely Polish.

*Danzig and the Polish Corridor.* On the north it is significant that Poland's 1918 frontier did not reach the sea except along a narrow corridor between East and West Prussia. This continued the long historical separation of the Poles from the sea, the Slavonic-speaking peoples in general being landsmen, not seamen. The town of Danzig near the mouth of the Vistula was, of course, the obvious sea outlet for the Vistula basin which forms the home-land of the Polish people, but its population in 1918 was 90 per cent German. In consequence, it was declared a Free State in 1919, together with a small area of land surrounding it, though it was included within the Polish Customs Union. This solution pleased neither Poles nor Germans, and the Poles set about building a new port, named Gdynia, on their short stretch of Baltic coast, to which access was provided via the narrow Polish Corridor, only about 30 miles wide.

*The Present Boundaries of Poland.* The traditional instability of Poland's frontiers was manifested again, both during the war of 1939–45 and on the collapse of Germany in the latter year. During the war, Germany and the USSR came to an agreement to divide Poland between them and carried this out in 1940. At the end of the war Poland accepted the Curzon line as her eastern boundary, *de jure,* and was recompensed by the *de facto* receipt of most of East Prussia, the Free City of Danzig, and a large slice of eastern Germany, as far west as the line of the Oder–Neisse rivers (see Fig. 51).

Fig. 51. THE CHANGED TERRITORIAL EXTENT OF POLAND

The shift of Poland's territory to the west has led to far-reaching changes in the country's geography. The most spectacular and disrup-tive changes were those in population: the evacu-ation or repatriation of up to 8 million Germans from Silesia, the Odra (Oder) valley, Pomera-nia, and East Prussia; and their replacement by about 5 million Poles, resettled there from territories lost to the USSR in the east, from overpopulated areas in central and south-east Poland, and by other Polish nationals returning from abroad. The major problems of postwar Poland, resulting from her new limits, have been how to integrate the resettled population into their new environment, and how to integrate the regained territories into the Polish economy. Factors assisting this integration have been: first, the wider resource basis for industrialisation following from Poland's acquisition of the German, and better part, of the Upper Silesian coalfield, as well as useful fuel, power, and mineral resources in Lower Silesia; second, the gain of some rich farmlands on areas of *Löss* and relatively good glacial soils, which represent a net gain for agriculture, despite the loss of fertile areas in the Lwow and Wilno areas; and third, the youthfulness of the resettled population and its high rate of natural increase, which provide a ready, and adaptable, labour supply.

*Poland a Transitional Area.* The concept of Poland as transitional between central and eastern Europe is a useful one, since transition is the keynote of so many aspects of its geography. There is a rapid increase in the severity of the winters from west to east in Poland, to such an extent that the icy hand of the true Continental winter is felt in the east, where on an average three to four months have a temperature below freezing. Culturally, there is a progressive falling-off in the degree of economic development, in the density of population, in the number of towns, and in the standard of living from west to east, though this is less marked in the south, on the *Löss* soils of Galicia. Broadly speaking, Poland is transitional between an eastern Europe which is a massive continental area of continuous lowland, and the rest of north-central Europe which is under semi-oceanic influence and is of very varied relief.

## GEOGRAPHICAL REGIONS

Four main types of physiographic region are found in Poland, arranged in zones running from east to west. In the north there are (*a*) the Baltic Heights, similar to those of Germany. These are succeeded farther south by (*b*) the great central lowlands with their *Urstromtäler*, here called *pradoliny*, and basins. These again are followed on their southern side by the (*c*) Hercynian Uplands, including the sub-Carpathian depression and the Silesian bay of lowland, while the southern borderlands of Poland are formed by (*d*) the northern chains of the Carpathian Mountains, which belong to the Alpides system. Poland, therefore, comprises the same types of morphological structure as are found in Germany, arranged in the same order, with the difference that there is much less contrast between the great lowlands and the Hercynian Uplands. The uplands consist mainly of low, level plateaus, generally below 1,000 ft, and as treeless as they are highly cultivated. Apart from the Łysogóry, which is partly forest-covered as its name implies, there are none of the rugged, forested horsts which are such a feature of the German *Mittelgebirge*. These plateaus were sufficiently low to be lightly strewn with glacial material in the maximum advance of the Scandinavian ice-sheet, but later were covered with thick deposits of *Löss*, sometimes reworked to form *limon*. In many respects they form a continuation of the great agricultural plains of central Poland.

**The Baltic Heights and the Coastal Zone.** To east and west of the lower Vistula below Bydgoszcz (formerly Bromberg; 231,000[1]) stretch the extensive morainic lake plateaus of East Prussia and Pomerania (including West Prussia). Seldom rising above 1,000 ft, their variety derives mainly from differences of soil, resulting in varied land uses, with forest, especially on the terminal moraines and sandy outwash plains on the south, meadows in the wetter patches, and expanses of cultivated land on boulder-clay. The surface is generally undulating, but in places develops many minor inequalities of relief, especially in the south where terminal moraines and lakes are especially well developed. The beautiful Masurian lakeland of East Prussia is well known, the lakes filling hollows apparently formed by sub-glacial streams. Although farming is fairly remunerative, especially for potatoes and livestock, (pigs, cattle, horses), the population density is rather low. There is a notable absence of towns, although forest and light industries have led to the growth of the town of Olsztyn.

Even the coastal plain on the seaward side of the Baltic Heights, with a higher percentage of fertile boulder clay, shows a mainly rural population, in part originally drawn to the large estates, whose break-up began only after 1918 in an area whose smooth concordant coast lacked good harbours.

Gdansk (Danzig; 286,000) and Gdynia focus the urban and commercial life of northern Poland, by virtue of the excellent route afforded by the lower Vistula and its valley, and of the facilities for harbour building, though neither port is really first class. Gdansk lies on an arm of the Vistula delta and can take only moderate-sized vessels; its tonnage in 1938 amounted to 7 million tons as against 9 million tons for the new port of Gdynia, which was constructed after 1919. The dune-edged coast of Pomerania and the *Haff* and *Nehrung* coast of East Prussia now included in Poland, afford no good harbours, except at Königsberg on the River Pregel, which as Kaliningrad, lies today within the USSR. Szczecin (formerly Stettin; 269,000) was almost entirely destroyed in the 1939–45 war, but has been rebuilt to become Poland's second largest port, handling 3·9 million tons of shipping in 1961. It is an important industrial

[1] Population figures are for 1960 unless otherwise stated.

centre specialising in metallurgical products and shipbuilding, although the latter is more developed at Gdansk.

**The Central Lowlands.** The morphological development of the central lowlands of Poland has already been described (see Chapter 21). As in the similar lowlands of Germany, the main drainage, here by the River Vistula, is from south to north, with *pradoliny* running from east to west. The Notec (Netze)–Vistula–Narew–Biebrza–Niemen line, now canal-linked, may be specially noted, and also the Warta–Bzura–Vistula–Bug line further south. Compared with the German lowlands the *pradoliny* are less numerous and there are greater areas of ground-moraine between them.

The monotonous plains of northern Poland present much the same series of pictures over hundreds of miles, the same flatness, the same wide expanses of cultivation on the ground-moraine, the same pale grey, light sandy soils, the same coniferous forests, the same alternation of sand-dunes and marshes, sometimes reclaimed, in the *pradoliny*. Monotony of relief does not however give monotony of scenery. The land is worked in strips or furlongs very similar in appearance to the pattern of common field cultivation in medieval England. River valleys may be cut only 4 ft below the level of the plain but are liable to flooding and the shallow water-table rises rapidly after a storm to give flooding in the sandy fields for short periods. Only a few areas show any departure from this general sameness, and in most cases it is rather a variation in economic development or in type of population than of physical features.

*Lowlands West of the Vistula.* There are some slight regional differences to be observed between the area looking to Poznań (408,000) as its centre, and that looking to Łódź (708,000). The Poznań area, though having a higher percentage of infertile marshy and sandy tracts than the Łódź area, was noted for its great agricultural productiveness. This was the area of large estates during the German occupation; it has now large state-owned farms on which mechanisation is more advanced than anywhere else in Poland. The crops are still the same but the earlier higher standards of farming with the use of artificial fertilisers are still evident in somewhat higher yields.

In spite of the considerable density of population (200 per square mile), there is only one large city, namely Poznań itself, situated on the River Warta. It is a regional capital and the only manufacturing town of importance in the area. It has various industries connected with agriculture, such as the manufacture of agricultural machinery, chemical manures, flour milling, and brewing. Under current plans a new industrial area is emerging to the west centred on Konin-Inowroctaw with aluminium and chemical industries, based on the mining of brown coal and the generation of thermal electricity.

Thirty to forty miles east of the town of Poznań and north of the River Warta is the Polish lakeland, apparently similar in origin to the Havel-Spree lakeland, i.e. formed by sub-glacial erosion. The area is interesting for its black loams of unknown origin, which, it is claimed, formed one of the few non-forested areas of early Poland, that is to say, before the tenth century A.D. Here also the glacial cover is only about 10-20 ft thick, and salt deposits were accessible below, and these gave the region an early importance. The region is said to be the cradle of Polish nationality and the place of origin of the Piast royal family.

The Łódź area, on the high plain or low plateau between the Vistula and Warta–Oder river systems, has an exceptionally large proportion of fertile boulder clay and a high density of population. The town of Łódź, the main centre of the Polish textile industry, was a nineteenth-century artificial creation on the part of textile manufacturers, mainly German, who wished to take advantage of its position in former 'Congress' or Russian Poland, inside the tariff wall, and so have the advantage of the vast Russian market. There is a large ready-made clothing industry, originally associated with the Jewish population. The only other town of any size is Radom (130,000 in 1960), about 80 miles south-east of Łódź; it has clothing and also textile industries. Other towns are growing as industry and population are decentralised from Łódź.

*The Valley of the Middle Vistula.* The distinctive feature of this sinuous valley is the marshy floodplain, margined by dry, fertile river terraces. In places the valley widens, as in the ancient lake basins of Warsaw and Płock, where water was dammed up in front of the ice-sheet (see Chapter 21).

The Vistula itself is braided in many places and flows through a broad valley, originally marshy and still very liable to floods. Elsewhere in the valley sand-dunes have been piled up, particularly on the eastern side, and these provide dry material, it is true, but generally they are quite useless for cultivation.

The distinctive human feature of this area is the city of Warsaw (Polish, Warszawa), with over a million inhabitants before 1939, only 479,000 in 1946, but 1,136,000 in 1960. It became the capital of Poland only at the end of the sixteenth century, the former capital having been at Cracow in Galicia. The city itself has a good site on a terrace on the left bank of the Vistula, above the level of flood, and at a point where the absence of marshes gave a fairly easy crossing. The central position is also good, and it may perhaps be said that any suitable site near that position would have given rise to an important town.  At the end of the second world war the almost complete destruction of the city raised the problem whether it was more desirable to abandon the site or to resurrect the city on it. Actually the 'old city' has been faithfully rebuilt within its ancient walls but elsewhere new wide streets have been laid out and most of the population lives in new blocks of flats.  Today Warsaw is the administrative and commercial centre of Poland and an important industrial city, manufacturing, in particular, textiles and machinery.

Between Warsaw and Gdansk are several ancient towns, of which the most noteworthy are Bydgoszcz and Toruń, formerly better known by their German names of Bromberg and Thorn.  Bydgoszcz, with timber and engineering industries, owes much to its position near the junction of the Vistula river and Bydgoszcz canal.  Toruń (105,000 in 1960) is renowned as the birthplace of Copernicus. Płock is a growing centre for petrochemicals, based on Soviet oil piped from the Volga-Ural oilfields.  This huge development is transforming the western part of the middle Vistula, where industry market gardening, dairying, and tourism are growing apace.

**Lowlands East of the Vistula.**  The lowlands are here known as Podlasia.  They are not so low-lying as the region to the west of the Vistula, and they are lightly dissected by river valleys.  This area formed the old water-parting between the Vistula and the Dnieper river systems before the Polish river Bug captured the upper waters of the Pripyat river, a tributary of the Dnieper.  There is little ground-moraine here, but much sand and gravel; in consequence a good deal of land is still under forest, and the typical crops are rye, potatoes and flax.  The somewhat sparse population is distinctly poorer and more backward than that of the Poznań and the Łódź areas.  Towns are few and small, having had formerly a large Jewish element.


## THE HERCYNIAN UPLANDS

South of the northern plains there is a band of country, some 100 miles wide from north to south, which has at least a few recognisable lines of relief and where the physiognomy is based on a less haphazard distribution of the subsoil.  From east to west there stretches a series of low plateaus and basins, mainly developed on Cretaceous measures which have usually been little disturbed. The resurgence of two old Hercynian blocks, however, has caused a tilting of the overlying strata west of the Vistula and has also caused denudation to expose (a) the Mesozoic rocks whose Jurassic limestones on the west form the Częstochowa–Cracow scarp and (b) the Palæozoic rocks in the Łysogóry, east of Kielce, and in the

Silesian coalfield. East of the River San, also, the Cretaceous
measures have been warped to cause the anticline of Rostocze
running north-westwards from Lwów (now in the USSR). This
belt may conveniently be called the Polish scarplands, though,
as in the scarplands of Germany, the wide plains rather than the
escarpments form the conspicuous feature over the greater part
of the area.

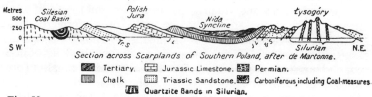

Section across Scarplands of Southern Poland, after de Martonne.

Tertiary.   Jurassic Limestone.   Permian.
Chalk      Triassic Sandstone.   Carboniferous, including Coal-measures.
Quartzite Bands in Silurian.

Fig. 52. SECTION ACROSS THE SCARPLANDS OF SOUTHERN POLAND

South of these Polish scarplands is a geosyncline, apparently
corresponding to that of the Alpine Foreland and similarly filled
in with Tertiary sediments and in places by glacial material. This
depression is drained towards the north by the Vistula and its
tributary the San and towards the south-east by the Dniester and
its affluents. The land rises gradually to the foothills of the
Carpathian system, here known as the Beskids.

**The Silesian Lowlands.** The valley of the upper Oder (Pol., Odra)
may be looked upon as an extension of the Germano–Polish plain.
It lies between the old rocks of the Hercynian highlands (Sudety) on
the west and the Triassic rock of the Hercynian uplands (Łysogóry)
on the east, and is encroached upon from both sides. It partakes
of the nature of the northern lowlands in its agricultural character,
though the third largest coalfield of Europe lies on its south-eastern
flank, while there is also considerable industrial development in the
Sudety.

Silesia, including much of the Sudety flank, had been under
German rule since 1526, first Austrian and later Prussian, but
following the advance of the Russian armies in 1945, the Poles
seized the whole of Silesia, even the part inhabited by Germans.
Ethnographically, the River Oder would seem to offer a reasonable
boundary in Upper Silesia, but farther north German-speaking
people had long inhabited both banks of the Oder.

Lower, i.e. northern, Silesia includes the sandy lands of the outer-
most belt of the young glaciation, and is largely heath-covered, but
south of the Katzbach and the Katzengebirge, on the *Löss*, are the
wide stretches of fertile loams which enabled Silesia to be one of the
main granaries of Germany, growing cereals, especially rye and

wheat, and such crops as sugar-beet and potatoes. The old town of Wrocław (formerly Breslau, on the Oder, 429,000) is the centre of this district and the regional capital of the whole of Silesia. In accordance with state plans, much new industry is developing in Lower Silesia, based partly on coal brought down the Oder river and partly on newly worked brown coal and copper resources which are available within the triangle between the Oder and Nysa (Neisse) rivers. The fertile soil is also continued in Upper, i.e. southern, Silesia, but only on the west side of the Oder, especially in the *Löss* belt at the foot of the Sudety. East of the Oder, from the River Stober southwards, are great forests, except where the *Muschelkalk* (Triassic) of the Chelm plateau comes to the surface.

**The Upper Silesian Industrial Region.** The Silesian coalfield indicates the near presence of the Hercynian system. It was one of the last of the great European coalfields to be developed, owing to its easterly and frontier position between Germany and Russia. It was developed by German capital and by German experts, but mainly with Polish manual labour.

The actual productive Coal Measures either outcrop or come very near the surface in the region of the great industrial conurbation of Gliwice–Bytom–Katowice–Sosnowiec. The measures sink south-eastwards until they are more than 3,250 ft below sea-level beneath the forests of Pszczyna (Ger., Pless), but rise again on the southern and south-western sides of the basin, are worked near Rybnik and Cieszyn (Teschen), and are believed to be workable near Cracow.

The industrial region forms a sprawling mass of Black Country in the heart of thinly peopled forest land on poor, sandy, glacial soils. The industrial development of the region was based on the presence of iron-ore, originally smelted by charcoal, and the intensive development of the coalfield came rather late in the nineteenth century, after the unification of Germany. The iron-ore is no longer considered economic to work, but the considerable supplies of lead and still more of zinc ores are important, Poland being one of the few countries of Europe to produce considerable quantities of the latter metal. The production of coal from the field, now wholly within Poland, reached 110 million tons in 1962, and is greater than the home market consumes, although Poland is now more industrial-ised. An outlet has been found in Scandinavia and in other agri-cultural countries which are poor in coal, such as Austria, Hungary, the Balkan countries, and Italy. To some extent the cheaper Polish coal had ousted British coal from the Baltic even before 1939.

The main branch of manufacture is of iron and steel goods, but on the whole the higher branches of metallurgy are not represented, the industry thus showing a lack of evolution common to the youth of most industries. Katowice (279,000) is the main industrial centre and here is located much of Poland's iron and steel industry and its non-ferrous metal industry. Iron-ore is imported chiefly from the USSR, but to a smaller extent from Sweden. The zinc and chemical industries make up other branches of industry, the latter partly based on by-products of the zinc-smelting and the coke ovens. The wartime expansion of industry by the Germans (e.g. synthetic rubber) has been inherited by the Poles, although the reconstruction of heavily damaged plants was necessary.

The industrial and urban growth of Upper Silesia has involved conflicting claims to the use of land for quarries, tip heaps, housing, and manufacturing industry. Accordingly, the attempt is being made to locate industry and to expand towns outside the conurbation, for example, at Nowy Tychy, and Tarnowskie Gory.

The Silesian corridor is also important in regard to communications as it gives an easy routeway to the Danubian basin.

**The Sudety.** This complex region has been much fractured by faults. There are a number of small horsts between which lie basins where the Permian and later strata have been preserved. The highest part lies in the north, where the Krkonoše Mountains (Giant Mountains, Riesengebirge) rise above the tree limit, the Snieżka (Ger., Schneekoppe) being above 5,000 feet. The most important basin is that of Walbrzych, where Coal Measures are preserved, yielding over 4 million tons per annum. This source of power gave fresh life to the textile industries of linen and wool which had already been established along streams giving water power. The coal is now chiefly converted into coke, which is greatly needed by the metallurgical industries of Upper Silesia. The very sinuous boundary between Silesia and Bohemia reflects the complex structure and topography of the Sudety.

**The Polish Jura.** Overlooking the Silesian lowlands is an escarpment formed of Jurassic limestone which extends in a north-west to south-east direction from Częstochowa on the Warta to Cracow on the upper Vistula. It appears to have no recognised geographical name, though the plateau on top is sometimes known as the plateau of Wolbrom, after a small town of the same name, but the term Polish Jura may serve to indicate its character, though its similarity is to the unfolded German Jura rather than to the Franco-Swiss Jura. It formed a well marked frontier feature for several hundred years, between the fourteenth century, when Silesia ceased to be under Polish administration, and the eighteenth century, when Poland ceased to exist as a state. Numerous ruins of old castles and fortresses bear witness to the former military importance of the scarp. The top of the plateau to the east of the scarp is bleak, it

POLAND

55 Spraying potatoes

56 A Polish farmer working his own farm

57 On the beach at Nowa Huta

58 Karlovy Vary (Karlsbad) is an internationally famous spa town at the foot of the Krusne Hory (Erzgebirge). This area was largely colonised by German speakers up to 1945.

CZECHOSLOVAKIA

59 Bohemia. A view from the foothills of Sudety into the undulating plateau country of northern Bohemia, near Turnov. Limestone eroded into fantastic shapes, is a feature of this area.

lacks surface water, and has a scanty population. Częstochowa (164,000) is a large industrial town on the Warta and towards the north-west end of the Jura; it is a centre of cotton manufacturing and of iron-ore mining while recently it has become an iron and steel centre. At the south-eastern end is the old capital of Poland, Cracow (479,000).

**The Nida Depression.** This depression, drained southwards by the Nida tributary of the Vistula, occupies the middle of the syncline between the two old Hercynian blocks of the Silesian coal basin and the Łysogóry. Its Cretaceous measures are covered by Tertiary sediments, and these again by glacial material, and as the latter are mainly sterile sands and gravels, or heavy clays which easily become boggy, the landscape in parts recalls the northern lowlands, with forest, heath, and marsh. Where the glacial soils have been denuded, however, the Tertiaries, which are mainly limestones, provide a good soil known as the *rendzina*, which is particularly rich in humus. The southern part of this region, together with the strip of country on the north of the Vistula from Cracow to Sandomierz is *Löss*-covered, and wheat appears in the rural economy as a change from the rye and potatoes of the glaciated northern plains. The area is backward, however, on account of its lack of railway facilities.

**The Łysogóry.** The parallel crests of the Łysogóry follow the prevailing strike of the country from north-west to south-east and reach over 2,000 ft in height. This old horst is largely a region of forests and ancient mines reminiscent of the Harz massif of Germany, but there is considerable cultivation in the valleys. Though the massif shows rounded forms in most places, the quartzite crests are often sharp and craggy.

**The Depression of the San and Upper Vistula.** The triangular depression between Cracow, Sandomierz, and Pryzemśl becomes increasingly fertile towards the south as the coarse glacial soils give way to the *Löss*. It also becomes lightly dissected into hills by the San and Vistula and their affluents, but without providing any obstacle to movement, and an important railway line runs from east to west at the base of the triangle along the foot of the Beskids. Along this line a number of small market towns lie at the entrances to the mountain valleys, the town of Przemyśl (46,000) being the largest. During the period 1936–39 the San–Upper Vistula Depression, as the Central Industrial District, was scheduled for economic development by the Polish government. The application of this plan, which involved the establishment of chemical, metallurgical, and engineering plants, was interrupted by the war, but it has now been largely carried out.

The city of Cracow (Pol., Kraków; 479,000) lies at an important position in the gap between the Beskids and the Jurassic scarp already mentioned. Its ancient importance was largely strategic, and it was chosen as capital by the kings of Poland in the thirteenth century and held that rank for three hundred years. Its old university, the ancient castle built on the rocky eminence, the Wawel, and the famous Cloth Hall, all survived the war, as did most of its other architectural features. Its present importance is mainly commercial, and it shows signs of playing a similar rôle in relation to the Silesian coalfield as the ancient city of Cologne played in regard to the Ruhr coalfield. A large new steel works and town of Nowa Huta have been built just to the east of the city during the 1950s; a new centre for aluminium refining lies just to the south.

**The Uplands East of the Vistula.** The plateau of Lublin consists mainly of chalk with a considerable covering of *Löss*. Wide tree-less horizons are here the rule, though wheat, the cereal typical of the *Löss* lands of Europe, takes second place to rye and sugar-beet is also important. The predominance of rye indicates the backwardness of the present economy of the area. Here houses are to be seen cut out of the *Löss*, as in parts of China. The old town of Lublin (181,000), on the old route which went along the northern margin of the *Löss* belt, is another of Poland's textile towns, but it is now more notable for its engineering and food-pro-cessing industries.

For the Polish Carpathians, see Chapter 30.

**Economic Summary.** The population of Poland was 24 million in 1946 and had risen to 30 million in 1961. Two features demand comment: first, the very high natural increase of 19·5 per 1,000 after the war had decreased to 13·1 in 1961; second, owing to the drift of population to urban centres, the percentage living in towns has grown from 27·4 per cent in 1931 to 48·5 per cent in 1961. There are now twenty-two towns with populations of 100,000 or more. Poland was essentially an agricultural country in 1938, some three-quarters of the employed population being then engaged in agriculture, and only one tenth in industry. With the acquisition of the whole of the Silesian coalfield in 1945, the situation changed rapidly. In 1961 47·8 per cent of the employed population was engaged in agriculture and 23 per cent in industry. About half of the total area is arable, a percentage exceeded only in Denmark and Hungary. The leading and most widely cultivated crops are rye, potatoes, and hay; sugar-beet is also important, especially in Poznań and on the *Löss* uplands. Even so, grain harvests are scarcely adequate and grain imports are needed. Forests cover one-fifth of the total area of the country, but though Poland is one of the richest countries of Europe in this respect, the figure given includes a fair amount of poorly timbered land, and the value of the forests should not be exaggerated. Nearly 89 per cent of the agricultural production comes from private farms of which there are 3·5 million in Poland with an average size of only 6½ acres. State farms contribute 10 per cent, mainly in western Poland, while cooperatives number less than 1,800 and produce only 1·2 per cent of the national output.

Mining is confined mainly to the southern part of the country, the chief minerals being coal, zinc ore, oil, and salt. The output from the Polish section of the Upper Silesian coalfield was 36 million tons in 1937; the total field produced about 110 million tons in 1962, and the amount is rising. The output of zinc from the same area and from the Łysogóry amounted to 107,000 tons in 1937, but 165,000 tons in 1961. The oil wells of the Galician foothills appear to be approaching exhaustion; part of the field has been lost to the USSR, and the total annual output reaches only about 200,000 tons. Crude oil is now being imported by pipeline from the Volga area to serve new petrochemical industries in central Poland. Of the other minerals, salt, the most important, is mined in the Carpathian Foreland around Wieliczka, and in the north of Poland, near Toruń. Recently discovered natural sulphur resources near the San–Vistula confluence in south-east Poland, and copper ores in south-west Poland give promise of future industrial developments. The exploitation of these, and also of brown coal deposits in western and central Poland for electric-power generation, are receiving attention in current five-year plans.

The metallurgical industry has grown greatly since 1945; home produced iron-ore amounted to 2·4 million tons in 1961, more than three times the prewar figure. The production of pig-iron was then 4·8 million tons and that of steel 6·6 million. This increase has resulted from the annexation of German Silesia, the planned re-organisation of the steel industry, the building of the vast new works at Nowa Huta, and the importation of high-quality ore from Krivoi Rog in the USSR. Other considerable branches of industry are connected with the timber, sugar-beet, and oil resources, while the chemical and engineering industries are of growing scale.

As regards exports, metallurgical products account for 28 per cent, coal and coke for 18 per cent, and foodstuffs for 17 per cent. Textiles have become less important at only 5 per cent of the total value of exports. The leading classes of import are engineering products, ores and fuels, notably oil piped from the USSR, textile raw materials, including Soviet cotton, and raw food materials for processing. Part of this pattern of trade results from the policy of economic specialisation which is being developed within COMECON,

the organisation for mutual economic aid of the Soviet-bloc countries.   This has been effective too in greatly stimulating ship-building
on the Polish coast to serve Soviet, Czech, and East German, as
well as Polish, needs.

## REFERENCES

L. A. Boyd, *Polish Countryside*, New York, American Geographical Society,
1937, contains some 500 photographs covering every aspect of country life.
On the boundary changes of 1945, see S. Leszczycki, 'Geographical Bases of
Contemporary Poland', *Journal of Central European Affairs*, viii, 1948.   On
economics, see J. Taylor, *The Economic Development of Poland*, New York,
Cornell University Press, 1952, and R. Hartshorne, 'The Upper Silesian Indus-
trial District', *Geog. Review*, 1934; H. G. Wanklyn, *The Eastern Marchlands
of Europe*, London, George Philip, 1941; N. Spulber, *The Economics of Commu-
nist Eastern Europe*, New York, Wiley, 1957.   See also G. North 'Poland's
Population and Changing Economy', *The Geog. Journal*, 124, 1958, 517–527;
N. J. G. Pounds, *Geographical Essays on Eastern Europe*, Bloomington, Indiana
University, and the Hague, Mouton, 1961; idem 'Planning in the Upper Silesian
Industrial Region', *Journal of Central European Affairs*, xix, 1959, and 'Industrial Geography of Modern Poland', *Economic Geography*, 1960.   *The Concise
Statistical Yearbook* published in English is available through the Polish Insti-
tute.   *Problems of Applied Geography*, Warsaw, 1961, was published by the
Polish Academy of Science and is available from the Institute of British Geographers.   A useful monthly publication giving information and analyses of new
developments, is *Polish Perspectives*.

CHAPTER 24

# CZECHOSLOVAKIA

ALTHOUGH Czechoslovakia is not very large, its total area of 49,700 square miles being about the same as that of England without Wales, yet its key position in central Europe, its natural endowment and the energy of its inhabitants make it one of the most noteworthy of the smaller countries of Europe.

The Republic was formed in 1918, when a National Council of Czechs and Slovaks took over the government of certain lands which had been formerly included in the Austro-Hungarian Empire. These lands comprised, first, the old historic Czech kingdom of Bohemia–Moravia; secondly, the small adjacent region of Austrian Silesia which had been administered from Vienna for several hundred years; and thirdly, the relatively backward lands of Slovakia and Ruthenia which had formed part of the Hungarian Empire since its inception. The bond of union between Czechs and Slovaks was primarily their common Slavonic language, there being less difference between Czech and Slovak than there is between 'standard' English and the English of Robert Burns.[1] A second powerful bond was their passionate desire for release from the oppression which had characterised Austrian and Hungarian rule. This oppression fell more heavily on the Czechs than on the Slovaks, for the Bohemian kingdom, including Moravia, had already had a long and distinguished history before it misguidedly chose an Austrian Habsburg as its king. Its 'Golden Age' was as early as the fourteenth century, when the Bohemian king, Charles IV (a Lorrainer), became Holy Roman Emperor, and Bohemia ranked among the most cultured states of Europe. The earliest university of the Empire was that of Prague, founded by Charles IV in 1348.

The election of a Habsburg to the throne of Bohemia in the sixteenth century marked the beginning of the policy of Germanisation, which gained in intensity when the Protestant reformer Jan Hus became identified with the cause of Czech nationalism. After the disastrous defeat of the Czechs at the Battle of White Mountain, just outside Prague, in 1620, the Czech leaders were executed and

[1] Of the three main founders of Czechoslovakia, Masaryk was born in Moravia, Beneš in Bohemia and Štefánik in Slovakia

421

their estates confiscated. From that time onwards every effort was made to prevent the Czechs from acquiring either wealth or influence. The use of the Czech language was forbidden for all official purposes, no university education could be obtained in Czech, Czechs were not allowed to occupy any responsible administrative positions, in many cases not even subordinate positions.

For 200 years it seemed that Bohemian nationalism would never raise its head again, but signs of life were discernible in the nineteenth century with the revival of interest in the Czech language and literature. The Czechs also made strenuous efforts to raise themselves from the status of illiterate peasants and so justify their claim to self-government. The rise of industrialism and the introduction of modern methods of farming brought an increase of wealth and power to the Czechs, but the justice of their claim to independence was not acknowledged until October, 1918, when the Austrian Emperor Charles offered them federal freedom, an offer which unfortunately came too late.

Czechoslovakia was broken up in 1938–39 to satisfy Germany's military rather than nationalist ambitions. Bohemia projected as a salient into the German lands, and no doubt was potentially dangerous to the fulfilment of Germany's revived ambition to dominate central Europe. The minorities question was used mainly as an excuse, for it is clear that the German minority received much better treatment than the Czechs had formerly obtained under German (Austrian) rule. Unfortunately, the world slump of the 1930s fell more heavily on the German (i.e. the manufacturing districts) than on the purely Czech areas, and thus favourable ground existed for anti-Czech propaganda. Following the Allied victory in 1945, its pre-1938 boundaries were restored, except that in the east Ruthenia was incorporated into the Soviet Ukraine. Of the 3·6 million German population of prewar Czechoslovakia, 2·9 million were expelled.

In 1948, after a quick revolution, Czechoslovakia became a communist state. It is now firmly integrated in the 'eastern bloc' of communist countries.

**Bohemia.** *Introduction.* Bohemia, the western section of Czechoslovakia, is a rather complex piece of Hercynian Europe. It is true that the whole area may be looked upon as a rectangular-shaped horst, with corners pointing north, east, south, and west, but it is a horst containing many minor horsts and basins and it is largely covered in the northerly parts with Mesozoic and Tertiary deposits. The region consists essentially of the peneplained stumps of a folded mountain system of Carboniferous age, with traces of earlier folding. The whole region was progressively denuded following its uplift in

Carboniferous times, and by the Cretaceous period most of the region was submerged, though from the marly and sandy character of the Cretaceous deposits it is evident that they must have been deposited in a shallow sea near land. Then in Tertiary times the present horst was raised up bodily as a consequence of the earth movements connected with the building of the Alps and Carpathians, but was considerably warped as well as faulted in the process. The main upwarpings took place in two regions, namely, along the south-eastern border, forming the broad swelling of the Moravian Heights, which reach only 2,739 ft, and along the south-western border in the Šumava (Bohemian Forest; Ger., Böhmerwald), which reaches nearly 5,000 ft. The main faulting took place along three lines of weakness, namely, along the outer or western side of the Šumava, along the southern or inner side of the Krusné Hory (Ore Mountains; Ger., Erzgebirge) which border Bohemia on the north-west, and on the north-east side in the Krkonoše Hory (Giant Mountains; Ger., Riesengebirge) and Sudety, where a complicated system of blocks and depressions arose (see p. 416). Volcanic outpourings of Tertiary age sometimes accompanied the dislocations, especially in the north-west. As a result of these warpings and faultings, the middle of the horst became a basin, in whose lower northerly part the Cretaceous and Tertiary cover was preserved. The Tertiary sediments still remain at the foot of the Krusné Hory in the Karlovy Vary–Teplice depression, which is partially filled in by Tertiary volcanic deposits and thereby divided into a number of basins, and the Mesozoic deposits remain in the plain of the Labe (Elbe). The rest of the Bohemian basin consists mainly of a featureless plateau of crystalline rocks, mainly granites and ancient crystalline schists, but, quite exceptionally, the Brdy Forest south of the River Berounka (Ger., Beraun) shows little changed Pre-Cambrian and Palæozoic rocks outcropping from north-east to south-west, with the hard quartzites standing up as ridges. The basin of Plzeň (Ger., Pilsen), on the Berounka, and the Kladno basin are excavated in Carboniferous rock. The two depressions of Budějovice (Ger., Budweiss) and Třeboň (Ger., Wittingau) in the south of the crystalline plateau are filled by Tertiary deposits.

The river system reveals the general slope of the land, the main river, the Vltava (Ger., Moldau), forming a diagonal from the southern to the northern corner, where it cuts through the surrounding mountains.

Climatically the bordering mountains are areas of heavy rainfall and raw climate, but the northern plain, by its position and relatively low relief (c. 700 ft), has little rain and high summer temperatures, though with somewhat severe winters, e.g. Prague: January, $-0.5°$ C

(31°F); July, 19·5° C (67° F), mean annual rainfall, 19 in. The Labe plains have almost a steppe climate, with *Löss* deposits and patches of Black Earth (*chernozem*), and appear to have been forest-free for long ages. The southern plateau also has little rain, but summer temperatures are not so high.

## THE NATURAL REGIONS

**The Mountain Border.** On two sides the mountainous frontiers of Bohemia are co-extensive with part of the German frontier and their nature has already been described in Chapter 22; the third side adjoins Silesia, Polish since 1945. Each of these sides is about 200 miles long, and the greatest heights are found in the Šumava in the south-west and the Krkonoše Hory (Ger., Riesengebirge) in the north-east, the former reaching a height of over 4,000 ft and the latter over 5,000 ft though the crests have the usual rounded forms common to the mountains of the Hercynian system. The Šumava on the south-west is the most densely forested and most scantily peopled of all the bordering mountains, forestry being the principal occupation. The Krusné Hory have been largely cleared and are under cultivation for hardy crops, and home industries (e.g. gloves, chair making) are carried on to a considerable extent. Jáchymov (Ger., Joachimstal) is noted for its radium mines. Throughout the mountainous border the people were almost entirely German-speaking[1] until the expulsions of 1945 onwards, and were descended from settlers who penetrated the Slavonic-speaking salient of Bohemia in the Middle Ages – part of the great eastern colonisation movement of the Germans. In places they also penetrated into the basins at the foot of the mountains.

**The Northern Plains and Basins.** (1) *The Tertiary Depressions of Karlovy Vary and Teplice.* These lie at the faulted foot of the Krusné Hory and consist of a number of basins separated by massifs of considerable height. The basins are particularly notable in having preserved quantities of Tertiary brown coal. In the west is the little basin of Cheb (Eger), which, however, has no workable brown coal and lies at a height of some 1,300 ft and is mainly devoted to pasture. East of this is the basin of Falknov–Karlovy Vary, (Ger., Falkenau–Karlsbad), both towns lying on the Ohře river (Eger). This basin possesses considerable and varied resources, namely, brown coal, mineral springs, which have made the fortunes of Marianské Lázně (Ger., Marienbad) and Karlovy Vary (Ger., Karlsbad), and kaolin from the neighbouring granitic Cisařsky Les

---

[1] The German versions of place-names, the only ones given in some atlases, are now purely historic. They are given in parentheses in this chapter for references purposes.

(Ger., Kaiserwald) for the Karlovy Vary porcelain industry. East of this basin is the volcanic massif of Doupov, reaching a height of 3,000 ft, but on the far side lies the *Löss*-covered Teplice basin (Ger., Teplitz; 42,900)[1] which is some 40 miles long and of great agricultural richness, as well as containing the largest deposits of brown coal in the country (the Chumotov field), some 40 million tons being mined in 1961. A flourishing glass industry is found here, and

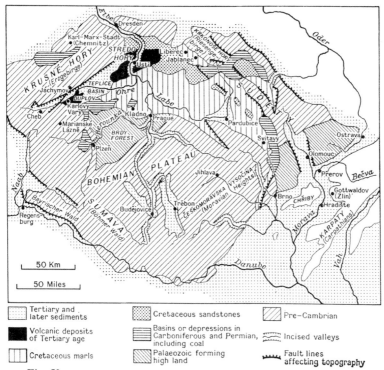

Fig. 53. MAIN PHYSICAL FEATURES OF BOHEMIA AND MORAVIA

machinery of various kinds is also manufactured. The volcanic plateau of the Středo Hoří (Ger., Mittelgebirge) succeeds this basin eastwards, but its fertile basalts render it suitable for cultivation up to a height of nearly 2,000 ft, and its lower slopes carry orchards, hops, and wheat. The River Labe crosses the plateau in a well incised valley. Usti (Ger., Aussig; 63,800) is a river port and manufactures chemicals.

The Tertiary depression was colonised by Germans from the

[1] All figures are resident populations at the 1961 census.

Erzgebirge in the Middle Ages, but increasing numbers of Czechs settled there, especially in the Teplitz basin, when the development of the mines called for an increase of labour.

(2) *Basins and Plateaus at the Foot of the Krkonoše Hory.* At the foot of the Krkonoše Hory lies a depression separated from the Labe plain by plateaus of hard Cretaceous sandstone. Here a considerable textile industry, mainly cotton, has developed from an old domestic linen industry using locally grown flax. Liberec (Ger., Reichenberg; 65,300) is the centre of this scattered industry. Jablonec (Ger., Gablonz; 27,300) manufactures beads and imitation jewellery of all kinds. The population of this region was also mainly German-speaking, of whom a few key workers were allowed to stay, especially in connexion with the glass industry, as their skill and experience were irreplaceable.

(3) *The Labe Plain.* This is the only large plain of Bohemia and stretches from south-east to north-west for a distance of 60 miles beginning near Svitavy (Ger., Zwittau) to beyond the junction of the Labe and Vltava. It is some 20 miles broad, lies mainly below 700 ft in height, and is of exceptional fertility, its Cretaceous marls being mainly covered with *Löss* on which *chernozem* soils have developed. Farming is on modern lines, including such commodities as sugar-beet and forage crops, as well as wheat and other cereals, while stall-fed cattle and pigs are also important. The fairly dense population is Czech-speaking, but there are few towns of any size, the nearness of Prague discouraging the growth of other urban centres.

The Cretaceous cover extends to the neighbourhood of Prague, and undoubtedly at one time extended farther south.

**The Bohemian Plateau.** Unlike the northern lowlands of Bohemia, which are a region of rich and varied agriculture as well as considerable industrial development, the uplands of southern Bohemia are regions of poor agriculture, only redeemed by the presence of a few rich basins and by the coal basins of Plzeň and Kladno.

(1) *The Basins of Plzeň and Kladno.* The former was excavated by the Berounka and its numerous tributaries in the rather soft Carboniferous sandstones and shales, and forms a little region of rich agriculture, whose barley and hops were the original basis of the brewing industry, which attains vast proportions. Plzeň (137,700) also possesses large metallurgical works (Škoda) in addition to its breweries, and was the great Austrian manufacturing centre of armaments, the iron-ore originally coming from the Brdy Forest to the south. The Plzeň coalfield, however, is now nearly exhausted, but the Kladno field, some 20 miles west of Prague, has an output of about 2 million tons per annum.

(2) *The Brdy Forest* still retains considerable forest cover (50 per cent).

(3) *The Crystalline Plateaus* are regions of undulating relief, varying in height from 700 to 2,700 ft. The rejuvenation of the drainage has caused the larger rivers to incise their beds, but the upper courses and smaller streams still show senile features and are often marshy (cf. Plateau de Haut Limousin in the Massif Central of France). The plateau is generally a region of rather poor soils, and potatoes and rye are the dominating crops.

(4) *The Tertiary Basins of Budějovice and Třeboň.* The latter, at a height of more than 1,400 ft, is little below the level of the surrounding plateau, while the former, at a little over 1,100 ft is considerably below. The Tertiary clays, though apt to be marshy and still covered with many lakes, are generally fertile. The lakes or 'ponds' are famous for carp rearing, and they are regularly drained for their 'crop' of fish to be harvested. České Budějovice (Ger., Budweiss; 63,900) has a well-known industry in the making of lead pencils, the graphite being obtained from Krumlov south of the basin. In this southern corner of the Bohemian horst the central plateau is not bounded by any definite heights, and communication is not difficult with the Danube valley.

**Prague** (Cz., Praha; Ger., Prag; 1,003,300). The capital city is situated on the Vltava on the southern border of the northern lowlands, almost in the middle of the Bohemian 'diamond'. It is the natural centre of Bohemia but is excentric to the united state of Czechoslovakia. Its name is said to mean 'threshold', from the banks of quartzite which outcrop in the river bed having produced fordable shallows, though at the same time they set a limit to navigation. The city is placed at an admirable nodal point and it was of considerable fame in the Middle Ages, but remained small until the middle of the nineteenth century, when industrialisation began to make itself felt in the country. The city itself has important manufactures, using the pig-iron made on the Kladno coalfield for all kinds of metallurgy, including locomotives, machinery of all kinds, agricultural implements, etc. The alimentary industries are well represented, and the products of the neighbouring Labe plain are manufactured as well as imported raw materials. The textile, glove, and glass industries are also of considerable dimensions. The choice of Prague as capital for Czechoslovakia added to the importance and population of the city, which is the commercial and intellectual centre of the country.

**Moravia.** Moravia, which comprises the greater part of the basin of the Morava, stretches from the Moravian Heights of the Bohemian horst on the west to the Carpathian zone on the east, and includes the lowlands of Tertiary and later sediments between the two. The former province of Austrian Silesia, with its coalfield, was also handed over to Czechoslovakia, with the exception of a small piece in the north-east near Cieszyn (Cz., Těšin; Ger., Teschen), which went to Poland.

The Moravian lowlands are rich lands from an agricultural point of view, but are perhaps better known to the world at large on account of their importance in affording one of the main highways of movement in Europe. By linking the lowlands of Silesia with those of the Vienna basin they afford the easiest line of movement between the great Germano-Polish plains and the great plains of the middle Danube, and so form part of the route which links the Baltic to the Mediterranean. The actual 'Moravian Gate' lies at the north-eastern end of the lowlands, and it is a narrow depression, only a few miles wide, closely approached by the Carpathians on the east and by the Sudety (Sudetes) on the west. It forms a low waterparting, just over 1,000 ft in height, between the head-waters of the Oder and those of the Bečva, a tributary of the Morava, or, in other words, between the Baltic and Black Sea drainage areas.

The north-western border of Moravia is formed by the Moravian Heights, which sink down gradually towards the south-east. As already mentioned, these are part of the Bohemian horst, and their gently rounded forms indicate an upraised peneplain. In the western part, centred on Jihlava (Ger., Iglau; 34,700), the granite uplands attain considerable heights (between 2,000 and 3,000 ft), and the region is mainly one of poor agriculture and rather scanty population. Farther east there is a north to south depression, presumably a down-warping of the crystalline horst, which has been partially filled by sedimentary deposits, largely of Cretaceous age. In these fairly easily eroded marls and sandstones the rivers have cut deep valleys and in particular the Svitava offers a line of movement below 1,500 ft which is followed by the railway between Prague and Brno, though the main line between Prague and Vienna goes over the granite heights farther west via Jihlava. East of the Svitava depression the horst rises again, but is practically cut off from the Sudety by the north-western extension of the Moravian lowlands along the upper Morava.

The Moravian lowlands themselves are divided into three main sections by 'islands' of higher and less fertile land, which run in a north-east to south-west direction and are outlying portions of the Carpathian system, partially submerged by later sediments. The most prominent is the Chřiby, east of Brno. To the east of them, below Hradište on the Morava, the lowland is less fertile than usual, and the Morava itself is bordered by marshes, which account to some extent for the old frontier with Hungary following the line of the river. To the north-west lies the fertile country of the upper Morava, surrounding Olomouc (70,100) and Přerov (30,500), and to the west lie the fertile lowlands east of Brno.

Agriculture is the dominating interest of the Moravian lowlands, and crops are rich and varied. Sugar-beet, barley, vines, wheat, maize, rye, and forage crops, cattle and pig rearing are all important. Manufacturing industries are to a considerable extent concentrated at Brno (Ger., Brünn; 314,400), the only really large city of Moravia. Textile industries predominate, though the sheep which formerly supplied the raw material have now disappeared from the granitic Moravian Heights in favour of cattle. The city is situated at the meeting-place of the route from Praha across the Moravian Heights with the route north-eastwards along the plain to Silesia.

The proximity of the Silesian coal basin is encouraging the growth of factories in Moravia (e.g. the Bata shoe factory at Gottwaldov, formerly Zlin (54,200), 40 miles east of Brno), but the heavy industries (coke, metallurgy) naturally remain on the coalfield itself, which produces more than three-quarters of the total coal output of the country. Ostrava (234,700), together with Otrokovice-Kvitkovice and Marianské Lázné form an industrial conurbation numbering more than 250,000 people.

**Slovakia.** Physically, culturally and economically Slovakia shows sharp differences from the western part of the country. In structure and physiography it belongs to the Carpathian province of Europe, and its regional geography is accordingly described in Chapter 30. Owing to its easterly position, its mountainous character, and its long history of subjection to Hungary, it is less well developed. Farming depends to a greater extent upon production for subsistence, towns are fewer and smaller, and the transport system was really developed only after the creation of the Czechoslovak state in 1918. Although the communist régime has made assiduous efforts to develop the area, by raising the standard of agriculture, and by rapid industrialisation in the Five-Year Plans since 1948, there still remains an economic gap. Before the war Slovakia accounted for only 8 per cent of Czech gross industrial production; by the end of the first Five-Year Plan, in 1953, this had been raised to only 16 per cent. Historically Slovakia has tended to have high birth and death rates, and a high natural rate of increase of the population which has been compensated by emigration overseas. But with the new emphasis on internal development this has changed, and the rate of population increase in Slovakia between 1950 and 1961 was twice as great as that of the Czech half of the country.

**Economic Summary.** As elsewhere in central Europe, the

agricultural pattern is marked by great regional contrasts associated with variations in relief, climate, and soils. In the whole country some three-fifths of the area are given over to agriculture, and of the agricultural area almost exactly three-quarters are arable, one quarter grass. But the proportions of farm land to total land, and of arable land to all farm land, are higher in the Czech west (and highest of all in Moravia, especially in the intensively cultivated southern lowlands) than in the Slovak east.

| LAND USE 1960 (FAO classification) | CZECHOSLO-VAKIA | CZECH (WEST) SECTION | SLOVAK (EAST) SECTION |
|---|---|---|---|
| | | per cent | |
| total | 100 | 100 | 100 |
| agriculture | 57 | 58 | 56 |
| arable | 42 | 45 | 38 |
| grass | 15 | 13 | 18 |
| forest | 34 | 33 | 37 |
| other | 9 | 9 | 7 |

Cereals made up half the arable acreage in 1960. Rye, formerly the most important cereal, has suffered a great reduction in acreage since 1950; it now stands fourth, behind barley, wheat, and oats. Sugar-beet is an important cash crop which can be grown only on the better soils of the lowland basins; it makes big labour demands, and is most important in the more densely populated districts of the west. Other cash crops (usually associated with more fertile soils and favourable climates) are fruit, vines, tobacco, and hops. In 1945 (and in 1949) land reforms swept away the former big estates and established a society of small to medium-sized peasant farms. Because of the obvious danger of uneconomically small farms, cooperatives were set up. Under the communist régime over 87 per cent of the land had been collectivised or turned into state farms by 1961. Yields of the most important crops appear to have increased greatly as a result.

Taken as a whole, Czechoslovakia has a remarkably good raw material base for industrial development. She is self-sufficient in many agricultural raw materials (sugar-beet, potatoes for distilling, hops and barley for the big brewing industry), in forest products, from the highland rim of Bohemia and from the Carpathians (for furniture, chemicals, and artificial fibres), and above all in coal and brown coal. Three-quarters of the bituminous coal output (26·2 million tons in 1960) come from the Czech part of the Silesian coal-field, around Moravská Ostrava; three-quarters of the brown coal (total output 55·5 million tons in 1960) from the Chumutov field in the Ohře valley in Bohemia. Much of the brown coal is used in electricity generation; most electricity generated is still thermal, despite the presence of mountain streams for hydro-electric development (especially in Slovakia) and of uranium ore at Jáchymov in northern Bohemia, which could supply nuclear power. Soviet oil, piped to Bratislava, will provide another source of energy. Iron-ore is mined in the Slovenské Rudohorie (Slovakian Ore Mountains), and is mainly sent west for processing, though under the first Five-Year Plan of 1948-53, a big new plant was opened at Huko near Košice in order to work up the ores on the spot. Petroleum, raw cotton, fine wool, specialised mineral ores and chemical products, and tropical produce must necessarily be imported; the USSR has been an important supplier of many of these products since 1948.

Manufacturing industry remains remarkably concentrated in the west, especially in Bohemia and in northern Moravia (Czech Silesia). In the highland rim of Bohemia, a tradition of peasant crafts developed into highly specialised manufacturing industries in modern times. The products characteristically are of high value in relation to their bulk, a necessary feature in these upland regions. Pottery and glass (including optical glass, and jewellery), and textiles—originally based on water-power and local wool and flax— are the main industries.

The industrial tradition of these areas is very similar to that on the German side of the frontier, and indeed many of the skilled workers were German up to 1945. Since the war the glass and textile industries have been decentralised to a large extent, especially to Slovakia, and there have even been closures of textile mills in the old German areas. Timber resources are exploited for the paper and furniture industries, which are especially concentrated in Slovakia (where they are being developed) and northern Moravia. Important engineering industries are found in Czech Silesia on the north-western brown coalfield of Bohemia, in Plzeň (Škoda) and in the capital. These firms have been nationalised by the communists, a measure partly necessary because so many of them were formerly owned by the expelled German population. Today Czechoslovakia occupies an important place within the economic system of Eastern Europe, for (parts of the German Democratic Republic apart) it has the most developed tradition of specialised industrial skill of all the communist countries. Over two-thirds of the country's external trade is now with other communist lands of the eastern bloc. The USSR is the main trading partner, sending principally raw materials and receiving Czechoslovakia's specialised manufactures. Poland has an important place because she supplies much needed coal and electricity from the Silesian field.   The trade links within the eastern bloc will be much enhanced by the Oder–Danube canal link (now under construction) which will give the inland state of Czechoslovakia direct water links with the Baltic at Szczecin and with the Black Sea.

## REFERENCES

The standard work in English is H. G. Wanklyn, *Czechoslovakia*, London, G. Philip, 1954.   Also important, especially for economic development, is V. Bušek and N. Spulber (Eds.), *Czechoslovakia*, New York, Praeger, 1957. See also H. G. Wanklyn, *The Eastern Marchlands of Europe*, London, G. Philip, 1941.   J. Moscheles, 'Natural Regions of Czechoslovakia', *Geog. Review*, 14, 1924, still has value.   An important work in Czech is M. Blažek, *Hospodářska geografie Československa*, Praha, Státní Gedagogické Nakl., 1953; it has been translated into German as *Ökonomische Geographie der Tschechoslowakischen Republik*, Berlin, Verlag die Wirtschaft, 1959.   A firm practical foundation for the study of the Czech lands is provided by the *Atlas Republiky Československé (Atlas of the Czechoslovak Republic)*, Praha, 1936, with explanatory text in French and English.   See also the references on central Europe.

### CHAPTER 25

# THE ALPINE REGION

## GENERAL INTRODUCTION

THE Alpine arc is some 500 miles long and varies in width from 80 to 140 miles. It contains many peaks above 10,000 ft high and, in spite of the comparatively low latitude (from about 44° to 47° 30′ N), it carries the largest valley glaciers of the mainland of Europe. The greatest average height and the greatest number of high peaks are to be found in the central portion where the range is narrowest, particularly in Bern and Valais in Switzerland and the adjacent French Savoie, where Mt Blanc is 15,782 ft in height, while many peaks in the Zermatt and Bernese chains in Switzerland are between 13,000 and 15,000 ft, e.g. the Weisshorn, Dom, and Matterhorn in the former, and the Finsteraarhorn, Jungfrau, and Mönch in the latter.

**Structure.** It is now generally accepted that the Alps are for the most part built up of a number of *nappes* piled one on top of the other (see Chapter 1). It is considered from the *facies* of the rocks, i.e. their lithological character and their fossils, that the material forming the *nappes* was derived from sediments deposited in a great geosyncline occupied by an ancient sea. The upper sediments deposited during Mesozoic times seem to have undergone little metamorphism and now form mainly limestones – believed to have originated in both the northern and southern parts of the sea – or else slates and shales, believed to have originated in the central part of the sea. The older and more deep-seated rocks of Palæozoic age underwent pronounced metamorphism, presumably owing to great pressure, and became very crystalline, but together with much intrusive granite they all became involved in the vast system of earth waves raised by the violence of the earth storm of Mid-Tertiary times. Consequently each *nappe* consists—or consisted originally before denudation set to work—of an inner core of metamorphic crystalline rock and an outer envelope of little changed sedimentary rocks, the actual *facies* of which varies very much from place to place according to their original position in the geosyncline.

The main *nappes* recognised are four in number; the Helvetic being the lowest in position, followed by the Pennine, the Grisonid, and the Tirolid, the two last often grouped together as the Austrides, while a fourth division, the Dinarid, though it has overridden the Tirolides in places, in general represents an earth wave that toppled backwards, as it were, and its strata are recumbent towards the south. The position of massifs and *nappes* is shown in Fig. 54, p. 435. A vast amount of denudation has taken place in the lofty Alpine chain and in places entire *nappes* have been removed, so that it is only conjectured that the Tirolid *nappe* was once present in the western Alps, west of the Vorder Rhein, where, indeed, denudation has advanced so far that old Hercynian massifs have been partially exposed to the light of day. Such as, from south to north, the Mercantour, Pelvoux, Mt Blanc, and Aar massifs, which are composed principally of hard crystalline rock such as granite and gneiss. It is considered that in parts of the western Alps erosion has removed deposits nine miles thick, though this does not imply that the Alps were once nine miles higher, for material was often eroded at a pace equal to uplift. In the eastern Alps, on the contrary, denudation has proceeded less far, apparently because there the *nappes* were piled less high, and this in turn may have been due to the underlying Hercynian floor being generally lower than in the west. It must be remembered, however, that the Hercynian massifs themselves were raised bodily by the earth storm.

In consequence of their less intense denudation, the eastern Alps generally retain the Tirolid *nappe*, though erosion has laid bare the underlying Grisonid and Pennine *nappes* in the Hohe Tauern and Upper Engadine regions. The exposure of these inliers may be due to the presence, relatively near the surface, of ancient Hercynian massifs, which have arched up the *nappes*, but this is only conjectural. The southern part of the eastern Alps belongs to the Dinarides, which are not represented in the western Alps, but probably are buried beneath the alluvial deposits in the North Italian Plain. From the geological point of view there is thus a fundamental distinction between the eastern and western Alps, the dividing line roughly joining Lake Zürich and Lake Como.

It must not be supposed, however, that the *nappes* are merely simple slabs of the earth's surface. In their movements in regard to each other they themselves developed every kind of overfold and sheared recumbent fold, so that, having been acted upon by erosion, one outcrop succeeds another in great complexity.

One of the facts that emerges from a study of the Alps is the small amount of relation that their structure bears to relief. Only in the autochthonous outer folds of the French Alps is it possible to trace the relations between the folds and the present mountains and valleys. The arcuate shape of the Alps and the parallelism of the chains and longitudinal depressions are features common

to most of the young folded mountain areas of the world, and
the longitudinal valleys of the Alps do, to some extent, correspond

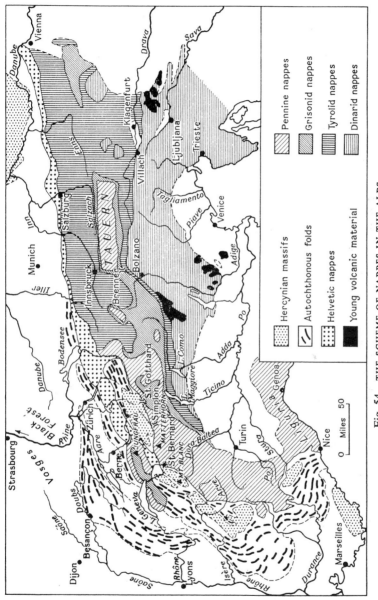

Fig. 54. THE SCHEME OF NAPPES IN THE ALPS

to lines of contact between the different *nappes* (as in the case of the Rhône valley above Martigny, the Inn valley below Innsbruck, and parts of the Salzach and Enns valleys), or to root zones, but the depressions show a disconcerting habit of passing from one zone to another. The reason why the transverse valleys, even the most important ones, such as the Adige and Reuss, are situated where they are is obscure. The relief, however, is related to the lithological character of the outcrop to some extent, and also to the later geological history of the region in late Tertiary and in Quaternary times.

**Quaternary Rejuvenation and Glaciation.** After the great paroxysm of folding which culminated in Miocene times, denudation reduced even the mighty Alps to a low range with mature rounded forms; in certain parts, indeed, peneplain features were copiously produced, particularly in the eastern Alps. The sea invaded the Vienna basin and the basins of Klagenfurt and Ljubljana in the east of the chain, and the Durance basin in the west. The Alps were saved as a mountain system only by a great new movement of re-elevation, but this time a vertical (epeirogenic) movement *en masse*, which was inaugurated at the close of Tertiary times and was largely responsible for the present great height.

This movement had already led to the rejuvenation of the river system and to an increased rate of erosion before the onset of the Ice Age, which was destined profoundly to modify the entire relief of the Alps. The whole of the Alps was covered by a great ice-sheet, with the exception of the south-eastern and south-western extremities, mainly in Steiermark, parts of Kärnten, and Provence. Only the higher peaks stood up above the level of the ice. The Pleistocene Period which included four periods of glaciation and three warmer and drier interglacial periods, produced many and various results. To glaciation must be attributed the sharp outlines to be found in the High Alps and the frequency of the horn or pyramid-shaped peaks, which were exposed to the fierce denudation of frost and ice as they stood above the snowfields. The valleys, also, which had begun to be incised owing to the epeirogenic movement, were filled with glaciers, whose pressure as they moved along scooped out the pre-existing main valleys and over-deepened them, leaving the typical flat-bottomed, steep-sided valleys known as 'U-shaped', e.g. Lauterbrunnen, upper Rhône, Vorder Rhein, and hundreds of others. The sides of the mountains beneath the peaks and above the main valleys were covered, on the other hand, with almost inert ice and were protected from both types of erosion, so that a shelf of gently rounded forms is usually to be found in this position, and the streams often tumble down from these shelves to the main valley by means of waterfalls. In the eastern Alps, especially on the outer borders where the mountains are lower, the higher parts more rarely rose above the snowfields and there are fewer sharply pointed peaks; on the contrary, the old peneplain surface can often be recognised at the top of steep-sided 'towers' or 'blocks' as in the Steinernes Meer south of the Königsee near Salzburg. Space forbids more than a brief mention of the Alpine cirques, the irregular profiles of the main valleys, and the numbers of small lakes, for whose origin the reader is referred to works on physical geography. The presence of the great lakes on the borders of the mountains is a distinctive feature of the Alps alone among the young folded mountains of Europe, although many similarly placed lakes are found in the Scandinavian highlands. Here in the Alps they usually occupy over-deepened U-shaped valleys and tongue basins, which are often blocked at the outward end by multiple accumulations of morainic material.

**Lithological Material.** The description of the main lithological zones of the Alps has been postponed until this point in the chapter in order to make clear that the present landforms are due more to the processes of peneplanation, rejuvenation, and glaciation than to the character of the rocks. For instance, though the high peaks are generally to be found in the crystalline zone, they are not confined to this belt, as the limestone giants of the Bernese Oberland testify, e.g. Eiger, Wetterhorn, Diablerets, etc., and even relatively unconsolidated deposits can form mountains of quite dignified dimensions, as in the case of the Tertiary conglomerates of the Rigi. Similarly, areas with rounded relief are to be found on all the formations.

Fig. 55 (p. 438) gives the main facts of the disposition of the rock zones. The interior zone, which consists mainly of highly crystalline rocks interspersed with bands of slates and shales, belongs to several *nappes*, including the Tirolid, Grisonid, and Pennine; mainly the Tirolid in the eastern Alps east of the Vorder Rhein and the Pennine in the western Alps. The old Hercynian masses also form part of this inner crystalline belt, and like the crystallines of the *nappes* are formed of highly resistant rocks, such as gneisses and granites which weather very slowly. In contrast to the crystalline rocks, which stand out as the main chains of the inner Alps, the slates and shales are much more easily eroded and the slopes are often milder than is usual for the High Alps, while excellent pastures are more than usually extensive, as in Canton Grisons (Switzerland) and the Kitzbühler Alps (Austria).

On the southern side of the crystalline zone in the eastern Alps is the southern limestone zone, belonging to the Dinarides. This thins out westwards and disappears altogether a little to the west of

Lake Maggiore.　Farther west the crystalline zone abuts directly
on the alluvium of the North Italian plain.

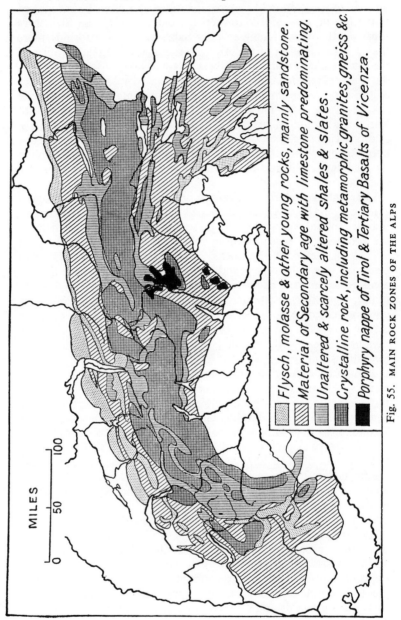

Fig. 55.　MAIN ROCK ZONES OF THE ALPS

Flysch, molasse & other young rocks, mainly sandstone.

Material of Secondary age with limestone predominating.

Unaltered & scarcely altered shales & slates.

Crystalline rock, including metamorphic granites, gneiss &c.

Porphyry nappe of Tirol & Tertiary Basalts of Vicenza.

MILES

0　　50　　100

A northern limestone zone lies on the northern side of the crystal-lines, but this is a very composite belt. In the eastern Alps of Bavaria and Austria the limestones belong to the Tirolid *nappe*; west of the River Arve in the French Alps the limestones do not belong to a *nappe* at all, and instead of being transported over long distances were folded more or less *in situ* and are therefore called autochthonous.

**Climate and Vegetation.** The Alps lie in two main climatic sub-divisions of Europe, the greater part falling within the region of central European climate and the southern part in the Mediterranean zone. The latter consequently is a region of summer dryness, while the mass of the range has precipitation all the year round, with a maximum in summer in the northern Alps, in autumn on the Italian side.

As in all mountain chains the climate varies very much according to the height and degree of exposure to the prevailing winds and to the sun. The slopes facing north are naturally colder than those facing south, and the wide valleys, which become veritable hot-houses in summer, yet suffer from a temperature inversion in winter and are colder than the slopes above. In winter, indeed, the region above 3,000 or 3,500 ft generally has a much more pleasant climate than the lower land, as it is above the level of maximum cloudiness and usually enjoys bright, sunny days with dry, still air, whereas the valleys may be filled with a chilly mist. In summer the cloud belt rises higher, owing to the greater warmth and consequent development of rising currents of air, and the lower valleys are sunnier than the higher regions, though the high peaks above 7,000 or 8,000 ft often rise above the clouds.

The precipitation is naturally heavier than that of the surrounding plains, but is not as high as that on much lower mountains in the Atlantic climatic region. The interior valleys in particular have a low precipitation, often less than 30 in, especially in Switzerland and Austria, hence the need for irrigation in many of the valleys. The outer ranges of the eastern Alps have copious precipitation, often exceeding 80 in, while the Venetian Alps deriving their rain from Mediterranean cyclones have twice that amount in places. The Alps of Savoy also have a heavy rainfall. The precipitation in winter usually falls in the form of snow, practically the whole range being snow-covered for at least three months in a normal winter, while the snow often lies for six months above about 6,000 ft. The lower limit of everlasting snow naturally varies with the latitude, with the exposure to the sun, with the amount of precipitation, as well as with altitude, and it comes down as low as 8,000 ft in the northern Swiss Alps and reaches as high as 10,500 ft in the drier central Alps. The lowest glacier (the Lower Grindelwald in the Bernese Alps) ends as low as 3,500 ft, but this is rather exceptional. Most of the glaciers are now in relatively rapid recession.

Owing to the great contrasts in temperature resulting from differences in altitude there are a great number of local winds. The *Föhn* wind is due, however, to differences of pressure between the Mediterranean basin and the plains of central Europe, and it blows when a marked cyclone is passing across Europe on the northern side of the Alps. It is usually described as a warm dry wind from the south and is a notorious 'eater of snow'. Hence it is welcome at the end of winter, but when the *Föhn* is roaring among the forest trees the sky is usually overcast and the rise of temperature from just below to just above freezing-point has the effect of making the atmosphere feel both damper and colder. Thus in mid-winter all welcome the end of the *Föhn* and the return to the typical winter climate with its warm, bright sunshine and calm air, even though the temperature *in the shade* is lower.

The vegetation of the Alps is naturally closely bound up with the climate. Where the central European climate prevails, magnificent summer pastures of grass (the true *alp*) are found below the snow line. Below these comes the zone of forests, whose upper limit is about 6,000 ft, but has often been lowered by man, while its lower limit is about 2,500 ft, though again it has been largely encroached upon. The forest generally remains both on the steeper and shadier slopes, and in spite of having suffered attack both from above and below, it is still the most extensive vegetation zone of the Alps. It is mainly composed of conifers, but includes deciduous trees near its lower margin.

In the Mediterranean Alps both grass and forests are more rarely found, and the prevailing vegetation consists of Mediterranean shrubs resistant to the summer drought. In regard to cultivated vegetation the Alps are a region principally of forage crops, used as food for dairy cattle, but in the broad longitudinal depressions, such as the valleys of the Isère and the Inn, maize is widely grown, and the vine also has a considerable place, being cultivated up to a height of about 2,600 ft on the sunny slopes. In the lower valleys of the Mediterranean Alps the olive is cultivated as well as the vine and other fruits, and on the higher slopes the pasture is utilised mainly by sheep, as it is generally not sufficiently rich for cattle.

**Alpine Routes.** The Alps with their sunny slopes and valleys provided a more favourable home for early man than the marshes and forests of northern Europe, and were well populated and the passes known and crossed in prehistoric times. In historic times the position of the Alps between Italy and the lands farther north led to their exploration by the Romans, and to the construction of roads connecting the homeland with the provinces across the mountain chains. This directed traffic on to a few lines of movement, such as the Mont Genèvre, Little St Bernard, Great St Bernard, and Brenner routes, which were used for centuries until the roads decayed with neglect in the Middle Ages, during which time hundreds of passes came into use again for the pack animals which transported the goods of the Mediterranean and the Orient to northern Europe. The construction of military routes by the rulers of Austria and Savoy in the eighteenth century, followed by Napoleon's military roads, of which the Simplon was the most noted, led once more to concentration on a few arteries of movement, a concentration intensified by the construction of the trans-Alpine railways, though the improvement of the motor car and the growing tourist traffic have led to the construction of a modern road network penetrating all the main valleys and utilising a considerable number of passes. A motor road has been tunnelled beneath the St Bernard pass to link Martigny (in Switzerland) with Aosta (in Italy), to which also another road, beneath Mount Blanc, has been tunnelled from Chamonix (in France). Other short tunnels for road transport and oil pipelines are planned.

In spite of their height and width, the Alps are a relatively open mountain range, mainly on account of their great longitudinal valleys. The transverse valleys also, such as the Ticino, Reuss, Adige, Dora Baltea, etc., provide most valuable lines of movement penetrating deeply into the mountains, but these are often obstructed by gorges, which baffled the early travellers, so that many of the apparently direct routes were not used until the late Middle Ages or early modern times. For instance, the St Gotthard route came into use in the thirteenth century following the building of a bridge across the Schöllenen Gorge which the Reuss has cut through the granites of the Aar Massif. Similarly, the direct route to the Brenner Pass by the Adige-Isarco valley was not used until the fourteenth century, owing to the obstacle of the Isarco defile through the porphyry plateau from Klausen (It., Chiusa = 'gorge') southwards. The Simplon was not much used until Napoleon's road was built across it.

The modern railways generally follow the most important of the old roads, partly because they utilise the same ways of approach to the main passes, and partly because the old roads selected out of the many possible routes those which afforded the shortest path between the goals of movement. It is fairly easy to cross the Alps by circuitous routes if time is no object, but good direct routes are few and far between. Most of the railway routes solve the difficulty by means of tunnels, which though difficult and costly in construction, enable the traveller to cross the western or central Alps in a little over two hours. The first of these great Alpine tunnels, the Mont Cenis, opened to traffic in 1871, is 7½ miles long, occupied fifteen years in construction, and linked Genoa and Turin with Lyons, Paris, and ultimately London. The valleys leading up to it are the Dora Riparia on the Italian side and the Isère-Arc on the French. Farther towards the east, the next two trans-Alpine railway routes, the Simplon and the St Gotthard, both traverse Switzerland and unite at Milan on the Italian side. The Simplon tunnel, 12 miles long, built a quarter of a century later than the Mt Cenis, took only eight years in construction as the result of the increase in experience during that interval. On the Italian side the tunnel is approached along the Toce valley, but on the Swiss side the route debouches on the longitudinal furrow of the upper Rhône – along which the railway continues westward to Lake Geneva and Paris – and another tunnel, the Lötschberg, had to be constructed (in 1912) in order to pierce the Bernese Alps and connect up with the Swiss plateau. The Lötschberg–Simplon line is widely used by English travellers coming from the Channel ports by the new route which traverses Champagne and avoids the détour via Paris. The St Gotthard route, which culminates in a tunnel 9¼ miles long, utilises the Ticino valley on the Italian side and the Reuss valley on the Swiss, and is the main route linking Genoa and Milan with Zürich and western Germany, and is also much used by traffic from England, Belgium, and Holland. Both the Lötschberg–Simplon and the St Gotthard routes serve much the same area and emphasise the importance of this line of movement. The St Gotthard had the initial advantage over the Lötschberg–Simplon in having only one mountain chain to cross and therefore needing only one main tunnel. The Brenner route connects the eastern part of the north Italian plain with central Germany. The approach valley of Adige–Isarco on the Italian side gives a direct south–north route for three-quarters of the way across the Alpine range, but on the northern or Austrian side the route leads down into the longitudinal valley of the Inn at Innsbruck, and further chains have to be tunnelled before the railway emerges on to the Alpine Foreland of Germany. The Brenner Pass is only 4,495 ft high and no long tunnel was necessary.

East of the Brenner the Alps are lower but broader and more complex, and routes tend to be more circuitous. Moreover, the main direction of movement, between Vienna and the head of the Adriatic, is oblique, and longitudinal valleys are considerably utilised, particularly the Mur–Mürz leading up to the Semmering

Pass, but there are several other important routes, like that utilising the Klagenfurt depression to the Venetian plain.

International expresses also use the composite longitudinal depression between Lake Constance (Bodensee) and Vienna, following the Inn, Salzach, Enns, and other valleys, though the trains are slow judged by English standards. Mountain railways are plentiful, especially in Switzerland, and carry tourists high up the mountains.

The main advantage which the railways possess over the roads in the Alps, at least, for trans-Alpine travel, is their greater freedom from obstruction by snow, so that the main lines and even most of the branch mountain lines are open all the year round, whereas the roads are apt to become impassable in winter; in fact, very few of the road passes are practicable from November to May or June, and the autobus services do not run.

**Industries in the Alps.** The main industries are those of forestry and dairying in the greater part of the range, and sheep rearing in the southern zone with a Mediterranean climate. The tourist industry is also of great importance in certain areas, particularly in Switzerland, and still newer is the hydro-electrical industry utilising the great water-power of the Alpine torrents. Manufactures utilising this power are increasing (see Chapters 26 and 27 on Switzerland and Austria respectively).

## REFERENCES

E. de Martonne, *Les Alpes*, Paris, 1926, gives an excellent short account from the geographic point of view. On structure the following may be noted, though they are intended for the geological rather than the geographical student: L. W. Collett, *The Structure of the Alps*, London, 1927, deals mainly with the central Alps in Switzerland and France. F. Heritsch, *The Nappe Theory in the Alps*, trans. P. G. H. Boswell, London, 1929, gives an impartial account of the various theories of structure. L. Kober, *Bau und Entstehung der Alpen*, Berlin, 1923, and R. Staub, *Bau der Alpen*, Bern, 1924, are classic geological works. On glaciation, A. Penck and E. Brückner, *Die Alpen in Eiszeitalter*, 3 vols., 1901–9, is the classic work. E. Bailey, *Tectonic Essays, mainly Alpine*, Oxford, 1939.

R. Blanchard, *Les Alpes Occidentales*, Vol. 5: *Les Grandes Alpes françaises du Sud*. Parts I and II, Grenoble, 1949–50; Vol. 6: *Le Versant piemontais*, Part I, Grenoble, 1952.

More modern works which may be studied are J. Cadish, *Geologie der Schweizer Alpen*, Basel, Beer, 1953; and the study by J. H. F. Umbgrove in *Symphony of the Earth*, The Hague Nijhoff, 1950, Chapter 3, 'Across the Swiss Alps'.

### CHAPTER 26

# SWITZERLAND

WITH an area of 15,900 square miles Switzerland is one of the smallest and most mountainous countries of Europe, with 60 per cent of its surface lying in the Alps and 11 per cent in the Jura Mountains. More than half the population is to be found in the plateau lying between these two mountainous zones, though 'plateau' is rather a misnomer, as the Tertiary sandstones, conglomerates, and marls (*Molasse*) of which it is composed are so dissected that in many places it appears to be only a succession of hills.

**The Swiss Plateau.** This stretches from Lake Geneva (Lac Léman) north-eastwards to Lake Constance (Bodensee), with a length of 180 miles and a maximum breadth of only 30 miles. Not only was it dissected by rivers, but it was afterwards covered entirely by a great ice-sheet formed by the fusion of the great Alpine glaciers at the time of maximum glaciation, though the last glaciation produced only valley glaciers in this area. The various phenomena resulting from the glaciation of a more or less lowland region are present here in great variety, namely disturbances of the river systems, deposition of ground moraines and formation of drumlins, deposition of coarser material from the terminal and lateral moraines which now often form hills, and deepening and broadening of the valley floors. The Swiss plateau, therefore, shows an alternation of flat-bottomed valleys, often rather wide, with somewhat steep-sided hills which tend to flatten out on top, though the unevenly deposited morainic material with its apparently haphazard distribution disturbs the general scheme. The plateau as a whole varies in height from some 4,600 ft near the Alpine border to some 1,300 ft at the foot of the Jura, and the difference in height between the valleys and summits varies from about a thousand feet on the south-eastern border to a hundred or so on the northern.

The Swiss plateau has the advantage over the neighbouring Alps and Jura in the greater ease of movement, the lower altitude and warmer summers; in consequence, two-thirds of the Swiss towns of over 10,000 inhabitants are sited on the plateau. The plateau carries routes south-westwards via the Rhône valley to the Saône–Rhône depression in France, northwards to the Rhine rift valley, and north-eastwards to the German part of the Alpine Foreland.

In itself the plateau is a region of intensive agriculture, for though the winters are cold, cloudy, and often foggy, the summers are warm and rainy and provide ideal climatic conditions for artificial meadows and the production of forage crops, as many as six mowings being sometimes possible in the year. Contrary to general belief, it is the plateau and not the Alpine or Jura zones which carries the greatest number of dairy cattle in Switzerland, though the cattle are mainly stall-fed and are seldom visible on the land, except in September, when they are turned out on to the mown fields. This great concentration on dairying is fairly recent. Before the era of cheap imported grain the Swiss plateau necessarily grew its own cereals, but their area is now much reduced. Other crops such as sugar-beet and tobacco are also grown, especially in the south-western part of the plateau. The vine is grown, mainly on the sunny slopes north of Lake Geneva and north-west of Lake Neuchâtel. Orchard trees are to be found planted along the roads in this land where no space is wasted on hedges. Where the hill slopes are too steep for cultivation they have been retained under forest, originally mainly deciduous, but generally replaced by conifers.

Considerable but scattered manufactures are to be found over the plateau, mainly using hydro-electricity as power. The manufacture of cheese is widespread, that of Swiss condensed milk and chocolate somewhat more localised. The textile industry is mainly in the north of the plateau: Zürich is the centre of the silk industry established there in the sixteenth century by Italian refugees, and St Gallen has a cotton textile and embroidery industry, which developed on the basis of an old hand-industry and received a fresh impetus from French refugees in the eighteenth century. The manufacture of machine-tools and of many types of machinery (textile, hydro-electric, etc.) is carried on in the north of the plateau and at Geneva. Since the industries are not usually dependent upon coal, they tend to be much scattered throughout the countryside (cf. Sweden).

The plateau also has its share of the tourist industry, particularly in the regions bordering Lake Geneva and Lake Lucerne, (Ger., Vierwaldstätter See).

Of the towns of the plateau, Zürich (440,170),[1] on the lake of the same name, is the largest, and possesses a very varied industry, including heavy engineering products, armaments, machine tools, textile machinery, cotton, and leather. It is also a very important commercial and intellectual centre, with the largest of Switzerland's seven universities. Geneva (176,180), at the western end of Lake Geneva, and formerly capital of the Calvinist state of the same name,

[1] Population figures are from the 1960 census.

is the largest town of the French-speaking part of Switzerland. A banking centre and a university town, it has watch-making and luxury industries. It became the seat of the League of Nations and is still the headquarters of many international bodies such as the Red Cross and International Labour Office. Bern (163,170), almost surrounded by a great incised meander of the River Aare, is the federal capital, a university town, and manufactures watches and textiles. Only three other plateau towns have more than 50,000 inhabitants; Lausanne (126,330), mainly a tourist centre, also has alimentary industries (chocolate, brewing, etc.); St Gallen (76,280) is noted for its embroideries, and Winterthur (80,350) manufactures machinery and textiles. The population tends to be scattered in small towns and villages, but attains a density of over 400 per square mile in many cantons (see Fig. 56).

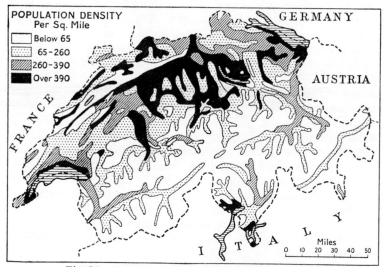

Fig. 56. SWITZERLAND: POPULATION DENSITIES

**The Jura.** The structure of the Jura has already been described (p. 272). Switzerland possesses the south-eastern folded portion with many parallel ridges and valleys. The range becomes lower and narrower towards the north-east, and, where it extends between Basel (Fr., Bâle, Engl., Basle) and the plateau, forms a comparatively slight obstacle. There is comparatively little arable farming in the Jura except for vine growing on the south-eastward facing outer slopes overlooking the plateau. The main rural occupations are associated with livestock and forestry. The fairly dense population of the valleys is associated not with any richness of the soil but with the development of industry associated with hydro-electric power.

The Jura is a barrier to communications. Only in three places do the rivers break entirely through it – the Rhône below Geneva, the Aare below Brugg, and the Rhine near Schaffhausen. The Biel–Basel railway route has needed relatively little tunnelling but the route is roundabout and the gradients are steep. However the importance of access to Basel and the Rhine has resulted in the construction of three tunnels through the Jura linking Basel to the Aare valley; these are the Bötzberg and Upper and Lower Hauenstein tunnels.

Basel (206,750) is the chief town of the area and the second city of Switzerland. Its position on the Rhine and virtually on the frontier with France and Germany has made it an important route and defence point since Roman times. Today it is a great railway junction, whence routes fan out all over Switzerland. Amongst its industries may be noted pharmaceutical chemicals, for which it has international importance, textiles (especially ribbons), and food processing, many of the industries relying upon the Rhine for the import of their raw materials. As one would expect, the tonnage movement of goods downstream is very small compared with the movement of goods up to Basel.

**The Swiss Alps.** The main lines of structure have already been described. Switzerland possesses a segment of the central part of the Alps where they are highest and narrowest, and in one place reaches across the whole width of the range to touch the North Italian Plain south of Lake Lugano. The main industries are forestry and dairying, transhumance of the livestock to the high summer pastures (*Sömmerung*) being widely practised. In some places milk pipelines are used to carry the milk from the summer pastures to the valley dairies, a great saving in labour, and labour is becoming increasingly scarce for agricultural work. The textile industry of St Gallen also extends into the Alpine zone. To these occupations has been added during the last eighty years or so the great tourist industry. This developed originally owing to the magnificent scenery of the Swiss Alps and their nearness to those countries of Europe whose inhabitants had money to spend on such holidays, and it has been fostered in every possible way by the provision of good hotels, roads and railways, and so on.

**The Swiss State and People.** Although possessing a total population of only just over 5½ million, Switzerland recognises four official languages. Various dialects of German are spoken by 74 per cent of the Swiss people, French by 20 per cent, mainly in the southwest, and Italian by 4 per cent, mainly in Canton Tessin. In addition, other languages descended from Latin are spoken in the Alps, particularly Romansch, which was recognised as the fourth official language in 1937, though it is spoken by only 1 per cent of the population. This recognition of the rights of people to speak their own language is in accord with the large amount of autonomy possessed by the separate provinces or cantons, and this dates back to the thirteenth century, when the four cantons round Lake Lucerne organised themselves into the Swiss Confederation on federal and democratic lines.

The considerable importance of Switzerland at the present day, in spite of its small size, is largely due to the remarkable exploitation by the Swiss of the advantages of their geographical position and resources, and to their armed neutrality, which they have maintained since 1815. The favourable position as a passage land across the Alps was early realised by the original cantons of the Swiss Confederation which lay athwart the St Gotthard route, while the development of the tourist industry on an unsurpassed scale is one of the latest examples of the grasp by the Swiss of the advantages of their situation and scenic resources. Their consistent neutrality, combined with their policy of asylum to the persecuted of other lands, led to the influx of many refugees, who brought with them various crafts, such as silk weaving, fine watch-making, hitherto not practised in the country, and also large amounts of capital. Also the democratic nature of the country, with an absence of landed aristocracy, meant that capital was not locked up in 'country seats' but was free for further investment in industry. Switzerland indeed offers many points of contrast with its neighbour Austria, which began also as a small country of the mountains, but expanded over wide areas eastward, only to be reduced once more to an Alpine state in 1919.

**Economic Summary.** The productive area in Switzerland covers 76 per cent of the country, of which 22 per cent is forested, 42 per cent grassland and 12 per cent arable. Agriculture is less important than formerly and employs less than a sixth of the occupied population. Just over half the working population is employed in industry and the remaining quarter in commerce, transport, professions and the hotel and catering industry. The principal industry is metallurgy and engineering employing 260,000, the textile industry 68,000, watch-making and jewellery 64,000, chemicals 35,000, and the hotel industry 43,000. A very large proportion of the total potential hydro-electric power resource is now harnessed; unlike Norway, Switzerland has not had the same development of electrochemical and electrometallurgical industries. Small amounts of coal and growing quantities of oil (increasingly by pipeline) have to be imported.

60 View over Berne. The Swiss capital situated in the heart of the plateau is almost completely surrounded by mountains which can be seen in the distance. Note the undulating nature of the plateau. The River Aare can be seen in the foreground and part of the Bernese Oberland in the distance.

61 View of Lake Brienz in the Bernese Oberland. Notice the string of settlements along the lakeside road and on the lower mountain sides. The tree line can be discerned as well as the clusters of farms on the lower mountain slopes.

62 The Lauterbrunnental: an impressive U-shaped valley in the Bernese Alps, with the village of Wengen and a lower drift- and fan-covered floor. Forested lower Alps with some meadow land and high peaks – Silberhorn, Grosshorn, Breithorn. The Staubbach Waterfall (right, centre) descends for 300 metres vertically from a hanging valley.

63 Vienna. This picture is taken from the Great Belvedere Palace. Notice the rim of hills which almost enclose the city.

64 Tirol. Grass is mown for hay on the Alp or shoulder above the glaciated valley but the steep valley sides remain in forest while the mountain slopes above carry little vegetation.

65 Kärnten (Carinthia): a glacial valley lake. Kärnten lies wholly within the high Alpine region, near the southern frontier of Austria. Note the limited amount of cleared land.

AUSTRIA

The combination of mountain and lake scenery, possibilities for winter sports, easy accessibility for many parts of Europe by the many passes and rail and now road tunnels, and the hospitable nature of the Swiss have led to the development of a considerable tourist industry. About 5 million foreigners visit the country each year and the money they spend provides not only a direct income for the hoteliers and *restaurateurs* but also makes an important contribution to the national wealth. The income from this invisible export helps to adjust an otherwise unfavourable trade balance since other exports are less than imports.

In spite of being a completely landlocked state Switzerland has possessed since 1940 an ocean-going mercantile marine (97,000 tons) and makes considerable use also of the Rhine waterway (cf. p. 356). The usefulness of this river will increase once the current improvements between Cologne and Basel are completed and the planned improvements between Basel and Bodensee undertaken. One day, too, Switzerland may be linked to the Mediterranean by the oft-mooted French scheme for a Rhine–Rhône deep canal via the Swiss plateau and lakes.

Imports include cereals, raw materials for the textile and engineering industries, metals, textiles, chemicals, including fertilisers, coal and increasing amounts of oil. The exports include a variety of textile goods chiefly silk and artificial silk, and embroideries, clocks, watches, jewellery, scientific instruments, precision instruments and dairy produce, especially condensed milk and cheese, and confectionery.

In order to be able to maintain her high standard of living Switzerland depends very much on imported raw materials, the export of manufactured goods and the tourist trade. These can only flourish in a peaceful and stable Europe where trade is unhindered. For this reason, and also because of her wish to maintain strict (but armed) neutrality, Switzerland has been reluctant to associate herself with the Common Market; her desire for freer trade has however made her a staunch supporter of GATT (General Agreement of Tariffs and Trade) and EFTA (European Free Trade Association).

### REFERENCES

*Dictionnaire Géographique de la Suisse*, 6 vols. and atlas, Neuchâtel, 1902–10, was for long the standard work. The monumental work is *Geographie der Schweiz*, by J. Früh, in 3 volumes, with a separate index volume (1930–46); a French translation is available; these deal thoroughly with every aspect of Swiss geography. P. Vossaler, *Die Landschaften der Schweiz*, Bern, 1928, is accompanied by a portfolio of 20 topographic maps, mainly composite sheets from official sources, which illustrate typical aspects of Swiss topography. See also A. F. A. Mutton, *Central Europe*, New York, Praeger, 1968, and 'Hydroelectric Power in Western Europe', *Geog. Journal,* 1951, and G. J. Fuller, 'The Trient Valley', *Geography,* 1955.

### CHAPTER 27

# AUSTRIA

THE break-up of the Habsburg dominions in 1918 reduced Austria from an Empire of 116,000 square miles excluding the Hungarian possessions to a small mountainous country of some 32,000 square miles. As the reduced population was almost wholly German-speaking, it would have been scarcely surprising if the country had turned for support to the German *Reich*, but political union was forbidden by the Allied Powers, and an economic union proposed in 1931 was declared illegal by the Court of International Justice. Eventually, in 1938, Austria was forcibly annexed by Nazi Germany and renamed the Ostmark. In 1955 the division of the territory of Austria into four zones of military occupation was terminated after ten years; the peace treaty established a neutral status for Austria as between the eastern and western blocs.

Austria is a typical Alpine area, though it includes a narrow strip of the Hungarian or Pannonian plain on the east, the Danube valley below Passau almost to Bratislava (Ger., Pressburg) in Slovakia, and a small part of the Böhmer (Bohemian) massif on the north.

The country is twice as large as Switzerland, but its population of 6¾ million is only a third greater. The Austrian Alps spread themselves more widely than the Swiss Alps, but are lower and their great valleys are longer and wider and so the range is more easily penetrated.

**Vorarlberg and Tirol.** The northern outer bands of Flysch and limestone lie inside Germany, from the Bodensee (Lake Constance) to the Königssee south of Salzburg, and the Austrian provinces of Vorarlberg and Tirol are situated south of this outer strip. In the west the Vorarlberg touches the eastern end of the Bodensee, which forms the frontier of three countries. The frontier also adjoins Switzerland for a short distance along the Vorder Rhein, and touches the tiny independent state of Liechtenstein farther south. The southern part of the Vorarlberg includes part of the central crystalline zone, the Arlberg railway line running approximately along the line of junction between the limestone and crystalline rocks from Bludenz to Landeck on the Inn. Vorarlberg is closely linked economically with Switzerland, the embroidery industry having spread here from

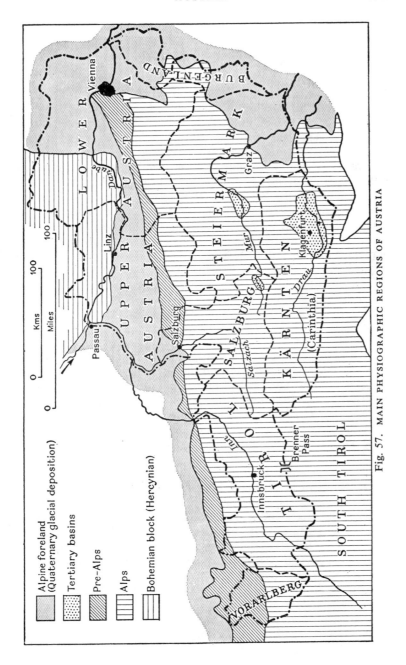

Fig. 57. MAIN PHYSIOGRAPHIC REGIONS OF AUSTRIA

Alpine foreland
(Quaternary glacial deposition)

Tertiary basins

Pre-Alps

Alps

Bohemian block (Hercynian)

St Gallen. The Tirol similarly consists of a northern limestone band and a southern crystalline band, both with many peaks, the Inn valley from Landeck to Innsbruck marking the line of junction in the west, but east of Innsbruck a broad belt of slates and shales (*Bündnerschiefer*) interposes between the limestone and crystalline belts, and the Inn as far as Wörgl follows the northern side of the slate zone and the southern side of the limestone belt. The longitudinal valley of the Inn between Landeck and Wörgl forms the heart of the Tirol. The valley averages about a mile wide, the river itself being usually incised; the broad terraces are very intensively cultivated, maize being one of the leading crops. Innsbruck (100,700),[1] the largest town in the interior of the Alps, grew up at the point where the Sill valley (Wipptal), leading down from the Brenner Pass, reaches the wide Inn valley. The old bridge over the Inn, from which the town takes its name, allowed traffic going northwards to München, Augsburg, etc., to use one of the short routes across the outer limestone zone instead of following the Inn valley towards the north-east. The town is now a regional capital and tourist centre. The part of the Tirol south of the Brenner Pass (Süd-Tirol) was lost by Austria to Italy in 1918, even though in the north it contained nearly a quarter of a million German-speaking people. In 1939, the majority of the remaining Germans opted for a return to Germany, which included Austria at that date. The Paris Agreement of 1946 between Austria and Italy provided for a considerable measure of autonomy for the German-speaking population. Since 1948 the region (which the Italians call Bolzano) has formed part of the administrative province of Trentino–Alto Adige; the 1961 population of the region was 89,070. It still contains a powerful and vocal German-speaking population, who have claimed that their rights have not been respected. In 1961 the dispute was referred to the United Nations but no definite resolution had been achieved by Autumn 1963.

**The Northern Sedimentary Zone from Salzburg to Vienna.** The outer Flysch zone reaches from Salzburg as far as the Wiener Wald ('Vienna Woods'), and its rounded hills and mountains are mainly devoted to pasture. The Flysch zone, however, is very narrow here, and the limestone zone which succeeds it on the south almost reaches the outer border of the mountains, and varies from forested mountains in the lower northern region to high, barren karstic plateaus in the inner and higher parts, e.g. Totes Gebirge, Steinernes Meer. This outer zone with its numerous lakes is well known to tourists, and so is the border town of Salzburg, which derived its name and wealth from the neighbouring salt mines of Hallein

[1] All population figures are resident populations at the 1961 census.

on the Germano-Austrian frontier. These important mines are still actively worked. Salzburg itself, with its castles, palaces, and gardens of the former archbishops, its musical festival and associations with Mozart, remains a city (108,100) of great charm.

South of the limestone zone a broad belt of slates and shales interposes in two places between the limestone and the crystalline zones. In the west the slates are continued from the Tirol and extend north of the Pinzgau, the longitudinal stretch of the Salzach, which marks their junction with the interior crystalline zone. East of the Pinzgau the slate strip is missing, so that the crystalline mountains of the Niedere Tauern abut on the limestone belt, until the slates once more appear north of the Mürz in the Eisenerz Alps, noted for their rich iron deposits, from which comes the greater part of the considerable amount of iron-ore produced annually in Austria. The slate-shale mountains are generally lower than the zones to north and south and give rise to softer forms and better pasture.

**The Interior Crystalline Zone.** The glaciated peaks of the Hohe Tauern generally rise above 10,000 ft but farther eastwards in the Noric Alps of Kärnten and Steiermark, where the heights do not generally exceed 6,000 ft, the ice-sheet seems to have been absent or only very patchy, and rounded forms reminiscent of the Carpathians are the rule and are often farmed up to their lower summits. The Mur–Mürz depression opens a way from the Hungarian basin well into the eastern Alps, the Mur penetrating deeply into the crystalline zone. Brown coal is found in these valleys. The town of Graz (237,100), situated where the Mur emerges from the Alps, is the regional capital for this Styrian (Steiermark) part of the Alps and for the productive foothills which border the lower valley of the Mur. This charmingly situated town[1] has become also an industrial centre, using mainly the iron-ore of Eisenerz and the brown coals of the Mur–Mürz depression in its metallurgical industry, and manufacturing also paper and textiles. It is the second largest town of the country.

On the southern side of the crystalline zone is the southern sedimentary belt, the Drau valley west of Villach marking the line of junction. The Klagenfurt depression east of Villach is one of the largest of the Tertiary-filled basins which form a marked feature of the south-eastern Alps. The basin is highly cultivated, cereals, vineyards, and orchards flourishing in the summer heat in addition to the usual forage crops and meadows. The limestone Karawanken Alps on the south of the basin form the present frontier of

[1] "La ville des Graces sur la rivière l'Amour", according to the French saying.

Kärnten (Carinthia), the southern part of Kärnten having been lost partly to Yugoslavia and partly to Italy in 1920.

**The Danubian Lands of Austria.** East of the old frontier town of Passau the Danube hugs the southern edge of the Bohemian crystalline plateau as far as Krems; indeed, in places denudation has removed the overlying Tertiary sands and gravels of the Alpine foreland to such an extent that the underlying hard old rocks sometimes appear even on the south side of the river, which therefore flows through an alternation of basins and narrows. The Danube valley in the stretch between Linz and Krems, i.e. the Wachau, is noted for its unspoiled beauty, and the river is here a wide, swiftly moving stream, whose speed can be realised from the fact that the tourist steamers take only seven and a half hours downstream between Linz and Vienna but seventeen hours upstream. In winter the river is often frozen and in spring the broken ice-floes sometimes get jammed and cause severe floods, hence the low-lying land bordering the river is usually avoided by homesteads and devoted to water meadows.

South of the Danube and north of the Alps the Alpine Foreland is continued from Germany where it is more widely developed. It narrows eastwards to a strip only about 6 miles wide east of the River Enns. In general, the Foreland consists of hilly country of Tertiary sands and conglomerates. The higher parts (Hausruck, 2,600 ft) are forested, the lower parts mainly devoted to grass and forage crops and stock rearing. Linz (196,000), on the Danube, is an old bridge town with considerable nodality, the Danubian route being crossed here by north and south routes from the Alps and the Bohemian plateau. North of the Danube between the German frontier and Krems is the Waldviertel (='forest quarter') on the southern extension of the Bohemian plateau. This is now largely cleared and devoted to pasture or to crops such as rye and potatoes, which tolerate both the poor soil derived from the granite and gneisses and the rather bleak climate, the area being some 1,300 to 2,300 ft above sea-level.

East of a line joining Krems to Znojmo (Znaim) on the River Thaya the old crystalline rocks sink under a mantle of Tertiaries, themselves usually covered by *Löss*. Here the fertile soil and lower altitude give possibilities for rich cultures, including the vine, which has given the name of Weinviertel to this region. The Weinviertel is continued northwards across the frontier by the plain of Moravia, and south-eastwards it merges into the Vienna basin.

**The Vienna Basin** lies on both sides of the Danube for some 60 miles from north-east to south-west, but is only about a third of that width across. The part north of the Danube is usually called the Marchfeld. The whole basin represents an area of sinking in which Tertiary sediments were deposited. It provides an area of lowland between the main ranges of the Alps and Carpathians, but is itself limited on the east by hills and mountains considered to be spurs of these ranges, namely, the Leithagebirge south of the Danube and the Little Carpathians north of that river. The Leithagebirge, though nowhere reaching more than 1,600 ft high and crossed by several railway lines, formed the frontier against the Hungarian plain, but the post-1918 addition of the German-speaking communities of the Burgenland in the western part of the Pannonian depression caused the frontier to be moved some twenty miles eastwards. The Tertiaries of the Vienna basin are mainly concealed beneath fertile *Löss* and river alluvium, and the area is highly cultivated, especially for forage crops and market gardening which supply the capital city. Well-known wines are produced round the hilly margins. The lowland is encircled by a chaplet of small towns, many of which have considerable industries, such as furniture making, brewing, and textile manufacture; while the metallurgical industry (locomotives, agricultural machinery, airplanes) has become increasingly important since 1919. Wiener Neustadt (33,800) is the largest of these small centres. A valuable oilfield was discovered in the Vienna basin during the 1930s, and has since been in active exploitation.

The position of the basin is so important that a large city was almost bound to arise somewhere within it. In this neighbourhood the great natural line of movement from east to west, i.e. from the Hungarian basin along the Danube valley between the Alps and the Bohemian plateau, is met not only by routes coming from the north, namely, from the Moravian Gate and from the upper Elbe, but also by routes coming from the south along the eastern edge of the Alps.

The actual site of Vienna (Ger., Wien) is at the foot of the Flysch hills of the Wiener Wald on a river terrace just above the Danubian floods. The city takes its name from the little River Wien, a feeder of the Danube, and the old nucleus of the town kept a discreet distance from the main stream, which is here a braided river, though it bordered a small western arm, now known as the Danube canal. In spite of works of regulation, very little building has taken place on the east bank of the main river, which is still liable to floods.

For several centuries Vienna filled the rôle of the most advanced bulwark of western civilisation against intrusion from the east, and continued to grow as the power of its rulers, the Habsburgs, extended eastwards and northwards. Its present large size (1939, 1,930,000; 1961, 1,627,600) dates from the time when it was the capital of a great empire, of 242,000 square miles and 50 million people. Before the war of 1914-18 it was the administrative and intellectual centre of the Austro-Hungarian Empire, as well as the commercial, banking, cultural, and recreational centre of a good deal of south-eastern Europe. It was also, with its satellite towns, the most important manufacturing centre of Austria proper. To a considerable extent it began to function again after 1918 as a centre for a wide area, especially commercially, on account of its long-established traditions and experience, its central position, and its widely known language, and because of the need for such a centre in this much divided part of Europe. As regards industry, Vienna possesses manufactures very similar to those of Paris, and specialises in the manufacture of fashionable clothes, fine furniture, pianos, and luxury articles noted for their good taste and elegance. Naturally these industries suffered from the second world war and its aftermath; for the border of communist Europe is less than forty miles to the east, and trade and cultural contacts are minimal. But there are now thriving engineering, vehicle, textiles, and glass industries. The old traditions of the city as a home of the arts, especially music, continue to attract many tourists.

**Economic Summary.** Austria presents an extremely sharp contrast between the capital city, which dominates the country, and contains close to a quarter of its population, and the provinces. Outside the capital Austria is overwhelmingly rural; the provincial towns, even Graz and Innsbruck, are small enough for the surrounding mountains to dominate the scene. The countryside is less well developed than the corresponding zones of Switzerland; over most of the country, the farm population is crowded on too small an area of land, holdings are very small and methods very backward. Austria has a much greater proportion both of forest and of arable land than Switzerland: in 1961 forest covered 38 per cent of the area, grass (including Alpine pasture) 28 per cent and arable land (including special crops) 21 per cent of the total area. The arable land is concentrated around the capital and in the Burgenland along the Hungarian frontier; very little is found in the Alpine provinces. Despite the general backwardness agricultural production developed to such an extent after World War II that Austria's dependence on outside food supplies has steadily diminished. By 1961 she produced enough to cover 89 per cent of her needs in bread grains, 100 per cent in potatoes, 92 per cent in vegetables and fruit, more than 100 per cent in beef, 96 per cent in veal and pork.

The high proportion of forest – mainly coniferous – gives Austria valuable timber resources. She is also better off than Switzerland in mineral resources, with considerable surpluses of iron and salt.

Important iron-ore sources in the Steiermark produced 3·5 million tons of iron-ore in 1961. There are large manganese deposits which are worked in the Steiermark, in the Carpathians and the Tirol. The capital depends on imported coal (bituminous coal resources are very limited) but some 5·7 million tons of brown coal were produced in 1961, about half from the Steiermark. An oilfield has been developed since 1938 in eastern Austria at Zistersdorf; 2·3 million tons of oil and 1·6 million cubic metres of natural gas were produced in 1961. The hydro-electric potentialities of the Alpine environment are much the same as in Switzerland; hydro-power accounted for 10·7 million kWh out of a total of 13·6 million kWh produced outside private industrial plants in 1961.

Thanks to iron-ore Austria has created a notable heavy industrial region in the Steiermark, around Leoben and Bruck on the Mur, and latterly on the Danube at Linz. Coal is necessarily imported: it comes from the Ruhr and Silesia. Linz also makes heavy chemicals. Apart from the traditional luxury industries of the capital, which suffered as a result of the war, there is little developed tradition of skilled light industry in the provinces, such as occurs in the highland zones of Germany and Czechoslovakia.

One of Austria's best economic prospects is the further development of the tourist trade, which has expanded so fast in western Europe since 1950. The small, picturesque towns prove a great attraction in summer, while in winter the same towns may flourish as ski resorts. The trade has developed more slowly than that of Switzerland, though in the summer half-year 1961 6·1 million staying guests and 36·8 million overnight stays were recorded; in the winter half-year 1961–2 the corresponding figures were 2·3 million and 12·0 million. The tourist trade should prove a special help in supplementing the farm incomes of the remoter, poorer agricultural areas.

## REFERENCES

For works in English see the references to central Europe. On postwar economic developments, note G. Kiss, 'TVA on the Danube?', *Geog. Review*, 37, 1947, 274–302; A. F. A. Mutton, 'The Glockner–Kaprun Hydro-electric Project, Hohe Tauern, Austria', *Geog. Review*, 41, 1951, 332–4; R. Cole, 'The Hydro-electric Power in the Glockner–Kaprun Area of Austria', *Geography*, 38, 1953, 93–100; A. F. A. Mutton, 'Carinthia, A Province of Austria's Southern Frontier', *Geography*, 38, 1953, 83–94. The standard work in German remains N. Krebs, *Die Ostalpen und das heutige Österreich*, 2nd ed., Stuttgart, Engelhorn, 2 vols., 1928; the same author contributed a short but valuable account in English to Baedeker's *Austria*, Leipzig, Baedeker, 1929. Postwar accounts include H. Gsteu, *Länderkunde Österreichs*, Innsbruck, Tyrolia-Verlag, 1948, and A. Becker and L. Helmer, *Österreich, Landschaft, Wirtschaft, Bevölkerung*, Wien, Deuticke, 1953.

### CHAPTER 28

# GENERAL INTRODUCTION TO
# SOUTH-CENTRAL EUROPE

THE countries included in this region are Hungary, Rumania, Yugoslavia, Bulgaria, Slovakia, and Albania, with certain portions of adjacent lands, particularly the Carpathian portions of Poland and of the USSR, and the European portion of Turkey. The Greek peninsula and islands are excluded on account of the contrasts in climate and in mode of life induced or fostered by differences in build and world position. On the other hand, the narrow coastlands of the north-eastern Adriatic and of the northern Ægean have been included here for the sake of clarity in dealing with structure, but climatically and to some extent culturally they belong to the Mediterranean region.

This region of south-central Europe includes two great systems of young folded mountains, the Carpathian-Balkan and the Dinaric, and these enclose two great basins, the Pannonian (or Hungarian) and the Lower Danubian (or Rumano-Bulgarian). The third important element is the crystalline mass of the Rhodope, which lies like a wedge between the Balkan and the Dinaric folded ranges and which probably continues beneath the Pannonian basin. The Pelagonian mass, which lies between the Vardar valley and Lake Prespa and extends into Greece, is similar in character to the Rhodope mass and is only divided from it by a very narrow strip of country. Geographically they may be treated together. There are a few minor structural elements, such as the Dobruja Platform and the Tekir Dagh, which stand apart from the rest of the area. Bessarabia and eastern Moldavia belong to the Russian Platform. (See Fig. 2, p. 5.)

**Physical Evolution.** The whole region probably lay beneath the sea in Cretaceous times. At the end of the Cretaceous period the Carpathian and Balkan folds emerged, to be followed in the Miocene period by the Dinaric system and by additions to the Carpathian system. At the same time the Rhodope mass came into evidence, but sustained dislocations, with the result that large segments sank and fault-bounded basins were widely developed.   In consequence, the ancient sea was split up into a number of lakes, of which the largest occupied the Pannonian basin.   As the waters of this lake stretched considerably beyond the present lowlands, sediments were deposited over the lands which now border the right bank of the River Sava as well as over the present Transylvanian basin.   Another large lake deposited its sediments in the region of the Rumano-Bulgarian basin.   This basin was connected with the Pannonian lake by means of a strait occupying a transverse depression between the Carpathian and Balkan Mountains; probably it was also connected southwards with the branching Ægean lake which occupied faulted basins in the present Rhodope and Pelagonian masses as well as covering what is now the northern part of the Ægean sea.

It must be stated at once, however, that the present height and relief of the young folded mountains of this area are not due to the preliminary folding nor even to the further folding which occurred in Miocene times.   Both systems of young folded mountains were subsequently reduced to plateau conditions and in some areas to peneplains; their present high elevation is due to subsequent epeirogenic uplifting at the close of the Tertiary era.   Thus, both the Carpatho-Balkan and the Dinaric systems show well developed plateau forms, several levels being usually recognisable.   As a rule, the mountains consist of rounded bosses and wide upland slopes which are often forest-covered and are reminiscent of the Alps or central Pyrenees.   Alpine forms are entirely lacking in the Balkan Mountains, as their low elevation precluded a Quaternary glaciation. In the Carpathian system glaciation was also limited so that only the highest mountains in northern Slovakia bordering on Poland show the characteristic Alpine forms, such as arêtes, cirques, horns, etc. The Dinaric system also presents few Alpine features and these are to be found mainly in the Prokletije (='Damned Land'), sometimes known as the North Albanian Alps, and in Montenegro.

In late Tertiary (Pliocene) times, the freshwater lake which had filled the Pannonian basin began to be drained off and became divided into a number of smaller bodies of water, of which the present Balaton and Neusiedler lakes are remnants.   Similar drainage took place in the Rumano-Bulgar basin.   The ancient Ægean lake and its branching arms remained for a somewhat longer time; in fact, they were not drained off until the foundering of the northern Ægean, which probably occurred in early Quaternary times (see Fig. 64, p. 513).

Many terraces bordering both the ancient lakes and present river valleys remain to bear witness to the intermittent manner in which these inland waters were lowered and finally disappeared.   These terraces, usually composed of soft rocks of Tertiary age, and often *Löss*-covered, are now often much dissected by subaerial erosion and form a transition between the flat grain-growing basins and the barren or forested mountains. They provide good land for mixed farming and fruit growing, and offer suitable sites for settlement. Consequently they are a feature of great social, economic, and geographical importance for this area. So, too, was another effect of the lowering of the base level of erosion; much river capture took place, and numerous gorges were formed offering good opportunities in modern times for the development of hydro-electric power production.

In connexion with the Tertiary earth movements there was much outpouring of volcanic material, though there are no recent volcanoes. It seems, however, that parts of the region are still undergoing elevation, at any rate in the Dinaric system, but the Pannonian basin and Walachian plain have continued to sink and are largely covered with very recent sediments. That the coastal Dinaric and central Rhodope areas in Yugoslavia are still somewhat unstable was emphasised in the tragic earthquakes at Makarska in 1962 and Skoplje in 1963.

**Modern Theories on the Tectonic Affinities of the Danube Region.** A beautiful, if somewhat startling, simplicity has been introduced into the structure of this area thanks to the work of Kober and other geologists. The whole area is visualised as essentially forming part of one tectonic system only (see Chapter 1 and Fig. 2, p. 5). The system of mountains known to geographers as the Dinaric is said to correspond to the upper or Dinaric *nappes* of the Alps; the Pelagonian and Rhodope masses are considered to represent the *Zwischengebirge* or 'median masses' similar to the masses of Corsica and Sardinia; and the Carpatho-Balkan system to correspond to the lower *nappes* of the Alps. The Rhodope mass is believed to extend beneath the Hungarian basin, as evidenced by hills with cores of an ancient rock, such as those between the Save and the Danube near Pécs, and the Bihor Massif. These theories are somewhat difficult to reconcile with the older ones, especially as regards the Rhodope mass, but they have many adherents.

**Climate and Vegetation.** The climate of the whole area – with the exception of the Mediterranean and Black Sea coastlands – is transitional between the maritime and continental. The region is dominated in winter and summer by the continental high-pressure system with its easterly winds. It brings in winter temperatures often well below freezing point, snow, and biting winds which periodically break into the Mediterranean coastlands. Generally the coastlands experience heavy winter rain alternating with moderately high temperatures resulting from cyclonic weather conditions. In summer the east winds give rise to hot, dry conditions causing droughts disastrous to agriculture in the south and west of the area, where extensive irrigation has had to await the recent reorganisation of farming on a large-scale basis.    The northern part, especially the Tatra mountains, however, experience a summer maximum of precipitation resulting from the penetration of maritime air over the North European Plain and Alps.    Maritime air in the form of cyclones intrudes into the region most frequently in spring and early summer, bringing most rain in this period to large areas of the interior.

The typical vegetation is deciduous forest, of central European type, grading into coniferous forest.    Hardly anywhere do the rounded summits rise above the tree-level except in Slovenia and Slovakia, so there is little *alp* or *alm*.    High pastures above the forest level have been formed or increased by clearing the timber to give summer pasture.    In the most sheltered parts of the basins, where low rainfall is combined with porous soil, grass has been the natural vegetation during historic times, as in the Alföld, in the Rumano-Bulgar basin, and in the basin of the lower Maritsa.    These areas have been utilised mainly for growing grain, but in a few cases they are too dry and offer only poor grazing.    Efforts are being made to increase their productivity by irrigation and fertilisation. Other exceptions to the usual forest cover occur in regions of very pure and often barren limestone, such as the Karst region of the Dinaric system, and on a smaller scale in parts of eastern Serbia and Macedonia.

The wide range of cultivated crops includes wheat and maize, sugar beet, the vine, cotton, rice and tobacco.    Fruit trees flourish, particularly plums and apples, and in parts of the south also apricots, the rapid transition from winter to summer reducing to a minimum the danger from spring frosts.

**Mineral Wealth.**    Before the second world war the area was largely considered to be poor in minerals.    Such a belief resulted chiefly from the region's economic function as a supplier of agricultural produce to industrial west-central Europe, combined with its lack of the capital, administrative organisation and economic policy to explore and exploit new resources.    Two factors have changed significantly the assessment of the area's mineral wealth since the war: the establishment in each country of communist governments applying policies for industrialisation which seek to use domestic resources to a maximum, including low-grade minerals such as brown coal; and linked with this, the intensive research undertaken for new resources which sometimes has increased substantially the size and range of known resources for the countries concerned. The discovery of sizeable new brown coal reserves in Yugoslavia and of non-ferrous metals in Yugoslavia, Bulgaria, and Hungary, provide examples. While the area's resources are greater – in some cases much greater – than was previously thought, they are inevitably limited. South-central Europe largely lacks high-quality coals and must rely for fuel and power on brown coal localised chiefly along the margins of the Pannonian Plain in south-western Slovakia, northern Hungary, northern and north-central Yugoslavia, and in basins in the Rhodope system. Much more important in quantity are the petroleum and associated natural gas resources in the Transylvanian basin and on the outer flanks of the Carpathians. Metallic ores occur in great variety in the mountains often in association with the Tertiary volcanic activity, but with the exception of copper, bauxite, and zinc, deposits are small. Iron-ore resources are, however, much greater than those previously known, largely as a result of intensive geological research in the service of the programme for large-scale metallurgical development. Iron-ores are particularly localised in the Dinaric mountains of Yugoslavia and in Bulgaria. Salt deposits, situated on both sides of the Carpathians and in northern parts of the Dinaric system, are also important.

**Water-Power.** Until recently the hydro-electric power potentialities of this region were much underestimated. Despite only moderate rainfall, no perennial snow, and few natural lake storages, the area has potential supplies of 'white coal' almost comparable with those of Scandinavia, the Alps, and Pyrenees. The availability of these resources, in contrast to limited coal reserves, has stimulated the development of a large number of hydro-electric power stations: especially in the Carpathians (in Slovakia and Rumania), in western and north-central Bulgaria, and in the mountain regions of Yugoslavia which possess a water-power potential second only to that of Norway.

The swift-flowing Danube will be profitably harnessed, notably at the Iron Gate (Kazan gorge), where it breaks through the Carpathian Mountains. Agreement has now been reached between Yugoslavia and Rumania for the development of two of Europe's largest water-power stations, one on each side of the gorge. At the same time the need of the Danubian lands for an integrated scheme of power stations, canals for navigation and irrigation, and drainage channels along the Danube is now in sight of realisation through COMECON or CMEA, the organisation for economic cooperation of the eastern European countries and the USSR. A further factor in the development of hydro-electric power stations in this region has been the reassessment of the potentialities of rivers crossing the Hungarian and Walachian plains, using the experience of the Soviet Union with its Dnieper, Volga, and other projects.

**Historical and Economic Developments.** The lands of south-central Europe must be looked upon as countries backward in relation to west and central Europe. It must be stated at once, however, that the most significant feature of these countries is their present rapid development in an effort to reach an economic level comparable with that of western Europe. These countries possess little good coal, but various metals, brown coal, water-power, and abundant timber (except in Hungary) are available to sustain a wide range of basic industries, not to mention engineering industries to serve the needs of developing industries, agriculture and transport. Perhaps most important of all, these countries possess considerable reserves of manpower. The reason for their backwardness does not thus lie in their lack of resources, but partly in previous under-estimation of resources. Much prewar development was financed by foreign capital concerned generally with its own extraneous interest rather than with that of the countries' economic development. Thus before the war, mining and primitive processing industries were developed chiefly to serve export markets and not to promote manufacturing within the area. Although, too, the area supplied food to industrial central Europe, particularly Germany, even farming was (and still is, in part) in a primitive condition, with the exception of Hungary and parts of north-western and north-eastern Yugoslavia. Before the application of the postwar collectivisation policy, now almost complete in Hungary, Slovakia, Bulgaria, Rumania, and Albania, subsistence farming was the rule, farm machinery was very primitive, and the rearing of livestock unscientific.

The backwardness of these lands must be attributed largely to the fact that they bore the brunt of the Turkish attacks on Europe, and also to their position on the line of movement of most of the great earlier incursions from eastern Europe and Asia. With minor exceptions they all fell under the blighting Turkish rule. The lands of the north and west were the last to be conquered by the Turks and the first to free themselves. Hungary, for instance, was conquered by the Turks in 1526 and obtained its freedom in 1699, but the liberation of the countries nearest to Constantinople came very late. Rumania freed itself from Turkish suzerainty only in 1878, though virtual independence was established in 1861; the nucleus of modern Yugoslavia was formed in 1817, but the Niš area was not added until 1881 and the Vardar area not until 1912–13; independent Bulgaria dates only from 1881 and Turkish suzerainty was not definitely abandoned until 1908.

One of the reasons for backwardness was that the Turkish invasions forced large numbers of peasants to desert the productive plains, which became largely depopulated, and to flee to the mountains where among broken, forested country it was difficult for the Turks to attack and where the poverty of the land made it not worthwhile to do so.  In the small fertile basins south of the Sava–Danube the Turkish conquerors forced the local population into serfdom whereas the peasants in the mountains remained free.  The Magyars alone managed to retain their position on the open plain chiefly as they themselves were a horse-riding nation organised on a military basis.  Thus, apart from the Magyars, most of the population of the Balkans may be looked upon as having become refugees in their mountain fortress, cut off from contact with western Europe and consequently from changes taking place there.  Naturally oriental influence remained strong where the Turks held sway for the longest time.  Most of Bosnia, for instance, is a living museum of cultural anthropology and many inhabitants still wear Turkish costume.  The Balkan Peninsula contains the only section of Europe west of the USSR where Mohammedanism is professed by any considerable numbers (over one million people).  Likewise serfdom lingered on long after it had disappeared from western Europe. The Hungarian serfs, including those of Slovakia, Transylvania, and Croatia were freed in 1839, those of Rumania in 1864, and in the Balkans only with the withdrawal of the Turks in 1912.  Liberation was not beneficial to the peasants because large areas remained in *latifundia* farmed by a few landowners while the bulk of the population lived off a small area.  With the increase of population this small area became divided and subdivided, and a condition of over-population arose towards the end of the nineteenth century.

This problem of overpopulation is another reason for backwardness, and accounts for the postwar efforts at industrialisation. More people are engaged in farming than the land can adequately feed.  Moreover, peasant subsistence farming does not necessarily, or even usually, make the best use of the land unless it is combined with cooperative production and marketing of the surplus produce, and such surpluses before the war were limited to the larger holdings on the best farmed land.

The predominance of peasant farmers had an adverse effect on the commercial and industrial development of the countries and on the smooth running of government and public services.  Except in Hungary, few people could be said to belong to a middle class and even these small numbers were often Jewish; south-central Europe was therefore handicapped in its attempt to catch up with the more advanced parts of the world, not only by the shortages of fuel and poorness of communications, but also by a marked shortage of trained personnel. Another drawback was that subsistence agriculture does not lead to the accumulation of domestic capital.

A further feature of south-central Europe as a whole is the intermingling of peoples and the difficulty of drawing boundaries on national lines. Largely as a result of the easy movement of peoples within the large empires of Turkey, Austria-Hungary, and Russia, and the deliberate attraction of settlers from without, this intermingling led to the inevitable inclusion of considerable and diverse minority populations in countries recently created as nation states. This gave rise to a political instability which was not conducive to the capital investment essential from outside.

Considerable efforts were made by all the countries between 1918 and 1938 to catch up with western Europe. For instance, substantial industrial expansion took place; communications, though very inferior to those west of Vienna, were markedly improved; education was made available to large numbers. Visual evidence of progress could be seen particularly in the rebuilding of cities on modern lines. Belgrade and Bucharest were almost entirely rebuilt, while many new houses and usually a new school could be seen in almost every village of Slovakia, Rumania, and Yugoslavia. The manufacture of cement for building was one of the most important and flourishing industries. The whole standard of housing and hygiene was rising.

Certainly most significant and far-reaching changes in the geography, demography, and economy of the south-central European countries have taken place since 1945. Political events during the years 1945–48 brought the area into the political, social, and economic sphere of influence of the Soviet Union. A revolution occurred, establishing socialist governments with policies new to the area. These policies entailed radical changes in the geography of south-central Europe involving significant alterations in the structure of population, the collectivisation of agriculture, and above all, the rapid growth of industry, not only in each country as a unit but also in new areas within each country. After the reconstruction of settlements and industry destroyed or damaged during the second world war, each country embarked on plans of economic development for periods ranging from three to five years. The Five-Year Plan became as much a feature of postwar south-central Europe as it had been in the Soviet Union in the thirties. Not all the changes and new developments planned were necessarily carried out, either within the periods or the areas prescribed by the plans. Frequent changes in plans have been made, most notably in Yugoslavia in 1948–49 when that country was subjected to a political and economic blockade by the USSR and her neighbouring European satellites. Nevertheless, one must view the postwar years essentially as a period of comprehensive planning resulting in a series of radical and inter-linked changes in the character of the countries concerned.

Industrialisation has been the major factor precipitating these changes. The need for industrialisation in the area was unques-tioned, since it is the only effective method for removing surplus population from agriculture. And it has so happened that a socialist revolution provided the means to effect this: centralised planning and direction of development, the reduction of consumption to a minimum and the raising of savings to a maximum for capital investment, and a wider educational system linked to the needs of the state to provide more trained technical and scientific per-sonnel. Modifications, and some decentralisation of the system since 1956 (most marked, however, in Yugoslavia since 1950) have to some extent overcome the serious drawbacks of the system, but the fundamental aims remain unchanged. The policy of industrialisa-tion is changing the former 'agricultural belt' of south-central Europe into a belt of 'agricultural-industrial' countries.

The nature of the policy for industrial construction has had far-reaching consequences for the geography of these countries. State policy has required the rapid expansion of basic industries – mining, power, metallurgy, engineering, and chemicals – which, generally, were least important before the war. Engineering has replaced textiles or food as the largest industry, while production in the other basic branches has increased rapidly since 1947–48. The application of the principles of industrial development and location, learnt from the Soviet Union, has encouraged a significant growth of industries near the raw materials these countries possess. There has thus been a uniform call for the 'development of backward regions' within all the countries concerned: by locating industries where overpopulation is serious, standards of living are very low, and agriculture is very primitive, and where industry was almost non-existent before World War II. Such regions include Solvakia, central and north-east Hungary, most mountain regions of Yugoslavia (except Slovenia), Bulgaria, north and central Rumania, and even Albania.

Particular efforts have been made to find resources for the develop-ment of basic industries in these backward regions. The postwar construction of iron and steel industries in central Hungary (at Dunaujvaros, formerly Sztalinvaros), in Yugoslavia (in Bosnia, Montenegro, and Macedonia), in western Bulgaria, and in the Danube delta lands of Rumania, provides examples. Many of these major developments have occurred in regions with fuel and power, metallic and non-metallic mineral resources: the central and eastern mountain areas of Yugoslavia, north and west-central Hungary, and west and central Bulgaria around the Carpathians. On the other hand, a remarkable growth of engineering, electrical, and precision industries has taken place in centres of earlier industrial importance and where trained labour is available. Most outstanding in this respect has been the expansion of industry in major towns, in Budapest, Belgrade, Zagreb, Sofia, Plovdiv, and Bucharest. Lighter industries, especially textiles and food manufacturing, have been developed also in the backward regions to employ surplus labour and help to intensify agriculture. Since 1958 the practical activation of COMECON has also begun to affect the pattern of industrial development. By the division of labour and by specialisation among the member countries, in respect of material supplies and manufactured articles, efforts are being made to increase the economic production of areas with special potentialities in each country. Such are those which produce bauxite and aluminium in Hungary, oil and petrochemicals in Rumania, non-ferrous metals and southern fruits and vegetables in Bulgaria. At present Yugoslavia is not a member of this organisation; Albania was expelled in 1962.

With the planned expansion of industry, major demographic changes in the area have been the decline in the proportion of the population engaged in, or dependent upon, agriculture and the increase in those engaged in industry, services, and especially administration. In turn this has resulted in a rapid growth of urban population. New industrial activities have largely determined the growth of town populations. Thus large centres with good transport and industrial facilities, such as Budapest, Zagreb, Belgrade, Sarajevo, and Bucharest, as well as mining centres, have expanded very rapidly. New towns or satellite settlements have become common features – new centres isolated for strategic, social, or economic reasons from major towns, developed often on a purely agricultural landscape and bound closely to new mining or manufacturing activities. Examples are the bauxite–aluminium industrial centre of Várpalota, one of five new towns in Hungary, and Novi Travnik, a centre for engineering and chemicals, and one of the eight new towns in Yugoslavia. Sometimes these pleasant modern towns have been developed to reduce commuting to large industrial centres (see Fig. 58).

Agriculture, too, has undergone radical changes, though these at present are more organisational in character, since peasant attitudes and habits are but slowly altered. The postwar repatriation of Germans from their large farms and estates in Hungary and northern Yugoslavia provided an opportunity for subdivision of available land among peasants resettled there from seriously overpopulated regions; alternatively the governments took over these estates and worked them as state farms.   This led to some temporary regression in agricultural production since settlers at the beginning often applied primitive methods on lands which were formerly efficiently farmed. More significant has been the rigorous programme of collectivisation

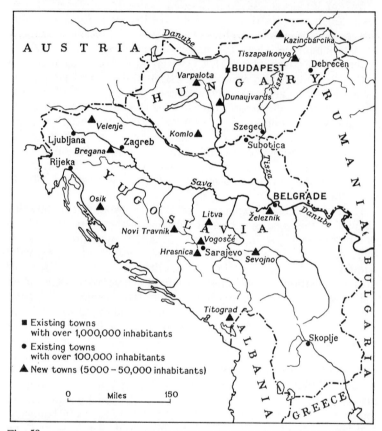

Fig. 58.   THE LOCATION OF NEW TOWNS IN HUNGARY AND YUGOSLAVIA

of peasant holdings introduced in the late 1940s and early 1950s in all the countries of south-central Europe.   Only in Yugoslavia has this policy been modified substantially.   There collective and state farms account for only 11 per cent of the agricultural land area, the rest being in private holdings, often organised in various forms of cooperative.   In Bulgaria, Rumania, and Slovakia a high percentage of land is under state management.

Three important points must be emphasised regarding collectivisation. The earlier social and economic problems arising from forced collectivisation and excess of bureaucracy have been overcome partly by modified forms of voluntary association and less centralisation. Secondly, the amalgamation of tiny peasant holdings into large farms with larger fields lays the foundation for replacing the old primitive hand methods by mechanisation and for an increase in agricultural production and yields. Thirdly, farming in countries where backward methods and traditional peasant values predominate can be made efficient only by thoroughly organised application of mechanisation, fertilisers, scientific cropping and scientific livestock breeding. Peasant farming has neither the means nor the possibility for achieving such changes without collective or cooperative production. Much of south-central Europe (with the major exception of Yugoslavia only) has been transformed, therefore, from an area of strips and patches into one of large square fields. This has been most easily and effectively accomplished on the plains of the Danube, Tisza and Maritsa and their tributaries where flat land permits large-scale mechanisation, and where most large estates were located. Farming in difficult mountain regions, especially in Yugoslavia, is not so easily modernised in this manner and must be organised on another basis. Connected with this problem, however, is that of rational land use. As mentioned earlier, peasant subsistence agriculture does not lead to rational land use, since basic crops such as grains are cultivated even where physical conditions are not appropriate. Cooperative organisation is necessary to introduce rational land use, as for example, to reverse the present land use pattern in many mountain areas of Yugoslavia where steep slopes are cultivated for crops and the fertile, moist valley lands are under grass. Effective organisation can also contribute to the improvement of agriculture in hilly regions of south-central Europe by encouraging and facilitating the investment, in tree crops or dairy farming, which the peasant is either unwilling or unable to make.

## REFERENCES

As reading for the physical and human backgrounds the following are recommended: Part II of E. de Martonne, *Europe Centrale*, Paris, Colin, 1931, dealing with the region north of the Sava–Danube line. For the region south of that line, J. Cvijić's *La Peninsula Balkanique*, Paris, Colin, 1918, is the classic work, though much of the detail is out of date now. A posthumous edition of the work of J. Cvijić is his *La Géographie des Terrains Calcaires*, Belgrade, Académie des Sciences, 1960, which brings the study of this region more up to date. Doreen Warriner, *The Economics of Peasant Farming*, Oxford University Press, 1939, deals with this important subject as a background to the postwar changes, regarding Poland, Czechoslovakia, Hungary, Rumania, Bulgaria, and Yugoslavia. H. G. Wanklyn, *The Eastern Marchlands of Europe*, London,

G. Philip, 1941, considers the geography of this region and its parts from an historical and political viewpoint.

For reading on developments since 1945, the following publications may be noted. N. Spulber, *The Economics of Communist Eastern Europe*, Bloomington, Indiana, 1960, containing useful information on the factors and changes which broadly influence the region's geographical pattern. A comprehensive book on the economics and political developments is E. Hoffmann, *COMECON: der Gemeinsame Markt in Osteuropa*, Opladen, Leske, 1961. I. T. Sanders, *Collectivisation of Agriculture in Eastern Europe*, Lexington, University of Kentucky Press, 1958, gives an overall picture of agricultural changes. The United Nations' annual *Economic Survey for Europe* contains useful information. Also recommended, for more specialised information and topics about the whole region and its subdivisions, are: N. J. G. Pounds and N. Spulber, *Resources and Planning in Eastern Europe*, Bloomington, Indiana University Press, 1957, and N. J. G. Pounds (Ed.), *Geographical Essays on Eastern Europe*, Bloomington and the Hague. Mouton, 1961.

CHAPTER 29

# THE MIDDLE DANUBE BASIN

THIS depression, also known as the Hungarian or Pannonian basin, rises on all sides to mountainous country. Its middle portion belongs to Hungary and its outlying parts are now divided between a number of states, namely, Rumania, Yugoslavia, Austria, and the USSR. As the area forms a physical unit, however, it will here be treated as a whole. In a sense the postwar political uniformity of the region – remembering that the Soviet Union also temporarily controlled that part of Austria lying within the basin – reinforces such an approach.

Not only was the area subsiding in Tertiary times, but it continued to sink during the Quaternary period. It contrasts, therefore, with the Transylvanian basin, where Tertiary material remains at the surface and has been much dissected. Sedimentation is still active in many parts of the Hungarian basin, particularly along the Tisza and the lower course of its left-bank tributaries, e.g. Körös, Maros, and Temes, which are still liable to floods, in spite of great efforts to regulate their beds. *Löss* is found on much of the higher ground such as the old lake terraces and on the bordering hills, and sporadically in the lowlands themselves, but alluvium and blown sand have covered up the *Löss* deposits in most of the low-lying parts.

The region is not entirely flat, though there are large stretches of level ground. A notable line of hills in west-central Hungary extends from the south-west to the north-east, crossing the Danube north of Budapest. Another series of hills lies between the Drava–Danube and the Sava, where they appear under a number of different names, but can be included under the heading of the Croatian–Slavonian hill country.

The Danube is the only river which breaks through the surrounding mountain ring, though there are a number of relatively easy exits in the form of saddles and passes which are followed by railways and roads. Indeed, the surrounding mountains are not the barrier they appear at first sight. They are threaded in numerous places by deep and broad valleys giving opportunities of penetration. Moreover, the surrounding ring of mountains both narrows and diminishes in height in a remarkable manner in two places. The karstic saddle in the south-west is the more important of these, as it leads from the

471

well-populated lands of eastern Austria and western Hungary to the head of the Adriatic. The second is the remarkable narrowing of the Carpathian mountain system near the headwaters of the Tisza in the north-east. In recent years the value of these routes has increased with the great rise of Yugoslavia's overseas trade in the first case, and with increased Hungarian-Rumanian-Soviet trade in the second.

**The Little Alföld.**[1] This small, hill-girt plain is situated in the extreme north-west of the basin. It is separated from the Vienna basin by a line of hills running at right angles to the Danube and forming a link between the Alps and the Carpathians, and from the Great Alföld by the Bakony Forest. The flat middle portion of the basin allows the Danube to divide into several arms in a district that formerly was very swampy. It has been largely reclaimed and is now used for pasture and dairying or for the growing of vegetables and sugar beet; agriculture in this region is being intensified under the stimulus of increasing demand from growing industrial and urban areas along the Danube and in the Bakony Forest. Southward the land rises, and late Tertiary deposits emerge from beneath the alluvium. Here grain cultivation becomes dominant, though there are also many orchards which increase in number towards the southern foothills. This region is one of ancient settlement, in contrast to recent development of the Great Alföld. It contains a number of old picturesque villages and small towns, mostly of German origin. One effect of the postwar political changes has been to introduce into these settlements social and communal facilities in the form of modern hospitals and schools and thus broaden their functional character.

Although predominantly agricultural and rural, the Little Alföld contains a few industrial centres. By far the most significant is Bratislava (Ger., Pressburg; Hung., Poszony; 260,000), a major river port on the Danube, and a centre of engineering, chemicals, textiles and various light industries. At present the Bratislava region is becoming a major petrochemical area with the construction there of Czechoslovakia's largest oil refinery based on oil piped from Kuibyshev in the USSR. The twin ports of Komarno (Slovak) and Komárom (Hungarian) also lie in this region, as does the engineering centre of Györ.

**The Hill and Plateau Region of Central Hungary.** This may be divided into three parts. First, the mountains, largely volcanic in origin, which stretch in an east–north-east to west–south-west direction from the River Bodrog to the Danube, and rise to a maximum of 3,300 ft. The economy of this region centres chiefly on

[1] 'Al' = low, 'fold' = country or land.

forestry and grain production though industry is of growing importance in a few centres.   On the northern margins of the region the
mining of brown coal is of increasing importance particularly for
nearby power, briquetting, and chemical plants.   One of the most
spectacular developments since the war has been the construction
of a large fertiliser and chemicals combine and associated new town
at Kazincbarcika, a symbol of modern industrialising Hungary and
of the effort to improve agriculture.   The Miskolc–Diosgyör region
is the centre of Hungary's expanding quality steel production, while
new rolling mills have been recently opened at Salgotarjan to the
west.

To the south-west of the Danube the Bakony Forest continues in
much the same direction, with a maximum height of 2,300 ft.   The
strata, varying from Carboniferous to early Tertiary, are lightly
folded and considerably faulted, and may perhaps be connected with
the Alpine folds.   These hills retain a considerable amount of their
deciduous forest cover, though much clearing has taken place.
Since 1950 three important points of industrial growth in this region
have had considerable effect in intensifying agriculture here and
continuing the process of forest clearance.   Zalaegerszeg in the
south-west has become an oil-refining and bitumen-producing centre
as a result of expanded local oil output.   To the north-east of Lake
Balaton on the margins of the Bakony Forest, the mining of bauxite
and the production of aluminium has increased very rapidly as a
result of Hungary's specialisation in this field within the framework
of COMECON.   Production is concentrated in Székesfehérvár and
in the new town of Várpalota (Inota-Pet) near by.   In the extreme
north-east, the Tatabanya area has assumed national importance
with the construction there of brown coal mines, coal-crushing
plants, power stations, engineering industries serving mining needs,
and limestone quarrying and cement production for local building
use.   Part of this growth is associated with the proximity of the
area to the Budapest market.

South-east of Lake Balaton, which lies at the southern foot of the
Bakony Forest and has a maximum depth of only 36 ft, lies the third
section of this region.   In reality it is a low, lightly dissected plateau
covered with *Löss* and intrinsically very productive.   From this
plateau north of Pécs and Székesfehérvár respectively, rise two hill
masses with granite cores, believed to be outliers of the Rhodope
block.   Like the Little Alföld, this region west of the Danube is a
land of old settlements.   Yet towns founded in the Middle Ages
are now being expanded on modern lines, and a population that has
long been devoted to a diversified agriculture is turning more to
other occupations.   Mining and manufacturing are increasing in

importance here with the extensive postwar development of Hungary's only bituminous coal-mining activity and with a new town at Komlo, new natural gas production, and porcelain industries at Pécs, timber manufacturing at Mohacs, and textiles at Kaposvar.

The capital city itself, Budapest, originated in a settlement on the right bank of the Danube where the hill country reaches the river. The original medieval town of Buda, with its good defensive position, has long been surpassed in size by Pest on the flat land on the east or exposed side of the river.   Before the siege of 1945 it was perhaps the most beautiful inland city of Europe.   Since the war, great efforts have been made to develop relatively self-contained housing settlements and small satellites around the city to ease the congestion of the centre.   The original settlement, situated where the river narrows, had a good position for trade on the north–south river route and in modern times also on the east–west route which uses a river gap through the mountains to the north-west of the town.

**The Great Alföld.**   East of the Danube, between Budapest and Belgrade, an area of flat land stretches to the foothills of the Carpathian mountain system to the east.   The main unity here is one of climate, for although flat, various parts of the area show important environmental and economic differences.   The Great Alföld has a more Continental climate than the foregoing regions, experiencing severe winter cold and severe droughts in late summer.   Formerly an area probably of wooded steppe and devoted to the rearing of horses, cattle, and sheep, it is now one of open, largely arable landscapes except in small areas of loose, infertile sandy soil.   There are few trees except the willows along the swampy borders of the few rivers, or where acacias, eucalyptus, pines, and other drought-resisting trees have been planted round farmhouses and villages as shelter-belts.

The region is overwhelmingly agricultural and crops are very varied.   Cereals, particularly maize and wheat, form the chief cash crops, though melons, tobacco, paprika, and many others are widely grown.   Cattle are reared in large numbers but are now mainly stall-fed instead of being turned loose to graze.   This is one of the results of cooperative farming which is also stimulating more dairy, fruit, and market-garden production.   Pigs and poultry, especially geese, are numerous, being fed mainly on the plentiful grain.   Implanted sporadically on this rural landscape, however, are the rising chimneys and modern buildings of important new industries and urban settlements.   They are part of the 'socialist transformation' of the countryside introducing 'proletarian elements' to a largely peasant society, a means to hasten the socialisation of agriculture itself.   Of note in this respect are the large metallurgical centre and new town of Dunaujvaros (formerly Sztalinvaros) on the Danube, built and operated at high cost, and the power and chemicals centre of Tisza-palkonya in eastern Hungary.

Between the Danube and the Tisza lies a region which is higher and drier than the low-lying swamp country to the east of the Tisza river. This region, Cumania, is largely covered with sand, now to a considerable extent devoted to vineyards, the vines on the sandy soil being especially free of phylloxera. Peaches and apricots are widely grown around Kecskemét (75,000), which is a great fruit centre, the explanation of the productivity of this region being the thinness of the sandcover permitting the mixing of the underlying *Löss* with the surface soil. Even so, the successful planting of trees in the Alföld demands great care and a special technique now being more widely adopted by state and cooperative farms. South-east of Kecskemét the soil is impregnated with salts giving a large area of *puszta* (='waste'), known as the Bugác steppe. Here may still be seen the original white Hungarian cattle. They can stand great heat and drought and make excellent draught animals, but provide little milk and fatten only slowly. Because of increasing mechanisation and growing needs for dairy and meat products, they are being replaced by crossbred cattle. In Yugoslavia, south of Subotica, which is a centre for agricultural marketing and processing and also for engineering, lies a fertile *Löss*-covered region devoted mainly to cereals and sugar beet cultivation. Being Yugoslavia's only large and fertile agricultural region, and her only region with large farms, collectivisation and mechanisation here have been most marked and most successful in the postwar period.

To the east of the Tisza lies low-lying swamp land which since 1950 has been one of Hungary's 'backward regions' and subject to a policy of intensive economic development which only now is having marked results. Reclamation of this land is providing areas of pasture for intensive livestock farming, while irrigation of the sandy region north of Debrecen is facilitating an extension of vegetable production, notably potatoes. Hungary's largest area of *puszta*, the Hortobágy, lying west of Debrecen, is being used more intensively for livestock raising. Industrial activities, however, are of increasing importance. Debrecen (140,000) is an expanding centre for the manufacture of precision and quality goods, while chemical industries, based on local straw and willow and on Rumanian natural gas, are bringing employment to the Tizsa valley region.

The population distribution on the Alföld shows some rather curious features. On the one hand is a concentration into large towns, which, however, usually retain much of the appearance of villages, or 'garden cities' as their centres have few large buildings or shops to give an urban character, while the houses are usually of only one storey and each stands in its own garden. Recently, with modern buildings and flats, they begin to look more like towns. On the other hand, between the towns the population is extremely disseminated and the countryside is dotted with scattered farmhouses on smallish holdings, known as *tanyas*. Some of these have disappeared or are disappearing and the rural population is becoming more concentrated in small agricultural workers' settlements with the process of collectivisation. Near Hodmézövásárhely, the *tanya* system gives a very geometrical pattern to the landscape.

**The Croatian-Slavonian Hill Country.** This region of Yugoslavia lies between the rivers Drava and Sava. It consists of a fertile, well cultivated lowland broken by the Papuk-Psunj masses of central Slavonia and the Fruška Gora hills running in a west-north-west to east-south-east direction. These hills all contain a core of ancient rock and are believed by some geologists to be connected tectonically with the Rhodope and by others with the central crystalline Alps. Most of the hills are partly forested, the rest being under orchards, vineyards, and subsistence farms. The Fruška Gora area bordering the Danube is especially renowned for its wines.

# HUNGARY

The Hungarians or Magyars entered the middle Danube basin in the ninth century, having come from their earliest known home between the Sea of Azov and the southern Urals. They found the plain occupied by a scanty population composed partly of the disorganised Avars and partly of Slav-speaking peoples. The Magyars were sharply differentiated from these people and their German neighbours by language, Hungarian belonging to the Finno-Ugrian language group of which Estonian, Finnish, and some Soviet national groups are the only other representatives today in Europe. Having established a solid and coherent state in the middle of the mountain-girt plain, they proceeded to extend their power and settlement along the routes which easily penetrate the surrounding mountains. Medieval Hungary, as a Christian kingdom, which received its religion from Rome, occupied a considerable territory from Dalmatia to Transylvania. Later it suffered domination by Austria from the west, and subjection by Turks from the east and, in the nineteenth century, the pressures of nationalist movements of the Slav and other peoples long subject to Magyar rule. As a result, in 1919 Hungary was reduced to a small state of 36,000 square miles with a population of $8\frac{1}{2}$ million.[1] Though allied to the Turks by

[1] The present population is about 10 million.

tradition, the Magyars became so devoted to the European Christian ideal that for long they formed a bulwark for western Europe against the Muslims. Unfortunately, Hungary's subjection by the Turks occurred when western Europe was emerging from medieval into modern times. She thus lagged behind in the process of cultural, social and economic development.

With its level surface of fertile soil, Hungary remains pre-eminently agricultural. This holds true despite the rapid expansion of industry since 1948, which has reduced the percentage of the population engaged in agriculture. About 60 per cent of the total surface is under the plough, a higher percentage than that of any other country in Europe except Denmark. Pasture covers about 19 per cent, forest 14 per cent, and vineyards, orchards and gardens 4 per cent. Of the ploughed land nearly three-quarters are devoted to cereals, but planned state and cooperative farming is effecting a change in land use, increasing the ratio of fodder and industrial crops at the expense of cereals. The number of pigs, cattle, sheep and horses is high and the livestock industry may be compared in intensity with that of the maize belt of North America.

More spectacular have been the changes in land ownership. The Land Reform of 1945 requisitioned the large estates, which had dominated Hungary's prewar agriculture, and the land was divided partly among 642,000 landless agricultural workers or dwarf land-holders and partly retained by the state. From 1949 collective farms were established, though their number decreased after 1956. Less than one-third of all agricultural land in Hungary is now organised on a state, collective or cooperative basis. Nevertheless more voluntary forms of cooperation are being extended to bring all peasant farmers eventually the benefits of larger-scale farming, mechanisation, an adequate supply of fertilisers, etc., to intensify land use and thus raise output.

Despite these aims and changes, the large surplus of agricultural produce available for export between 1918 and 1938 has not been so readily available since 1945. Quite apart from the early disadvan-tages of forced collectivisation, a major reason for this lies in the growth of urban and non-agricultural populations. This has absorbed more of the surplus within the country. Hungary's post-war agricultural trade pattern, however, has completely altered, partly to her benefit. In contrast to her difficulties in selling food abroad before 1939, since 1945 Hungary has always been assured of finding markets for her grain, fruit (peaches, apricots, melons), wines, eggs, and poultry, in the Soviet Union and Czechoslovakia. In this respect the use of refrigerated vehicles and air transport in recent years has partly overcome the problem of Hungary's inland position for the supply of perishable produce to the large but distant markets of the USSR. This, too, is stimulating more intensive land use in Hungary.

One would not expect to find great mineral wealth in a plain of Quaternary sediments. Hungary's limited mineral deposits thus impose heavy restrictions on her industrial development and necessitate large supplies of materials and semi-manufactures from abroad. Undoubtedly the most important resource is bauxite, followed by small reserves of oil, brown coal, some bituminous coal, and building materials. Jurassic coal is mined at Komlo near Pécs, brown coal near Salgotarjan and Miskolc in the north, and in the Dorog–Tatabanya area in the Pilis Hills north-west of Budapest. Present production (1963) runs at about 3 million tons of bituminous coal and 27 million tons of brown coal.

Industries are more developed than might be expected, and are growing relatively fast, using partly domestic resources and partly materials imported from the USSR (iron-ore, oil, non-ferrous metals), Rumania (natural gas and timber), Poland (coal and coke) and Bulgaria (non-ferrous metals), all member countries of COMECON. Manufacturing industry now employs over one million workers, three times the figure for 1946. The engineering and electrical industry has become the largest and most rapidly expanding, thanks both to planned industrialisation and to agricultural mechanisation with emphasis on the demand for capital equipment. The policy to use domestic materials more intensively has led to a growth in mining industries (especially coal, bauxite, and limestone), and in food-processing with the accent on preserves, sugar and brewing. The textiles, tobacco, leather, and shoe industries are also quite substantial.

Budapest is by far the largest manufacturing centre, still concentrating 45 per cent of the country's industry, but the Hungarian government is attempting to reduce the dominant position of the capital by its policy of developing backward areas by the construction of large industries or new industrial centres in rural areas with little industry, especially in west-central Hungary, Transdanubia, and the regions along and east of the Tisza. Development in the last region is being greatly assisted by improved transportation with the USSR. In part these new development areas compare in character with the Soviet Union's centres of 'complex industry'. Examples are the new towns of Dunaujvaros (metallurgy, engineering, cement and cellulose), Várpalota (power, aluminium and chemicals), Tiszapalkonya, and Kazincbarcika (power and chemicals), and medium and small towns like Debrecen (140,000), Szeged (110,000), Gödöllö, Pécs, Mohács, and Tatabanya. The construction of Hungary's largest oil refinery and power station (supplied with piped Volga–Ural oil) at Szazhalombatta, a few miles south of Budapest, is symbolic not only of the compromise being reached in developing industries in what are becoming satellite settlements of the capital, but also of the changing distribution of Hungary's modern industries.

Budapest, with a population in 1963 of 1,950,000, holds a dominating position in Hungarian life. The city is not only the capital of the country but the chief commercial and manufacturing centre with its largest engineering, textile, leather, tobacco and food-processing industries. It is also the principal cultural and educational centre, with the leading university, and has the distinction, unusual in a capital city, of being the chief health resort and holiday town largely owing to the occurrence of many kinds of natural springs which have been turned to good account for both recreation and health purposes.

Apart from Budapest, none of the towns is of any great size. The oldest towns occupy defensible positions west of the Danube, such as Székesfehérvár, which was the capital as early as the tenth century. Few towns are situated along the two great rivers because of their liability to flooding. Within the last eighty years, however, great regulation works have been carried out and hundreds of miles of protective dykes erected. This has facilitated important changes in the settlement pattern since 1945 – the construction of new industrial settlements alongside the Danube, Tisza, and their tributaries. There are now good prospects that central and east Hungary may become an important region of new industrial, commercial and urban developments associated with the construction of dams, hydro-electric power stations, irrigation and drainage channels and navigable waterways on the Danube and Tisza and with aid from the COMECON organisation.

## REFERENCES

K. Treiber, *Wirtschafts-Geographie des Ungarischen Grossen Alfölds*, Kiel, 1934. Clive Holland, *Hungary*, London, Jenkins, 1935; H. G. Wanklyn, 'The Rôle of Peasant Hungary', *Geog. Journal*, 1941. A. Basch, *The Danube Basin and the German Economic Sphere*, London, Kegan Paul, Trench and Trubner, 1944, is valuable for a view of this area in the period immediately before the war.

More recent publications include the United Nations, *Economic Bulletin for Europe*, 1957, 'The Hungarian Economy in Spring', 1957; much useful information on current social and economic events is to be found in the monthly publication of the Hungarian News and Information Service, *New Hungary*.

### CHAPTER 30

# THE CARPATHIAN SYSTEM

THE Carpathians, from the Vienna basin to the Iron Gate, have about the same length as the Alps, but only about half their average height, with no summit exceeding 9,000 ft. Owing to their geographical position they have played an unimportant rôle in history and have a small and backward population. They are, however, of growing economic importance as a result of the social and political changes engendered by the second world war and its aftermath. They are easier to cross than the Alps and can be more easily welded into an economic unit since more railways cross them. Less is known about the geological structure of the Carpathians than about that of the Alps, and they are much less adequately mapped, though the quest for mineral, fuel and power resources is changing this situation. Owing to their lower height they possess no glaciers and there was less glaciation during the Pleistocene period. Accordingly they present relatively little Alpine scenery and are less attractive to tourists. The Tatra Mountains alone were intensely glaciated, though the Transylvanian Alps show Alpine forms sporadically.

To a certain degree, the Carpathians may be considered to be a prolongation of the north-eastern Alps, though the longitudinal zones do not correspond closely and the *nappes* and *Decken* are much less developed. One of the peculiarities of the Carpathian system is the great amount of block subsidence on the inner side of the mountain arc. The Hungarian basin almost divides the arc into two sections near the headwaters of the Tizsa, and lesser subsidences are numerous. These were usually accompanied by volcanic outpourings of Tertiary age; there is thus an inner ring of volcanic ranges sometimes associated with precious metals.

It is usual to subdivide the Carpathians into four sections according to physical and structural characteristics. The fact that the whole system is divided between four countries – Poland, Czechoslovakia, Rumania, and the USSR – with partly different histories does not diminish the significance of the physical division, since today all these countries are moving together along one path of development with similar basic social, political, and economic characteristics. Cooperation between these countries will increasingly develop the Carpathians as an economic, as well as a physical unit. The physical

**66** The Attila Josef housing estate, biggest of the new housing estates in Budapest. The area which lies alongside the road to the airport, was once one of the worst slums in the city. 10,000 new flats will be open on this estate by the end of 1965.

HUNGARY

**67** Part of the town of Dunaújváros.

HUNGARY

**68** Dimitrovgrad. The chemical plant.

RUMANIA

69  Hydroelectric plant in the Vah valley  CZECHOSLOVAKIA

70  Hunedoara Iron and Steel Works  RUMANIA

divisions are as follows.  The western Carpathians stretch from the Vienna basin to the River Hornad, the central Carpathians comprise the narrow stretch between the latter river and the upper Tisza, the eastern Carpathians continue almost as far as Braşov, and the southern Carpathians or Transylvanian Alps continue as far as the Iron Gate on the Danube.  The Transylvanian Basin, bounded on the west by the Bihor Mountains, constitutes the fifth division (see Fig. 59).

No single longitudinal zone continues throughout the whole length of the chain, though an outer sandstone or flysch zone is

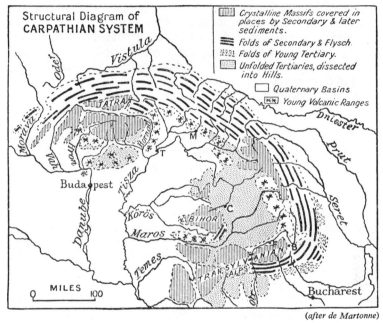

(after de Martonne)

Fig. 59.  STRUCTURAL DIAGRAM OF THE CARPATHIAN SYSTEM

present everywhere except in the Transylvanian Alps.  Also a fore-land of lightly folded Tertiary material is almost complete; certain important fuel resources are associated with this zone.  An inner discontinuous zone of crystalline rocks, well represented in the Western Carpathians, appears as a narrow band in the Eastern section, while it forms the core of the Transylvanian Alps and Bihor Mountains.  In places these contain useful metallic mineral and fuel resources.

**The Western Carpathians.**  This section differs in many ways from the rest of the mountain chain. The Carpathians are here at their widest, highest, and most complex. Longitudinal rivers such as the Vah, Hron, and Hornad flow towards the Pannonian basin, deeply penetrating the range, as in the Alps. These valleys, with the numerous tectonic basins, permit relatively easy internal movement and the region is fairly well penetrated by railways. The longitudinal routes have assumed major importance for communications between west and central Czechoslovakia on the one hand and the USSR on the other. The main railway from the Ukraine via Košice to Prague has been electrified.

The Carpathians here consist of a series of structural zones which are concave to the south, with the exception of the most southerly one, and which are not easily distinguished one from the other on the relief map as they are only occasionally separated by well-marked depressions. These zones may be termed briefly the northern, central, and southern, each with different physical, human, and economic characteristics.

The northern or outer zone belongs to the Flysch *nappe*, which consists largely of Mesozoic sandstone. It forms a long range of hills and mountains generally forested and of rounded form, here known as the Western Beskids. The range seldom exceeds 4,000 ft in height and is fairly easily crossed: indeed the name Beskid is said to mean 'passes'. Thus the Jablunkov Pass (1,808 ft) in Czechoslovakia affords easy connexions between the Ostrava coal basin and industrial area and the developing region of the Vah valley in Slovakia, the Rabka Pass gives access to the tourist region around Zakopane (in Poland), and the Dukla Pass (1,653 ft) links economically developing areas in south-eastern Poland and eastern Slovakia; all are followed by railways and will increase in importance in coming years. While relatively backward compared with western Europe, the economy of the Western Beskids does show marked internal differences. The western parts are falling more and more under the influence of the Ostrava and Upper Silesian industrial areas and becoming areas of scattered but important industries, as in the Żywiec region, with significant consequences for the patterns of settlement, land use, and communications. The eastern parts still suffer agricultural overpopulation, poverty, and relative isolation, though industry and tourism are planned to have important effects there.

Separating the northern from the central zone is a fairly well marked line of depressions developed in soft marls but not occupied by any master river. These depressions are areas of relatively intense agriculture centred around small market towns, e.g. Nowy Targ (= New Market), amid the largely forested or pastoral mountains to the north and south.

The central zone follows the same general course as the Beskids, but comprises more varied material. Here crystalline rocks, though often covered by sedimentary rocks, appear in the higher mountain masses such as the Tatra. The zone is divided into outer and inner ranges, only clearly separated from each other around the Liptor–Poprad depression in the valleys of the upper Vah and Poprad. In the outer zone the Mala Fatra and High Tatra Mountains are among the best known ranges. The latter reaches a height of over 8,700 ft and is the highest and most picturesque range of the whole Carpathian system. It is composed of resistant granites with limestone in places and was sculptured during the Great Ice Age into a fine series of horns, cirques, arêtes, and with numerous lakes and waterfalls is similar to those of the High Alps. Their apparent height is enhanced by the relatively low height of surrounding basins. The Polish boundary here bends south in this region to include part of the northern side of the Tatras. A Polish-Czechoslovak agreement has opened the whole of the High Tatras to visitors from both countries, so that a more flourishing tourist trade is supporting a number of growing resorts, e.g. Zakopane. The inner line includes the Velka or Great Fatra and Lower Fatra ranges. These are composed largely of granite and gneiss with an envelope of Triassic limestone. To the east of the Lower Tatra are the Spiš Ore Mountains. Composed of Palæozoic schists with ancient volcanic intrusions, these are a source of minerals, especially iron, providing a basis for the industrialisation of eastern Slovakia. All these mountains are heavily forested and timber industries are important. Finally the Slovakian karst, composed of Triassic limestone, adjoins the Pannonian basin north of the Sajo depression.

The third, or southern, zone of the Western Carpathians consists of young volcanic material, and is very discontinuous. The largest section, lying athwart the middle Hron, is often known as the Slovakian Ore Mountains. The medieval tradition of mining ores (gold, silver, and copper) here is being revived in a new form with the recent development of large-scale iron-ore mining; this, combined with the opening up of magnesite resources, provide raw materials and refractory bricks for the growing metallurgical industries of this region. The industrialisation of the Western Carpathians, based on varied metals and non-metallic minerals and on hydro-electric power from the Vah river, is leading to important social changes. Among these one can note the decline in the habit of wearing colourful local costumes, the addition of modern quarters to many picturesque and once primitive small towns, and the growth of a group of people commuting daily from rural areas to the factory.

South of the Ore Mountains and karst lies a well-marked depression filled with Tertiary and Quaternary deposits and studded with young volcanic material. The Ipel and Sajo occupy part of this depression, which separates the Western Carpathians proper from the volcanic Mátra and partially volcanic Bükk (='beech') hills of Hungary.

To the east of the central crystalline zone occurs a broad faulted depression, traced by the north-south section of the Hornad river. The Torysa valley continues the route northwards almost as far as the River Poprad, which cuts transversely through the Flysch zone so offering a route between the plains of Hungary and Poland. The longitudinal valleys of the Western Carpathians open into it, so that the depression is a crossroads region, now assuming increasing importance within the economic organisation, COMECON. Košice (87,600), the most important town of the region is located on this route, and as a result is the most rapidly growing industrial centre. Iron and steel, textiles, metalworking, and machinery, timber and food industries are of expanding importance. East of the Hornad fault lies a long line of volcanic hills lying between the depression and the great bay of lowland that bites into the Central Carpathians. Tokaj (in Hungary), celebrated for its wine, lies at the southern end where these hills reach the Tisza.

**The Central or Forest Carpathians.** Here the width of the mountains is reduced to about 60 miles only. The mean height is much lower than elsewhere, and several low passes (e.g. the Dukla, Lupkov, and Jablonica) connect the Hungarian Plain with the upper Dniester corridor and the plateau of Podolia. Between 1919 and 1945 Podolia belonged to Poland, while Ruthenia to the south formed part of Czechoslovakia. Both areas were annexed by the USSR in 1945, the latter giving her the north-eastern corner of the Hungarian Plain. The ease of communications in this region is proving vital to the economic integration of adjacent regions: for the linkage of south-east Poland with developing areas in Slovakia and north-east Hungary, and that of the USSR with Hungary.

Only the Flysch zone is to be found here, known generally as the Eastern Beskids, accompanied by an inner line of volcanic hills; there is no crystalline zone. Small deposits of oil and natural gas are found in the northern foothills and are worked mainly along the Polish-Soviet frontier and at Borysław; salt is worked in the Tisza plains to the south. The region was much affected by the population changes following the boundary changes and associated political events of 1945. Areas in south-eastern Poland and neighbouring areas of the USSR are thus thinly peopled or completely deserted; areas of former grassland and cultivation now form a wilderness of secondary bush and young tree growth.

**The Eastern Carpathians.** This region stretches from the source of the Tisza almost as far round as Braşov and lies chiefly in Rumania. Apart from the foreland they consist of three main zones, an outer zone of parallel ridges of Flysch (sandstone and conglomerates), a central crystalline schist zone with resistant limestones in places, and an inner or western zone of chiefly young volcanic material. Easy weathering of the first two zones has given rise to rounded mountains almost everywhere. They average 5,000 ft in height so that only the few higher summits were affected by glaciation, for example the Rodna Massif (7,560 ft). The Eastern Carpathians are well forested, with deciduous trees, especially beech, on the lower slopes, and conifers on the upper slopes. They supply much timber, which is floated down rivers especially on the eastern, Moldavian side, and manufactured into wood products and paper in factories located near larger population centres. The upper limit of tree growth is about 5,000 ft here, so there is little high pasture except for sheep.

Human habitation is scanty apart from a few longitudinal depressions, which appear as islands of settlement and cultivation in a sea of forested mountains. In the north these depressions lie in wide, shallow, longitudinal valleys not yet reached by the cycle of erosion, for example, the Moldavian Bistriţa, above Vatra Dornei; in the centre the depressions are former lake basins, while in the south they are of tectonic origin. The inhabitants of these depressions cultivate maize and vegetables, rear sheep and pigs, and combine these activities with forestry. Some mining and industrial activity is beginning to change the landscape and the social and economic life of the population in a few areas: copper and manganese mining and processing in the Bistriţa area around Vatra Dornei, brown coal mining, power, salt- and oil-extraction industries in the middle Trotus valley. The central basins of Gheorgheni and Ciuc lie between the central crystalline and western volcanic zones. The latter, stretching south from the Borgo Pass south-west of Vatra Dornei, are heavily forested. They appear to have dammed back the drainage flowing westwards from the crystalline zone and produced lake basins of Gheorgheni, drained by the upper Mureş, and Ciuc, drained by the upper Olt. Both are fertile, sheltered basins intensively cultivated for wheat, some fruits and vegetables, and with industries based on Carpathian timber supplies.

Two other basins of similar appearance but of tectonic origin lie farther south in the angle between the Eastern Carpathians (here represented only by the Flysch zone) and the Transylvanian Alps. These are the basins of Trei Scaune[1] (Hung., Három Szek) and of

---

[1] The name means 'three seats' or 'settlements' in both languages.

Brasov. From the latter the Predeal Pass leads south carrying the railway from Budapest to Bucharest and linking the Transylvanian Basin with the Walachian Plain within Rumania. The Eastern Carpathians themselves are crossed by several single-track railways but by no main railways; the need for such a line is growing, however, with the increasing needs of economic development of the lands to the east.

The Eastern Carpathians are mainly inhabited by Rumanian-speaking people, but two other linguistic groups are represented. In the region known as Maramureş to the north of the Rodna Massif, the people speak Ruthenian (Ukrainian). This area was Hungarian before 1918, subsequently Rumanian and is now in the USSR. Ruthenians also inhabit the Bucovina ('beech land') area lying to the east of Maramures; this area was ceded by the Turks to Austria in 1775, became Rumanian in 1918 and is now also within the Soviet Union.

The Gheogheni, Ciuc, and Trei Scaune intermontane depressions, in contrast, are inhabited by Magyar-speaking people called Székely.

**The Southern Carpathians.** The Transylvanian Alps are not, in fact, very Alpine in appearance, though like the Western Carpathians they contain certain massifs which show well-marked pyramidal forms and other results of glaciation. Generally, their summits rise above the forest zone and they often present fine scenery. The rocks composing the mountain chain have been acutely folded as in the case of the Alps, but present topography rests upon a later sequence of events. At least three periods of extensive peneplanation and rejuvenation can be traced in three series of flat-topped plateaus or platforms at different levels in the Transylvanian Alps. True Alpine forms occur only where occasional monadnocks were left standing above the level of the highest plateau which itself is but slightly fretted by cirques, giving an Alpine appearance only from below. Most platforms or *plaiuri*[1] are on the middle and lower peneplain surfaces. The real Vulcan Pass is not the wild gorge of the River Jiu, but lies on one of the *plaiuri* frequented by shepherds and used as far back as Roman times, though the modern road and railway route is carried along the river gorge. While the region is heavily forested, there is much pasture on the lower and middle platforms and this is grazed by sheep during the summer months. Before the coming of winter, during which season the mountains are under heavy snow, the sheep are driven down to the lowlands. So far the only significant economic development of this area lies in the mining of bituminous coal near Petria. Communications must be improved before further development, even of timber industries, can be realised.

[1] In Rumanian this means 'paths'.

The Southern Carpathians become lower towards the south-west and, as the Banat Mountains, change to a north–south direction. These begin west of the River Temeş, where the height is less and the structure different. Here sedimentary rocks of Palæozoic and Mesozoic age appear as well as the crystalline. Coal is mined in the Anina basin and iron near Reșița and Hunedoara. These have given rise to Rumania's most important metallurgical and engineering industries located in the Reșița and Hunedoara areas. The Porta Orientalis affords an important route for road and railway links between the otherwise isolated area of western Rumania and the Walachian Plain.

The Bihor Massif and its neighbouring mountains, known in Rumania collectively as the Apuseni (i.e. 'western') Mountains, almost shut off the Transylvanian basin on its western side from the lower-lying Hungarian basin. This, however, does not prevent the rivers of the Transylvanian basin from finding their way westward to join the Tisza in the Hungarian Plain. The Bihor Massif consists partly of ancient crystalline rocks, various Palæozoic and Mesozoic sediments and recent volcanic material. The whole mass is greatly penetrated by fault basins. With its meadow platforms and forested slopes, its economic life is similar to that of the Transylvanian Alps. In the south, formerly important gold and quicksilver mines now operate on a very small scale. In the north, however, recent discoveries of uranium have caused a revaluation of the region.

**The Transylvanian Basin.** This basin lies at a height of 1,500 to 2,000 ft above sea-level. It is composed of almost undisturbed sediments of Tertiary age such as underlie the recent deposits of the Hungarian basin. Owing to the continued sinking of the latter basin, most drainage from Transylvania goes westwards and the relative height of the two basins causes active erosion in the higher one. The Transylvanian basin is thus dissected into very hilly country. Hill summits are rounded, and the clays and sandstones of the area favoured the development of smooth and gentle slopes very favourable for agricultural use. Around the margins of the basin, particularly in the south and east, are a number of small flat-bottomed basins of special fertility: e.g., those of Sibiu and Făgăraş, Braşov, Trei Scaune, Ciuc, and Gheorgheni, though the last three are more properly intermontane.

The peculiar manner in which the River Olt breaks through the lofty Transylvanian Alps represents a beautiful example of river capture which took place when the land north of the mountains stood at a higher level than at present. The resultant gorge, the Red Tower Pass, is of major significance for movement in south-central Europe and is followed by a railway.

The climate of the Transylvanian basin is markedly Continental, with hot summers and cold winters, but is not so extreme as that of the Hungarian basin, while precipitation is heavier, owing to the greater altitude. Originally the area was wooded and not a grassland. Owing to the combination of favourable soil and climate, most of the region has been cleared for cultivation, with maize and wheat as the leading cereals with some orchard land and many vineyards, especially on south-facing slopes along the Mureş river and its tributaries. A good deal of pasture land is to be found, often now being improved by better management in larger, more highly capitalised cooperative farms, so that the area is one of mixed farming. In parts, especially in the north, potatoes are commonly grown, in the centre, hemp, and in the south-east, some sugar-beet. The cultivation of vegetables and industrial crops and the output of dairy produce are being increased by investment and land use planning applied through the collective and cooperative farms. This policy is being applied to support more industrial development, e.g. food- and textile fibre-processing, and to provide more food for the growing non-agricultural labour force. However, the basin is particularly favourable to man for it offers a great variety of resources for productive agriculture and industrial development. These are now being brought into fuller and more intensive use through government investment, although the region is already one of the most advanced in the country.

Considerable mineral deposits are to be found: salt in many localities, natural gas in the interior, some brown coal on the southern border and small deposits of iron-ore in the south-west. Under the postwar policy of economic development the Rumanian government has invested much capital in new industries in all the medium and larger population centres of the basin. Pipelines now link the main sources of natural gas to domestic and industrial consumers in these centres. While used chiefly for fuel and power, the gas also serves as a raw material for new chemical works developed in Făgăraş, the Cluj–Turda area, Sibiu, and the Tirgu–Mureş–Mediaş areas. Salt is processed into soda and other chemical products, primarily in western and south-western Transylvania. New engineering industries are being developed to serve the growing needs of transport and agriculture, and have replaced in importance the historic textile industries in such towns as Braşov (formerly (Oraşul–Stalin), Cluj, and Sibiu. Industry has begun to modify the character of many centres, which were formerly based on marketing predominantly agricultural produce. Originally most towns were German foundations, many built to guard vulnerable passes across the encircling mountains. Thus Braşov (223,000) stands at the northern end of the Predeal and Brau passes, and Sibiu (100,000) at the northern end of the Red Tower Pass. Cluj (201,000) is situated on the main road and railway connecting Budapest with Bucharest. All three centres are well placed in regard to communications over the whole basin and Cluj also with the Hungarian plain. They are thus ideal for the development especially of assembly industries. Braşov, owing to its fine position and proximity to the Ploeşti–Bucharest areas, has surpassed Cluj as the largest city in the basin.

The mountain rampart served in defending Transylvania against the Turks, so that for long it was the most eastern outpost of West-European civilisation. The natural beauty of Transylvania, its medieval towns, its picturesque inhabitants, and its unspoiled countryside combine still to present a scene of strange enchantment, despite the social and economic changes since 1945.

### REFERENCES

B. Uhlig, *Bau und Bild der Karpaten*, Vienna and Leipzig, 1903, is the standard work, though now out of date. See also the relevant chapters in F. Machatschek, *Landeskunde der Sudeten und West-Karpatenländer*, Stuttgart, Engelhorn, 1927, and E. de Martonne, *Europe Centrale*, Paris, Colin, 1930 and 1931, 2 vols.

More recent publications containing material of geographical value are S. A. Fischer-Galati (Ed.), *Romania*, New York, Praeger, 1957, and *Facts and Figures, A Handbook of Czechoslovakia*, Prague, Orbis, 1959, containing a section on Slovakia. Also the *Annales de Géographie*, 1958, Tome LXVII, contains useful short notes on developments in Rumania before that year.

### CHAPTER 31

# THE RUMANIAN LOWLANDS

**The Walachian Plain.** This region has much physical similarity to the Hungarian lowlands, but on the whole its climate is hotter and more arid, especially when compared with the northern part of the Alföld. In some ways it is more monotonous. There are fewer trees and also fewer signs of habitation, and, with relatively few exceptions of poor and mean private farmhouses, the great increase in state and cooperative farming has brought brick buildings in the place of the traditional wood or daub and thatch. The plain is covered by a thick mantle of recent deposits derived from the wastage of the Transylvanian Alps. There is a top-dressing of *Löss*, especially east of the River Olt, and considerable stretches of sand west of that river. The Walachian lowland is separated from the Bulgarian bank of the Danube not only by the main stream of that river, but by its floodplain (known as the *Balta*), a band of swampy country, some 6 to 9 miles wide, studded with lagoons and with deserted river channels. Cliffs border the floodplain on either hand, and although those on the Bulgarian side are higher (rising to some 300 ft above the swamps) and come closer to the river, those on the left bank remind us that the Rumanian plain is just as much a plateau as the Bulgarian 'platform'. Indeed the two are not unlike in soil, climate, and products, but the Danube acted, and still partly acts, as a very real barrier between them owing to the difficulty of building bridges across the broad river and its broader swamps, or of finding a landing-place for a ferry on the northern side. Until 1950 only one bridge, that at Cernavoda, crossed the Danube in the 660 miles of the Rumanian section. For military reasons, and to achieve easier economic integration in south-central Europe, new bridges have been built linking the two banks at Giurgiu and Calafat. A series of broad terraces rise by very gentle stages from the cliff bordering the swamps and floodplains of the Danube until the foothills are reached, roughly at a height of 600 ft. In turn the foothill zone rises to the mountains to the north.

The rivers have mostly incised their beds sufficiently near the water-table for water to be procurable at no great depth, even though rivers from the mountains contain little water in summer and those from the foothills often dry up completely. Springs occur along the

490

valley sides. In August and September, however, the water shortage is acute, even at such a town as Craiova, situated by the River Jiu, one of Walachia's principal rivers, and *before* the river crosses the plain.

Exposed to biting north-east winds in winter and blistering heat in summer, the treeless, waterless plain caused great hardship to the colonists who came from the foothills to people the plain in the nineteenth century. Population is not dispersed here but concentrated where water is available The plain is more suited to large-scale

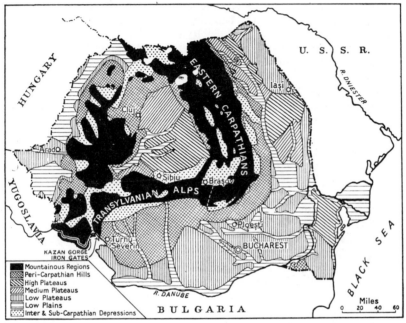

(*after Pelham and Mihăilescu*)

Fig. 60. MORPHOLOGICAL DIAGRAM OF RUMANIA

than to peasant-farming; thus since 1946 there has been much development of state, collective, and cooperative farms to bring farming methods and practices more into harmony with the possibilities offered by the plain. Many areas formerly covered by long narrow strips, worked by ox-drawn ploughs, and under peasant management have been replaced by large square fields worked by tractors and other machinery under collective management. Most of Rumania's export comes from these plains and those beyond the Siret river. For a time exports were much reduced compared with those of pre-1914 as the peasants preferred to grow maize, a crop of which they have more knowledge and which forms their staple food. The state and collective farms have restored the former emphasis on wheat.

Communications across the plain were poor and still are in places, though they are being improved. Many roads are still dirt roads suited only to country carts. There is nothing here to compare with the fine new 'international' road, which runs from Oradea through Transylvania via Braşov to Bucharest. This is being extended to Constanţa on the Black Sea. One railway runs the length of the plain linking settlements along the foothill zone with Bucharest, and sending off branches to the Danube.

In Oltenia, to the west of the River Olt, the land is higher with rather more than half the region between the mountains and the Danube occupied by foothills which send long forest-covered fingers southwards. Here it is difficult to say where the foothill zone ends and the plain begins. The steppelands here are themselves less steppe-like, and have more variety of relief, a heavier rainfall, more numerous springs, and a more diversified agriculture. Besides cereals, cotton, tobacco, the vine, soya beans, sunflowers, and fruits are cultivated, mainly near the valleys and on the slopes.

The most favourable portion of the Walachian plain is that in which Bucharest was built. This region, extending between Ploeşti and the confluence of the Rivers Danube and Arges, is known as Vlăsia. Here are precisely those supplies of water and woodland which are generally lacking elsewhere on the plain. The two main rivers, Argeş and Dâmboviţa,[1] and their higher tributaries come from the high mountains and contain water even in summer, despite the fact that the Dâmboviţa at Bucharest is hardly more than an insignificant brook, now partly carried underground. It seems that the erosion gradient in this region is less now than formerly; rivers have not incised their beds to any extent, and are nearly all level with the plain. In any case, the water-table is near the surface so that trees will grow easily; considerable patches of natural woodland still remain. In addition to these natural advantages, the region has benefited from its position on the overland route between Constantinople and Transylvania via the Bran Pass at the head of the Dâmboviţa and the old Danube crossing at Giurgiu. Along this route in the past an active exchange of products took place between the Orient and central Europe. Today its major importance lies in its relationship to Bucharest, the capital, and to its cross-roads location for land routes between the USSR and western

[1] Pronounced *Dimbovitsa*.

Bulgaria on the one hand, and between eastern Bulgaria and Transylvania on the other.

*Bucharest*. In medieval times Bucharest became a princely residence and flourished as a market place on two small hills originally
selected to serve the need for a defensive and flood-free site above
the cultivated plain. After suffering plunderings, burnings, and
epidemics, the town grew to about 100,000 inhabitants in 1800; as
an outpost of the Ottoman Empire, it was very oriental-looking
with an extraordinarily cosmopolitan population drawn from as
far away as Germany, Italy, Turkey, Armenia, and Bulgaria, in
addition to the Rumanians. A new era began after the Russo-
Turkish wars in the late eighteenth century, and the city grew with
the emergence and expansion of the Rumanian state. With only
121,000 inhabitants in 1860, by 1912 it numbered 341,000, and in
1962 1,355,000. The city had lost its oriental character by the
early twentieth century, but the greatest changes have taken place
since 1918. It is now modern in appearance, with an impression
not only of the bustling life of a capital city but also of orderliness,
with long straight avenues of new flats and offices, and of cleanliness.
The administrative, commercial, and cultural interests of Rumania
are all concentrated, indeed over-concentrated, in Bucharest; hence
efforts to decentralize its functions by developing backward areas
or by creating satellite towns such as Jilava. Its industrial growth
has been spectacular, keeping pace with Rumania's overall industrialisation. The city remains the largest centre of manufacturing,
localising one-sixth of the country's industry, notably engineering
and machinery, food processing, oil refining, rubber manufactures,
and clothing.

Apart from Bucharest there are no towns in the midst of the plain.
All the others are on the margins, either near the foothills or along
the Danube.

The position of the two chief Danubian ports, Galaţi (110,000) and
Brăila (117,000),[1] strikes the eye as curious in that they are only nine
miles apart. Originally they were rival ports, the first being in the
principality of Moldavia and the latter in the principality of Walachia
before the union of the two in 1859. Each stands on a piece of
firm ground that approaches the river on the northern side, but
both have been long losing trade to Constanţa (148,000) on the
Black Sea coast. The Brăila–Galaţi area is now becoming of great
industrial significance in the Rumanian economy with large new
iron and steel, chemical, timber-working, cellulose, and paper
industries.

The population of the Walachian plain is entirely Rumanian and

[1] Population figures for 1962 from the *Statistical Yearbook of Rumania*, 1963.

was settled from the foothills of the north, mainly in the nineteenth century.

**The Rumanian Foothills.** These form a fairly narrow but economically important band of country in Moldavia and also in Walachia as far west as the Dâmboviţa district. The folded Tertiaries of this eastern section contain important deposits of petroleum in the Prahova and Dâmboviţa districts. Large deposits of salt are worked near Slănic and less important amounts of salt and petroleum in the Bacău district of Moldavia. Bacău (73,000) has become an important centre for chemicals. West of the Dâmboviţa, a region of much dissected foothills stretches out in front of the Carpathians, separated from them by the sub-Carpathian tectonic depression. The whole region is a land of ancient settlements, smiling villages, old monasteries, and a fairly dense population now being modified by the effects of postwar government policies. New housing and collective or cooperative farm buildings appear more and more. Wooded uplands usually separate the valleys from each other. Smaller holdings, cooperative rather than state farms, and a great diversity of crops are the rule, catering increasingly for the food demands of the Ploesti–Braşov, Galaţi–Constanţa, and Bucharest market areas. Through the cooperatives there has been a great increase in pig rearing here for the same purposes. Fruit trees, especially plums, are abundant and the vine is widely grown. The population is more dispersed than in the plain. The most favoured zone of the foothills is the sub-Carpathian depression, which may be regarded as the cradle of Rumanian nationality. At the outer edge of the foothills, standing on the plain, are a number of market towns which are also becoming manufacturing centres. The development of factories producing fertilisers, other chemicals, paper, and electrical apparatus illustrates this change; they are partly dependent on local resources (oil, gas, timber), on the local agricultural market (fertilisers), and on local labour (the electrical industry). Craiova (133,500), Bužau (78,000), and Slatina are the most important. Ploeşti (167,000) is experiencing very rapid growth associated with the expansion of Rumania's oil-drilling and oil-refining activities. The output of petroleum in 1962 was 12 million tons, compared with 1·9 million in 1913 and 6·6 million in 1938.

**The Moldavian Platform.** From the foothills of the Eastern or Moldavian Carpathians begins the great east European or 'Russian' platform, stretching away towards the east. The Moldavian section of this platform lies between the marshy floodplains of the River Siret on the west and the Prut on the east, and is developed on slightly tilted sedimentary rocks of Tertiary age. The region is by no means flat, especially in the central portion which reaches 1,300 ft in places.

In relief, eastern Moldavia falls naturally into three regions: a northern lowland, a central dissected plateau, and a southern plain. The northern lowland consists of sandstones and clays which have been weathered into rounded, broad-backed hills, though on the west the land overlooking the River Siret is higher and more plateau-like. The whole region, except for this plateau, is a hilly steppe. The valleys, however, tend to be waterlogged after the spring snow melt while the more important ones, which are cut down to the clay, are marshy for most of the year. In contrast, the hills are mainly *Löss*-covered and the soils mainly *chernozem*; these are excellent for grain, but the region is liable to disastrous droughts. Only now are the extensive drainage and irrigation works, necessary to stabilise conditions for agriculture, being undertaken here. Except in the extreme west the landscape is singularly naked-looking, and the little villages appear bare and miserable, without trees to protect them from the biting blizzards of winter and the blistering heat of summer.

This lowland continues as far south as Iaşi, where it is overlooked by the great limestone scarp marking the northern edge of the central plateau. The higher northern part of the plateau has been protected to some extent from erosion by a thick capping of Tertiary (Sarmatian = late Miocene) limestone, though the rivers have cut deep, steep-sided valleys (cf. the English Cotswolds or the French Plateau de Langres). Farther south, the limestone sinks beneath layers of sandstones, gravels, and clays, and the landscape has softer forms. The whole plateau region recalls the Walachian foothills in physical appearance and human and economic geography. Woods and pastures cover the heights, the less steep slopes are cultivated, the moist valleys are devoted to meadows or maize; vineyards are common while regional specialities are pumpkins and beans. The villages lie among orchards in the shelter of valleys. The plateau is a region of ancient Rumanian settlement and so also are the terraces bordering the Siret and Prut floodplains.

The plateau sends fingers of upland southward (as in Oltenia), so it is difficult to say where the upland ends and the southern plain begins. South of Bârlad, however, the land is almost flat, trees are very rare, water sources are scanty, and *Löss* becomes increasingly prevalent until the real Black Earth is reached. The treeless steppe is devoted to cereal growing as in northern Moldavia, although sugar-beet has become important on large cooperative and state farms.

Eastern Moldavia is underdeveloped economically, with few railways, few good roads, and few towns. However, it is one of Rumania's 'backward regions' and considerable efforts have been made since 1948 to develop it, chiefly by means of industrialisation. New industries are based primarily on local timber, agricultural produce (sugar-beet, vines, sunflowers), oil, and salt from the Carpathians, or on the use of local labour in industries such as textiles, pharmaceuticals, and light engineering. Iaşi (157,000) is the capital, the largest town, and a rapidly expanding industrial centre, while Bârlad, Botosani, and Roman have acquired their first industrial establishments. A nuclear power station has been located at Roman to provide the power needed for developing industries and to electrify the towns and villages.

**The Dobruja.** Rumania's trans-Danubian province is a treeless peneplain. Its surface is *Löss*-covered and underlain by chalk so that the region is particularly lacking in surface streams, but it is seamed by *wadis*, especially in the middle portion where the arid plateau looks like a slice of Africa. The Dobruja (Rum., Dobrojea) falls abruptly both to the Black Sea coast and to the Danube. It undoubtedly accounts for the northward bend of the Danube, which once more turns east at Galaţi, when freed from this natural embankment. The greater part of Dobruja is now under the plough, chiefly for wheat, though also for flax in the south, tobacco in the north, and sunflowers everywhere. Yields tend to be low, but through the application of fertilisers and more scientific farming the cooperative and state farms are achieving better results. Sheep are still important, though on the hill pastures. The northern hills still carry some trees but are now being transformed into a copper-mining area which is cutting into the higher forest. The only town of any size is Constanţa; however some charming seaside resorts have lately developed here, for example Mamaia, with its fine skyscraper hotels. The seaport of Constanţa is artificial, but is of great and growing importance to Rumania as it is practically ice-free and serves as the port for Bucharest. Engineering, textiles, and canning industries are notable and partly based on the commerce of Constanţa. An oil pipeline connects it with Ploeşti.

The southern part of Dobruja, which was annexed from Bulgaria in 1913, reverted to the latter country in 1945.

**Lowlands in the Pannonian Plain.** Because the eastern fringe of the Pannonian Plain was mainly inhabited by Rumanians who came from the mountains during the eighteenth century, it passed under Rumanian rule at the break up of the Austro-Hungarian empire in 1918. This fringe consists for the most part of fertile agricultural land, growing wheat, maize, sugar-beet, tobacco, and fodder crops, and carrying considerable numbers of livestock including cattle, pigs, and geese. In former days the rivers flooded far and wide, but the marshes were largely reclaimed in the nineteenth and early twentieth centuries, though the drained soil unfortunately frequently developed alkali patches. A number of medium-sized towns served as exchange points for the products of the plain with those (chiefly timber) of Transylvania. Such towns as Oradea (120,500) on the Crişul Repede ('Rapid' Criş), Satu Mare (61,000) on the Someş, Arad (124,000) on the Mureş, and Timişoara (better known as Temesvar; 145,000) on the canalised River Bega, have become locations for varied industries, particularly engineering, railway equipment, machinery, electrical, light chemical, textile, and timber processing.

**Rumania.** The state of Rumania has grown in a remarkable fashion since 1859. In that year the two Rumanian-speaking principalities of Walachia and Moldavia united, and from that year dates the beginning of the country's westernisation. Previously the region had been under Byzantine, Turkish, and Russian influences and was extremely backward economically. The first bank, founded as late as 1857, was a complete failure, and the first railway was not opened until 1869. The boundary changes of 1918, adding Transylvania, Bucovina, Bessarabia, and eastern Pannonia, doubled the area of Rumania, and almost doubled the population, but rendered it less homogeneous. World War II brought the territorial loss of Bessarabia and Bucovina to the USSR. In 1962, of the 18·6 million inhabitants, some 1½ millions were Magyars and Szekely, 390,000 were Germans, and 140,000 Jews.

The Rumanians claimed to be descendants of the colonists and Romanised inhabitants of the Roman province of Dacia, though there has been considerable intermixture with Slavonic-speaking peoples. The language has a Latin basis and the country looked to the Romance-speaking peoples for support and guidance, though also to Russia, since by religion the people belong to the Greek Orthodox and Uniat churches. Since the second world war Soviet political and economic influence has been very strong and has reoriented the country's outlook.

Rumania is overwhelmingly agricultural, though the number of people employed in agriculture is decreasing and the non-agricultural and urban population has rapidly increased since 1945. Now one-third of its inhabitants live in the towns and work outside agriculture, compared with only one-fifth in 1930. Even so over 60 per cent of the people live on farms. Following the agricultural reform laws of 1917, large estates were broken up to satisfy the land hunger of the peasants, and the amount of agricultural produce available for export somewhat decreased. There was little industrial development owing to the shortage of coal and iron and insufficient knowledge of those resources, to historical backwardness, and to lack of capital, so that the country depended on its exports of petroleum, cereals, and timber for its ability to import the necessary manufactured goods.

Major changes followed the second world war and still continue. Agriculture has been reorganised into state, collective, and cooperative farms to embrace now over 85 per cent of all land. Wheat is the principal cereal exported, since maize is the staple food for home consumption. Rumania may still be looked upon as one of the granaries of Europe. Forestry is also very important and has become more so with the intensification of the use of timber in industry; scientific forest management and reafforestation are now in progress. Some progress had been made towards industrialisation before World War II but the major developments in this field have come since then. With help from the more developed members of COMECON – the USSR, Czechoslovakia, the German Democratic Republic, and Poland – production has been expanded to 7 million tons of hard coal in 1962, $4\frac{1}{2}$ million tons of brown coal, and $1\frac{1}{2}$ million tons of steel. Oil production and refining in the Ploeşti region is by far the largest industry. Among other industries are the various chemical industries using Transylvanian natural gas, the scattered textile industry, the widespread timber and cellulose-paper industries, the engineering industry of Resiţa, the growing iron and steel of Hunedoara, and the cement industry. Bucharest is concerned with numerous secondary industries. New areas of industry are being created, however, by deliberately planning the economic development of backward areas. This can be seen most clearly in the location of new manufacturing plants in Moldavia based on three points of industrial growth: at Galaţi (iron and steel), at Roman (nuclear power), and in the Bacău region (salt and oil processing). The development of hydro-electric power in the Transylvanian Alps and southern foothill zone provides the prerequisite for the industrialisation of western and south-western Rumania. The villages still rely on their own hand-made textiles, pottery, and rugs, now largely organised on a cooperative basis and partly aimed at the growing tourist trade.

## REFERENCES

E. de Martonne, *La Valachie*, Paris, Colin, 1902, is still a classic monograph on this region. Among the many books on the economic geography of Rumania the following may be noted: G. D. Cioriceanu, *La Roumanie Economique de 1860 à 1915*, Paris, M. Giard, 1928, and by the same author, *Les Grands Ports de Roumanie*, Paris, M. Giard, 1928. H. Conrad, *Die Wirtschaft Rumäniens, 1945–1952*, West Berlin, 1954, may be added for the early postwar period. The most recent book, by M. Haşeganu (Ed.), *An Economic Geography of*

*Rumania,* Moscow, Foreign Literature Publishing House, 1962, is in Rumanian and Russian only.

For the human geography, H. J. Fleure and R. A. Pelham (Eds.), *Eastern Carpathian Studies*, London, Le Play, 1936, and H. J. Fleure and E. Estyn Evans, *South Carpathian Studies*, London, Le Play, 1939, contain interesting material.

The Bulletin of the Rumanian Geographical Society, Bucharest, contains many interesting articles, often with French or German summaries, including some recent issues, though its postwar successor is largely only in Rumanian and Russian.

### CHAPTER 32

# THE BALKAN PENINSULA (I)

## YUGOSLAVIA AND ALBANIA

OWING to its position and shape the south-eastern or Balkan peninsula is the least Mediterranean of the three southern peninsulas of Europe, though paradoxically it includes Greece, parts of which provide textbook examples of a Mediterranean country. The broad base which joins the peninsula to the rest of the Continent not only allows the penetration of continental influences, but also the development in the northern and central areas of high pressure in winter and low pressure in summer. The result is that most of the peninsula has severe, snowy winters and hot, rainy summers. Thus the natural vegetation, agriculture, and the pattern of human geography generally are necessarily different from those of the other two southern peninsulas.

The Balkan peninsula is a region of even higher and more broken relief than either Iberia or Italy, being mainly above 1,200 ft with a large part over 3,000 ft. It lacks the level plateaus of central Iberia, and has nothing comparable to the Ebro basin or to the northern Italian plain. It lacks any considerable lowland to form a nucleus around which a really strong political state could be built up. The largest areas of lowland lie on the eastern periphery, in the very teeth of invasions from Asia. In fact the stormy history of the Balkan peninsula may be attributed very largely to a combination of unfavourable position and unfavourable relief, the former rendering it a conflict area of different types of civilisation, and the rugged relief rendering it a difficult area for political unification, human circulation, communications, profitable agriculture and industry. Moreover in place of the high mountain barriers which largely cut off each of the other two peninsulas from the rest of the continent, the Balkan peninsula lies open and exposed to the north. Its five political units reflect its rôle of a meeting place for different types of culture. The postwar history of fluid political and economic orientations of member states, particularly Yugoslavia and Albania, serve to emphasise this point.

Both in structure and relief the Balkan peninsula is complex, though the broad outlines are deceptively simple. It consists essentially of young folded mountains lying against the northern and western sides of an ancient crystalline massif (see Fig. 2, p. 5), generally known as the Rhodope (or Rodopi) block.[1]  The massif, which represents the stumps of an old folded system, is composed mainly of crystalline schists, with considerable outcrops of granite, gabbro, and serpentine.  Its north-west corner reaches nearly to Belgrade, its eastern corner almost to Istanbul (Constantinople), and its

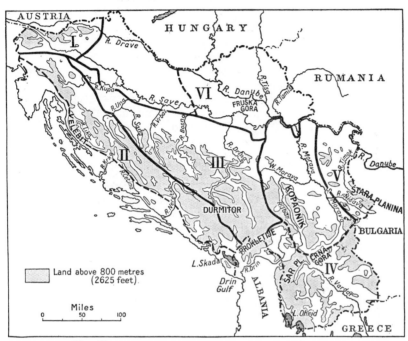

Fig. 61. GEOGRAPHICAL REGIONS OF YUGOSLAVIA
I. The alpine zone.  II. The Western Dinaric region, comprising the Karst and the coastal fringe.  III. The eastern Dinaric region.  IV. The Morava–Vardar corridor lands.  V. The Balkan mountains of north-east Serbia.  VI. Yugoslav lands in the Pannonian lowlands.

southern corner to Thessaloniki (Salonika).  Its south-western extension to the Gulf of Volos is sometimes known as the Pelagonian massif.  Part of the massif has foundered beneath the Ægean Sea.

The young folded mountains belong to two systems.  On the north-east lie the Balkan folds (known in Bulgaria as the Stara Planina, i.e. 'old mountains').  These appear to be a continuation

[1] The Rhodope Mountains proper, which lie in Bulgaria, form only a small portion of the massif.

of the Carpathian system.    On the west lie the Dinaric folds, a much
broader and longer range.    The present relief is due not so much to
the original tectonic movements as to subsequent events.    By late
Tertiary times the whole Balkan peninsula had been reduced to a
peneplain, showing mature relief features, and with arms of the sea
invading all low-lying parts.    New earth movements, mainly epeirogenic, caused re-elevation of the greater part of the area at the close
of Tertiary times.    A good deal of faulting occurred, mainly in a
north-west to south-east direction, but occasionally in an east to
west direction, as along the western Morava river and Gulf of
Corinth.    Warping or torsion seems to have taken place along the
Adriatic coast, so that parts of the western Dinaric folds remained
near sea-level.    With the re-elevation a new erosion cycle began,
resulting in the drainage of most of the area covered by seas and
lakes, rejuvenation of the river system, much river-capture, and the
development of gorges where hard rocks were encountered or where
streams were flowing across the grain of the country.

## THE WESTERN PART OF THE BALKAN PENINSULA

**The Dinaric System.**    This system extends from the Ljubljana
basin on the north to the southern tip of the Greek mainland.    It
is broadest in Yugoslavia where it trends north-west to south-east,
and where also the distinctive feature of the Karst is widely developed.
This high Karst desert offers, and has always offered, a great barrier
to communication between the excellent harbours of the Dalmatian
coast and the fruitful lands of industrial resources and good agricultural potentialities in Bosnia, Croatia, and Serbia.    Air transport
is helping to overcome the barrier at least for perishable goods and
for tourist traffic to and from the coast.

Near the Drin Gulf and Lake Scutari (Skadar), the north-west to
south-east trend is brusquely interrupted by the Prokletije Mountains running at right angles to the main Dinaric trend.    The direction of the coastline also changes, and runs from north to south to
Cape Glossa; the mountains south of the Prokletije resume almost
the same trend as further north.    In this north–south Albanian
section the mountains are fronted seaward by still partly malarial
lowlands poor in natural harbours.    Prewar Italian investment in
roads and postwar Soviet investment in port and railway construction, however, somewhat altered the situation.    Today, though, it
is the political orientation of Albania which decides the value of
such development for penetration into the interior.    Thus the Balkan
peninsula turns its back, as it were, on the Adriatic and Italy, though
it is open to the north, to the east, and to the south-east.    Physically,

therefore, its 'natural' orientation is towards the Danube and its tributaries, to the Black Sea, and ultimately, the Soviet Union.

The Yugoslav Section of the Dinaric System. This section falls into two main regions. On the west and south-west is the Karst region, composed of highly permeable limestone, with a fringe of more productive country in the islands and along the coast. On the north-east lie the forested mountains and hill country of the Sava drainage area; because of their mineral wealth these are sometimes called the Dinaric Ore Mountains.

*The Western Dinaric Region. The Coastal Fringe.* Along the drowned concordant coast occur the strata of Cretaceous and Eocene age. Usually, strips of limestone form the forested or denuded islands and ridges, and alternate with strips of Flysch, forming depressions and the major areas of cultivation.

The climate may be called Mediterranean in type, with dry summers and usually brilliant skies, a major factor in the rapidly growing tourist industry there. The annual rainfall is rather heavy, however, Rijeka (Fiume), Dubrovnik, and Split on the coast having respectively 63, 59, and 34 inches.

Mediterranean crops such as olives, vines, and figs are grown on the very limited amount of lowland and on terraced hillsides, provided the soil is suitable. On the limestones even of the coastal belt, however, only meagre pasture for grazing sheep and goats is to be found. Italian influences (e.g. in architecture) are ubiquitous and until 1945 the towns of the region were inhabited by a considerable number of Italian-speaking people. The whole population is Slav, though they have adopted a Mediterranean mode of life and are largely occupied with horticulture and fishing. A major problem of this region, however, has been, and still is, division of the land into tiny 'pocket-handkerchief' patches as a result of a rapid growth in population and the laws of inheritance. Only since 1947 has a vigorous policy of economic development in Yugoslavia generally begun to reduce overpopulation here by removing people from agriculture into industry, commerce, transport, and tourism. This in turn is beginning to affect agriculture and to intensify the region's specialisation on horticultural produce, especially fruit.

Although the coastlands have changed hands politically many times in the past, yet the chief towns retain some of their character of Mediterranean city-states, engaged in commerce by land and sea. In the Middle Ages, when ships were smaller and commercial goods consisted mainly of small or valuable commodities, the latter could be brought on mule-back across the difficult mountainous interior, and more towns were engaged in commerce than at the present day; consequently, the coasts of both the mainland and islands are dotted with picturesque little Italianate towns complete with city walls, loggias, campaniles, piazzas, and Renaissance buildings. These are now being transformed into growing tourist centres, with new hotels, camping sites, and other service facilities changing the character of their social and economic life.

The tide of economic development is changing even more significantly those towns served by the few railways and which, nowadays, are commercially important. The towns of Rijeka (Fiume–Sušak, population 100,000)[1] and especially Split (99,000), are expanding rapidly with modern housing estates, following the great growth in Yugoslavia's seaborne trade since 1948 and in associated ship-building, engineering, and chemical industries in both centres. The cement industry near Split is also expanding to meet growing home and overseas demands. Šibenik, traditionally like Split, handles local trade in wine, olive oil, and other Mediterranean goods; far more important, however, are its exports of local bauxite and its growth as a major Yugoslav aluminium industrial centre based on the bauxite and hydro-electric power from the Cetina and Krka rivers. Zadar (It., Zara; 25,500), which lost its rôle as capital of Dalmatia when the town became an Italian enclave in 1918 and was thus separated from its hinterland, may recapture something of its old position now that it has been provided with railway connexions. It is developing into an auxiliary port to Split, with new light industries to provide employment in an underdeveloped region. The considerable growth of tourism has stimulated the expansion of Dubrovnik in particular. The recent completion of an Adriatic highway from Trieste–Rijeka to Dubrovnik, is encouraging the growth of tourism also in intermediate small towns and villages along the coast, and is facilitating the development of many more isolated and backward areas.

Through migration, these changes are tending to increase the density of population in the Adriatic coastal zone relative to that in the high karstic region further east, despite the limestone character of the coast.

*The High Karst.* The high, barren limestone Karst of Yugoslavia is the most outstanding example in Europe of a type of topography which is found on a smaller scale in numerous other places, cf. the Causses of the Massif Central in France, and the Slovakian Karst. It stretches for 350 miles from north-west to south-east, and has a maximum breadth of about 50 miles. It has a maximum height of over 8,000 ft, though it is not so much the height or the breadth which makes it such a barrier, as its barren waterless character.

Although developed on a folded mountain system, yet the region

[1] Figures for 1961 from the *Statistical Yearbook of Yugoslavia*, 1962.

was so thoroughly peneplained that it now consists largely of barren stony plateaus, ribbed from north-west to south-east by flattish ridges, known as *planine*, and containing elongated basins known as *polja*.

The limestone of which the whole region is composed is singularly

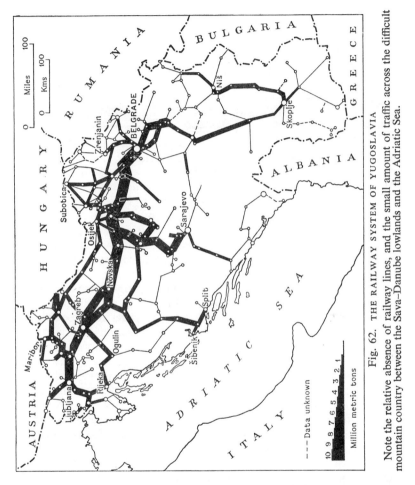

Fig. 62. THE RAILWAY SYSTEM OF YUGOSLAVIA

Note the relative absence of railway lines, and the small amount of traffic across the difficult mountain country between the Sava–Danube lowlands and the Adriatic Sea.

porous, so that there is a general absence of surface water. This is not owing to any lack of rainfall; on the contrary, the rainfall is one of the heaviest in Europe, in places reaching over 180 in. This precipitation, however, disappears underground and forms a vast network of subterranean drainage which is useless to the inhabitants of the region, who are obliged to procure their water supply by storing snow in caves and rainwater in cisterns. Only one river, the Neretva, traverses the whole of the zone above ground, and this only maintains itself because it has been powerful enough to cut a deep cañon which reaches below the water-table and so is fed from subterranean springs at the sides of the gorge (cf. the Tarn gorge in the Causses of France). It seems likely, however, from the presence of dry valleys on the plateau surfaces, that there was more surface drainage in former times than at present. This view is borne out by a number of now dry *polja* which have fresh-water Tertiary deposits, indicating that karstification was undoubtedly intensified by the re-elevation of the whole area and the consequent lowering of the water-table.

The scanty vegetation of the Karst can support only a few sheep and goats, apart from the occasional depressions where a little soil has accumulated and where cultivation can accordingly be carried on. These depressions fall into two main classes, the *polja* (sing., *polje*, a Serbian word meaning 'field'), which are large depressions running parallel to the strike of the rock, and *doline* (sing., *dolina*), which are small round depressions formed by the solution of the limestone and floored with a residual soil of a bright red colour. To these may be added the lowlands of the lower Neretva valley. Many *polja*, unfortunately, are inundated in autumn and spring, which are the rainiest seasons, and are therefore useless for perennial cultures such as trees, or for crops which need a long growing season. They are therefore devoted almost entirely to cereals, maize in the lower *polja*, e.g. Popovo, and wheat in the higher, though attempts are being made to expand the new cotton acreages in these areas. Unduly prolonged inundation can still cause serious local grain shortage. Plans are being drawn up to control and improve water-supply conditions in selected areas of the Karst country by developing hydro-electric power projects, with linked schemes for drainage and irrigation of the *polja* and lowlands to permit the intensive cultivation of tobacco, fruits, and vegetables. Lake Scutari (Skadar) may be looked upon as a *polje* which is permanently flooded, though a scheme is pending for the reclamation of some 150,000 acres. The *polja* concentrate most of the scanty population of the High Karst. There are few urban centres with over four thousand inhabitants, the main exception being Mostar, the old administrative centre of Hercegovina, situated at an important crossing place of the River Neretva, and a market centre for the lower Neretva valley. Since the second world war the construction of new mines to exploit substantial bauxite and brown coal resources, the location of large textile, timber-manufacturing and engineering industries, and the intensification of agriculture with the associated growth of food-, cotton-, and tobacco-processing factories in the vicinity, have greatly strengthened the economic position of the town. As a result, its population increased from 31,500 in 1953 to 50,000 in 1963. Cetinje, although the former capital of Montenegro, is now of only local importance. The new town and capital, Titograd (30,500), a centre of a large new aluminium industry, and Nikšić (21,000) with its bauxite mines and steel industries are now far more important.

The High Karst descends to the coast by abrupt gradients. Accordingly, although movement along the grain of the Karst is relatively easy (hence the new industrial developments along the Mostar–Nikšić–Titograd axis), it is very difficult to find practicable routes down to the coast either by road or rail. Only three railway lines reach the coast, and these are all single-track. In the north the port of Rijeka (formerly the twin ports of Fiume–Sušak) are served by a standard-gauge line with very steep gradients; the Split–Šibenik–Zadar area is connected with the Lika *polje* and now with the middle Sava lowlands (via Sisak-Novska) by other standard gauge lines; but communication to the rapidly growing 'industrial core' region of central Bosnia is still by narrow-gauge through difficult country. The Dubrovnik-Gruž area has only very circuitous narrow-gauge connexions inland, with two rack-and-pinion sections. The haulage of heavy loads and a frequent railway service are unimaginable on these narrow-gauge, single-track lines, with their many steep gradients and sharp curves, so that little traffic from the Sava–Danube lowlands finds its way across the Karst to Yugoslavia's ports. Changes now taking place will, when complete, revolutionise the trade relationships of the coast and interior. A new standard-gauge line is being constructed from Sarajevo to a new port at Ploče near the mouth of the Neretva river in order to link industrial Central Bosnia more effectively with the coast and with overseas markets. Similarly a new line is under construction from Belgrade to Bar in Montenegro to give Serbia a direct outlet. Roads running inland from the coast are relatively numerous, but usually possess hair-raising zig-zags and gradients. Though these are being improved too, they are unsuitable for heavy traffic at present.

*The Albanian Section of the Dinaric System.* The great Prokletije range, sometimes called the North Albanian Alps, forms the frontier between Yugoslavia and Albania.

The little country of Albania is unique in the Dinaric lands in not having a concordant coast, but a triangular-shaped lowland, seamed with lines of low hills, developed on the Flysch and Tertiaries of the coastal zone. The base of this lowland is the Adriatic coast between the Drin Gulf and Cape Glossa; its apex is near Elbasan. Despite the alternation of malarial, waterlogged depressions, and *maquis-*covered limestone hills giving pasture only to sheep and goats, this lowland focuses the country's economic life.   As a satellite country of the Soviet Union from 1946 to 1962, Albania received much money and equipment for the economic development of this lowland.   Extensive drainage and pest control made considerable areas suitable for agriculture, especially for grain, while the region between the mouth of the River Drin and Valona (Alb., Vlona) specialises on growing some cotton, tobacco, and citrus fruits as secondary products, and that north of the Drin on tobacco and dairy products. Farming is organised chiefly on a cooperative basis.

The lowland has also been the scene of Albania's very recent industrial development, based on local oil, salt, and asphalt resources, surplus labour, and trade, which for ideological reasons, is forced to go through Albanian ports and not through Yugoslavia or Greece. The construction of Albania's first railways after 1948, linking Elbasan and Tirana with the port of Durres, greatly assisted this development.   Oil production and oil refining have been expanded along the Seman river, especially just south of Elbasan, as also has salt output along the coast.   Durres has been converted into a sizeable artificial port serving northern and central Albania, and this function has stimulated the growth of industries processing imported materials, such as rubber and metals, and serving local needs. Tirana (130,000), the capital, has become the country's main industrial centre with varied food, textile, timber, engineering, and glass industries.   It is also the centre of administration and of the road network.   Of the settlements of notable size which lie mainly along the foot of the mountains or just within them Elbasan is the most important, with food, tobacco and timber industries.

The southern section of Albania consists of lofty mountain ranges trending north-west to south-east, alternating with deep river valleys along which Greek influences penetrated.   The inhabitants of the southern valleys, Viosa, Dhrino, Osum, are Greek in religion and to some extent in culture, affording a bone of contention between Greece and Albania.   Pastoral life prevails, as on the southern side of the frontier, though there has been some industrial development in the extreme south based on local brown coal, water power, food and tobacco products.   Where the ranges run out to sea, the excellent natural harbour of Valona is developed in an intermontane depression; it is a centre of growing trade, and cement, food, and brown coal mining industries.

The high mountain zone of interior Albania stretches south from the River Drin to the southern end of Lake Prespa.   Four, in places five, more or less parallel zones can be recognised.   The outer or western mountain zone consists of barren ranges through which rivers flow in difficult gorges to the lowlands, and which offer good possibilities for future hydro-electric power development. There is an inner tectonic depression, occupied by the upper courses of various rivers and filled by young sediments, offering facilities for intensive agriculture. This discontinuous depression is succeeded eastwards by the lofty central zone, where there is much forest providing the raw materials for rapidly developing timber manufacturing

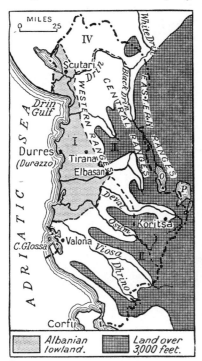

works. In this zone, too, there is much new mining activity, mainly extracting chrome, copper, and nickel-iron ores. The range is very difficult to cross, except in the north and south. It offers a great barrier between the western longitudinal furrow and the next depression which is occupied by the Black Drin, Lake Ohrid (Ochrid), and the Koritsa (Korče) basin. This eastern furrow is not so traversable as might appear from a small-scale map since it is divided physically into compartments and politically between Yugoslavia and Albania. As a result, only the Korče basin, accessible by roads from Elbasan, is being developed significantly. Agriculture here is being improved and intensified mainly to increase cereal and dairy production to meet the growing needs of the local urban and

Fig. 63. ALBANIA: GEOGRAPHICAL REGIONS

industrial population. The mining of brown coal for power and the production of cement, manufactured foods, textiles, and leather goods are developing in this region. A fifth zone, a mountainous one, which lies mainly in Yugoslavia, intrudes into northern Albania (see Fig. 63).

These zones are separated by the River Drin from the Prokletije mountains. This river takes advantage of a lowland bay in the coastal Tertiaries and of the absence of the Karst belt to develop a transverse valley, and river capture has enabled it to tap the Metohija basin by means of its tributary, the White Drin. The Metohija basin is in Yugoslavia, though its population is largely Albanian.

The tiny land of Albania has an area of only 11,000 square miles and a population of just over 1·6 million. Until the years following the second world war her people and economy have remained the most backward in Europe. This backwardness results from the interplay of a number of factors. The extreme physical division of the country, and the acceptance of Islam by the Albanians at the time of the Turkish conquests cut the nation off from the advances that came through contact and cooperation with other peoples, especially those of western Europe. A patriarchal social organisation prevailed until the 1950s and blood feuds were rife until recently. And after their independence from the Turks in 1913, their economic progress became the sphere of political dictates. In the 1930s Albania became an appendage of Italy and much investment was made in roads, oil, and cement production for military purposes, even before the 'conquest' of Good Friday, 1939. After 1945 Albania became a satellite of the Soviet Union and assumed an importance disproportionate to her size, population, and resources. Her strategic position on the Mediterranean, and her useful resources of oil and non-ferrous metals encouraged the Soviet government to develop Albania economically. Between 1945 and 1961 some seventy mines and factories were constructed in the country using equipment imported from the USSR, Czechoslovakia, and Poland. The main towns grew from small to medium size, especially Tirana, and agriculture was modernised and collectivised to a considerable degree. Since 1962, however, Albania has reoriented herself politically and economically to the Chinese People's Republic, and all ties with the USSR have been severed.

*The Eastern Dinaric Region.* The Karst belt is succeeded eastward by a zone of forested mountains with normal river drainage. The rocks are very varied, their character and associated environmental elements offering wide and varied possibilities for economy activities. Mesozoic sandstones, limestones, and shales predominate, although the rocks range from Tertiary sedimentaries in the north-eastern foothills bordering the Sava valley to Palæozoic and pre-Cambrian crystalline schists in north-central Bosnia. Limestones here cover less extensive areas so that they do not affect the surface supply of water, and indeed there is much forest. The main ranges tend from north-west to south-east with summit levels at or over 6,000 ft. The whole area is highly dissected, and movement in any direction is confronted by rugged country. Although the Eastern Dinaric Region is drained by the right-bank tributaries of the Sava, such as the Drina, Bosna, Vrbas, and part of the Una–

Sava and Kupa systems, yet these rivers offer singularly little help to movement since their valleys cut across the grain of the country and contain long gorge-like stretches.

Nevertheless, very considerable efforts have been and are being made to provide this tangle of forest mountains with transport facilities. Communications, once difficult with the outside world and largely by narrow-gauge railways, have been improved by the construction of new standard-gauge railways linking all the main towns with each other and with the rest of the country, and by new road construction. The main stimulus in opening up this region lies in its resources fundamental to Yugoslavia's industrialisation: timber, varied minerals, abundant hydro-electric power, and several fertile basins of potentially intensive agriculture.

About 40 per cent of Yugoslavia's timber is situated here, about half the total surface of Bosnia being forest covered, with beech, oak, and conifers predominating. The postwar industrialisation policy has transformed this region from a timber-exporting into a timber processing region, many new woodworking, cellulose, and paper factories having been developed along the main valleys and in the basins. Teslić, on the Usora, a left-bank tributary of the Bosna, claims to have the largest wood-distillation factory in the world. Among the minerals, important salt and brown coal deposits in north-east Bosnia are supporting growing mining and chemical industries in the Tuzla basin. Noteworthy deposits of iron and brown coal at the northern end of the Sarajevo basin have led to the establishment of a large ferrous metallurgical and chemicals combine at Zenica (50,000). The Sarajevo basin forms the fertile heart of Bosnia, an increasingly important industrial and commercial region. It forms a large isolated agricultural clearing, stretching some 50 miles from north-west to south-east, developed on the lightly dissected site of a Tertiary lake basin, and entirely surrounded by lofty mountains. Sarajevo (200,000) is now Yugoslavia's third largest city and is still rapidly expanding. Its central location in the country, and its proximity to Yugoslavia's most rapidly-developing mining and industrial region in central Bosnia, have been major factors in the transformation of Sarajevo into an important centre of engineering, timber processing, and other industries.

The Eastern Dinaric region is one of the regions in south-central Europe changing most rapidly. A backward, poor peasant society is being projected into the modern urban industrial age with the result that it is a land of change and adjustment to change. The growth of mining and manufacturing has led not only to the great expansion of such towns as Sarajevo, Zenica, Tuzla, Banja Luka. It has been accompanied by the growth of new towns for mine and factory workers, as in the Sarajevo, Tuzla, and west Bosnian areas. Many villages of timber-and-thatch or Turkish-style houses have been engulfed by the construction of sizeable estates of concrete buildings with shops and other services. Yet many workers still divide their time between farm and factory and commute daily over miles of country.

Along the north-eastern margins of the East Dinaric zone the young Tertiary hill-country slopes down to the Sava lowlands (Posavina). The land has been largely cleared for cultivation and is densely populated. Mixed farming is practised, orchards are numerous with plums predominating (for the production of prunes and plum brandy), maize is the chief cereal, while cattle- and pig-rearing are of growing importance. The region is, however, over-populated and forms a labour supply area for industrial centres along the Sava valley and in north-central Bosnia.

**The Mountain-and-Basin Corridor Lands.** Between Belgrade on the north and Salonika in Greece on the south (about 300 miles) and about 90 miles wide from east to west, lies a stretch of rugged country developed mainly on the crystalline rocks of the Rhodope Massif. It is threaded by a remarkable series of tectonic basins, lying mainly along the courses of the Morava, Ibar, Vardar, and Struma rivers. These basins are generally aligned along a north-north-west to south-south-east axis, giving the shortest route possible through the Balkan peninsula from central Europe to the Mediterranean Sea. The corridor area is confined by the lofty, wild, and difficult Dinaric ranges on the west and by the Balkan and Rhodope Mountains on the east, the only exit being where the basins and gorges of the Nišava tributary of the Morava have been traversed by a railway leading to Sofia, Istanbul, and the 'land' route to Asia via the Bosporus.

The 'corridor lands' lie mainly in Yugoslavia. Here there is a double line of movement; an easterly route which was formerly followed by a Roman road along the Morava and lower Vardar valleys; and a westerly one which was used by the medieval 'Carski Put' or Imperial Way, going via the Ibar valley and Kosovo *polje* and joining the first route near Skoplje. Both are now followed by a railway. Until the late 1950s the more easterly route carried the main line; now the more important route is the westerly one owing to the progress of economic, especially industrial, development of western Serbia and Kosovo. A possible continuation of the western route lies southward of Skoplje through the Pelagonian basins. The Struma valley (Bulgarian) is a less important thorough-fare since it affords a less direct line of communication between central Europe and the Mediterranean, but a railway links Sofia to the Ægean coastlands by this route.

71 Ploesti oilfields

RUMANIA

BULGARIA

72 Kremikovtzi. The biggest metallurgical plant near Sofia in Bulgaria

73 Mamaia beach

RUMANIA

74 Threshing wheat at one of Hungary's co-operative farms, on the Great Alföld.

HUNGARY

75 Work with a tractor-drawn sprinkler in the vineyards of the Helvécia State Farm, Cumania.

As mentioned earlier,[1] all the basins have bordering terraces more or less dissected by subaerial erosion while the middle portions tend to be flat.    The gorges naturally offer difficulties to road and railway construction and neither the Vardar–Morava nor the Vardar–

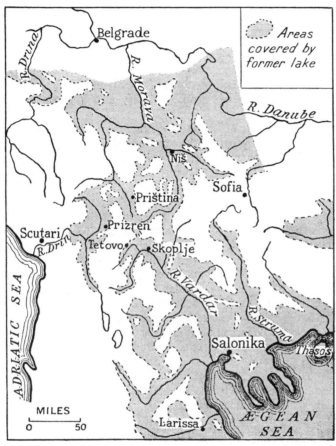

*(after Cvijić)*

Fig. 64. THE ÆGEAN LAKE OF THE LATE TERTIARY AND EARLY QUATERNARY PERIODS IN YUGOSLAVIA AND ADJACENT REGIONS

Ibar route is particularly easy, though there is no high watershed to be crossed in either case.    The water-parting between the Vardar and Ibar is indefinite, the feeders of both rivers rising in Kosovo *polje*, and the water at the source having an indeterminate flow.    Thus

[1] See the introductory section on South-central Europe, p. 459.

here, as in some basins, such as Pelagonia, drainage of flat areas is necessary if agriculture is to be practised. Turkish rule and increasing overpopulation in these lands led to a neglect of the ill-drained lowlands because of lack of funds and techniques, while the hill slopes became over-farmed. Postwar agricultural policy in Yugoslavia is trying to modify the pattern of land-use in these basin-lands. The arable land under grain, arranged in strips and patches, is being improved by protective measures, and orchards and permanent grass introduced, as the extension of cooperative farming allows, in order to minimise soil erosion. Drainage and irrigation are being applied to the flat low-lying areas to expand the cultivation of cereals, sugar beet and other industrial crops, and they also improve remaining grassland areas.

Despite their many similarities, there are certain differences between the northern part of the corridor lands, the Morava drainage area, and the southern, or Vardar drainage area. The Šar Planina and the Skopska Crna Gora, which trend north-east to south-west, almost cut off the Morava basin from the Vardar basin so that climate and vegetation as well as the population and economy differ between the two areas. Unlike the northern region, the Skoplje basin is subject to tectonic movements, as was so tragically underlined by the disaster of July 1963 which destroyed much of Skoplje. These should be reckoned with in planning the location of settlements, industrial plants, lines of communication, and so on in the area. The basin has the rather dry summers that recall the Mediterranean régime; consequently the low-lying tillable lands tend to be devoted to wheat rather than to maize which is characteristic further north, and irrigation is being increasingly practised for such crops as tobacco, rice, oilseeds, and even cotton. The mountains carry less forest than further north, and many summits are entirely bare. The Vardar drainage area carried the name Macedonia, a name applied in 1945 to the People's Republic of Macedonia, one of Yugoslavia's six federated republics. The area was Turkish until 1912, hence its extreme backwardness. It contains people claimed by Bulgaria as Bulgarians and by Yugoslavia as Yugoslavs, in addition to small groups of Albanians, Greeks, Vlachs, and Turks. Macedonia (called 'South Serbia' between 1929 and 1939) contains many market towns which date back at least to Roman times. Owing to the region's economic stagnation under the Turks, these market towns were often small. Since 1945 new mining and manufacturing activities, and the increasing collectivisation and commercialisation of agriculture, have been factors of great importance for the revival of these towns. Until its recent destruction, Skoplje was by far the largest and most rapidly developing centre.

It is Macedonia's administrative capital, with its best facilities for communications, and industries based on local raw materials (chrome, iron-ore, limestone, tobacco). Metallurgical, engineering, food, tobacco, textile, and chemical industries had become important. It is possible that the city will not be rebuilt to the size it had achieved; it may be replaced by a new town on a new site or by a series of decentralised settlements dispersed in safer areas around the Skoplje basin. Other market towns are growing rapidly as a result of new and varied developments: Bitolj (50,000) with engineering, sugar refining, and leather processing industries, Prilep (40,000) with tobacco and mineral working industries, and Veles (27,000) and Štip (19,000) with varied textile and non-metallic mineral activities. Part of this development is based on hydroelectric power from the upper Vardar.

The Morava drainage area, especially the northern Šumadija area, was the nucleus of modern Serbia. Until the mid-eighteenth century it contained no towns but the fortress settlements of Belgrade and Smederevo on the Danube. In the present century it has been actively developed owing to its better communications and its proximity to the Belgrade market. The region is relatively densely populated and cultivated mainly for maize, sugar-beet, and vegetables; there are also many orchards and vineyards. As a result food-processing industries were already important in 1939 as well as textiles and clothing which employed rural labour. Since 1945 there has been more active exploitation of the region's considerable mineral wealth. The mining of various non-metallic minerals, magnesite, lead-zinc ores, and brown coal has stimulated the growth of large processing industries and engineering in all the medium towns along valleys served by railways. The most notable centres are Kragujevac, Kruševac, Kraljevo, Arandjelovac, and Smederevo. Yugoslavia's economically most backward region is also included in this northern section: Kosovo-Metohija. Here much new capital is being applied to develop the area by improving agriculture and introducing the cultivation of industrial crops such as sugar-beet, by expanding lead-zinc mining at Trepča and other centres, and by opening up Europe's largest brown coal deposits at Kosovo-Polje.

**The Balkan Mountains.** These bound the mountain-and-basin corridor lands on the east, and in Yugoslavia are known as the Mountains of north-east Serbia. They continue the same direction and character as the Banat mountains on the northern side of the Danube. The crystalline zone contains the mineralised regions of Bor and Majdanpek with substantial copper and pyrites resources and growing refining and chemical industries. The mountains are studded with a number of fertile tectonic basins (e.g. Zaječar on the

Timok, Pirot, and others on the Nišava), often separated from each other by gorges. Despite the expansion of bituminous and brown coal mining in the Timok basin this is an area of depopulation. At the northern end of this basin, however, the small town of Prahovo is being developed into a port on the Danube to serve the new fertiliser factory there which uses imported phosphates, and sulphuric acid from Bor. Niš (85,000) is a town of marked nodality near the confluence of the Nišava and southern Morava rivers; it has developed into one of Yugoslavia's major engineering, textile, and tobacco centres.

**Yugoslavia.** The political nucleus of Yugoslavia is the Šumadija region, which in 1821 won its freedom, as the kingdom of Serbia, from the Turks. The collapse of the Austro-Hungarian Empire enabled the Croats and Slovenes to join up with the Serbs and the Macedonians, but the new state included peoples in very diverse stages of development; thus, as in the case of most new composite states, its post-1918 history has been stormy. The formation of Yugoslavia into a federal state of six autonomous republics since 1943, and the postwar policy of social and economic equality for all peoples in the country, have done much to consolidate and unite the country under Tito's communist rule. Yet a longer period of social, cultural, and economic development is necessary in Yugoslavia before the primitiveness of the mountain peoples and the higher standards of the Slovenes are evened out.

The interest of the outside world in Yugoslavia has centred mainly on her command of the routes to the Ægean and the Bosporus. In fact, its political geography has overshadowed all other aspects. The Central powers wished to keep Serbia and Bulgaria weak, dependent states, in order to pursue their 'Drang nach Osten' policy to bring the region under German domination: hence the annexation of Bosnia-Hercegovina by Austro-Hungary. Italy, likewise, in 1919 did not welcome a powerful neighbour on the other side of the Adriatic, and annexed parts of the Yugoslav coast until 1945. The Slavonic language of the Yugoslavs predisposed them to Russian sympathies, but their desire for full political and economic independence led to the blockade of Yugoslavia by the Soviet Union in the years 1948–56. The long-term result, however, has been to Yugoslavia's political, social, and economic benefit, bringing her more readily into contact with western Europe and North America and, most significantly, the underdeveloped Afro-Asian and Latin American countries.

Yugoslavia has now an area of 99,000 square miles; it is thus rather larger than Great Britain. It has a population of 19 million, of whom about 83 per cent are Serbs, Croats, or Slovenes.

Owing to the mountainous nature of much of the country, the population density is not high, but in 1961 varied from about 400 per square mile in low-lying hill country of north-west Croatia to about 225 per square mile in much of the Vojvodina, Serbia, and Kosovo-Metohija, and only 80 per square mile in much of the Karst country. Local population densities in the *polja*, however, may be high.   The

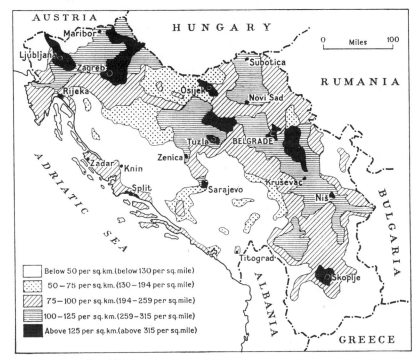

Fig. 65.  POPULATION DENSITIES IN YUGOSLAVIA

Note the belts of comparatively dense population along the Sava–Drave lowlands and the Morava corridor with their focus on Belgrade.   These are separated from the moderate densities of the Adriatic coastlands by the scantily peopled Dinaric Alps, in which the basin of Sarajevo stands out as a population 'island'. Low densities also occur in the Vardar basin and in the mountains of north-east Serbia.

population is mainly rural, though industrialisation in particular is leading everywhere to a rapid increase in the urban population at the expense of the numbers living in rural areas.   Sweeping measures of agrarian reform were carried out in 1918–19 and 1945, after both world wars, to satisfy the land hunger of the peasants.   The changes of 1945 also involved the resettlement of peasants with little or no land in the over-populated mountain areas on the expropriated estates of former large landowners, mainly foreigners, in the plains of the north. Agriculturally, Yugoslavia can be divided into two basic zones. The grain and sugar-beet region of the northern plain and bordering valley lands is the most important agricultural area. South of the Sava–Danube line forests and pasture occupy more land than cultivated crops. The forested and agricultural nature of the country was well borne out before 1939 in the list of exports which included timber, followed by eggs, grain, pork, raw copper, animals, hops, meat, cement, and prunes. Much has been, and is being changed by the programme of industrialisation applied since 1946. Apart from livestock and hops, food products are exported now in processed form, and the export of raw materials has been largely replaced by that of semi-finished or finished products. The country is in a rather better position than Hungary and probably Rumania for industrial development. Her deposits of iron-ore are large, and in 1962 Yugoslavia ranked first in Europe west of the USSR in the production of lead, antimony, and chrome, second in bauxite and copper, and sixth in zinc. Metallurgical industries are thus well founded. While lacking substantial deposits of bituminous coal, her energy resources comprise considerable brown coal, oil, and natural gas, and a large hydro-electric power potential approaching that of Norway. Since 1946 there has been a rapid growth of metallurgical, chemical, fuel, and power industries, and particularly of the engineering and electrical industries, to serve growing needs in equipment and machinery. Employment in industry has risen from under 250,000 workers in 1945 to over 1 million in 1962.

Of the cities Belgrade (Serb., Beograd) grew very rapidly after 1918, from 112,000 in 1921 to 240,000 in 1931 as a result of its expanded administrative, commercial, and industrial functions. These trends have continued during the years following the second world war and now the city numbers over 600,000 inhabitants.[1] Largely rebuilt in western style, the heart of the town lies on a hill-promontory overlooking the Sava, just west of its junction with the Danube. To the north, east, and west of Belgrade the Danube and Sava have marshy banks, so far as the Iron Gate on the east and the Drina on the west. A superb modern town for 250,000 people is being built on the drained marshland north of the city, so linking Zemun to Belgrade. Its position at the northern end of the corridor lands exposed it to frequent attack in the past, but it is excellent from a commercial point of view. Since the formation of Yugoslavia in 1919, Belgrade has been the centre of two important agricultural and transportation regions. In association with the country's

[1] Figures for 1962.

general postwar economic development, the Belgrade area has become a centre of engineering and electrical industries with an emphasis on assembly industries, chemicals, and consumer products.

Zagreb (500,000), the capital of Croatia-Slavonia, is the second city of the country. However, it is the major commercial centre, being famous for its International Trade Fairs, and it equals the Belgrade–Zemun area in industrial importance. It manufactures machinery and electrical equipment, alimentary produce, textiles, furniture, and chemicals.

### REFERENCES

An excellent general account of the Balkan countries is given in Y. Chataigneau and J. Sion, *Géographie Universelle*, Vol. VII, entitled *Italie, Pays Balkanique*, Part 2, Paris, Colin, 1934. The works of J. Cvijić contain much interesting material, *La Peninsule Balkanique, Géographie humaine*, Paris, Colin, 1918, and *La Géographie des Terrains Calcaires*, Belgrade, Academie des Sciences, 1960.

For prewar assessments of Yugoslavia's resources see M. R. Shackleton, 'Economic Resources and Problems of Yugoslavia', *Scot. Geog. Mag.*, Nov. 1925, and R. Aranitović, *Les Ressources et l'Activité économique de la Yougoslavie*, Paris, Bossuet, 1930. These should be compared with information contained in the following postwar publications: M. Mellen and H. Winston, *Yugoslavia's Coal Resources*, New York, Praeger, 1956; G. W. Hoffman and F. W. Neal, *Yugoslavia and the New Communism*, New York, Praeger, 1961, which also has much of value on postwar political, economic, and geographical changes in that country in general and in detail; and F. E. I. Hamilton, 'Yugoslavia's Hydro-Electric Power Industry', *Geography*, XLVII, 1962. For a study of industrial changes, consult F. E. I. Hamilton, 'The Changing Pattern of Yugoslavia's Manufacturing Industry', *Tijdschrift voor Economische en Sociale Geographie*, Rotterdam, April, 1963.

For Albania, see S. Skendi (Ed.), *Albania*, New York, Praeger, 1957. Specific studies on the human aspect are R. Bičanić, 'The Effects of war on rural Yugoslavia', *Geog. Journal*, CIII, 1944; A. E. Moodie, *The Italo–Yugoslav Boundary*, London, Philip, 1945; and D. Warriner, *Revolution in Eastern Europe*, London, Turnstile Press, 1950.

For a short introduction to the political geography of the Balkans, see G. W. Hoffman, *The Balkans in Transition*, New Jersey and London, Searchlight Book, Van Nostrand, 1963.

### CHAPTER 33

# THE BALKAN PENINSULA (II)

## THE BULGARIAN LANDS, TURKEY-IN-EUROPE, MACEDONIA, AND THRACE

THE Bulgarian lands border the middle corridor lands of the south-eastern peninsula on the east and fall naturally into a number of roughly east–west parallel zones. The Bulgarian Platform rises on the north to the Balkan Mountains, which are succeeded in turn by a long line of depressions. These depressions are followed on the south by the Rhodope Massif which lies at a high level in the west, almost disappears in the middle, and rises again in the Istrandja Mountains of European Turkey.

**The Bulgarian Platform.** This region has been compared already with the neighbouring Walachian plain. It is covered by a mantle of *Löss* which conceals the underlying unfolded layers of Cretaceous limestone and sandstone overlain by Tertiary material in the north. The Platform has a gently undulating surface, but is cut into a number of segments by almost cañon-like valleys traversing the region from south to north. These render east–west movement difficult, in contrast to the general ease of movement on the Walachian plain. Apart from these valleys there is a marked absence of surface water, and settlements are accordingly agglomerated round wells or in the narrow valleys; there are very few villages on the interfluves. The land is treeless and lends itself to the cultivation of cereals, of which there is a considerable surplus for export. The postwar period has seen major changes here from peasant small-scale to large-scale socialised agriculture, as is general in Bulgaria. This has laid the foundation for the region's economic development. By extensive drainage and irrigation works the cultivation of sugar-beet, flax, and rice has been expanded to support new industries such as sugar-refining, flax spinning and linen textiles. Fertiliser and machine industries have been developed in the region's most central town and river port, Ruse (85,000), to serve the needs of agriculture. Vegetable production has also increased to supply growing markets in other COMECON countries. An important result of these changes has been the great amount of rebuilding in the countryside and the provision of facilities which have reduced substantially the social, economic, and cultural differences between town and country.   Recently large straw-cellulose industries have been constructed alongside the Danube to make use of vegetable matter growing along the river.   The chief towns of the region are Varna (125,000) and Ruse.   Varna, formerly Stalin, on the Black Sea coast, is the country's main port, a growing centre for ship-building and other industries, and a thriving tourist resort.

**The Balkan Mountains.**   The Bulgarian Platform rises gradually southward to the Balkan Mountains, or Stara Planina as they are known in Bulgaria.   Like the Carpathian system, they owe their present height to uplifts following the peneplanation of the original folds.   Considerable traces of this peneplain remain, especially east of the longitude of Sliven where re-elevation was not very great.

The transition zone between the mountains and the Bulgarian Platform is marked by a line of small towns (e.g. Vratca, Pleven, and Trnovo) on or near rivers and routes leading into the highlands.   As a result of their situation between the platform and the mountains, these centres are experiencing considerable industrial development, while the cultivation of industrial crops, such as sugar-beet and flax, increases to the north and mining, forestry, and hydro-electric power develops in the mountains to the south.

The northern ranges consist chiefly of varied Cretaceous material, with long limestone bands forming ridges which are penetrated, however, by numerous passes.   Two railways traverse the range, the most important going via the Isker valley to Sofia, the other via the Šipka pass to Kazanlik in the Tundža basin.   The whole Balkan mountain area is well forested and is the source of much of Bulgaria's timber.   Timber processing, and machine industries serving forestry needs, are growing fast here, especially in settlements served by railways and better roads.   The highest zone is found near the south and consists mainly of Palæozoic shales interspersed with granite, and rises above the forest, giving pasture for sheep.   Wool is supplied to textile and carpet industries situated in towns to the north and south.   The mining of coal is beginning to change the landscape and the economy of small towns to the north of Sliven, east of Gabrovo, and north of Sofia.   The eastern Balkan mountains, which run out to sea at Cape Eminé, lack Palæozoic and granite material and are lower; yet they are less easy to cross because of the dense cover of forests and paucity of transverse valleys.   The economy of the hinterland of Varna is changing, under the growing stimulus of that centre.   Agriculture is being intensified for the greater production of sunflower seeds, sugar-beet, fruits and vegetables along the valleys and railways to Trnovo and Ruse.

Growing building demands have required the construction of new cement industries using local limestone. Manufacturing industries are developing in the market centres, especially Kolarovgrad, to process local agricultural products and salt, or to serve local needs.

On the south the mountains fall rather abruptly to a series of basins. Beginning in the west with the Sofia basin, they are continued eastwards for almost the whole length of the chain, mainly by the longitudinal sections of the Striema and Tundža valleys. The Sofia basin is shut in on the south by a branch of the Balkan mountains which leaves the main chain south of the Pirot basin in Yugoslavia and runs south-south-east to come up against the Rhodope mass. The basin lies at a height of 1,800 ft and is surrounded on all sides by high mountains, yet is very accessible owing to peculiarities of the river system, especially the extraordinary course of the Isker in this section of the south-eastern peninsula. The Isker rises in one of the highest points of the Rhodope (the granitic Rila Planina), traverses one of the many mountain-girt basins (that of Samokov) in the region, breaks through another ancient granitic massif to enter the Sofia basin, and continues to the north to break through the Balkan Mountains. Three other river systems – the Nišava, Maritsa, and Struma – radiate from this complex area of basins and mountains and offer several routes leading up to the Sofia basin. The nodality of the basin is unique in the whole Balkan peninsula, but its small size has hindered the realisation of its full advantages. Nevertheless, together with the adjacent Dimitrovo basin, it forms the most important economic area in Bulgaria today. It contains the capital city, Sofia, whose population has grown from 287,000 in 1934 to 650,000 in 1959. Sofia is the seat of Bulgaria's centralised administration, of its culture, and also of one-fifth of the country's manufacturing industry, localising chiefly the lighter branches of the engineering, electrical, chemical, textile, and food industries. The city, however, lies close to Bulgaria's heavy industrial area, the Dimitrovo basin, with its mining of brown coal, iron-ore, and manganese ore, and its iron and steel, and engineering industries. To the north bituminous coal is mined near Kurilo. The ores of the Dimitrovo basin and Kurilo coal provide the raw materials for Bulgaria's large new iron and steel and coke industries now being constructed near the capital. Under the impact of these changes, agriculture in the Sofia basin is today less concerned than formerly with the production of rye and the raising of sheep, and more with vegetable cultivation.

The eastern basins are shut in on the south by the Anti-Balkans or Sredna Gora (= 'middle mountains'). This is a zone of low rounded mountains composed of crystalline schists covered by forest, with granite masses supporting pasture, and young volcanic areas used for cultivation. Copper is mined and refined here, and sulphuric acid produced as a by-product. The fertile low-lying basins of the upper Strienna and Tundža are particularly well sheltered and have been called the garden of Bulgaria because of their vegetable, fruit, cereal, and grape production. The extensive rose gardens of the upper Tundža produce oil for the famous scent 'attar of roses'. Other industries are developing in this belt based on power from hydro-electricity plants in the Tundža valley.

To the south of the Sredna Gora lies a considerable stretch of lowland. This is occupied chiefly by the upper Maritsa basin, one of the many old lake basins of the Balkan peninsula. It is one of the richest and most progressive agricultural areas in Bulgaria owing to the fertile alluvial soil, hot summers, and abundance of water. Very varied products are grown, including maize, cotton, the vine, tobacco, tomatoes, and rice; irrigation has been widely extended in this area since 1950. The villages, now taking on a modern appearance, lie picturesquely sheltered among walnut, sweet chestnut, and cherry trees. The region is deriving considerable benefit from the export market for its agricultural produce which is expanding as a result of closer trade contact with western Europe and from Bulgaria's developing rôle within COMECON as a specialised producer of fruits and vegetables. Plovdiv (170,000) is the main population, commercial, and industrial centre of this region and stands second in importance only to Sofia.

**The High Rhodope.** Between the Struma and Maritsa rivers the central portion of the Rhodope massif remains as a fairly continuous area of high land presenting considerable areas over 6,000 ft high and rising to 9,613 ft in Mussalla, in the Rila Planina. The forested mountains generally present rounded slopes recalling the former peneplain character, but the Pirin and Rila highlands are residual masses rising above the general level of the dissected plateau, and were high enough to develop glaciers during the Pleistocene period; cirques and moraines are thus numerous. Until investigations for mineral resources were carried out in the postwar period, the whole central area was very little known to the outside world. The area contains no railways, but new roads penetrate the larger valleys from Plovdiv and Velingrad. It remains still a region of sheep rearing on highland pastures and forestry in the extensive lower regions; but the construction of hydro-electric power plants on the larger rivers and the exploitation of timber are giving rise to small industrial developments, notably at Velingrad.

Eastwards, the Rhodope Mountains sink gradually to uplands composed of young volcanic rock (andesite), drained by the Arda tributary of the Maritsa. Lead, zinc, and chrome are mined and this provides the only significant economic activity in an area largely devoted to sheep rearing. In turn these mountains merge into the hills through which the Maritsa and Tundža break their way just north of Adrianople (Turkish, Edirne). These hills are formed of crystalline schists and link the Rhodope mass to its outlying portion, the Istrandja Mountains whose little-explored forested heights extend from the Bulgaro–Turkish frontier to the roots of the Istanbul peninsula.

**The Bulgarian State and People.** The Bulgars came into their present home in the eighth century, having previously been neighbours of the Magyars in the lower Volga region. They evidently mingled with the Slavonic-speaking peoples and adopted their language. Their traditions, however, have prevented them from throwing in their lot with the Yugoslavs. They finally secured their freedom from Turkish suzerainty between 1885 and 1908, but despite its proximity to Constantinople, Bulgaria does not seem to have suffered so much from Turkish occupation as might be expected and the somewhat dour peasant farmers have shown tremendous powers of resistance and recovery.

Larger than Hungary and Albania, but smaller than any of the other states of south-central Europe, Bulgaria has a population of nearly 8 million, who are still largely dependent upon agriculture and forestry. One-third of the area is under forest, two-fifths are agricultural, and the rest (one-quarter) is unproductive mountain land. The main exports are agricultural products – tobacco from the Struma and Mesta valleys followed by wheat and maize, eggs, rapeseed, fleeces, silk cocoons (from the coastal and Maritsa areas), and rose oil. Nearly full collectivisation of agriculture has been achieved in Bulgaria in the effort to raise production. This, together with plans for Bulgaria's specialisation on these items, as well as on fruit and vegetables, within COMECON, has led to a great increase in exports of foods in fresh and processed form. Industries are underdeveloped, though growing as a result of heavy capital investment (partly by other COMECON countries), of the increasing use of Bulgaria's little known but varied mineral resources, and of improvements in agriculture providing more produce for industrial manufacture. The mining of coal has developed rapidly, though the output consists chiefly of low-grade brown coal. In 1961 production reached 18 million tons, most being mined in the Sofia–Dimitrovo (Pernik) area. The output of metallic ores has increased considerably, in part to meet export requirements. Iron ores are the most important though increasing quantities of lead, zinc, copper, and chrome are being produced from the Balkan and Rhodope mountain systems.   Of all Bulgarian industries, food processing is still the most important, but engineering, metallurgy, chemicals, and textiles have grown rapidly too.   Bulgaria has two seaports. Varna and Burgas (75,000) on the Black Sea; both are undergoing considerable expansion and modernisation to cater for increasing Bulgaria–USSR trade.


## TURKEY-IN-EUROPE

The basin of the River Ergene and the lower Maritsa, also known as the basin of eastern Thrace, extends south-westwards from the Istrandja Mountains.   It is filled with Tertiary sediments, which are covered in places with Quaternary gravels and more recent alluvium. It is very level in the middle, but is dissected into undulating country around the border.   It is mainly a region of steppe, caused by its basin configuration, permeable soil, late-summer drought, and cold winter winds.   The lower portions of the basin provide only pasture, though the higher regions with a heavier rainfall are cultivated and here wheat, maize, and sugar-beet are important.

Climatically this area seems to combine the bad points of both the south-central and Mediterranean régimes.   The prevailing winds are northerly all the year round, giving cold dry winters which are too cold for Mediterranean crops and dry hot summers which are too dry for those of central Europe.   In autumn and spring the region shares in the Mediterranean 'former and latter' rains, but June to September inclusive are almost rainless months.   In winter occasional cyclones passing from the Mediterranean to the Black Sea bring southerly winds and thaw, so depriving the ground of its protective snow cover.   It is evident that the evils of this marginal climatic position are enhanced by the shape of the basin, since the bordering Istrandja and Rhodope Mountains have much heavier rainfall and a consequent timber covering.

The basin is enclosed on the south by a line of bare hills composed of folded Cretaceous and Tertiary material with a core of ancient rock.   These border the Gulf of Xeros and the Sea of Marmara, and form the boundary between the Thracian steppe and the narrow coastal fringe of Mediterranean climate.   Natural gas has been found in the young Tekir Dagh range and is providing industrial possibilities for settlements along the neighbouring coastlands and steppe.

**The Marmara Region and Istanbul (Constantinople).**   The Straits zone has possessed great international importance since the days of the struggle between the Greeks and the Trojans.   The narrowness of the Black Sea entrances means that this piece of water can be controlled under modern conditions by a land power not possessing a single ship. The economic importance of this ice-free sea exit to the Russian people was at one time very great. During the Stalin era when the economic self-sufficiency of the USSR was the aim, this had less significance. The postwar, and especially recent, changes in the relationship between the Soviet Union and the outside world and especially her development as a sea power have made the region again of great strategic importance.

The Dardanelles and the Bosporus are both drowned river valleys, and the harbour of Istanbul – known as the Golden Horn – is a drowned tributary valley. Shipping can lie in the harbour out of reach of the strong current that streams through the Bosporus from the Black Sea. With the decay of the Ottoman Empire, Constantinople declined in importance and the removal of the Turkish capital to Ankara was another very serious blow. Nevertheless, the nodality of the site and city is of great importance and this, together with its mixed population composed of trading Greeks, Jews, and Armenians, has enabled Istanbul to expand its economic, commercial, and cultural activities. Since the Greeks were driven out of Smyrna and the Anatolian coastlands, more efforts have been made to concentrate trade and industry in Istanbul and its neighbouring areas. New industrial development, linked with Turkey's postwar economic expansion, has been considerable so that the city is a centre of chemical, machinery, iron founding, textiles and clothing, glass, timber-processing, and rubber industries. Its cultural life has been enhanced by the development of a modern university with an academic staff consisting partly of Jewish refugees from German universities. In 1960 the population of Istanbul, one of Europe's most historic cities, numbered 1,500,000, and so it is the second largest city of south-central Europe, being exceeded in numbers only by Budapest.

## THE GREEK LANDS OF MACEDONIA AND THRACE

As a result of the second Balkan war and World War I, Greece secured the coastlands round the head of the Ægean, thus cutting off Yugoslavia and Bulgaria from direct access to this sea. These lands are developed on the southern part of the Rhodope massif. They consist of deltas and faulted basins separated by mountain zones running out to sea. They have a Mediterranean climate favourable to agriculture, but the swampy, malarial nature of the lowlands has required the extensive application of modern drainage methods to make these areas suitable for cultivation. The foothills are well adapted to Mediterranean horticulture, and this, together with the excellent position for controlling trade with the interior, attracted the Greeks from early times. The rest of the population is Slavonic-speaking, though whether their language is a dialect of Bulgarian or not is a matter that has been hotly debated in dozens of volumes. There are also numerous Jews, and before 1923 there were considerable numbers of Turks. The establishment here of large numbers of Greek settlers driven out of Turkey in 1923 has caused a great preponderance of Greek-speaking people. With the help of foreign money, mainly from Britain, USA, and France, the basins were converted into excellent agricultural lands, growing many crops, largely under irrigation, but with tobacco as the most important export. Postwar planning has led to further improvements in agriculture and to some industrial development aimed at processing agricultural produce.

Thessaloniki (250,000 in 1961) is easily the largest town, an important port, and a manufacturing centre, owing to its favourable position at the southern end of the Morava–Vardar corridor lands. It stands to the east of the Vardar delta and its port is out of the way of the silt from that river which is carried westwards by marine currents. Kavalla (44,500) is the port of the fertile Drama basin and similarly stands clear of deltaic silt. The growth of tourism is affecting the economy of the Thracian coastlands at the present time.

## REFERENCES

Two recent books dealing with a wide range of aspects are L. A. D. Dellin (Ed.), *Bulgaria*, New York, Praeger, 1957, and A. Beškov, *Volksrepublik Bulgarien*, Berlin, Verlag die Wirtschaft, 1960. An informative article regarding the process and results of agricultural collectivisation is 'Le Collectivisation Agraire en Bulgarie: L'exemple du village de Petrač', *Annales de Géographie*, LXIX, 1960. See also G. W. Hoffman, 'Transformation of Rural Settlement in Bulgaria', *Geog. Review*, LIV, 1, Jan. 1964. See also S. H. Beaver, 'Bulgaria: A Summary', *Geography*, XXV, Dec. 1940.

# SECTION VI – EASTERN EUROPE

### CHAPTER 34

## GENERAL INTRODUCTION TO EASTERN EUROPE

THIS region of eastern Europe embraces about half the total area of the whole continent. It stretches from about 43° N to 70° N, that is, approximately from the latitude of the French Riviera to that of the North Cape within the Arctic Circle, a distance of some 1,900 miles, and from about 23° E to 60° E, a distance of some 1,500 miles, equivalent to the distance between the west of Brittany and Constantinople.

The greater part of this region forms a single morphological and relief unit, stretching from the Arctic Ocean in the north to the Black and Caspian Seas in the south, and from the Pripyat Marshes and the Carpathian Mountains on the west, to the Ural Mountains on the east. As indicated in Chapter 1, the region is mainly built up of unfolded sediments dating from Palæozoic to recent times, the whole forming a slightly raised peneplain of undulating or level relief. It is possible to traverse the whole region from north to south and from east to west along the great slow-moving rivers and their linking canals and not rise above a height of 650 ft. It thus comprises the greatest stretch of lowland in Europe and, indeed, one of the greatest in the world. The lowland is known geographically as the Russian Lowland. For the purposes of this book the bordering mountains will also be included within eastern Europe.

Eastern Europe is markedly different from the rest of the continent in the absence of interior mountains which divide up the region into compartments, or which act as frontiers to climatic, political, or any other types of division. With such an extension in latitude, however, there must obviously be differences in climate, vegetation, and products from north to south, and, in fact, the vegetation of the Lowland changes from tundra in the north, through forest in the centre, to steppe in the south; with minor elements on the margins. Both the climatic and vegetation divisions merge into one another almost imperceptibly and there is an absence

of the abrupt transitions and the sharp contrasts which are characteristic of western Europe.  At the same time there is an absence
of the fragmentary character and mosaic-like distributions, which
necessitate such detailed studies for the rest of the Continent.
Eastern Europe is built on broad, simple lines, so that one can
perhaps compare it to an Egyptian pyramid, which though massive
is easily described on account of the simplicity of its design, whereas
western Europe has the intricacy of a Gothic cathedral.

Politically almost the whole of eastern Europe has been included
within the frontiers of a single state since the end of the eighteenth
century, and its boundaries practically correspond to what used to
be known as Russia-in-Europe.  After World War I (1914–19)
a strip on the western side of the Russian Lowland, comprising the
independent states of Estonia, Latvia, and Lithuania, together with
part of Poland and the Rumanian province of Bessarabia, broke
away from Russian control, but reverted to Russian rule during and
at the end of World War II (1939–45).  During the nineteenth
century and the early part of the twentieth century, Russian rule
had stretched westward beyond the limits of the Lowland to include
Finland and much of the Vistula basin, but although the latter
regions show differences of structure there are no marked changes
of relief, vegetation or climate between the Lowland and the
adjacent morphological regions in these areas.

On the eastern and south-eastern sides the internal boundaries
of the new Russia which emerged after World War I, that is, of the
USSR (Union of Soviet Socialist Republics), largely ignore the
traditional division into Europe and Asia, a tendency which the
older boundaries foreshadowed by taking the eastern boundary of
one province right across the Ural Mountains and well into western
Siberia.   Both old and new boundaries emphasise the fact that the
old division between Europe and Asia had little meaning.   It never
rested on any secure geographical base, for the lands of Russia
east and west of the Ural Mountains possess the same type of relief
and climate, have broad similarities of soil and vegetation, the same
continental vastness and remoteness from the oceans; moreover,
owing to the colonisation of the past three hundred years they now
have the same Russian inhabitants.   The Continental features are
naturally intensified as one goes east, but Russia-in-Europe more
closely resembles western Siberia than it resembles central or western
Europe.   The Ural Mountains form a relatively low wall, easily
crossed in many places, between two similar expanses of country.
Nevertheless, in themselves they form a distinctive morphological
region of considerable individuality, since they are composed of
folded and fractured strata belonging to the Hercynian system.

They therefore interpose a belt of rugged country, rising to heights of over 5,000 ft in places, between the plains which lie to east and west, and they also form an important watershed between the tributaries of the Volga and Pechora to westward and those of the Ob to eastward. It is interesting to note that the large Soviet World Atlas of 1954 shows the Urals as lying just within the European section of the USSR, and they will be treated as belonging to Europe in this volume.

At the southern extremity of the Urals, low ridges, originally wooded, now mainly scrub-covered, run out into the steppes, becoming lower and narrower until they peter out completely. Between the Urals and the Caspian Sea lies a treeless plain, some 400 miles from north to south, across which nomadic peoples from Asia invaded Europe from prehistoric times until Ivan IV ('The Terrible') defeated the Tatars in the middle of the sixteenth century. There are here, in the Ural–Caspian Gap, no effective natural obstacles, though the Ural river used to be taken as the conventional dividing line between Europe and Asia. Asiatic influences are still much in evidence in the Ural–Caspian Gap, for the scanty population on the dry untillable steppe is of Asiatic stock and speech (Kirghiz), as far west as, and beyond, the lower Volga, a distance of some 500 miles west of the Ural river.

On its southern side the Russian Lowland stops at the northern foot of the great Caucasus Mountains and at the small Yaila Mountains of the Crimea. Both these belong to the young folded mountains (Alpides) of Eurasia. North and South Caucasus, with their great diversity of nationalities, religions, and languages, were conquered by Russia during the nineteenth century, while the Crimea with its Tatar elements came under Russian rule at the end of the eighteenth century. The old conventional boundary of Europe along the Manych depression, some 100 miles or so north of the Caucasus foothills, has no longer any validity, and the most useful frontier of eastern Europe coincides with that of USSR *vis-à-vis* Persia (Iran) and Turkey. The term European USSR will be used here to include both North and South Caucasus.

It is noteworthy that over the whole of the vast area of the Russian Platform there are no physical obstacles, except low hills, rivers, swamp, and forests, and these were not sufficient to stop the expansion of the Russian state from its nucleus in the Moscow region, an area which Kropotkin, the famous Russian geographer, called Russia's 'Ile de France'. The rivers, indeed, far from being obstacles, were important highways. In contrast to western Europe there is found in eastern Europe a marked homogeneity, not only of structure and relief, but also of political organisation, and to a less extent of peoples and languages. Only on the borders can much diversity be found.

## STRUCTURE AND RELIEF OF EASTERN EUROPE

**The Crystalline Base.** It is believed, from the evidence of numerous borings, that the sedimentary strata everywhere rest on a base of ancient crystalline rocks, comprising granites, gneisses, and other similar igneous and metamorphic material. This crystalline floor is not everywhere at the same depth below the surface; in some places it is several thousand feet below sea-level, in others it is either exposed or has only a very slight covering of superficial deposits. The crystalline floor emerges altogether from the sedimentary Platform in the north-west, in the Kola peninsula and Karelia, where it forms the eastern margin of the Pre-Cambrian Baltic or Fennoscandian Shield (see Figs. 2, 63). The crystalline base also appears at or near the surface in southern Russia, in a belt some 550 miles long, running from north-west to south-east between the Dniester and the Don. It has been called the Azov–Podolian 'shield' by some writers, but other authorities refer to it either as the Dnieper 'horst' or Ukrainian 'massif'. It forms a plateau of no great height, some 600–1,000 ft in Podolia and Volhynia in the west, as also in the eastern section north of the Sea of Azov, but it sinks to less than 600 ft in the centre near Krivoi Rog, and also on both sides of the great bend of the Dnieper. The crystalline rocks of the Dnieper horst are in most places masked by thin layers of sandstone, limestone or clay which, in turn, are often hidden by *Löss*, but many of the rivers have cut down to the crystalline floor so that rapids have been formed, notably just below Dnepropetrovsk near the great bend of the Dnieper, on the River Don and on the River Dniester near Mogilev. It seems that the epeirogenic elevation of this horst is fairly recent, and has had a very considerable effect on the river system, particularly on the formation of the Polesian or Pripyat marshes (see p. 565), and of course on the formation of the rapids mentioned above.

The great value of these ancient rocks lies in their mineral wealth, for example, the iron of Krivoi Rog, still the chief single producer of ore in the USSR, and the manganese of Nikopol, are well-known assets of the Ukraine, while from the Russian portion of the Fennoscandian Shield come great quantities of apatite, used in making phosphatic fertilisers; nepheline, used in the aluminium and ceramic industries, as well as smaller amounts of copper, nickel, and iron.

There are other inequalities of the crystalline floor which affect the relief to some extent, notably a downfaulting in the Donets region which preserved Coal Measures of Carboniferous age, and incidentally the 'roots' of an old folded system. Owing to the resistant nature of these 'roots' the area appears on the surface as a plateau. Upthrustings are in evidence in the Kursk region, which serves to form the southern part of the Central Russian Uplands (see Fig. 67, p. 541), and also in the Volga Heights which lie west of the River Volga between Kazan and Volgograd, in the Stavropol plateau north of the Caucasus Mountains, and in the Ufa plateau west of the Urals. It would be a mistake to exaggerate the rigidity of the crystalline base, which shows faulting and warping at all geological epochs.

**The Moscow Basin.** The north-western part of the Russian Lowland, between the Kursk–Voronezh horst in the south-west, the Fennoscandian Shield in the north-west, the Timan Mountains in the north-east and the Ufa horst to the east, is covered to a great depth with sedimentary deposits, mainly of Palæozoic age. This great accumulation was only possible because the crystalline floor continued to sag slightly throughout Palæozoic times, and indeed well into the Mesozoic period, for in the middle of the basin occur rocks of Triassic, Jurassic, and even Cretaceous age. Rocks of the Tertiary era are generally absent, showing that the land emerged from beneath the waters before this period. Extensive peneplanation followed this recovery, so that the younger rocks were stripped off the periphery, with the result that the rocks now outcrop in roughly concentric circles; the older rocks of Cambrian and Silurian age are on the margins, while the youngest, of Cretaceous age, are in the middle and reach the surface over large areas between the rivers Volga and Oka. These rocks are usually masked by superficial deposits of glacial drift which are sometimes of great thickness, but the underlying strata are of considerable importance, particularly with regard to the mineral deposits; for instance, the brown coal of the Tula district, the oil shales from the Cambrian and Lower Silurian strata in Estonia, and the bauxite of Tikhvin in the Leningrad *oblast*.[1]

The nature of the underlying rocks also had more influence on the glacial deposits than might be suspected, for the very materials of which the drift is composed were derived very largely from the underlying sedimentary rocks. Moreover, in the process of denudation, scarps were often formed, and those which faced towards the north-west held up rock material in front of them

[1] This word is pronounced 'or-blast' and is an administrative unit of greatly varying size within most of the constituent republics of the USSR.

when the ice-sheets were advancing, and also prevented the escape of melt-water when the ice-sheets were retreating.

**The Tertiary Basin of the Southern Russian Lowland.** The southern part of the Russian Lowland not only has a much more disturbed crystalline floor than the northern part, but over large areas Palæozoic strata appear to be absent and rocks of Mesozoic age rest directly on the old crystalline base. The Cretaceous system is well represented, and there is a great thickness of marine and lacustrine Tertiary strata. The latter are particularly important for their deposits of oil, which are widespread in various horizons: to the long worked deposits on the flanks of the Caucasus must now be added those of the incomparably richer 'Second Baku', an extensive region stretching between the Urals and the Volga. It is clear that the main emergence of the land took place much later here than in the northern half of the Lowland; in fact, the waters of the Caspian are believed to have spread far to the north and west, even in post-glacial times (see Fig. 66), but the bulk of the area seems to have become land just before the Ice Age began. Unlike the northern part of the Lowland, the southern part was not covered by ice-sheets, except for two great 'tongue basins', but received a mantle of *Löss*, which conceals the minor inequalities of the surface except in the south-east, where the waters of the Caspian Sea extended until geologically recent times.

**Effects of the Ice Age.** Although the main relief features of the Russian Lowland are due to the solid geology, yet the detailed topography is chiefly due to events which took place during the Quaternary glaciation, when parts of the Lowland were swept clear of soil, while others received a mantle of superficial deposits of various kinds.

The sequence of events was much the same as that already described in connexion with the Germano-Polish lowland. The main centre of expansion of the ice-sheet was the Scandinavian highlands, though there were minor centres of dispersion in the Timan Mountains, the northern Urals, and Novaya Zemlya. The maximum advance of the ice-sheets probably took place here in the second glaciation stage (known as the 'Riss' glaciation) which largely obscured the work of the earlier ('Mindel') glaciation. The 'Riss' ice-sheet reached about as far south as Smolensk on the Dnieper, Kaluga on the Oka, and Gorki (Nijni-Novgorod) on the Volga, but sent two advanced tongues down the valleys of the Dnieper and Don, nearly as far south as the great bends of these two rivers (see Fig. 66). It is significant that the Volga Heights and the Central Russian Uplands south of Kaluga were not glaciated; although only of modest height, they were sufficiently elevated to

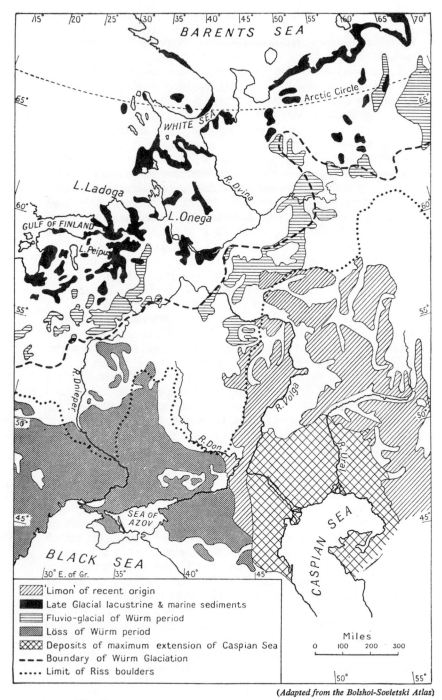

(*Adapted from the Bolshoi-Sovietski Atlas*)

Fig. 66.  SOME GLACIAL FEATURES OF EASTERN EUROPE

divert the ice-sheet, which was here probably fairly thin owing to the great distance from the centres of dispersion. The work of the 'Riss' glaciation has been partially obliterated by morainic deposits and outwash sands from the latest ('Würm') ice-sheet in the north, and by deposits of wind-blown *Löss* in the south, but its existence was detected by the presence of erratic boulders and stones. Moreover, the 'tongue-basins', where the advanced lobes of ice formerly lay, still show traces of the former marshes which succeeded the lobes of ice, and still have rather poorly developed river systems. The results of the latest advance of the ice-sheet are still clearly visible. Its southern edge probably lay near Minsk and Moscow; farther eastward its limits are hidden in the northern forests, but probably lie along the watershed which separates the Arctic drainage of the northern Dvina river system from the Ponto-Caspian drainage, of the northern tributaries of the Volga (Vetluga, Kama, etc.).

The work of the ice-sheet may be broadly classified into three main types which may also be associated with actual space relationships:

1. Erosion by the ice-sheets in the north-west (Finno-Karelia, the Kola peninsula, and a small part of the Baltic provinces).

2. Accumulation under the ice-sheets in the northern part of the Russian Platform.

3. Deposition by wind and water beyond the edges of the ice-sheets in the southern part of the Platform.

**The Erosion Territory on the North-West.** On Fig. 66 is shown the approximate boundary between the erosion territory and the accumulation territory. If this figure is compared with Fig. 2 (p. 5), it will be seen that this boundary almost coincides with the edge of the Fennoscandian Shield, for the very good reason that the ice-sheets stripped off the sedimentary rocks which are believed to have covered the crystalline shield at one time. The Kola peninsula and the northern part of Finno-Karelia show the same combination of barren rocks and lake basins which characterises Finland. Eskers, which are sandy ridges formed by sub-glacial streams, are also frequent, as well as confused masses of boulders, but ground-moraine of boulder-clay type is absent. Across the south-eastern part of Finno-Karelia, however, there is a great end-moraine, composed of boulders, rubble, sand, and gravels, which marked a period when the edge of the retreating ice-sheet remained stationary for a long time. The ice was far from being 'dead' but relatively rapid movement of the ice was balanced by rapid melting along the edges. This moraine, which is a continuation of the Salpausselka of Finland, runs in a north-east to south-west direction north-west

of Lake Ladoga; a similar end-moraine runs south of the Shuya
river between Lake Ladoga and Lake Onega. This picture is
slightly blurred in Karelia by the late-glacial submergence which led
to the deposit of marine clays in the low-lying areas. There are
a large number of lakes, due to the erosion of rock basins, to
tectonic faults, and to the great disturbance of the pre-glacial
drainage.

**The Accumulation Territory.** The northern part of the Russian
Platform shows glacial deposits which are similar to those of the
Germano-Polish lowland, and particularly of the Vistula basin.
For various reasons they have been studied in less detail, but in
many localities it is possible to trace end-moraines as well as parallel
fluvio-glacial valleys similar to the *Urstromtäler* and *pradoliny*
already described (see pp. 362–364). The main end-moraines
trend from north-east to south-west for the most part. The
two head-waters of the River North Dvina, the Sukhona and the
Vichegda, appear to occupy an ancient glacial valley, caused by
the blocking of the north-bound drainage by the edge of the ice-
sheet. Generally speaking, conditions were less favourable to the
formation of well-marked end-moraines and parallel *Urstromtäler*
than in Germany. Towards its outer edges in Russia, the ice-sheet
was a long way from the highlands of Scandinavia, where its
plucking action was most intense, and it was moving over an area
of low relief which offered little opportunity for glacial plucking.
There was no obstacle comparable with the *Mittelgebirge* of central
Europe to prevent the expansion of the ice-sheet southwards or to
prevent the southward escape of melt-water. Except in Karelia
and adjacent regions of the north-west, the load carried by the ice-
sheet was derived from the sedimentary rocks of the Russian
Platform itself, and these were fairly easily ground up into clay with
a greater or smaller sprinkling of boulders according to the type of
rock passed over. The proportion of fairly level clay plains in
Russia is therefore similar to that in Poland and greater than that
in Germany; these plains may perhaps be compared with the
boulder-clay region of East Anglia. However, 'knob and basin'
topography, as the Americans call it, is by no means absent, and is
particularly well represented in the Valdai Hills. The hilly end-
moraine type of scenery gives some variety to the level expanses
which are so characteristic of the northern forested half of the
Russian Lowland. Small lakes also break the monotony, and
are fairly frequent owing to the disturbance of the drainage in
glacial times, while the same cause is responsible for the numerous
rapids on the streams of the north and on the tributary streams and
head streams farther south.

Boulders are naturally most apparent towards the north-west, and these are particularly numerous where the advancing ice-sheet met a relief obstacle, though this was not necessarily of any great height. Thus the escarpment known as the 'glint' which borders the Baltic coast, and sometimes coincides with the coastal cliffs, led to a marked accumulation of boulders below it on its northern side (see Fig. 67, p. 541). Similarly, the ridge of Carboniferous limestone which forms the main core of the Valdai Hills arrested the progress of the ice-flow and the region is strewn with boulders. In some places extensive stretches of sand were deposited as outwash plains (*Sandr*), and sand also predominates in the *Urstromtäler*. The distribution of the main areas of these fluvio-glacial sands is shown in Fig. 66, p. 534. Normal sub-aerial denudation has not had enough time to remodel the surface features, except on the smallest scale, though the shallow late-glacial lakes have often been drained wholly or in part, and now form swamps or cultivable peaty bottom-lands.

**The Deposition Territory of the Southern Part of the Russian Platform.** South of the edge of the last ice-sheet ('Würm' glaciation) a large part of the surface is covered by a mantle of either *Löss* or *limon*. The latter is believed to have been derived from *Löss*, as its chemical composition is very similar, but unlike the *Löss* it is more or less stratified and therefore appears to have been re-sorted by the action of water. The extent of the deposits of pure *Löss* is shown in Fig. 66, from which it will be seen that in some places, particularly in the middle Dnieper region, it covers the glacial drift laid down during the period of maximum glaciation. The *limon* gives rise to soils which are usually just as fertile and just as free from stones as the *Löss*, while the alluvium of the floodplains along the rivers is also very fertile as it is mainly derived from these deposits. On the north-western side of the *Löss-limon* belt, however, there are extensive areas of sand, representing outwash plains and *Urstromtäler*. These occur particularly in the upper Dnieper area, north of Kiev and east of the upper Don, the two depressions here forming easy ways of escape for the melt-water of the most recent ice-sheet. Throughout both the *Löss-limon* region and the sandy tracts, stones are generally conspicuously absent but, in a few areas, boulders of the maximum glaciation can still be found on the surface, as in Volhynia, west of Kiev, where enough stones were found to pave part of the old highway between Kiev and Brest-Litovsk (now Brest), while the houses actually have corner-stones, a rare occurrence in southern Russia. Outside the glaciated area the solid rock comes near the surface in the granites of the Dnieper Heights, but generally speaking there is a remarkable lack of building or constructional stone of any kind in southern Russia.

To the south-east of the *Löss-limon* belt there is a larger expanse of superficial deposits of different type. These are the lacustrine sediments laid down beneath the former extension of the Caspian Sea, which at one time spread as far west as the scarp of the Ergeni Hills and as far north as shown on Fig. 66, p. 534. These sediments consist of clays and sands often impregnated with salts, as semi-desert conditions prevail owing to the low rainfall. The sand in many places forms shifting sand-dunes.

**The Marginal Mountains.** The old crystalline base of the Russian Platform was too rigid to buckle to any extent, though it experienced faulting and warping, and in fact behaved like the Fennoscandian Shield of which it is the hidden continuation. Round its margins less resistant rocks were subjected to intense folding and were built up into mountain ranges of various ages. Of these the Timan range is believed to be the oldest, though it has doubtful tectonic affinities, the Urals belong to the Hercynian system of folding which took place at the close of Palæozoic times, and the Caucasus and Crimean Mountains to the Alpides system of Tertiary times. In the south-west, the Carpathian Mountains, part of which now lies within the USSR (as a consequence of World War II), may be included among the Alpides. The Donets folding, though leaving little impression on the landscape, belongs to the Hercynian system.

The Timan Mountains, whose folding is possibly Caledonian (see p. 13), have undergone such prolonged denudation that they exceed 1,000 ft only at one or two points, and they appear as discontinuous lines of rounded hills which, however, are often sufficiently high to rise as tundra-covered moorlands above the surrounding forest. The remains of five parallel ranges have been traced.

The Ural Mountains are of the same geological age as the Massif Central of France, the Erzgebirge, Harz Mountains, etc., and have undergone similar peneplanation and rejuvenation. The range stretches for over 1,400 miles from north to south, and falls naturally into three sections, a northern, central, and southern. The northern section, which is about 900 miles long and lies north of latitude 61° N, is little known, but summit levels appear to average 2,000 ft or so, while heights of 5,000 ft and over are occasionally reached. It varies in width from about 50 to 75 miles, and consists of several parallel ranges; it was extensively glaciated during the Quaternary Ice Age and shows U-shaped valleys and many 'cirques', thus resembling the highlands of Norway and Scotland. The southern half of this section is forest clad and forms a hunting ground for the peoples of the north, but it is devoid of permanent habitations, except in the extreme south where minerals are worked. Further geological investigations may reveal the presence of minerals farther north, where already a railway crosses from Vorkuta to Salekhard on the River Ob. The central portion of the Urals, which is only about 150 miles from north to south, is the lowest section, and partly for that reason is particularly important. Its rounded massifs seldom exceed 1,200 ft in height, and its low passes were utilised by the Russian pioneers of the sixteenth century on their way to Siberia. The southern Urals are about 350 miles long and attain a width of some 160 miles in the middle. They consist of several parallel ranges which fan out southwards from the middle portion, but become lower as they do so. The greatest height of the southern Urals occurs at Yaman-Tau (5,378 ft) in the most westerly range, but the mountains have everywhere the characteristic Hercynian form of long, flat-topped ridges, usually forest-clad to their summits, except where they have been cleared to provide charcoal for the iron industry. Movement is fairly easy here from north to south along the longitudinal valleys, but by no means easy from east to west, the railway from Ufa to Chelyabinsk having to climb to 1,950 ft just east of Zlatoust. Farther south, in the region of Magnitogorsk, not only are the ranges lower, but they are separated by wide and shallow valleys, there is little timber, and communications are much easier.

The core of the Urals is largely composed of very highly disturbed metamorphic rocks with igneous intrusions, with which are associated a great range of metals; iron-ore, copper, gold, nickel, chrome, manganese, platinum; in fact, it is claimed that the Urals contain a thousand different minerals in 1,200 locations. Precious stones, such as amethyst, topaz, and emerald, occur in considerable quantities. The sedimentary rocks on the flanks of the Urals are rich in other minerals, especially oil, potassium salts, and, to a lesser extent, coal.

**The Caucasus Mountains.** Some 900 miles in length, with some ten or eleven peaks higher than Mt Blanc, the lofty snow-clad Caucasus offer a splendid example of the Alpides system of folding. In many important features, however, they resemble the Pyrenees rather than the Alps; first, their straight alignment is in contrast to the Alpine arc; secondly their transverse edges on east and west are washed by seas; thirdly, to north and south they are flanked by depressions which stretch from sea to sea. Consequently, though difficult to cross, their flanks can easily be turned, so that they lack the busy, well-worn routes and passes of the Alps.

**Mountains of the Crimea.** These mountains, which border the south-eastern coast of the Crimean peninsula, are only about 100 miles long from north-east to south-west and some 25 miles wide. Their structure is quite simple. They represent the north-western flank of a denuded anticline whose south-eastern flank has foundered beneath the Black Sea; the axis of this anticline lies approximately along the present coastline. The vault of the anti-cline has been denuded to expose Jurassic limestones and shales along the coast between Balaklava and Feodosia, and these are succeeded to north-westward by Cretaceous measures, (chalk and conglomerates), and these again by Tertiary limestones, marls, and sandstones. The harder layers, particularly the limestones, form well-marked scarps facing south-east, between which lie plateaus and depressions. The fracture line along the coast was accompanied by Tertiary volcanic activity, the remnants of which can be seen in numerous rugged hills.

**Summary.** A summary of the physical regions of European USSR is given in Fig. 67, which is adapted from the *Soviet World Atlas, 1954*. The following notes explain the numbers given in the map and also afford a résumé of this chapter.

I. Kola peninsula and Karelia. An ancient crystalline plateau, cut up by faults, with evidences of recent glaciation.

II. Regions in which relief is mainly conditioned by morainic deposits, but influenced by pre-glacial physique.

III. Low-lying regions on the edge of the Quaternary glaciation; *Sandr*; sandy, lacustrine and marshy stretches, sometimes with dunes. Includes the Don–Oka glacial tongue-basin.

IV. Upland regions with strongly eroded relief; mainly covered with *Löss* or *limon*.

V. Plains; mostly outside the glacial zone, but excluding VI.

VI. Recent plain of Caspian depression.

VII. Timan Mountains, Donets plateau. The former is com-posed of low ridges, and vestiges of old ridges; the latter forms a rolling plateau, deeply dissected by the river network.

VIII. Mountainous districts; relief mainly due to tectonic folding, faulting and epeirogenic elevation. Includes parts of Urals, Caucasus, and Crimean Mountains.

IX. Volcanic mountains of Armenia.

X. Low mountains and hills; relief mainly conditioned by tectonic processes.

XI. Foothill region; relief showing erosive forms due to river action.

XII. Alluvial and fluvio-glacial plains along foothills of Caucasus and the abraded platform at eastern foot of Urals.

## CLIMATE AND VEGETATION

**The Tundra Zone.** This occupies most of the territory north of the Arctic Circle, except in the Kola peninsula, where the strip of

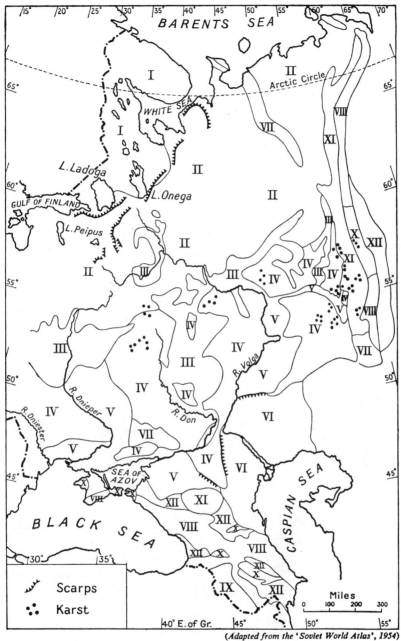

(*Adapted from the 'Soviet World Atlas', 1954*)

Fig. 67. GEOMORPHOLOGY OF EASTERN EUROPE

For explanation see text, p. 540.

tundra along the Arctic Ocean is comparatively narrow, though
tundra occurs above the forests on the mountains of the interior.
The tundra sends tongues southwards into the forest zone along the
Timan and Ural Mountains, roughly as far south as 63° N in
the latter.

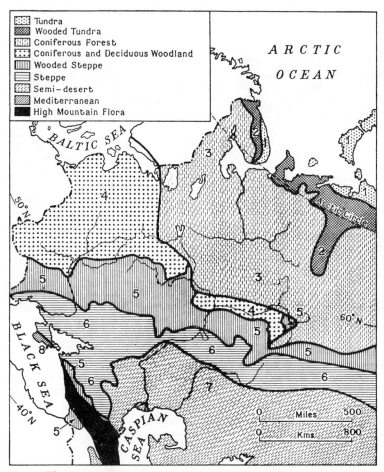

Fig. 68.  MAJOR VEGETATION ZONES OF EUROPEAN USSR

Winters are long and severe, with both soil and subsoil frozen,
and with snow covering the ground for about eight or nine months.
Cold winds blow with enormous force.  Summer is short, being
limited to about six weeks, and although the summer days are

very long, frosts may occur. The precipitation is spread evenly throughout the year, and clouds cover the sky almost all the time; although the total amount of precipitation is slight (8 to 12 in per annum), even this small amount hardly evaporates at all, but remains on the land as shallow stretches of water which often become transformed into marshes. As a result, mosquitoes are very troublesome in summer.

**Coniferous and Mixed Forests. The Taïga.** The coniferous forest zone in eastern Europe extends farther south than it does in central and western Europe. Its southern margin dips from the neigh-

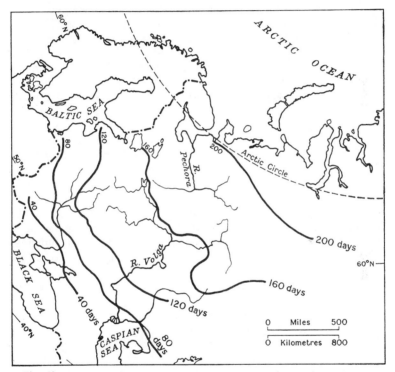

Fig. 69. AVERAGE DURATION OF SNOW-COVER IN EUROPEAN USSR

bourhood of Leningrad (60° N), south-east to the neighbourhood of Kalinin (Tver) on the Volga (56½° N), and thence to Kazan (about 55½° N), in correlation, no doubt, with the dipping of the winter isotherms towards the south-east. Winters are both long and cold, with six or seven months in which the average temperature falls below freezing, with snow lying on the ground for about

five and a half months in the south and for seven or eight months
in the north. The thaw sets in during late April or early May, so
the growing season is short, for the average temperature drops
below freezing in October even at Kazan. The average summer
temperatures are fairly high, e.g. 60·4° F (15·8° C) at Archangel,
67·5° F (19·7° C) at Kazan for July, but night frosts are liable to
occur even in the warmest month.

A marked feature of the vegetation of the Taïga zone is the
development of peat bogs (see p. 32).

**The Sub-Zone of Mixed Forest.** The proportion of deciduous trees
in the mixed forest zone remains small, and they form important
patches only in the southern portion of the zone. The chief
deciduous trees are the lime, oak, elm, and maple. It may be asked
why this zone need be taken as anything more than a transition belt
between the taïga and the purely deciduous forest. The answer
lies partly, (a) in the width of the belt, some 600 miles from north
to south along the meridian of Leningrad (30° E), whereas the zone
of purely deciduous forest is considerably narrower and much
intermingled with steppe, and (b) in the great importance of this
zone in the human geography of Russia. The main portion of this
sub-zone is triangular in shape, with its northern limit running from
Leningrad to Kazan and its southern limit from Zhitomir, via
Kiev and Ryazan to Kazan, which forms the apex of the triangle.
It continues east of the Volga only as a narrow strip. On the west,
it merges, of course, with the great zone of mixed forest which
covers Europe from the 60th parallel of latitude to the head of the
Adriatic Sea (c. 46° N). This triangle or wedged-shape zone of
mixed forest is the heartland of Russia, the only part suited to
agriculture in early days; in terms of human geography the history
of Russia may be described as the advance of the agriculturalists
of this zone against the hunters of the northern taïga and the
nomads of the southern steppes.

Climatically the region is marked off from the taïga by its longer
growing season, and particularly by a longer period free from killing
frosts. The duration of the snow cover is still long, varying from
about 160 days at Leningrad to 80 days at Kiev. At Moscow
there are five months with mean average temperature below freezing,
and at Kiev four months; the Neva, the Moskva and the Oka
all usually freeze before the end of November and remain frozen
until the middle of April. Summer temperatures, on the other hand,
are high for the latitude compared with those of central and western
Europe, e.g. Moscow, has a mean average July temperature of
66° F (19° C) and Kiev of 66·6° F (19·2° C), and although the precipitation is higher than in the taïga, the greater insolation dries up the

76  Neretva gorge

YUGOSLAVIA

77  Sarajevo: new housing

YUGOSLAVIA

78  Morskie Oko (the
Eye of the Sea), Tatra
Mountain.

POLAND

79    Academician Paton Bridge in Kiev

THE USSR

80    Volga hydro-electric station named after V. I. Lenin

land in summer and in consequence there is much less tendency to peat-bog formation, except in low-lying ground which is by nature badly drained.

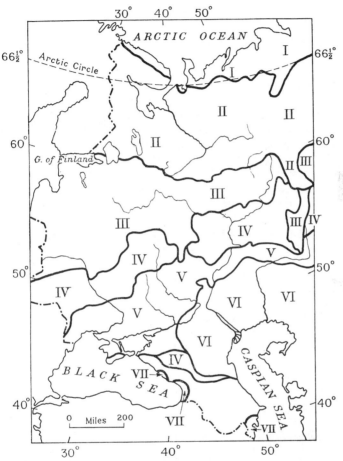

Fig. 70. MAJOR SOIL ZONES OF EUROPEAN USSR

I. Tundra and bog region. II. Podzol-peat region. III. Sod-podzolic region. IV. Degraded chernozem. V. Chernozem. VI. Chestnut and brown soils and saline soils. VII. Zheltozem (yellow soils) and Krasnozem (red soils).

**The Steppes and Wooded Steppes.**   South of the mixed forest zone there is a large area which is somewhat loosely termed 'the steppe'. Actually it consists of three zones as far as vegetation is concerned, and this difference in vegetation cover reflects slight but significant differences of climate.

In the greater part of the vast steppe area, trees will not grow except along water-courses or where water is supplied artificially. An exception occurs, however, in the northern fringe, where bordering the zone of mixed forest is the wooded steppe, or parklands.

*The Wooded Steppe.*　This area, which was once covered by steppe grasses and associated herbaceous vegetation, was invaded by deciduous trees in post-glacial times.　Oak, lime, maple, and ash are the predominating trees, with an undergrowth of shrubs or smaller trees, such as the spindle, cherry, hazel-nuts, and dog-roses, etc.　The deciduous trees were able to invade this area owing to the smaller liability to drought than in the true steppe.　Not only is the precipitation actually heavier (generally over 16 in), but it tends to be spread out more evenly in the year, and there is less evaporation than farther south owing to the lower summer temperatures and somewhat cloudier skies; moreover, the thicker snow-cover moistens the ground more thoroughly.　The wooded steppe appears always to have had considerable clearings in which steppe vegetation flourished. These were known as *polia* or *polyany*, meaning meadows or fields (cf. the *polja* of Yugoslavia). Owing to the extension of cultivation into the wooded-steppe belt, few woods now remain.

*The Tillable Steppe or Prairie.*　The tillable steppe or prairie corresponds with the distribution of the true *chernozem* or 'black earth'.　The annual precipitation here is usually less than 16 in but more than 10 in, with a maximum in spring and early summer. Winter precipitation occurs in the form of snow, but towards the drier margins tends to be not sufficiently thick for adequate ground protection.　In summer temperatures are high (e.g. Odessa 72·7° F: 22·6° C, and Saratov 72·1° F: 22·3° C in July), and evaporation exceeds precipitation.　In consequence the area is generally tree-less.

*The Non-tillable Steppe or Semi-desert.*　The non-tillable steppe is found round the northern end of the Caspian Sea, and east of the Ergeni Hills, where the annual rainfall is less than 10 in.　This region is sometimes known as semi-desert, but most of it carries seasonal grazing, though there are some completely bare patches which increase in frequency and size towards the south-east. The humus content is moderately high and the soils are therefore relatively fertile under irrigation.　Unfortunately a good deal of the surface is impregnated with salts of various kinds, and though the salt-loving vegetation which grows on some of these stretches is appreciated by livestock, completely bare salt pans cover considerable areas.

A good deal of confusion is caused by the word 'steppe' being applied both to the tillable as well as to the non-tillable grasslands. No doubt before the days of agricultural expansion the difference was not so noticeable as it is today, but a fundamental contrast in land use exists between the two types. In the following chapters, to avoid confusion, the term prairie will be used for the tillable steppe south of the wooded steppe, the term semi-desert for the non-tillable steppe.

## REFERENCES

See p. 619.

### CHAPTER 35

# THE NORTHERN LANDS OF THE USSR

THE northern lands of tundra and taïga are mainly non-agricultural, with a considerable percentage of their scanty population speaking languages belonging to the Finnish group. For these reasons they stand apart from the land further south, though they have been important to Russia on account of the port of Archangel since the mid-sixteenth century, and that of Murmansk in this century. In the past four centuries there has been considerable Russian penetration.

The whole area may be sub-divided into two major sub-regions:

A. The Kola peninsula and Finno-Karelia on the Fennoscandian Shield.

B. The northern part of the Russian Platform, draining towards the Arctic and White Seas.

**A. The Kola Peninsula and Finno-Karelia.** The Kola peninsula consists mainly of a dissected plateau formed of gneiss and granite, with rounded forms predominating. Newer maps issued by the USSR give the plateau a greater average elevation than did earlier maps based on incomplete surveys, and most of the land appears to be between 600 to 1,000 ft high, with the Khibin Mountains rising to over 4,000 ft. The northern shore of the peninsula lies just within the tundra belt; the coniferous forest farther inland is poor and thin, and peters out at an elevation of a few hundred feet. Consequently the timber industry is only poorly developed, while agriculture is equally unimportant, since the surface was largely swept bare of soil by the ice-sheet; the low-lying regions are often lake-filled or swampy, and the scanty soil is poor and acid. The short growing season renders even the hay crop very precarious. Until the war of 1914–19 the peninsula was largely the domain of some 2,000 Lapps, who lived a semi-nomadic existence, following their reindeer, with fishing to supplement their food supply, together with immigrant Finnic-speaking Zyrians (now called Komi), and a sprinkling of Russian and Norwegian fishermen. It is true that the Russians of Novgorod had explored this area in search of furs and had founded small settlements (e.g. Kola) before the fifteenth century, but the furs were neither so good nor so plentiful as those of the taïga farther east, and there was nothing to induce the Russians to settle here.

The need to bring in supplies from Great Britain during the war of 1914–18 marked the beginning of a great change in the Russian attitude towards the peninsula. Although Murmansk lies so far north (69° N) it can be used throughout the winter, owing to the Gulf Stream which hugs the shore. The Kandalaksha–Murmansk railway, which was built in 1914–16, utilises the depression in which lie Lake Imandra, the Kola river, and lesser rivers and lakes, and it is in about the same latitudes as the Scandinavian railway from Gellivar to Narvik. In spite of the railway Murmansk was only a small place of some 9,000 people in 1926, but by 1959, with 226,000 inhabitants, it had become the largest town in the world at such high latitudes. Many activities lie behind this remarkable growth. Murmansk is a naval base with yards for repairing and building ships and it marks the western limit of the summer northern sea route from Vladivostok. Further it is the administrative centre of the peninsula, and the base and processing centre for the Barents Sea fishery. It serves the peninsula too by exporting apatites.

Apart from Murmansk, the main importance of the Kola peninsula springs from its wealth of minerals and water power. The new Soviet town of Kirovsk (38,400), east of Lake Imandra, is the main centre for the mining of apatites and nepheline. Fertilisers, using the apatite, are manufactured there, and aluminium is refined from the nepheline; superphosphates are made at Kandalaksha. The new mining town of Monchegorsk was founded in the mid 1930s to work copper-nickel ores while, in the extreme north-west, are the nickel mines and plant of formerly Finnish Petsamo (now Pechenga) which is linked by rail with Murmansk. Mica deposits also occur. The Kola peninsula has the most northerly electric grid transmission system in the world, utilising the powerful falls on the Niva and Tuloma rivers, and the railway from Murmansk has been electrified. It is not surprising, in view of the economy and climate, that the population of Kola, which has doubled since 1939 to nearly 600,000, is grouped – to the extent of 92 per cent – in the towns. Indeed the rural population is shrinking: in 1959 there were only 43,000, living in an area of over 50,000 square miles, so that most of Kola is uninhabited. Even so, some of the potatoes, fresh vegetables, meat, and milk needed by the towns and mining settlements are produced locally.

While the Kola peninsula bears a strong resemblance to Norwegian Finnmark and Finnish Lapland, Finno-Karelia, now organised as the Karelian ASSR, greatly resembles the central lake section of Finland. This likeness is increased by the inclusion within the USSR of a strip of country which was part of Finland before World War II. After the departure to Finland of the Finnish inhabitants of this ceded territory, the USSR downgraded the Karelian–Finnish SSR, at the same time changing its name. Even so, Russians not Karelians form the preponderant group within Karelian ASSR's population of 649,000. The first Russians there entered chiefly from the White Sea, drawn to the excellent fisheries along the coast south of the Kem river. During the Soviet period they have immigrated in step with industrial development.

Karelia is distinguished from Kola by the excellence of its forests and the abundance of its lakes. It resembles the peninsula in the importance of its routes and the abundance of water-power which is increasingly harnessed at electric power stations. Its agriculture is clearly of little importance, except regionally, less than 3 per cent of the land being cultivated. Indeed more than half of the population is engaged in lumbering; the mining of mica and the quarrying of building stone are other industries which provide products for shipment.

The routes on which the economy of Karelia chiefly depends are the Leningrad–Murmansk railway and that which leaves this at Belomorsk to connect with the Archangel–Vologda railway, as also the great water route which, via Lakes Vig, Onega, and Ladoga, and various rivers, almost links the White Sea to the Baltic. This water route, with its portages, has been in use from the fifteenth century, but was supplemented in the 1930s by the Baltic–White Sea canal. This gives access from the White Sea to Lake Vig and from the latter to Lake Onega, and thus enables vessels to ply between the two seas during the open-water season and to relieve the railway of bulky freights – timber and apatites, building stone and mica. As the supply of hydro-electric power continues to increase, so has Karelian production of timber and timber products, notably cellulose, paper and plywood.

Karelia has only one large town, its capital Petrozavodsk (Peter's Mill), founded by Peter the Great on Lake Onega, and the spearhead of industry in the north-west during pre-Revolution times. Standing on the Murmansk–Leningrad railway, with 135,000 inhabitants, it manufactures machinery for the timber industry at the Onega plant. Belomorsk is a timber-exporting port on the White Sea. Vyborg (51,000) is by far the oldest of the Finno-Karelian towns, having been fortified by the Swedes at the end of the thirteenth century. It is a seaport approached from the Gulf of Finland lying in the Karelian isthmus through which pass the main routes between Leningrad and Helsinki. Before 1940, as Viipuri, it belonged to Finland but now finds itself within the Leningrad *oblast.*

It flourished as a Finnish timber-exporting port, being connected by waterways with an extensive hinterland now truncated by a political boundary. As a result, it has declined both in trade and in population.

**B. The Northern Drainage Area of the Russian Platform.** This vast area of 460,000 square miles comprises more than a fifth of European USSR or nearly four times the area of the British Isles. Yet its total population was only 3·4 million in 1959, or about 8 per square mile. This may be compared with 35 per square mile in Finland which lies in roughly comparable latitudes but enjoys a more favourable sea frontage. Some idea of the rôle of this northern region in Soviet economy is suggested by the fact that only 1 per cent of its surface is cultivated, nearly 80 per cent is forest or bog-land, and about 19 per cent has tundra vegetation.

The relief of the region is low and monotonous, mainly below 600 ft, except in the Timan Mountains. Minor inequalities of the land are concealed in the interminable forests, but there are many swampy and boggy depressions. The main water-parting between the rivers draining northwards to the Arctic and those draining southwards to the Caspian Sea is a long low ridge running north-east to south-west, which appears to be a terminal moraine left by the great ice-sheet. It is commonly taken as the southern boundary of the northern region.

The chief means of communication is still by water, for there are few railways and fewer roads in the region. The Northern Dvina river system has about 3,000 miles of navigable water, and the Pechora about 1,000 miles, but their usefulness is unfortunately much curtailed by their northerly latitude, Archangel (*c.* 65° N), near the mouth of the Northern Dvina, being frozen for seven months on an average, while the mouth of the Pechora is often frozen or seriously impeded by ice for about nine months in the year. Freezing is less severe in the upper courses of the rivers, so that internal navigation begins some time before the mouths are open for the export trade. The use of nuclear-powered ice-breakers helps to reduce the closed period.

This northern drainage area may be subdivided into (1) the tundra, (2) the taïga, and the latter into (*a*) the west, or Archangel region, (*b*) the north-east, or Pechora–Mezen area, (*c*) the south-west, or Vologda region. This subdivision depends on considerations of position and of the stage of economic development rather than on physiographic grounds.

**The Tundra.** Practically all the land north of the Arctic Circle belongs to the cold desert, or tundra. It begins just north of Mezen on the river of the same name, and broadens eastward, owing to the north-easterly trend of the coastline. The scanty population, consisting of Nentsy, formerly known as Samoyeds, and Komi (Zyrians), both Finnic in speech, together with some intrusive Russians, are organised in the Nenets National Area within Archangel *oblast* and numbered only 45,000 in 1959, that is less than one per square mile. Naryan-Mar (13,000), situated on the right bank of the lower Pechora river, is the capital of this area and a timber-exporting port. The reindeer-keeping Nentsy live on the fringes of the taïga in winter and engage in trapping, but move to the coasts in summer. They were falling an economic prey to the Komi, who had developed marked commercial aptitudes in modern times, and were buying up reindeer herds and grazing rights. It remains to be seen whether the recent state establishment of collective reindeer farms, schools, and medical stations will arrest the decay of the Nentsy who numbered only 23,000 in the whole USSR at the 1959 census.

**The Taïga.** It is only within the last 100 years or so that the northern forests have been valued for their timber. Before that time furs, and to a lesser extent salt, were the only commercial products. The people of Novgorod and Muscovy looked upon the region much as the Hudson's Bay Company looked upon the northern forests of Canada, and small fur-trading posts were established throughout the region at suitable collecting points along the rivers.

(*a*) *The Archangel Region.* The discovery by the English in the sixteenth century of the White Sea route to Russia led to a great increase in the importance of the western part of the taïga, and especially of the Northern Dvina river system, for the only practicable route between Archangel and Moscow was via the Northern Dvina and its tributary the Sukhona, and thence via the Vologda tributary of the latter. With the opening of the Baltic route by Peter the Great in the early eighteenth century the Archangel route was neglected, until the world demand for timber became so great that it could not be met by more accessible supplies. Archangel grew from 18,000 in 1900 to 77,000 in 1926, and 256,000 in 1959, and is the chief sawmilling and timber exporting port of the USSR. It has various activities, chiefly connected with wood, such as the manufacture of plywood, pulp, and paper, as well as ship-building, fishing and whaling industries. The Archangel region was connected by rail to the agricultural regions of the mixed forest belt at the end of the nineteenth century, and a direct line runs from north to south, linking Archangel with Vologda, and thence to Moscow.

Apart from the land near the navigable rivers and the railway line, the forest still retains much of its primeval character. The average population density of only eight per square mile means, in fact, that large tracts of country are completely uninhabited. The rural population – less than half of the total – is engaged in lumbering and subsistence agriculture, growing some rye, oats, barley, and flax, and rearing cattle in the natural meadows. There is an abundance of game birds and fresh-water fish.

(b) *The Pechora-Mezen Area.* The forested portion of the Pechora basin, together with the upper Vichegda and Mezen basins and the Timan Mountains, make up the Komi ASSR. This region, which is larger than the British Isles, is remarkable for the low, but sharply rising, density of population – now nearly seven persons per square mile. It is still one of the most inaccessible parts of Europe, for its rivers, on which transport much depends, lack the canal links with central Russia which are available in the western taïga. Until the 1940s it had neither surfaced roads nor railways. The discovery of coal at Vorkuta situated in the north-east beyond the Arctic Circle and of petroleum (and natural gas) at Ukhta in the centre of Komi has been successfully exploited and has stimulated transport improvements, notably the building of a railway south-westwards across the republic from Salekhard (17,000) on the lower Ob via Vorkuta and Ukhta to Kotlas, from which access can be had northwards to Archangel and southwards to Kirov and the Urals. The Pechora coalfield, of which Vorkuta (55,000) is the urban centre, was yielding 17·5 million tons of hard coal (including coking coal) in 1960, while the Ukhta wells produced then over half a million tons of oil. The population of Komi had risen to over 800,000, three-fifths of which is urban. The rivers provide only seasonal transport for timber, while dairy farming forms the chief agricultural activity. Komi, like the Archangel region, cannot supply its requirements of grain, which is railed from Western Siberia and the middle Volga via Kotlas. The capital of Komi and a centre of the timber industry is Syktyvkar (64,000), an old settlement on the Vichegda river in the extreme south-west of the region. Pechora coal supplies Leningrad and Archangel as well as local needs and will also supply Ural industries when railway access has been improved.

(c) *The Vologda Region.* With 23 people per square mile, this is the most developed part of the northern forest, but it is not, in fact, situated very far north, Vologda (59° 30′ N) being in the latitude of Stockholm, and Kotlas (61° N) in that of Tampere. The southern part of the region may be regarded as transitional between the taïga and the mixed forest zone of the Moscow region. Agriculture has been important here for a long time, and many of the settlements are centuries old. Vologda (138,000)[1], at the head of

[1] The population figures for towns of 50,000 or more inhabitants are from the census of 15 January 1959.

navigation on the Northern Dvina system of waterways, is the most important town and administration centre, and was one of the chief points on the old Moscow–Archangel route, as its wealth of sixteenth and seventeenth century architecture testifies. Nowadays, as the crossing-point of the Leningrad–Perm railway with the Moscow–Archangel line, its nodal position is enhanced. The collecting centre for the market produce of a large area, with flax, linseed, oats, hemp, butter, and eggs as the main commodities, Vologda also produces equipment for railway and water transport and for the timber industry. Cherepovets (92,000) has grown fast since the second world war as an iron and steel centre providing metal for the European North of the Union; it lies west of Vologda, at the northern end of the Rybinsk reservoir (filled in 1941), and has good waterway facilities and railway access to Leningrad. It will benefit by the Baltic–Volga waterway which is under construction (see p. 557). Smaller urban centres are: Velsk, with rail connection to the Vologda–Archangel line; Kotlas, on the Northern Dvina, with rail connexion south to Kirov (Vyatka), both centres of the timber industry; Ustyug at the junction of the Yug and Sukhona rivers; and Solvychegodsk, at the junction of the Vichegda and Northern Dvina, whose salt-pans founded the fortunes of the famous Stroganov family. The three last-named towns were important points on the old 'fur route' to the Pechora basin and Siberia.

## REFERENCES

See p. 619.

### CHAPTER 36

# THE CENTRAL ZONE OF MIXED FORESTS

THIS triangular area is widest in the west where it stretches for some 600 miles from the Gulf of Finland in the north to Kiev in the south, but it tapers to a point in the east near Gorki (Nijni Novgorod) at the junction of the Volga and Oka rivers. Within this area the Russians developed their characteristic mode of life, and, apart from the early Kiev trading ventures, it was only in the seventeenth century that they began to move south-eastwards into the steppe lands.

The western part of this Russian homeland lies almost exactly in the same latitudes as the British Isles (cf. the Gulf of Finland with the Orkneys, *c.* 59½° N, and Kiev, 50° 29′ N, with Plymouth 50½° N), but the real heartland of Muscovy, around whose nucleus the Russian state developed, lay to the north of England's heartland, Moscow being in the same latitude as Glasgow (55° 40′ as against 55° 52′). The more continental position of the Russian lands, however, gives rise to colder winters and a shorter growing season, which conspired to produce difficult conditions for settlement, especially for early and medieval farmers. For instance, although Moscow is 7° F (4° C) warmer in July than Glasgow, on an average, yet it is 36° F (20° C) colder in January, and the average Easter temperature at Moscow is no higher than the average Christmas temperature at Glasgow.

Soils are rather similar to those of the British Isles, and vary from podzols to the brown forest soils. There is a greater extent of fluvio-glacial sands, which contain little plant food, and if the boulder-clays contain fewer stones than in Britain, they are particularly heavy and sticky in spring with the melting snows. The adverse effect of unfavourable climate and soils is reflected in the much lower percentage of deciduous trees in this belt than in the British Isles, the boulder-clays as well as the sandy tracts being clad with conifers. Also, a far larger proportion of the land is covered with peat bog than in Great Britain, though not perhaps more than in Ireland.

The mixed forest zone is difficult to divide into natural regions owing to the absence of well marked physical features or physical contrasts, but owing to differences of historical and economic development there are certain distinctive nuclear regions.  These are:

(a) the Leningrad–Novgorod region, whose position on the Baltic led to the growth of trading interests, as exemplified by medieval Novgorod and later St Petersburg (Leningrad);

(b) the region round Moscow and Ivanono, mainly between the upper Volga and its tributary the Oka, historically known as Muscovy, and

(c) Byelorussia or White Russia in the upper Dnieper basin, which was historically a buffer area and only finally became politically part of Russia in the seventeenth and eighteenth centuries.

**The Leningrad-Novgorod Region.**  This region comprises that part of the Russian Platform whose rivers drain to the Gulf of Finland.  For convenience, Lake Peipus and the River Narva may be taken as the western limit, as these form a political as well as an ethnic frontier, but on physical grounds the whole Narva basin should be included.  Administratively this region consists of the *oblasts* of Leningrad, Novgorod and Pskov.

The region is remarkably transitional.  It lies at the junction of the northern coniferous forest (or taïga) and the central mixed forest, and therefore at the practical northern limit of agriculture. It lies between the sea-based culture of the Baltic and the land-based culture of Muscovy.  It is the meeting place of Finns, Estonians, and Karelians of Finnish speech, Scandinavians of Teutonic speech, and Russians of Slavonic speech.

Thanks to the stimulus of the Scandinavian 'Rusmen' it developed precociously before Moscow was founded, and during the later Middle Ages its towns of Novgorod and Pskov were trading republics, affiliated to the Hanseatic League, while Muscovy still dwelt in isolation.  Yet because of the short, damp growing season, the ice-bound winters, and the buffer situation politically, the Novgorod region failed to maintain its earlier importance.  Only Peter the Great's foundation of St Petersburg (now Leningrad) at the beginning of the eighteenth century, following his conquest of the Neva area from the Swedes, galvanised the region into new economic activity.  This is remarkably concentrated in Leningrad which, with its suburbs, has 3·3 million inhabitants, more than half of the region's total (6·25 million).  The rural population, although it is numerically dominant in both Novgorod and Pskov *oblasts*, is surprisingly scanty: indeed total population for the whole region averages only 32 per square mile.

The story of Leningrad's foundation amid the marshes of the Neva is a familiar one.  The Russian city was laboriously built on piles (cf. Venice and Amsterdam), and it provides an excellent example of the importance of position as compared with site.  The deltaic mouth of the Neva was the sole place where the Russians could wrest a foothold on the Baltic at that time, and so gain access to a practicable sea route to western Europe and the world at large.[1] Leningrad has relatively good inland communications by both waterways and rail. The first canal link with the Volga system was completed as early as 1710, only seven years after the laying of the foundation stone of the fortress of St Peter and St Paul, but the later Mariinsk canal system (*c.* 1808) linked the Neva and Svir with the Sheksna tributary of the Volga, while the Tikhvin Canal (1811) linked up the Neva and Volga systems via the Mologa tributary of the Volga. The Neva waterway is also connected by a short canal with the Northern Dvina system. The Baltic–Volga waterway to provide a deep-water replacement of the old Mariinsk system, is scheduled for construction during 1959–65.

Leningrad has long been a manufacturing city: in fact, it was the first Russian city to feel the impact of the Industrial Revolution, though its earliest functions were administrative and commercial, owing to its establishment as the capital of Russia, and to the busy traffic of its port. In spite of its abandonment as capital at the time of the Revolution, Leningrad continued to grow, owing to its importance as a manufacturing centre. Yet it had few obvious advantages for industry. Its hinterland provided few raw materials except scanty supplies of bog-ores and flax, and no fuel except charcoal and peat – in fact, its chief source of industrial fuel was imported English coal.[2] Today Leningrad draws its coal supplies from the Vorkuta and Donets coalfields, but relies very largely for power on hydro-electricity derived from rapids on the Svir and Volkhov rivers and for gas on supplies piped from Estonia. The chief manufactures are shipbuilding, machine-building for electric power stations, light engineering, precision tools, textiles, cellulose (including paper and rayon), and chemicals (including fertilisers from Kola apatite and rubber goods), leather and alimentary industries.

Leningrad remains the chief Baltic port of the USSR, especially for the export of timber, but there are now more Soviet ports further west, notably Riga. The use of ice-breakers helps to reduce the period of two to three months when the port is ice-bound.

The immediate hinterland of Leningrad is agriculturally poor, and the total land area is much restricted by the presence of Lakes

[1] They had formerly had to make shift with the Archangel route (see p. 552), for the Black Sea coast was held by the Turks until the very end of the eighteenth century.
[2] When under siege during World War II, many stoves in Leningrad were kept burning with coal-dust dredged up from the Neva, where it had accumulated from the unloading of colliers over a period of some 200 years.

Ladoga and Onega, which are respectively the largest and second largest lakes in Europe.   Even so, two agricultural zones around the city have been developed to serve the Leningrad market: vegetable growing and dairying based on locally produced fodder in the inner ring, and dairying and potato growing in the outer.   On the southern and south-eastern sides of the city the country consists mainly of a succession of swampy depressions and lake basins on the site of former glacial 'tongues'; surrounding these are low morainic ramparts, which are drier but less fertile.   The climate is unfavourable to cereals, but the glacial clays of the tongue-basins, when drained, are suitable for growing flax, hay, and fodder crops. Immediately to the west of Leningrad, along the Gulf of Finland, Silurian limestones appear on the surface, with only a thin sporadic glacial cover; and, in contrast to the rest of the area, there is a lack of surface water, but goodish soils of *rendzina* type.   It was in this area that the tsars erected their summer palaces, e.g. Tsarskoe Selo.[1]

The old urban centres of the area, Novgorod, on the Volkhov river, and Pskov (81,000) on the Velikaya, have declined to market towns, with small manufacturing industries of flax, timber, and leather, though Novgorod (61,000) is said to have had 400,000 inhabitants in the fifteenth century, at the time of its greatest trading period.   Modern centres are no larger, although the important bauxite deposits mined near Tikhvin supply the aluminium refinery at Zvanka, situated close to the Volkhov rapids.

**The Moscow–Ivanovo or Central Industrial Region.**   This region lay on the margins of the latest (or 'Würm') ice-sheet, and accordingly morainic deposits alternate with fluvio-glacial sands.   There is little variety of relief, though there are occasional low morainic ridges, while the fluvio-glacial sands are still often subject to flooding and were avoided by early agricultural settlements.   The early Russian settlers probably cultivated only the *polyany* (sing. *polie*= field).   These occurred chiefly in the southern and central parts of the zone, and probably had a light vegetation cover of deciduous woodland interspersed with meadow.   These *polyany* occupied the best-drained sites on the boulder clay, or were developed on patches of limestone which were sufficiently near the surface to improve either drainage or soil, or both.   The decay of the leaves from deciduous trees and of the meadow grasses naturally produced a richer soil to a greater extent than did the pine needles of the coniferous forest; in consequence of this and of the better drainage, the soils of

---

[1] The name Tsarskoe Selo is believed to have been derived from the Finnish 'Saari Mojs' or 'high place', which became 'Sarskoe' in Russian and subsequently 'Tsarskoe Selo' or 'Tsar's village'; this was later named 'Detskoe Selo' or 'children's village', and is now called Pushkin.

these clearings are *not* podzolised, but resemble the brown forest soils of the English lowlands, and in especially favoured areas approximate to the *chernozem* of the steppes.

Elsewhere, however, podzolised soils and coniferous forest prevailed, and though large areas have been cleared, a good deal still remains in the northern part of the zone round Ivanovo. Peat bogs increase in size and frequency towards the north, and in recent decades the peat has been utilised in great electric power stations to add to the power resources of the region.

The southern margin of the mixed forest zone, where it merges into the wooded steppe, lies roughly along the River Oka in this region, and thus the Oka would seem to be its obvious southern boundary. Yet even before the development of the Tula coalfield (now called the Moscow coalfield), which lies south of the Oka, the Tula region was associated with the Moscow area, for the Russians found a favourable habitat in the meadows and deciduous woods of the wooded steppe, and they tended to seep southwards whenever Tatar pressure weakened. Thus the Oka was usually only the second line of defence of Muscovy and not its main defensive moat.

The Moscow–Ivanovo region is the main urbanised section of the whole of the USSR, and until the 1930s was the main manufacturing area of the whole country, in spite of the development of the Donets region in the third quarter of the nineteenth century. Industry began there because the towns offered markets, while ungrateful conditions for farming led the peasants to eke out their incomes by cottage industries, particularly textiles and blacksmith's work. Bog ores were used at first. The state also established industries, especially that of armaments, while owners of serfs employed them in various manufactures. The discovery of the Tula brown coals proved very important, although the calorific value is low and the ash content and mining costs are high; the output for the year 1958 reached 47 million tons. By the early years of the twentieth century the Moscow–Ivanovo–Tula region had developed flourishing factory industries specialising in pig-iron and steel, engineering, hardware, and various textiles, though the textile industry remained at least partially a hand-loom industry. Much of the necessary coal and all the coke came from the Donets coalfield. With the development of the Ukraine and Ural industrial areas, the Moscow industrial region became *relatively* less important, but *actually* it produces more manufactured goods than ever before. The economic stature of the Central Industrial Region is evident when we note that, although its area is a mere 1 per cent of that of the USSR, it contains nearly 10 per cent of the USSR's population including nearly 20 per cent of its urban population; further, its industrial output accounts for about a quarter of that of the whole country.

The dominant industries of the region are machine building, textiles and chemicals, but the range is very wide, including food, clothing, footwear, as well as those producing building materials and using timber. Although the region lies far from supplies of raw cotton and wool and although attempts have been made to develop textile industries near to the sources of raw material, it still dominates the Union's production of cotton, linen and woollen goods. The chemical industry draws materials from the coalfield and from locally available phosphorites, and produces *inter alia* fertilisers, dyes and synthetic rubber. The machine building industry produces lorries, automobiles, aircraft, ships, equipment for electric power stations, for the textile industry and for agriculture, as well as precision instruments. The enormous energy requirements for this large-scale industry are drawn only in part from the Moscow brown coal field which yields fuels for power stations. Three new hydro-electric power plants on the upper Volga contribute their supplies, while hard coal is railed from the Donets field and petroleum is piped into the region from the Volga-Ural oilfield and natural gas is piped from the Ukraine and North Caucasus (see Fig. 71).

Moscow, the capital of the USSR, was already a great city with 1·8 million inhabitants in 1913, although it had ceased to be the capital of the Russian Empire two hundred years previously. Its population slightly exceeded the 5 million mark at the 1959 census, and immediately around it, as well further away up to some 15 miles from the Kremlin, lie a dozen or so sizeable industrial towns, chief of which are Perovo, Kuntsevo, Babushkin and Mytishchi. In 1960 the limits of Moscow were extended to include such towns, together with a broad Green Belt, well wooded but containing also many state and collective farms, so that its area – 342 square miles – has more than doubled. An outer ring road is being built to serve Greater Moscow which, so constituted, has a population exceeding 7 million; government policy is to try to reduce its rate of growth.

Moscow's industries epitomise those of the whole region – machine tools, precision instruments, motor vehicles, food processing and distilling, textiles and clothing, but include also printing and publishing, while in Soviet education and culture the city occupies pre-eminent status. Its position as the USSR's capital is now somewhat excentric, in view of the achieved and continuing settlement and economic growth of the vast lands beyond the Volga, but reflects its great rôle in the making in turn of Muscovy and the

Russian Empire.   Its central position in European USSR, together
with its facilities for transport by water and by rail, clearly give the
city advantages as a distribution centre for finished goods.   Although
Moscow's original site is on the small Moskva tributary of the Oka,
it is accessible for barges and other river vessels, and the construction
in the 1930s of the Moscow–Volga canal puts it into communication
not only with the main river, but also, by means of the Mariinsk
canal system, with Leningrad and the north.

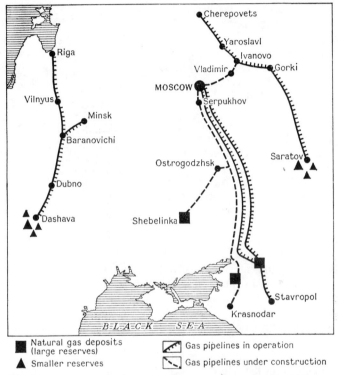

Fig. 71. PIPELINES FOR NATURAL GAS IN EUROPEAN USSR

The Moscow coalfield is mainly associated with iron and steel
production and metal working, Tula and neighbouring centres
being the Russian equivalent of England's Birmingham region, and
similarly, little of the iron is now obtained locally.   Tula (345,000)
specialises in samovars, small arms, sewing machines, etc.; Kaluga
(133,000) concentrates on agricultural machinery, including tractors;
Kolomna (106,000) has an old-established locomotive and rolling-
stock industry; Ryazan (213,000) makes agricultural machinery.

The last three towns mentioned are all situated on the Oka river. The phosphates which occur just north of the coalfield are worked up into fertilisers at Novomoskovsk (107,000) and elsewhere. This town is Stalinogorsk renamed.

Another group of manufacturing towns lies along the upper Volga, and has the advantage of this great waterway. In the west lies Kalinin (261,000; formerly Tver), situated at the head of navigation on the Volga, where the River Tvertsa joins the main river. It is one of the most important centres for manufacturing rolling stock, and has textile, leather, flour, and timber industries. Rybinsk (181,000; formerly Shcherbakov), on the Volga just below the large Rybinsk reservoir and electric power plant, and at the southern end of the Mariinsk canal system, makes rivercraft, and has important sawmills, flour mills, and rope factories. Yaroslavl (406,000), situated where the Moscow–Vologda–Archangel railway crosses the Volga, is one of the old historic cities of Russia, but has added synthetic rubber, rubber tires, oil refining, and engineering to its old manufactures of textiles, leather, timber, and flour milling. Kostroma (171,000), another ancient city, lies at the junction of the Kostroma and Volga rivers, and is an important saw milling centre, since it taps the whole of the forested Kostroma basin. It will be seen that these towns on the upper Volga make use of the timber coming down from the northern tributaries, the grain and petroleum coming up the Volga, as well as local products such as flax, but they are also tending to develop engineering industries.

The textile industry, specially important in the central region, is particularly associated with the name of Ivanovo (332,000). In this boggy and infertile area, with few alternative means of livelihood, conditions in the cottage industry and in the early factories were notoriously bad, and Ivanovo together with Orekhovo-Zuevo (108,000) were main centres of the revolutionary movement. Various requirements of the textile industry, such as dyestuffs, starch, and some types of machinery, are manufactured in the numerous small towns of this textile belt.

**Agriculture in the Moscow–Ivanovo Region.** As elsewhere in the USSR, agriculture in this region is still in transition. Right down to the 1920s the old uneconomic three-field system prevailed over much of the land; rye was the chief food crop, together with potatoes in more recent years, and flax was the chief cash crop, though oats, barley and hemp were also grown. Some market gardening was carried on. Pressure on the land had brought about a reduction in livestock, and this curtailed the supplies of meat and manure, though butter was produced for the towns in some areas. Since the 1920s the system of collective farming and the war of 1941–45 led to a further reduction of livestock,[1] but marked recovery in the numbers of cattle and pigs is recorded under Khrushchev's régime. Given the latitude (cf. Denmark), the comparatively damp summers, and the urbanisation of the area, the natural evolution seems to be in the direction of animal husbandry, particularly for dairy cattle and pigs, for which much grassland is available, supplemented by hay, silage and clover. The yield of grain, still mainly winter rye, remains relatively stable, though its area has decreased during the last ten years and is far from sufficient given the region's high density of population and high degree of urbanisation. Accordingly, large shipments of grain, as also of sugar and fats, are necessary; grain supplies now come mainly from the middle Volga region, Western Siberia and Kazakhstan. The need of drainage works and the heavier use of fertilisers are well recognised as means to increase regional supplies. The growing of vegetables and potatoes are well developed, notably in suburban belts as well as on the farms.

**The Western Section of the Mixed Forest Zone.** This region is transitional between Muscovy, which was the heart of Russia, and the Vistula basin, which was the heart of Poland, and thus is politically a buffer area. It is climatically transitional between central and eastern Europe. A Russian writer (S. P. Turin) writes of its 'mild and even climate', though the average January temperature is about 17° F (—8·3° C), and the annual range of temperature about 47° F (26° C).

Physically the area includes: (a) the northern part of the Central Russian Uplands forming the watershed between the Volga and Dnieper systems, coinciding roughly with the *oblast* of Smolensk; (b) the cultivated lowlands along the upper Dnieper, Berezina, and Sozh rivers, which corresponded with the Byelorussian SSR before World War II; and (c) the marshy region bordering the Pripyat river, known as Polesie (Polish) or Polyessie (Russian).

As the towns are mainly route centres, the distribution of the urban population can best be considered in relation to all three sub-sections.

(a) *The Smolensk Section of the Central Russian Uplands.* The Central Russian Uplands in this region consist mainly of high, rolling plains, relieved only by low hills and broad, marshy valleys. In the north, however, are the Valdai Hills (see pp. 536–7), while the most advanced terminal moraine of the latest (Würm) glaciation

---

[1] This was not intended when collectivisation was started but the peasants killed and ate their livestock, either because they feared that the animals would be confiscated or because they believed that the 'government' would supply the collective farms with animals. (See *The Russian Peasant and Other Studies*, by Sir J. Maynard.)

runs from east–north-east to west–south-west, just north of the upper Dnieper valley, whose course it has affected. It is well seen just to the north of Smolensk. South of this ridge the uplands were not glaciated, and in many areas they carry a covering of *limon* or *Löss*, while the river valleys draining the uplands are covered with fertile alluvium derived from the *limon*. Soils are therefore mainly fertile, and agriculture gives good crops of oats, barley, flax, hemp, potatoes and fodder. Stock rearing is fairly important, especially for pigs and beef cattle. The rural density of population, 40 per square mile, is twice that of the Leningrad *oblast* and much higher than that of Byelorussia.

Peat is abundant to provide fuel for the electric power stations, while mineral resources include phosphorites and building materials. Smolensk (146,000), an old city on the upper Dnieper mentioned as early as the ninth century, was a trading intermediary between Novgorod and Kiev. After being in dispute for many centuries between Russians, Lithuanians and Poles, it was finally secured to Russia in 1686, and played an important part in its intellectual, religious and economic life. Situated where the Warsaw–Moscow railway is crossed by the Orel–Riga line, it became a vigorous commercial centre and, like Minsk, developed various industries connected with the produce of the countryside, such as distilling, brewing, and the working of flax and timber. Bryansk (206,000), a river port on the Desna tributary of the Dnieper, is also a railway junction and the chief town of this western part of European USSR for metallurgical industry, specialising in locomotives and rolling stock. It lies on the margin of the mixed forests and the wooded steppe.

(*b*) *Byelorussian SSR.* This region became politically Russian at the first and second partitions of Poland in 1772 and 1793. It lies mainly in a 'tongue-basin' of the maximum (Riss) glaciation, though its northern extremity, north of Orsha and Minsk, comes within the terminal moraines of the latest (Würm) glaciation. South of these moraines there are considerable areas covered with outwash sands. The soils of both the glacial clays and the sands tend to be podzolised. There are also large areas of swamp and bog, which increase in area and frequency towards the south, and begin to be a dominating feature of the landscape along the lower Beresina, along the Dnieper near its confluence with the Pripyat, and more especially along the Pripyat river. The poor drainage of this area is partly due to its receiving a great deal of water from the surrounding higher land, but it has been aggravated by the epeirogenic rise in post-glacial times of the crystalline floor of the Russian Platform in the Dnieper Heights south of Kiev. Owing to the resistance of these crystalline rocks to erosion, the Dnieper has not been able to erode its bed in pace with this elevation, and in conse- quence of the 'bottleneck' below Dnepropetrovsk, the waters of the upper Dnieper and its tributaries have been ponded back. The name of the town Bobruisk (from Slavonic *bober* = beaver) indicates the watery habitat in which beavers used to flourish. The marshes are not generally of the sphagnum or northerly type found round Leningrad and Ivanovo, but of the sedgy type, and when drained they provide fertile soils, though on the whole the soils of Byelorussia tend to be sandy and infertile, and a good deal of forest still remains on the morainic hills of the north, and on the least amenable of the soils farther south. The livestock (particularly pigs and cattle) of this region have long been well known throughout Russia, with the by-products of hides, pig skins, and bristles. Oats and barley, largely grown for fodder, supplement the water-meadows and rota- tion grasses. Potatoes, hemp, and flax are important here as else- where in the west of European Russia.

(c) *The Pripyat Marshes of the Russo-Polish Borderland.* Most geologists now believe that the marshes of Polyessie (or the Pripyat Marshes) occupy the site of a great glacial *Urstromtal* or *pradolina*, and it is not now generally held that they occupy the site of an ancient lake. Both the pre-Quaternary and post-Quaternary events had considerable influence on the evolution of the area; to north and south it is bounded by anticlines whose axes run east-west, while west of Brest–Litovsk (now called Brest) it is bounded by another anticline with axis running north-south. The edge of the ice-sheet, during the most recent glaciation, lay for a long time in a great curve concave to the south-east along the western and northern anticlinal margins, and an enormous quantity of melt- water was available, which could not escape directly southward, owing to the presence of the southern anticline. An exceptionally large *pradolina* was formed, whose waters could escape only by the eastern or unenclosed side, until they found an easy way south- ward down the old 'tongue-basin' of the Dnieper valley.

After the ice-sheet had disappeared the *pradolina* was not com- pletely drained by the Pripyat, owing to the check imposed on the escape of the water by the epeirogenic uplift of the Dnieper Heights, as mentioned above.

A further consequence of this reduction of gradient is still in progress, and may eventually result in the natural drainage of the marshes. It is evident that the waters of the upper Pripyat lie nearer the Baltic than the Black Sea, and as a result the head- waters are in process of capture by the Polish river Bug.

The marshes of Polyessie form one of the poorest regions of

Europe.   The area resembles the English Fens before their drainage, though the scale of the Polyessie marshes is much larger.   Innumerable streams thread the area in all directions, and permanent 'broads' and marshes abound.   During low water, which occurs in late summer and again in winter, there is a fair amount of more or less dry land, but with the spring thaw the waters rise and wide areas are inundated.   In some places sand-dunes occur which are survivals of a drier climatic period, but the main exception to the watery picture is the peninsula of *terra firma* at whose eastern end stands the small town of Pinsk.   Trees, such as birch and alder, grow thinly in the marshes; pine trees occur on the drier sandy stretches, and timber plays a great part in the life of the people, houses and boats being made of wood, and timber being the chief fuel. Agriculture is, of course, not very important, but rye, potatoes, and flax are cultivated in the areas above flood-level, hay is cut from water-meadows, and marsh grass from land which remains swampy throughout the year.   Fishing and fowling, together with the rearing of ducks and geese provide additional food, though some pigs and poultry are reared.

Communications are naturally difficult, except in winter when both water and ground are frozen, and in summer by boat, and although a single-track railway was built from Gomel via Mozir to Pinsk, the trains cannot attain a high speed.   Many areas are accessible only by punts.   The economy is necessarily backward owing to the lack of communications, and the need for large-scale drainage works persists, though some drainage works have been carried out.   The population density was 80 per square mile in the Polish section (census 1931), and 62 per square mile in the Russian section (census 1939).   The region is now wholly included in Byelorussian SSR.

**Towns and Industries of Byelorussia.**   Most of the towns in the western section of the mixed forest zones are of medieval origin. They are usually route centres, situated at river crossings.   The old north–south route from Novgorod to Kiev crosses the east–west route leading from central Europe to Moscow in the neighbourhood of Orsha.   The former route linked regions of contrasting natural resources, the latter linked regions in contrasting stages of economic and cultural development.   On the east–west route, now followed by the Warsaw–Moscow railway, lie Smolensk, Orsha, Borisov and Minsk.   This was the line of Napoleon's advance on Moscow, a route which goes between the Pripyat marshes on the south and the morainic hills on the north.   In modern times many of the towns have greatly developed industrially but not to the same extent as towns situated farther from the western frontier.

The lack of coal and other minerals handicaps great industrial development, though peat is used to a considerable extent in electric power stations, while phosphates and some iron-ore are mined in the Central Uplands.

Minsk (509,000), situated at the crossing point of the Moscow–Warsaw and Liyepaya–Kharkov railways, owes its size partly to its administrative functions as the Byelorussian capital but also to the industrial growth which has followed its reconstruction after the heavy damage inflicted upon it during World War II.   In particular, it has factories making bicycles, tractors and automobiles, as well as others concerned with clothing, textile and wood-working. Vitebsk (148,000), in the north of Byelorussia, stands where the Leningrad–Orsha railway crosses the Moscow–Riga line, and is noted for its linen and knitwear industries.   Gomel (166,000), in the south, lies on the Sozh tributary of the Dnieper at a point where it is now crossed by several converging railway lines: it has a flourishing timber industry and manufactures agricultural machinery.   The timber industry is also important at Bobruisk (97,000), where cellulose and paper are made on a considerable scale.

The population of Byelorussia declined during the inter-censal period 1939-59 from 8·9 to 8·1 million, although the postwar growth of its towns has meant an increase in the urban share of its population from 21 per cent to 31 per cent.   Byelorussians make up 80 per cent of the population; the rest are Russians, Poles, Ukrainians and Jews – the last now accounting for only 1·9 per cent.

## THE BALTIC STATES: ESTONIA, LATVIA, LITHUANIA

The three east Baltic states or republics in the aggregate have an area as large as that of England, Wales, and Northern Ireland together.   Even Estonia, the smallest, is half as large again as Belgium or Holland, and somewhat larger than Denmark.   Nevertheless, they are little known even to most English people, despite their maritime position.   It is true that their population (about 6 million) is not very large.   It is more than that of Scotland, and Lithuania has almost as many people as the Republic of Ireland. The major reason for ignorance of these countries lies very largely in their past history.   This area of the eastern Baltic states lay generally outside the sphere of British interests, and their position linked the Ests, Letts, and Lithuanians with Russian, Polish, and Swedish history.[1]   Yet between the two world wars their closest economic ties

[1] Chaucer had evidently heard of Latvia, for he says of his Knight, in the Prologue to the Canterbury Tales: 'In Lettowe had he resed (journeyed) and in Russe, No Christened man so oft of his degree'.

were with the United Kingdom, which figured as the leading importer of their produce, and as first or second in the list of suppliers of manufactured goods.

**Position in Relation to Russia.** The three Baltic republics stand in somewhat the same relation to Russia as the Netherlands (Holland) do to Germany. From the point of view of the larger neighbour they are essentially *transit* lands. The best means of access from the USSR to the North Atlantic lie through the Estonian port of Tallin and the Latvian ports of Riga, Ventspils (Windau), and Liyepaya (Libau), while the much disputed port of Memel (Klaypeda) has also some importance as an outlet for the Byelorussian SSR via Minsk. These ports have the great merit of being much less hampered by ice than those near the head of the Gulf of Finland; in fact, the ports which stand on the bulges of the coast, such as Liyepaya, are normally open to shipping throughout the winter without the use of ice-breakers, while the average duration of the winter freeze at Paldiski and Tallin is only four weeks and seven weeks respectively, compared with four or five *months* at Leningrad. Before World War I, when the Baltic states were under Russian rule, Liyepaya was a great exporter of produce both from the Ukraine and Siberia. It was also an important naval base.

The strategic significance attached to this east Baltic area by Russia was attested by the very powerful fortresses (e.g. of Daugavpils and Kaunas), and the great military roads, which took no account of local needs, but went straight across country.

**The People.** In spite of forming part of the Russian Empire from the eighteenth century onwards until 1918, the people of the Baltic states are much less Russian than the Dutch are German. Their national individualities were proclaimed in the establishment of their independence in 1918, and have been acknowledged since their re-inclusion within the Soviet realm after the war of 1941–45 by the status accorded to them of member republics of the USSR.

The Estonians speak a language which is akin to the Finnish, while the Latvians and Lithuanians speak non-Slavonic Indo-European languages, which are peculiar in showing many archaic characteristics.

Before 1918, however, only the Lithuanians had ever possessed an independent organised state. There is, indeed, a very striking contrast between the success of the Dutch in maintaining their independence against powerful neighbours and the lack of such success on the part of the east Baltic peoples. The reasons are varied and complex, and are by no means entirely geographical, but it may be noted that these Baltic states lay far removed from the civilisation of the Roman world, whereas the Dutch (Batavians) got an early start owing to their more favourable geographical position, which their peculiar genius turned to good account.

The east Baltic people remained heathen, and therefore cut off from the learning and organisation of the Mediterranean and Western world, at least until the fourteenth century. The Lithuanians, who had a nucleus on the lower Niemen, were the most southerly of the three peoples and therefore enjoyed better climatic conditions for agriculture, actually founded an empire of considerable size (see p. 406) at the expense of their eastern neighbours the Tatars and Russians. Through its union with the Polish crown, however, Lithuania lost its individuality and its ruling class became Polonised. The country as a whole stagnated. The undeveloped state of the country itself and of its Russian hinterland prevented the development of an important transit trade, while such sea-borne trade as existed in the Middle Ages and early modern times was in the hands of the German-controlled Hanseatic League. For the Lithuanians, like their Slavonic-speaking neighbour, appear to have been purely landsmen. At the third partition of Poland, 1795, Lithuania fell to Russia.

Estonia and Latvia were conquered by a crusading order, the 'Teutonic Knights' during the thirteenth century, and both countries were Germanised to the extent that the land belonged to this German religious order, and after the order was secularised in the sixteenth century the land passed to the German 'Baltic Barons'. Trade was conducted by German merchants, Riga and Tallin being Hansa towns. In the seventeenth century, Estonia and northern Latvia passed under Swedish control, while southern Latvia was transferred to Poland. In the eighteenth century (in 1721 and 1795) both areas fell to Russia.

National feeling developed much later in this part of the world than in western Europe. It was mainly in defence of their language that each of the three peoples developed their political nationalism, in the face of a strong attempt at Russification during the second half of the nineteenth century. The Lithuanians alone had a tradition of former independence and of imperial glory to uphold their nationalist ideal. The ostensibly tolerant policy of the USSR towards national minorities did not preclude some deportation of the native inhabitants and the settlement of Russians in the former republics. Actually, as a result of emigration and enforced migration, the population of Lithuania declined slightly between 1939 and 1959, from 2·88 to 2·71 million, although both Latvia and Estonia registered small increases. The numbers of the Baltic nationalities recorded in 1959 as living within the USSR outside their national republic are proportionally small – about 8 per cent of the Estonians, and only 5 per cent of the Lithuanians and Latvians. Russians have intruded into Latvia SSR and make up 26·6 per cent of its total population; comparable figures for Estonia and Lithuania are respectively 21·7 per cent and 8·5 per cent.

**Physical Background.** The most northerly point of Estonia is about lat. 59° N, and the most southerly part of Lithuania about 54° N, that is to say, the region lies in the latitudes of Denmark and southern Sweden and of Scotland, and thus on the borders of the deciduous and coniferous forests, in the zone of rye, oats, potatoes, and flax. Owing to the position on the Baltic, with a large stretch of water to the west, the climate is rather damp and suited to grass and fodder crops.

Very little of the land is over 600 ft high, so none is too high for cultivation, but as the region was all glaciated, the superficial deposits give rise to soils of very varied fertility. The disturbance of the drainage system which was bound up with the glaciation has been responsible for many waterfalls and rapids, some of which have been used for hydro-electricity. None of the republics is rich in minerals, though the oil shales of Estonia have considerable value regionally.

**Surface Features Resulting from the Quaternary Glaciation.** This area presents a classic example of morainic deposition on the edge of a great ice-sheet. Only in north-western Estonia is the drift so thin that the solid rock appears at or near the surface and here the great ice-sheet scraped off most of the soil, but the low plateau of Cambro-Silurian limestone which resulted (zone A in Fig. 72) is streaked with eskers.

At first sight the arrangement of the morainic landforms seems quite haphazard, for outwash plains, terminal moraines, *Urstromtäler*, drumlins and other ground-moraine landscapes succeed each other rapidly and without any clearly marked order or sequence. The clue to this puzzling situation may be found in Fig. 72. At its greatest extent, and in its most active form, the last great ice-sheet threw up a great girdle of end-moraine (marked in the figure as zone C) with characteristic 'knob and basin' topography. This, broadly speaking, forms the 'rim' between the Baltic drainage and the Black Sea drainage, and forms a belt running from north-east to south-west some 70 or 80 miles wide. Daugavpils and Kaunas lie on the Baltic side of this belt and Minsk lies just to the south of its south-eastern edge. The 'knob and basin' topography generally presents a wildly haphazard arrangement of little hills and lake-filled basins, but in the Vilnyus region there is a well-marked 'tongue-basin', girdled by morainic ridges.

At a later stage, when the ice-front had retreated somewhat, the ice-sheet was evidently thinner and its edge became frayed into a series of great ice-lobes which occupied the hollows (tongue-basins), now partially filled by lakes Peipus and Pskov, the Gulf of Riga, and probably the Memel Gulf also. These long vanished ice-lobes gave rise to the main topographical features of zone B (Fig. 72).

End-moraines were thrown out in great festoons round the ice-lobes in the tongue-basins, and accordingly the direction of the moraines bears no relation to the *generalised* edge of the ice-sheet, but is closely connected with the shape of the ice-lobes. As it appears that the ice-lobes retreated spasmodically, each stage or pause was associated with the formation of a new morainic girdle. From these moraines the melt-water escaped on the outer sides across outwash plains, or along narrow fluvio-glacial valleys where sands were deposited on the floor of both outwash plains and *Urstromtäler*. Occasionally the water was ponded back in ice-dammed lakes, of which the Vyrtsyarv (Estonia) is a surviving remnant, and better soils resulted. As the lobes of ice melted, a ground-moraine landscape, sometimes rich in drumlins, emerged from beneath, as in central Estonia, west of Tartu. Sometimes however, this fertile drift was concealed beneath later terminal moraines or outwash plains.

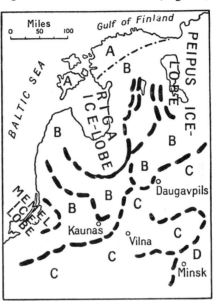

Fig. 72. SOME GLACIAL FEATURES OF THE EAST BALTIC REPUBLICS AND ADJACENT AREAS

A = Esker, or 'Harju' region, with solid rocks at or near surface.

B = Ice-lobe region. A late stage of the ice-lobes is depicted. Festoons of end-moraines (shown in black) outline the tongue-basins.

C = Main Baltic end-moraine, with 'knob and basin' topography, except for the Vilnyus tongue-basin.

D = The main outwash plain. (In Byelorussia.)

The picture is further slightly complicated by the fact that the edge of the ice-sheet receded towards the north or north-east in its later stages, instead of towards the north-west as in its intermediate and earlier stages. Thus, there tends to be, especially in

Lithuania, two sets of morainic ridges, running almost at right angles to each other, and this has resulted in a very confused topography which hinders the development of an adequate drainage system. This, in turn, means that large areas of land are liable to flood, particularly in spring after the thaw has set in, and to a certain extent in autumn. This flooding has an adverse effect both on farming and communications, while even the forests which grow on these areas consist of poor quality wood.

After the withdrawal of the ice, various oscillations of level affected the region. The waters of the Yoldia Sea, the Ancylus Lake, and the Litorina Sea rose over the coastlands, sometimes depositing fertile clays, at other times giving rise to sands and subsequently to peat beds. Later the lowering of the water-level led to a slight rejuvenation of the river system, and in consequence the rivers have somewhat incised their beds, and in places have cut down to the solid rock beneath the glacial deposits, as at the falls on the River Narva, which are utilised for the cotton textile industry at the town of the same name and, since 1955, by a hydro-electric station.

**Estonia.** Estonia, with an area of 17,800 square miles, is the smallest of the Baltic republics, but is rather larger than Denmark. Being the farthest north, it has the least favourable climate and suffers from the shortness of its growing season. The density of population (65 per square mile) is lower than in Latvia or Lithuania, but the country was reckoned to be the most progressive of the three republics, and between the two world wars the energy of the inhabitants was able to effect a considerable improvement in the standard of living. The distribution of the large estates of the German 'Baltic Barons' among the peasants in 1918 was accompanied by the development of a cooperative dairying industry on the Danish model. During the more recent Soviet phase, the agricultural emphasis in Estonia has continued to be on dairying and pig and poultry breeding for which much meadow and rough pasture exist; of the total area only about one-sixth is under crops, especially coarse grains, potatoes and fodder. The remarkable economic change in Estonia since its incorporation into the USSR has been its fast rate of industrialisation – twice that for the Union as whole. Nearly 60 per cent of the population now lives in the towns, and the rural population, which not long ago was preponderant, is steadily decreasing, both relatively and absolutely.

*Northern Estonia (the Esker Belt).* Estonia consists of three physical regions. In the north, rising from the Gulf of Finland by means of a steep cliff (the 'Glint'), is a low plateau which attains a maximum height of about 550 ft. Its Cambro-Silurian limestones are crossed by eskers ('Larju'), trending mainly from north-west to south-east, and the area is not very fertile. A belt of oil-shales runs parallel to the Gulf of Finland, about 6 to 10 miles inland, and the shales are processed at the integrated processing plant at the new town of Kokhta-Yarve: half of the shales, which are mined by shaft and by open pit method, are used to produce gas which is piped to Tallin and to Leningrad; oil is extracted to fuel electric power stations, the railways, Baltic shipping, and to supply domestic users, residual ash is used to make cement, while the by-products of shale offer many further opportunities to the chemical industry. The completion of the Baltic Regional Electric Station at Narva, scheduled for 1963, will make available 600,000 kW, and this capacity will later be doubled.

The practically ice-free port of Tallin is of great value to the country. Tallin (280,000 in 1959), the capital of Estonia, an old town of picturesque appearance, standing on a deep bay at the entrance of the Gulf of Finland, now accounts for more than half of Estonia's growing industrial output, mainly machines and textiles.

*Central Estonia (the Drumlin Belt).* A broad depression runs from Pyarnu on the Baltic via Tartu to Lake Peipus. Though sand and peat-bog cover much of the area round Pyarnu, most of the region is characterised by the presence of drumlins, running from north-west to south-east, with fluvio-glacial valleys (*Urstromtäler*) threading their way through the countryside. The boulder clay of the drumlins gives rise to fertile soil, and the region is highly cultivated, except in the west where forested sands are found. Tartu (74,000 in 1959), on the Ema river, is the second largest town of Estonia; it owes its fame chiefly to its university, founded by the Swedes in 1632.

*South-east Estonia (the Morainic Belt).* This region attains only moderate elevations (e.g. Great Munamägi in the East Livonian Heights = 1,054 ft), but is distinguished by extreme surface irregularity, since morainic material from both the Peipus and Riga ice-lobes was piled up here. Cultivation mingles with woodland; flax is widely grown.

**Latvia.** Latvia has the advantage over the other two republics of having no less than three good ports, each possessing good rail connexions with the interior. By virtue of its navigable river the Daugava (known as the Western Dvina in its Russian section), Riga became the most important port of the whole of the east Baltic at an early date, and with 605,000 inhabitants in 1959 it is the largest town of the three republics. Liyepaya (71,000) and Daugavpils (65,000) are much smaller. Latvia is the chief timber exporter among the three countries concerned, mainly on account of the timber floated down the Daugava from Byelorussia, though some is locally produced, about a quarter of Latvia's surface being forested. Before World War I Riga claimed to be the largest timber-exporting port in the world. It concentrates two-thirds of Latvia's industrial production, which includes ships, rolling stock, electrical equipment, textiles, chemicals, rubber articles, and processed tobacco. Its seaport does not however enjoy the advantages of Liyepaya and Kaliningrad (formerly Königsberg) further to the west which virtually escape the winter freeze.

Latvia's agriculture, like that of Estonia, yields principally animal and dairy products, as also flax, so that it is able to contribute supplies of butter, bacon and flax to other cities of the Union. Industrial enterprises will be stimulated by the new hydro-electric plant on the Daugava river at Plavinyas, scheduled for completion in 1963 with a capacity of 600,000 kW.

The main artery of Latvia is the Daugava river, which links the various physical regions together. In the extreme south-east of Latvia the Daugava drains (a) the 'knob and basin' country of the main Baltic end-moraine; then by means of its Aiviekste tributary it drains (b) the southern edge of the Peipus tongue basin round Lake Luban. It then incises its bed in hard, red Devonian sandstone, with (c) the morainic South and East Livonian Heights on the north-east, and runs into (d) the Riga depression. With the latter may be included the Jelgava plain. The only remaining physical region is (e) the Courland plateau.

(a) The 'Knob and Basin' Country is strewn with small lakes, and is more suited to woodland than cultivation, though much of it is cropped. The area has the old regional name of Latgale.

(b) The Valley of the Aiviekste is the only large part of Latvia which is quite unsuitable for farming, owing to the presence of very infertile sands. The whole region is forest-clad except for the swampy areas. The sands may presumably be considered to be the outwash derived from the morainic heights on the north-west which covered up the clays of the tongue-basin.

(c) The Livonian Heights, which are dotted with small lakes, are partially wooded. Their maximum height is 1,017 ft.

(d) The Riga-Jelgava Plain is a horseshoe-shaped depression encircled on the landward side by the most recent end-moraines of the Riga ice-lobe. After the ice-tongue had withdrawn somewhat to the north, this area was covered with the waters of an ice-dammed lake, which deposited clays and sands in somewhat haphazard fashion. It is mainly fertile and well cultivated, except along the coasts, where sand-dunes are accompanied by dreary bogs.

(e) The Courland Plateau carries a good deal of boulder-clay, and is mainly highly cultivated and thickly populated, though the coastal region has poor sandy soils, covered with forest and bog.

**Lithuania.** Lithuania lies mainly in the basin of the lower Niemen, though its northern border is drained by the upper courses of rivers whose mouths are in Latvia. It cannot be said, however, that the Niemen and its tributaries adequately drain the country, whose low-lying stretches become notoriously flooded especially during the spring thaw.

On broad lines the country may be divided into two main sections, a small area known as 'High' Lithuania in the east, and a larger area known as 'Low' Lithuania in the centre and west. 'High' Lithuania, developed on the main Baltic end-moraine, is mainly over 500 ft in height. The Niemen in this zone has cut down to the solid rock between Grodno and Kaunas, and foams over at least fifty rocky sills and rapids. 'Low' Lithuania, though mainly low-lying, is crossed by festoons of end-moraines (see Fig. 72, p. 571). Of these, the most notable form the heights of Telsiai and Shyaulyay, and run in a generalised north-west to south-east direction, with heights of over 500 ft. These heights appear to have been formed chiefly by the Riga ice-lobe, but also represent the outer rim of the Klaypeda (Memel) tongue-basin. Another fairly well marked ridge runs from north-west to south-east, just north-east of a line joining Klaypeda and Tilsit. This represents part of the inner end-moraine of the Klaypeda tongue-basin. In northern Lithuania part of the rim of the Riga tongue-basin is found south of Jelgava.

Boulder-clay predominates in the lowland region, except on the morainic ridges, where sandy and pebbly beds are common, especially in the Shyaulyay Heights; also west of Kaunas there are wide expanses of sand which seem to represent an outwash plain from the Shyaulyay end-moraine.

The population of Lithuania is denser (180 per square mile) than that of either Estonia or Latvia, although the country might appear more underdeveloped. Nearly three-fifths of the population live in dispersed farms and villages and are mainly engaged on the collective farms, cultivating rye, oats and wheat, potatoes, flax and fodder grasses, and in dairying and pig and poultry rearing. Timber is also a surplus product although less than a fifth of the country's area is still under woodland.

Kaunas (214,000 in 1959) on the Niemen was the capital of independent Lithuania during the interwar years when Vilnyus, which Lithuanians claimed as their chief city, lay in Poland. Nearly half of the country's industries are carried on there, being supplied with hydro-electricity from a plant on the Niemen above the city.

Klaypeda (89,000) is the only port. This city, formerly known as Memel and inhabited mainly by Germans, reverted to Lithuania in 1945. Yet earlier, when the Lithuanian S.S.R. was set up as a member state of the USSR, its area was expanded to include the disputed city of Vilnyus and the territory around it, together with a narrow strip of Byelorussian territory which was mainly Lithuanian in population.

**The Vilnyus Area.** This small and hitherto much debated area occupies a tongue-basin within the main Baltic end-moraine. The rim of this ice-lobe, shown in Fig. 72, p. 571, forms a rampart of less fertile heights surrounding a low-lying plain of productive soil. The farming inhabitants of this area were (and remain) of Lithuanian speech, although the majority of the townspeople of Vilnyus were Polish. Vilnyus had been the capital of the former Grand Duchy of Lithuania, and it was there that Lithuanian independence was proclaimed in 1917, although the city was seized by Poland in 1920 and held during the interwar years. It had 215,000 inhabitants in 1918 and now as capital of Lithuanian SSR, it has grown slightly to 235,000. Its size and importance result largely from its nodal position, which is emphasised by the railway lines which cross there (Leningrad–Berlin, and Minsk–Liyepaya).

REFERENCES

See p. 619.

**81** Forestry in the Soviet Union. The ground is being cleared for the planting of a new forest in the Tambov area of the central Black-earth Region.

**82** Kiev: capital of Ukraine SSR

**83** Ploughing in the Ukraine

84 Tea-picking machines in operation, Georgia.

THE USSR

85 Students of the Tbilisi Polytechnic Institute camping in Bakuriani valley, Georgia.

### CHAPTER 37

# THE BLACK EARTH REGION

SOUTH-EAST of the zone of mixed forest, the country belongs mainly to the Black Earth or *chernozem* zone which corresponds broadly to the prairie or tillable grassland region. This zone stretches as far south as the Black Sea near Odessa, and encircles the Sea of Azov. On the west it dies away at the foot of the forested Carpathians. On the east, its limits are the Ergeni Hills and the Volga between Volgograd (Stalingrad) and Saratov. It continues eastward across the Volga between the latitudes of Saratov and Kazan, but the belt is here much narrower, being replaced east of the lower Volga by semi-desert. The Black Earth belt attains its maximum width from north to south of some 700 miles between the Oka river and the foothills of the Caucasus, but it is only about 300 miles wide east of the Volga.

Along the northern edge of this zone there is a transitional region, averaging about 100 miles from north to south, where the soil, strictly speaking, belongs to the type known as 'degraded *chernozem*'. This strip, which is known as wooded steppe or parkland (see p. 546), extends southwards about as far as Voronezh on the Don and Saratov on the Volga. From the practical point of view there is not much difference between true *chernozem* and degraded *chernozem*, since both are deep, fertile soils, becoming sticky when damp and dusty when dry, and both are very suited to the growth of cereals. There is, however, one very important difference between the wooded steppe zone and the prairie zone. Although the trees in the wooded steppe have mostly been cut down, yet both trees and bushes can be grown here with little difficulty, so that *potentially* this belt is suited to mixed farming, with orchard trees (apples, pears, cherries) as an important element as in the Ukraine.

**Russian Settlement of the Black Earth Region.** The Black Earth region is the scene of relatively recent colonisation, for early Russian attempts to settle here were frustrated by such warlike nomads as the Pechenegs (tenth century A.D.) and the Cumanians or Polovitsi (eleventh to thirteenth centuries). In the fourteenth century the Tatars of the Golden Horde drove the Russians northwards and north-westwards, even from the wooded steppe, while as late as the sixteenth century the Tatars of the Crimea habitually raided as far north as the edge of the central mixed forest belt and thus checked any expansionist tendency. It was only towards the end of the sixteenth century that a Russian counter-advance began. This took place from two directions: (*a*) from Muscovy, and (*b*) from the Lithuanian–Polish lands between Kiev and Lwow. The latter colonisation was associated with the word *Ukraine*, meaning a frontier or marchland, and the term was particularly applied during the seventeenth century to the wooded steppes or parklands on both sides of the Dnieper; later it was extended as the settlers moved eastwards and southwards. It is noteworthy that steady, agricultural advance down the Dnieper did not reach the southern limit of the wooded steppe until the beginning of the seventeenth century, though Cossacks or military pioneers lived in fortified camps below the Dnieper rapids (cf. Zaporozhe = 'beyond the rapids'). From the Moscow area the advance of the tillers of the soil was also slow, but by about the middle of the seventeenth century a continuous, fortified barrier ran along the southern side of the wooded steppe, from Byelgorod on the Donets to Voronezh on the Don, and thence north-eastwards to Kazan and even beyond. Behind this fortified line the agriculturalists had some measure of security. In advance of this fortified line were communities of 'Great' Russian Cossacks (as distinct from the 'Little' Russian Cossacks of the Ukraine), who lived in fortified villages, particularly along the lower Don and the middle Volga, and engaged in fishing and piracy.

The advance into the true grasslands or prairies did not come until the second half of the eighteenth and the early part of the nineteenth century, for until the very end of the eighteenth century the Tatars, under their then suzerain, the Ottoman Empire, held the northern shores of the Black Sea, including the land round the Sea of Azov. The prairie was not a friendly environment for people from the mixed forest zone or even for those from the wooded steppe, if only because timber played such a large part in the everyday life of the forested Russian 'homelands'. On the treeless prairie the people had to find substitutes for timber as a material for house construction, the wooden walls and roof of the forest lands being replaced by adobe walls and thatched roof. No satisfactory substitute was found to replace wood as fuel, and up to modern times the villagers burned straw and dried dung, which gave little warmth to counteract the low winter temperatures. Village settlements clung to the valleys where timber and brushwood were available, and where water could be obtained by sinking wells, even if, as often happened, the stream ran dry in summer. Many of the streams are dammed back to provide ponds for watering livestock, and in earlier days provided heads of water for driving flour-mills. In contrast to the forested lands, settlement is here highly nucleated.

**Some Harmful Results of Unsuitable Agricultural Methods.** Practically the whole of the prairies region has now been under cultivation for over a hundred years, while most of the wooded steppe has been under cultivation for some 200 to 250 years. Both regions are justly famed for their fertility, but several bad effects have resulted from injudicious agricultural methods. The destruction of the trees of the parklands has been carried very far. Writing in the 1840s, the Russian writer Turgeniev said: 'In the eastern part of Orel the village generally lies among cleared fields, near a ravine which has been somehow turned into a dirty pond. Except a few bushes, which serve every purpose, and two or three gaunt birches, you won't see a tree for a mile round.' Yet the parkland near Voronezh, even farther south, had supplied all the timber for Peter the Great's fleet in his attack on Azov about 150 years earlier.

The word 'ravine' in the above quotation suggests another very serious effect associated with the advent of the plough. The removal of timber in the wooded steppe, and of the natural protective carpet of grass and its associated herbaceous vegetation in the prairies, has exposed the Black Earth to erosion by both rain and wind. As the rain, though small in amount, comes mainly in torrential thunderstorms, it has a very powerful erosive action. Moreover, as the underlying subsoil is *Löss*, which is very friable and easily eroded, once gulleys begin to form they deepen very rapidly. The low-lying floodplains and 'young' plains, which were under the Pontic Sea in recent geological times, are, indeed, not much affected by gullying, but the greater part of the wooded steppe and prairie zones consists of low plateaux in which the river system is incised, and accordingly conditions are naturally conducive to the development of ravines. The cause and results of gullying are the same here as in the Middle West of the USA, and are similarly due to applying methods of agriculture which are suited to the damper, forested homelands of the pioneers to an unfamiliar environment, with the result that a great amount of soil has been lost, and many formerly gently sloping surfaces have become deeply cut up and rendered useless. The régime of the rivers has also changed for the worse, with the alternate floods and droughts both being accentuated. Soviet authorities and experts are well aware of the need for further measures, such as contour ploughing, to arrest this heavy wastage of their national capital – an estimated 600,000 acres (240,000 hectares) of soil has been lost by gullying in the Ukraine alone. It is more difficult to counter the loss of soil due to wind erosion, for the extremely fine, powdery Black Earth is easily carried away by wind. The planting of shelter belts of trees in the wooded steppe is an attempt to check the effects of dust storms. A decrease in the amount of ploughland, and an increase in the area under cultivated grass, would no doubt prove as beneficial here as in the USA. Actually a small decrease of crop land is recorded in this region during recent years.

**The Central Black Earth Region.** This region, comprising the *oblasts* of Orel,[1] Kursk, Voronezh, Tambov, and the southern part of the Tula and Ryazan *oblasts*, presents two main types of relief.

On the west is the plateau of the Central Russian Uplands, with Orel and Kursk as the chief centres, while on the east is the Don–Tsna plain, centred on Tambov. The former, varying in height from about 600 to 900 ft, is a dry area in which water is obtainable only at depth. It appears hilly near the relatively few rivers, but otherwise is an undulating plateau deeply cut up by ravines which are avoided by railways and roads alike. The Eon–Tsna, or Tambov, plain is flat or gently undulating and is traversed by many small rivers, and water is easily obtainable. During the spring thaw the plain is notoriously muddy; for instance, the name of the town Gryazi literally means 'the muds'.

The River Don forms a convenient line of division between the two relief regions, for it hugs the plateau closely, having undercut the edge to form an escarpment which overlooks the plain. In this escarpment the underlying rocks of the plateau are revealed; Carboniferous and Devonian limestones in the north, and chalk farther south. The Don itself is not one of the most navigable of Russia's rivers, in spite of its length of 1,240 miles and its low gradient, its source being only 590 ft above sea-level. Unlike the Dnieper and the Volga, the Don has its course entirely in the wooded steppe and prairie regions, and there is no marshy or forested land in its basin to maintain the flow of water during the summer; moreover the snow cover is thinner here than in the forest belt and lasts a shorter time, while evaporation in summer is high. Consequently the river suffers from very low water in late summer and early autumn, though it may be a broad, tumultuous, swirling torrent during the spring thaw.

*Agriculture.* As the whole of this region lies within the wooded steppe vegetation zone and has similar soils throughout, the type of produce grown is also much the same over the whole area: cereals are naturally important; winter wheat and rye, spring barley,

[1] Pronounced Oriol or Oryol.

rye, oats, maize and millet are all grown; hemp is a traditional crop, valued for its oil as well as for its fibre. Sunflower seeds form an important source of fats for human consumption, besides being used as poultry food; children and even adults chew the seeds like sweets. Tobacco is widely cultivated throughout the region, while the Kursk–Voronezh area is second only to the western Ukraine for the production of sugar beet. Most of the region was already noted in the nineteenth century for good breeds of cattle and horses, and there was a good deal of bee-keeping, both honey and wax entering into commerce. Sheep were reared towards the drier south, but were decreasing in numbers even before the Revolution of 1917. Dairying and pig rearing are now well developed and there is a certain amount of non-commercial fruit growing.

The tendency, noted just before World War II, towards an increase in the area under permanent grass and root crops has been accelerated of late in the effort to increase the numbers of livestock. There is also a tendency towards specialisation in industrial crops. Pigs and poultry are on the increase. It must be remembered, however, that the old three-field system prevailed down to 1929, and the dislocation consequent upon collectivisation continued well into the 1930s, while after 1941 the war interfered with normal development. Collectivisation has brought about greater specialisation, stimulated by urban growth, than prevailed under the system of peasant farming, where each family aimed at self-sufficiency, and greater specialisation is likely to emphasise minor differences of soil, water supply, and position with regard to markets.

*Industry.* The Central Black Earth region has long had a range of industries depending on agriculture, such as flour-milling, tanneries, oil-pressing, hemp-carding, rope-making, which were established in the chief towns at the end of the nineteenth century and at the beginning of the present century. Within recent years, factory industry has greatly increased; to the established industries, such as the manufacture of boots and shoes, butter, starch, alcohol, and sugar, have been added those which produce synthetic rubber, aircraft, iron and steel, and machines of many kinds.

The Kursk iron-ores constitute a great reserve for the future, but as the metallic content is low and the deposits occur at great depth, they have been as yet of only small consequence; their exploitation was hastened under the 1959–65 Plan. The iron-ores near Lipetsk are smelted at that rapidly growing centre (156,000 in 1959; 21,000 in 1926), and, thanks to Donbas coal, and hydro-electricity from the Volgograd plant, the region has good industrial prospects; already its industries include aircraft and machine tools at Voronezh, and agricultural machinery at Kursk, Orel, and

Michurinsk. The last town, formerly known as Koslov, is an important railway junction and manufactures rolling-stock.

*Towns.* Voronezh (454,000 in 1959) is the largest town of the region and has been important since the end of the seventeenth century. It quadrupled its population between 1926 and 1959 owing to its development as an industrial, administrative, and cultural centre. It lies just to the east of the River Don, where it is joined by the Voronezh river which drains the western part of the Tambov plain. In modern times, however, the position of the city on the main railway from Moscow to Rostov-on-Don is of more import-ance than its water communications, which, though much used in the past, are of poor quality.

Tambov (170,000), founded in 1636, stands on the Tsna river which drains the eastern part of the plain. It is a very important grain-collecting centre, though it revealed its proximity to the central forest belt by being partly built of wood.

Kursk, now rather larger (203,000), is a much older founda-tion, and actually dates back to the eleventh century, when it was an important stage on the salt route from the Black Sea to the central forest belt. Kursk, which lies on the River Seim, an affluent of the Dnieper drainage system, also stands about half-way between the sources of the Donets and Oka. Today it is an import-ant railway junction, where the line from Moscow to Sevastopol, which traverses the plateau from north to south, is crossed by the Kiev–Voronezh line. Up to modern times it was famous for one of the most important fairs of mid-Russia.

Orel (152,000), which lies farther north on the plateau, though founded in 1564, remains only a medium-sized town, in spite of being a railway junction, the Moscow-Sevastopol line being crossed by the Riga–Smolensk–Volgograd line at this point.

# THE UKRAINE

The Ukraine SSR is a member state of the USSR based on com-munity of language and history, and is not a natural unit on ground of physiography or vegetation. It is true that the greater part of the Ukraine lies in the prairie and wooded steppe regions, but the area north of Kiev is in the region of mixed forest, and is floored with glacial clays and sands instead of the *Löss* of the steppes. The Ukraine is sometimes called 'Little Russia', in contra-distinction to 'Great Russia' of the Muscovy region, but the people rather resent this appellation and prefer to be called Ukrainians, meaning the 'border' or 'frontier' people.

The differences between the Ukrainians and the Great Russians are of the same order as those between English and the lowland Scots. In fact, the speech is basically the same, though pronounced somewhat differently, while in Ukrainian there are more South Slav words and an absence of the Finnish words characteristic of Great Russian. In appearance the Ukrainians are often darker and less 'Finnish', or, more properly, less 'Lapp', than the Great Russians. The Ukrainians, unlike the Great Russians, tend to look towards Kiev as the centre of their national life. Moreover, contacts with the west were more apparent than in Muscovy; not only were the Tatar nomads driven from the Ukrainian steppe under Lithuanian and Polish auspices, but both literature and material culture showed western influences (at least before 1917), while the people themselves migrated into the region very largely from the plateaus which lie to the north-east of the Carpathians. It is note-worthy that Poland held the land west of the Dnieper until 1793, with the exception of Kiev, which Moscow acquired in 1667. The Ukrainian people seeped eastward from Polesia, eastern Galicia, Volhynia, and Podolia during the seventeenth, eighteenth, and nine-teenth centuries, and while outstripping Polish control they came eventually under the rule of Moscow owing to the break-up of the Tatar Khanates. The 1938 boundaries of the Ukraine did not exactly correspond to the distribution of Ukrainian speech, there being considerable numbers of Ukrainians outside and considerable numbers of Great Russians inside. After the destruction which it suffered during World War II, Ukraine SSR emerged with additions of territory to the west annexed from Rumania, Czechoslovakia, and Poland. Its population thus increased to 41·9 millions, one-fifth of the Union's total. Of this population, 76 per cent are Ukrainians, 17·7 per cent Russians, and 2 per cent Jews; the remainder is made up mostly of Byelorussians, Moldavians, Bulgarians, Hungarians, Greeks, and Rumanians. The Ukraine is not only one of the most densely populated parts of the USSR but also one of the most outstanding economically. It is famous not only for its agriculture, but also for its mining and industrial development, and has the advantage of a long sea coast, which is frozen only for a comparatively short time, while the Dnieper has the longest navigation season of any Russian river.

**Geographical Regions of the Ukraine.** From the point of view of natural vegetation the Ukraine is divisible into three regions: (a) a small mixed forest belt in the north where conifers pre-dominated, (b) the wooded steppe in the centre, and (c) the true steppe or prairie in the south.

*The Mixed Forest Belt.* This lies north of the latitude of Kiev (50° 30'), and the subsoil consists of glacial sands and clays deposited in the old glacial 'tongue-basin' of the Dnieper valley. The soils are either podzolised, or at best are brown forest soils. Woods and even forests still remain, and agriculture is concerned mainly with dairy farming, with cereals occupying only a small acreage.

*The Wooded Steppe and the Prairies.* Together these constitute some of the most important grain lands of the USSR. The boundary between them is not clear cut; indeed, the plateau portion of the wooded steppe west of the Dnieper is as devoid of trees as the prairie or true steppe, but generally speaking there is a contrast between the mixed and more intensive farming of the wooded steppe and the somewhat precarious cereal farming of the prairie. The yield per acre in the former is considerably higher and not so highly variable. Moreover, the wooded steppe is a land of relatively old-established settlement. For instance, Kremenchug on the Dnieper was founded in 1571, and Kharkov in 1650. The boundary between the wooded steppe and the prairie runs in a south-west to north-east direction, a little to the south of these two towns, and the greater part of the prairie was not colonised until the last quarter of the eighteenth century (e.g. Dnepropetrovsk, formerly known as Ekaterinoslav, was founded in 1783), and it remained uncultivated and devoted to 'ranching' until the middle of the nineteenth century.

The wooded steppe is divided into two parts by the River Dnieper. On the west are the plateau lands of Volhynia, Podolia, and Bessarabia, most of which now lies in the Moldavian SSR, while on the east lies the plain of the middle Dnieper. The plateau, which is composed of sedimentary strata, underlain by the granites of the Azov–Podolian massif, is highly dissected by incised river valleys and ravines and covered with a great thickness of *chernozem*; it is treeless, except in the valleys. The plateau is swept by violent winds in winter, to such an extent that the railway track has to be protected against drifting snow by special palisades, while in summer the air is dusty, and streams tend to dry up. Nevertheless, the region is noted for its productivity, wheat, maize, and sugar-beet being produced in vast quantities, while vineyards clothe the sides of numerous valleys. (Note the place-names: Vinnitsa, Vinograd.) Orchard trees, restricted to the valleys, include apples, pears, plums, and cherries. Livestock and poultry are kept in considerable numbers. On the plain of the Dnieper the wooded steppe is even more productive. The same crops are grown with the addition of tobacco, and as the water-table is nearer the surface, trees grow well. The whole region has long been noted for its air of prosperity. The villages are set amidst orchards, every house having its own garden with flowers and vegetables, which include sunflowers, melons, and onions. The villages strongly resemble those of the Carpathian foothills, and are in marked contrast both to the timber-built villages of the central mixed forest belt and the bare, gaunt villages of the prairie.

In the prairie, bordering the Black Sea and the Sea of Azov, agriculture is handicapped not only by the scanty rainfall, but by the great variation in the amount received from year to year. Moreover, in the areas where the old granitic core comes near the surface the soil is very thin. Except along the actual coast, and near the watery and wooded floodplains of the great rivers, the land was very forbidding to agriculturists, and although it is now under the plough, the yields often fall far short. However, the presence of a large coalfield and great deposits of iron-ore and manganese add a powerful supplement to the economy.

*Industrial Development in the Ukraine.* Up to the war of 1941–45 the Ukraine was not only the most important agricultural region of the USSR, but also the most important industrial unit. This development was made possible by the great Donets coalfield which stretches from west to east on the southern side of the Donets river, and lies mostly in the Ukraine but partly in the Rostov *oblast.* The rich iron deposits in the crystalline complex at Krivoi Rog (386,000) and the manganese ore near Nikopol (81,000) to the west of the Dnieper river, are also very important, and to a less extent the salt found in the Permian rocks near Slavyansk, north of the coalfield, and the mercury near Artemovsk.

The Donets coal basin (or Donbas), of Carboniferous age, was producing about 80 per cent of Russia's coal in 1913, nearly 60 per cent in 1938, and 37 per cent in 1958. Its share of the total output has thus clearly declined, in step with the development of other fields, especially of those in Asiatic USSR. Nevertheless the actual production from the Donets mines has greatly increased in this century, despite their temporary destruction during World War II. They produced (in million tons) 25·3 in 1913 and as much as 182 in 1958. Donets contains coking coal (yielding half the Union's supply), gas coal, and anthracite, the last named mainly at the eastern end of the coalfield in Rostov *oblast.* Exploitation began on a considerable scale in the 1870s, following the construction of the railway from Kursk via Kharkov to Azov in 1870. A Welshman named John Hughes set up the first coke-fired furnace on Russian soil, and the town which was named after him (Yuzovka) remains the centre, and has become the largest town, of the Donets industrial area (701,000 inhabitants), although its name was changed to Stalino, and again in 1960, to Donetsk. For a long time the area specialised in pig-iron and steel for the older established metal-lurgical industries of the Tula–Moscow area, but more complex metallurgy and engineering gradually developed, especially in and after the 1930s. Heavy chemicals are also produced. The immediate surroundings of the Donets coalfield present more than one drawback to the establishment of large-scale industry, notably the seasonal scarcity of water, while the land is agriculturally poor. The necessary iron-ore has to be hauled for considerable distances, either by rail from Krivoi Rog, 225 miles west of Donetsk, or from Kerch in the Crimea, about 200 miles south of Donetsk. Ore from the latter source has a lower iron content and output, but can travel much of the distance by sea. The Ukraine still produces half the USSR's pig-iron and two-fifths of its steel.

The Donets coalfield is the site of numerous medium-sized industrial towns, such as Slavyansk (83,000), Kommunarsk, formerly Voroshilovsk (98,000), and Artemovsk (61,000), but there are only two really large towns, Donetsk and Lugansk (274,000) which was for a time called Voroshilovgrad. Many of the towns near the salt mines have chemical, glass, and ceramic industries.

There is also considerable industrial development in other parts of the Ukraine, notably iron and steel works at Krivoi Rog, Dnepropetrovsk, Zaporozhe, and at the ports of Odessa, Nikolayev, and Zhdanov. Heavy engineering is carried on in the great cities of Kiev and Kharkov. The harnessing of the River Dnieper began with the construction of a great dam near Zaporozhe which was enlarged when rebuilt after its destruction during the second world war. In more recent years two other large hydro-electric plants have been built, one at the new city of Kremegs near Kremenchug upstream, the other at Novaya Kakhovka downstream, and three others are either under construction or planned. The works already carried out have improved navigation on the Dnieper and provide increasing supplies of energy for the large-scale industries of the middle Dnieper area, although they have created great lake-reservoirs and have involved the resiting of many villages. Electric power is provided too by thermal stations, especially from one east of Dnepropetrovsk (Pridneprovskoye) which has a capacity of 1·2 million kW and uses natural gas – another rich resource of the Ukraine (see Fig. 71, p. 561). The main types of industry are, first, engineering, and secondly certain others which need large amounts of electricity, such as aluminium refining, ferro-alloy manufacture, and the extraction of atmospheric nitrogen. Dnepropetrovsk (658,000) nearly trebled in size between 1926 and 1959, while Zaporozhe grew from 56,000 to 435,000 during this period.

One of the most astonishing changes of population grouping ever to take place in times of peace occurred in the Ukraine between the two censuses of 1926 and 1939. The urban population increased by about 6 million, chiefly at the expense of the rural population, who were actually 4 million fewer in 1939 than in 1926. This 'flight from the land' was not looked upon as a disaster; on the contrary, it was regarded as a great step forward, since it resulted from mechanisation of the farms which thus increased output with a smaller labour force. The drift to the towns has continued and about half of Ukraine's population is now urban.

The Ukraine now possesses five cities, each of over half a million inhabitants, two of which have already been mentioned – Donetsk and Dnepropetrovsk; another (Odessa) is referred to below. Kiev (1,102,000) and Kharkov (930,000) are respectively the third and fifth largest cities of the USSR. Kiev, picturesquely situated on the high right bank of the Dnieper, and thus in an excellent position for defence against attacks from the east, dates from the ninth century, and in the eleventh century was incontestably the capital of the Russian world. In spite of its eclipse under the Tatar conquest, Kiev eventually resumed its role as a leading cultural and religious centre. It is now capital of the Ukraine SSR, though Kharkov held that position during the first flush of revolutionary enthusiasm, when there was a strong desire to break with the past Kiev's manufactures include heavy engineering, sugar, leather, tobacco, and printing. Kharkov, founded in the seventeenth century, has been developed rapidly, thanks to its excellent railway connexions with Moscow, the southern seaports, and the Donets coalfield, together with its position within a densely populated countryside. It has similar industries to those of Kiev, although it is particularly noted for electrical engineering, machine tools, and its great tractor plant.

The port of Odessa (667,000), the fifth largest town of the Ukraine, was founded in 1795 soon after the conquest of the coast from the Turks. It rapidly became the leading Russian port on the Black Sea, exporting agricultural produce from the Black Earth region, such as grain, oilseeds, and later sugar. The city is not at the mouth of any river. The Black Sea coast is here bordered by lagoons and sandspits, like the similar low, tideless shores of the Baltic Sea; it follows that the mouths of the great rivers are shallow and partially cut off from open water by sand-bars, while the smaller streams have no visible exit at all. Good sites for ports are therefore few and far between. Odessa is ice-bound for a much shorter time than the river ports of Nikolayev (224,000), Kherson (157,000), and the Azov ports of Berdyansk (65,000) and Zhdanov, formerly Mariupol (284,000). Odessa and Nikolayev engage in shipbuilding and marine engineering; Odessa also makes agricultural machinery and has oil refineries, tanneries, flour mills, and other food processing industries.

*The Lower Don Industrial Area.* South-east of the Ukraine is the region around the lower Don, which is politically divided from, but economically linked to, the Ukraine with which it shares the Donets coalfield: Shakhty (196,000) is the industrial centre of this eastern sector of the coalfield. Taganrog (201,000), on the Sea of Azov, has similar exports and industries to those of Zhdanov, coal being a prominent export. Rostov-on-Don (597,000) has important manufactures of agricultural machinery, tobacco, and footwear; it is also a collecting centre for goods from the Donets towns and for those from the fertile and oil-producing Caucasus foreland. The new 63-mile canal, opened in 1952 to connect the lower Don and Volga cities, has stimulated Rostov's port activities as it provides transport for coal, above all to Volgograd. The Caspian and Azov–Black seas are thus interconnected, while the last two have now water access, via the Volga, to the Baltic and White seas.

## REFERENCES

See p. 619.

### CHAPTER 38

# THE LANDS ALONG THE VOLGA

THE lands along the River Volga from the town of Gorki (Nijni-Novgorod) to the Caspian Sea may be grouped together as the Povolzhye or Volga economic region (cf. Posavina and Podravina in Yugoslavia). Although these lands fall into several vegetation regions – forest (coniferous and mixed), wooded steppe, prairie, and semi-desert – yet they have long been closely linked economically by the great artery of the Volga, which below Gorki is never less than half a mile wide, and is over two miles wide for the greater part of its middle and lower course.

The Volga and its tributaries carry about half of all river-borne traffic in the whole of the USSR, although closed by ice in winter and impeded by sandbanks at low water in autumn, and from early times it has been a noted waterway, carrying salt, dried fish, and Asiatic goods northwards and timber southwards. In modern times mineral oil has become the chief commodity carried, and about half the total Volga traffic is concentrated in the stretch between the Caspian Sea and Volgograd. Before the coming of mechanical propulsion the upstream journey was a slow and painful haul.

The Volga has significance for Russians not only as the greatest of all Russian highways, but also as the meeting-place of Muscovite and Tatar cultures, and the region still contains an appreciable number of Tatar folk, together with Tatarised Volga-Bulgars, Chuvash, and the Finnic Mordvinians and Mari, who were formerly subject to the Tatar Khanate of Kazan. The presence of these minorities was acknowledged by the creation of a number of autonomous republics, namely the Tatar, Mari, Mordvinian, and Chuvash ASSRs. The adjacent Bashkir and Udmurt republics, though not strictly in the Povolzhye region, also reflect the presence of other large non-Russian elements in the population. Although Kazan, the headquarters of the Tatars and the Tatarised Volga-Bulgars, fell to Ivan the Terrible in 1552, and the great emporium of Astrakhan was conquered in the same decade, yet actual Russian colonisation proceeded very slowly.

Russian settlement along the Volga was at first restricted to a number of forts which were established in the sixteenth and seventeenth centuries, but which remained purely military establishments until late in the eighteenth century. Samara (now Kuibyshev) was founded in 1586, Tsaritsyn (now Volgograd) in 1589, Saratov in 1599, Simbirsk (now Ulyanovsk) in 1648, and Syzran in 1684, but as late as 1799 Tsaritsyn had a population of little over a thousand souls (as against 591,000 in 1959), while even in 1851 Samara had only 15,000 inhabitants (as against 806,000 in 1959). Peasant pioneers gradually moved eastward across the Oka and settled in the forests and wooded steppes on the Volga Heights west of the Volga, among the primitive Chuvash and Mordvinians. East of the river the country was more open and in fact almost devoid of trees south of a line joining Simbirsk (Ulyanovsk) and Ufa; moreover, it had little surface water, while the best lands and the best watering places were already taken up by the Tatars, who though mainly pastoralists, also practised some agriculture. The river itself, particularly in the gorge-like stretch near Kuibyshev, was haunted by pirates, who on more than one occasion joined with the oppressed peasants of the west bank, under the leadership of the free (and free-booting!) Cossacks, such as Stenka Razin in the sixteenth century and Pugachev in the eighteenth century, with the object of overthrowing the crushing feudal rule of Moscow. It was only during the latter years of the eighteenth century, and more especially during the nineteenth century, that Russian agriculturists settled in the prairies and parklands between the Volga and the Belaya rivers and reached out eastward along the Samara river to Orenburg, while up to very recent times the middle Volga area was considered a 'poor, God-forsaken place, where drought, famine and a lack of culture in the inhabitants were the natural features' (S. P. Turin).

The wooded steppes and prairies east of the Volga below Kazan have proved to be very productive grainlands in spite of periodic catastrophic droughts, but the poorer steppes and semi-deserts south of a line joining Saratov, Uralsk and Orenburg remain grazing lands, thinly populated by the Mongol Kirghiz, while the similar semi-deserts west of the lower Volga, below Volgograd, are thinly populated by Mongol Kalmuks.

The actual banks of the river provide more favourable conditions for agriculture, or rather for horticulture, than the land farther away, owing to the greater shelter from wind and the facilities for obtaining water. The apple and cherry orchards of the middle stretch between Gorki and Kuibyshev are noted, while grapes, water-melons, peaches, plums, and apricots are widely grown lower down the valley.

**Regional Divisions.** The Povolzhye does not divide neatly into the parallel vegetation zones which are encountered farther west. It is true that the southern margin of the coniferous forests, which occupy the northermost section of the Povolzhye, runs roughly from west to east. This forest region, which stretches away to the north into the vast 'backwoods' of the Komi territory (see p. 553), reaches southward almost to the lower Kama, and to the Volga between Gorki and Kazan, but once the Volga has turned from its east-west course to its north-south course at Kazan, both relief and climate combine to produce different vegetation conditions on the west side of the Volga from those occurring on the east. Between Kazan and Ulyanovsk the natural vegetation on the west side appears to have been similar to that of the mixed forest zone of Moscow, while east of the river the woods were more open, and were entirely deciduous, and were in fact of wooded steppe character; farther south, between Ulyanovsk and Saratov, the lands on the west side belonged to the wooded steppe, while those on the opposite side were devoid of trees and belonged to the true steppe or prairie; farther south again, between Saratov and Volgograd, the west side continued to have the advantage on showing prairie lands as against the untillable semi-desert on the east side. It naturally follows that agriculture also differs on either side of the river.

This asymmetry is partly due to the dying out of Atlantic climatic influences towards the east, but the peculiar sharpness of the contrast on either side of the Volga axis between Kazan and Volgograd is chiefly due to the presence of the Volga Heights. These reach a sufficient elevation (maximum 1,400 ft) to experience extra precipitation and slightly lower temperatures; in other words, the extra height gives rise to differences of climate, which though slight in themselves, are cumulatively able to cause very important differences in natural vegetation and therefore in agriculture. On the whole the balance of advantages lies with the western bank.

The asymmetric character of the actual banks of the Volga, with high cliffs on the west and low-lying floodplains on the east, serves to emphasise the differences already mentioned, for there is also a physiographic contrast between the dissected Volga Heights and the eastern plain. The difficulty of bridging the great river further leads to the conclusion that a real 'frontier', or break in continuity, would occur along this line were it not for the facilities for transport afforded by the river itself.

As the Povolzhye area is obviously too large and too diverse to be treated as a single unit in any regional study, the following sub-divisions will be adopted: (1) the northern coniferous forest-lands north of the Volga–Kama junction, (2) the Volga Heights,

(3) the tillable steppes east of the Volga, (4) the semi-deserts and the Volga delta.

(1) **The Coniferous Forest-lands North of the Volga–Kama Junction.**   As mentioned above, the coniferous forest region reaches almost to the lower Kama river and to the Volga between Gorki and **Kazan.**   It is drained principally by the Vetluga tributary of the **Volga** and the Vyatka tributary of the Kama and is mainly low-lying land with no outstanding relief features.   Timber is shipped down these rivers and the Volga, the trade being a very ancient one. Soils and agriculture are similar to those of the Vologda and Ivanovo regions (see pp. 553 and 558).   Much land is devoted to the cultivation of flax, rye, hay, root crops, and similar products of the forest clearings, and dairy cattle are relatively important.   Industry is mainly occupied with the working up of the poorer timber into cellulose and paper. Small quantities of iron-ore are mined near the headwaters of the Vyatka, and deposits of phosphates, said to be the largest in the USSR, occur between the Vyatka and the headwaters of the Kama.

The main importance of the area in past times lay in its position on the route to Siberia via the Sukhona, Vyatka, and upper Kama rivers, and today it is relatively less important than it was during the Middle Ages.   This northern route was developed by fur and salt traders from Novgorod as early as the thirteenth and fourteenth centuries, when the more southerly route via Kazan and the lower Kama (later used by the Muscovites) was still in the hands of the Tatars.   A main railway line now traverses this region from west to east; lines coming from Moscow via Gorki and from Leningrad via Vologda unite at Kotelnich on the Vyatka river, thence the line goes eastwards to Kirov, an old fortress town formerly known as Vyatka, and thence to Perm and the Urals.   Kirov (252,000), the only large town of this region, is an important route and manufacturing centre, but was small until the railway era, having only 15,000 inhabitants in 1860.   In addition to its paper, matches, and other timber industries, and the sheep-skin garments which are well known throughout Russia, it now produces transport equipment. There are no other urban centres of comparable size, but Yoshkar-Ola (formerly known as Krasnokokshaysk and earlier as Tsare-vokokshaysk), the capital of the Mari ASSR, has grown fast; its inhabitants numbered 88,000 in 1959. Population densities are about the same as those of similar agricultural regions in the same latitude, as in Estonia and Latvia, e.g. Kirov *oblast* 41 to the square mile, Mari ASSR and Udmurt ASSR having 73 and 82 per square mile respectively in 1959 (cf. Estonia and Latvia 60 and 76 per square mile at this date).

(2) **The Volga Heights.**   The Volga Heights (more properly the

Volga plateau) are discernible on the right-hand bank of the Volga, some little distance below Gorki, and stretch southwards almost to Volgograd. On the west they rise imperceptibly from the Don lowlands, but on the east they fall abruptly to the Volga. Few travellers on the Volga have failed to record the impressive picture afforded by the lofty right bank which reaches heights varying from 300 ft to 900 ft above river-level, sometimes falling steeply in cliffs, sometimes sloping back from the river in wooded hills. This steep face is seamed by numerous valleys and ravines in which nestle picturesque villages, whose wooden houses cluster among trees beneath the characteristic green cupola of the village church.

Although seldom attaining more than 1,000 ft in height, the Volga plateau, especially in its northern part north of Syzran, displays more variety of relief and rock formation than any other region of similar size on the Russian Platform. The plateau is deeply dissected, the rivers flowing in incised valleys, which are especially deeply cut between the Sura and the Volga, and in the Zhiguli Heights.

The Zhiguli Heights, reaching over 1,200 ft, lie within the great bend made by the Volga near Kuibyshev. They owe their origin to faults which have brought Carboniferous and Permian rocks to the surface on both sides of the Volga, and here occurs the only stretch of the river on which both banks are lofty. The Permian formation is also found in the northern part of the plateau, where gypsum beds occur which are pitted with swallow holes into which the rivers disappear. Farther south occur sands and marls of Jurassic age, which in turn are succeeded southward by pure white chalk, sometimes capped by Tertiary sands. The superficial deposits show a significant variety, degraded *chernozem* not only alternating with clay-with-flints, but itself varying considerably in texture from place to place, being generally more sandy and less rich in humus than in most parts of the Black Earth regions. On the other hand, the southern and south-western parts of the plateau, for example, round Penza, have large areas with little variety of relief and with good 'Black Earth'. The difficult nature of the dissected and formerly forested country between the Sura and the Volga seems to have been a factor in enabling the Chuvash to preserve their primitive mode of life and their individual characteristics until a late date; west of the Sura the forests which sheltered the Mordvinians seem to be connected to a considerable extent with the deposition of fluvio-glacial gravels in the Don tongue-basin, though the relief is also somewhat broken. Incidentally the Mordvinians, though small in numbers outside their autonomous republic, are scattered throughout the central parts of the Volga plateau among the Russian settlers.

Trees grow easily on the plateau as far south as Saratov, with extensions southwards along the Khoper and Medveditsa tributaries of the Don. Owing to the diversified terrain and the possibility of tree growth, a great variety of crops can be grown in the northern parts of the Volga Heights, although owing to the high density of population and the consequent great pressure on the land, the peasants of former days had to concentrate on subsistence crops. Mixed farming (with such crops as flax, hemp, sugar-beet, potatoes), dairy farming, and fruit growing were being developed in the 1930s.

The Volga Heights show a high density of rural population—the populations of Chuvash ASSR and Mordvinian ASSR reach respectively 125 per square mile and 76 per square mile; and there are no towns of large size except Penza, since urban settlement is inevitably attracted to the main line of movement, the Volga. Penza (254,000), an important route centre situated where the main line from Moscow to Kuibyshev and Orenburg crosses the upper Sura, has flour mills, woollen mills, and tanneries, drawing upon raw materials from the surrounding area. The capitals of the Chuvash and Mordvinian ASSRs are relatively small. Cheboksary (83,000), capital of the former, now has railway facilities; Saransk, the Mordvinian capital, lying west of the Sura river, has a large con-densed-milk combine which indicates the type of agriculture in this formerly well-wooded area.

(3) **The Tillable Steppes East of the Volga.** East of the Volga and south of the Kama the land stretches for mile after mile in plains and low plateaus, whose rich 'Black Earth' is as suited to the cultivation of cereals as are the similar soils of the Central Black Earth region and the Ukraine, but where the uncertainty of the rainfall rendered agriculture a very hazardous undertaking and is still reflected in sharply varying yields from year to year. The average annual rainfall varies from about 12 in in the south (e.g. at Uralsk) to about 17 in in the north (e.g. along the Kama), but unfortunately the variation from year to year is very great.

The wooded steppe with a slightly higher precipitation, roughly north of a line joining Ulyanovsk and Ufa, allows for a greater variety of crops since the danger of drought is not so acute. This is reflected in the higher population density (cf. 110 per square mile in the Tatar ASSR, as against some 65 per square mile east of Kuibyshev, and 40 per square mile in the Orenburg *oblast* to the south of the tillable steppe). The southern margin of the Black Earth, and also of widespread village settlement, is to be found near the railway line connecting Saratov and Orenburg.

The wooded steppe region, which lies mainly in the Tatar ASSR, is suited to mixed farming, and has had a relatively prosperous past. Industries dependent on agriculture, such as the production of soap, candles, leather, and felt boots, have long been established here.

Farther south, in the treeless parts of the Saratov and Kuibyshev *oblasts* which lie east of the Volga, the production of cereals has been almost a monoculture; the arable land was customarily devoted to small grains for several years and then left fallow for several years to allow it to recover. About 40 per cent of the land lay fallow every year before the Revolution, so as to give time for moisture to accumulate in the soil. Peasant farming was at a grave disadvantage in this type of region, this being exemplified by recurrent crop shortfalls and even famines. The farming of the region does much better now with extensive mechanised farming on large state and collective farms: the principal crops, grain especially wheat, but also sugar-beet, sunflower, and fodder, are rotated, while sheep, pigs, cattle, including dairy cattle, are reared, South of Kuibyshev on the lower and drier eastern side of the Volga, state farms have sprung up in the course of the ploughing-up campaign which started in 1954. The cultivation of wheat is here the chief objective, although sheep ranches have also been established. The Volga region now accounts for 10 per cent of the Union's grain area, although the yield may still vary between 5 per cent and 10 per cent of the Union's harvest. Even so, basic foodstuffs are relatively abundant to sustain the remarkable urban growth of the region and, in good years at least, to provide surpluses for western and northern cities. In the older settled parts of the middle Volga the rural population is mainly grouped in very large villages, originally sited where water supplies were available. The implementation of the Great Volga Scheme has meant so far the removal and resiting of many towns and villages and the flooding of 6,000 square miles of valley land: indeed the middle Volga now appears as an elongated lake, several miles broad (see Fig. 73). The Scheme has meant too the provision of stored waters for the irrigation, especially of the left-bank lowlands, and also to drive the turbines of hydro-electric power plants above Kuibyshev and at Volgograd which, it is claimed, are the largest in the world.

No less than an industrial revolution continues to take place in the middle Volga region which was traditionally regarded as an agricultural area, dependent on a river of very irregular régime, marginally placed in relation to the old, populous and developed centres of Russia and, being without coal deposits, unlikely to develop industrially in a large way. Yet the region, stimulated industrially during the second world war, forged ahead during the 'fifties as it will probably continue to do in the decades ahead. It occupies a strikingly advantageous geographical position commanding the Volga waterway, now greatly improved for navigation and paralleled by a railway on the right bank; moreover it is crossed by railways which link the industrial regions of central and southern European USSR to the west with the Ural industrial region to the east. Also the middle Volga region commands the resources of the Volga–Ural oilfield which extends from Saratov north-eastwards to Perm and Ufa; here lie (as at present estimated) 80 per cent of the USSR's oil reserves and from here is derived three-quarters of the Union's current output. Natural gas, no less than oil, is available for regional needs and for export. In addition, the Volga river is now producing electricity on a scale which more than satisfies the region's requirements: the Kuibyshev and Volgograd hydro-electric power stations have respectively a capacity of 2·3 and 2·5 million kW, and another large station is under construction at Volsk, which lies between Saratov and Syzran. Only in respect of coal is the region dependent on outside sources – now mainly the Asiatic fields of Kuznetsk and Karaganda but also the Donets, with which Volga–Don canal provides transport. Kuibyshev more than doubled its population between 1939 and 1959; it outstripped both Kazan and Saratov, and is already the eighth city of the Union. In view of the growing development and settlement of Asiatic USSR and of its remarkable transport facilities, it might well seem geographically cast for the future capital of the USSR.

South of the Saratov–Uralsk–Orenburg railway the 'Black Earth' gives place to the chestnut soils, and the moisture available is too small for cultivation, except along the main rivers and a few *wadis*, which flow towards, but never reach, the Caspian Sea.

(4) **The Semi-deserts and the Volga Delta.** The semi-deserts stretch on both sides of the lower Volga below the elbow bend by Volgograd. On the west, the scarp of the Ergeni (a Kalmuk word meaning 'heights') marks the approximate boundary between the 'desert and the sown', while east of the Volga the Torgun and Eruslan, feeders of the Volga (*c.* lat. 50° N), mark the southern limit of cultivation. The sandy soils are not without surface water immediately after the snow has melted, but moisture rapidly sinks into the permeable soils, or evaporates leaving saline deposits where the soil is less permeable. In some places true desert with moving sand-dunes occurs, but in most areas there is sufficient vegetation for nomadic flocks of sheep, kept by the Buddhist Kalmuks on the west of the Volga, and the Moslem Kazaks on the east. The population density in the semi-desert is very low, less than 12 persons per square mile.

Through this inhospitable region runs the lower Volga in a

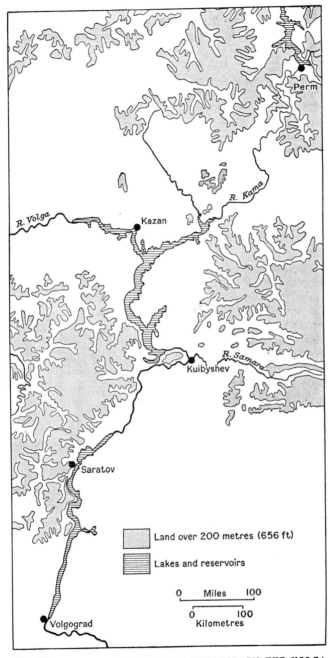

Fig. 73. SOME LAKE-RESERVOIRS CREATED ON THE VOLGA
BY HYDRAULIC WORKS

network of channels, a watery belt which strongly resembles the 'balta' and delta of the Danube (see p. 490), and has been compared by some authors to Upper and Lower Egypt. It must, however, be remembered that the Volga is frozen on an average for twenty-one weeks at Volgograd, and for fifteen weeks at Astrakhan, so that plant-growth comes to a standstill during the winter months. On the other hand, summers are very hot and, although much of the broad floodplain and delta lies under flood-water in May and June, the area provides an oasis of cultivation and sedentary life. Semi-tropical crops can be grown, and on the drier margins peach and apricot trees flourish, together with the vine. The lagoons and distributaries of the Volga, like those of the Danube, abound with water-birds, as well as with various types of sturgeon which yield the famous caviare.

**Towns of the Povolzhye.** All the large towns of this area are situated on the Volga with the exception of Penza. Most of the cities originated as fortresses, but developed as administrative and market centres. As elsewhere in Russia the coming of the railway greatly assisted their growth, and the towns situated where the five main trunk lines cross the great river are naturally in an exceptionally favourable position.

In the north the two outstanding urban centres are Gorki (Nijni-Novgorod) and Kazan. Both are old historic cities, which have taken on a new lease of life with the industrialisation of the USSR. Gorki (942,000 in 1959 as against 222,000 in 1926) lies at the extreme west of the region under discussion, and at the extreme east of the old Great Russian lands. By virtue of its position at the junction of the Volga and the Oka it possesses great natural nodality, and it also proved a favourable market place for goods coming along the Volga and Kama from various parts of Asia. Furs (from Siberia), tea (from China), silks, carpets, raw cotton (from Turkestan), and wine (from the Caucasus) were among the many things sold at its celebrated fair which flourished during the nineteenth century. At the present day it is noted chiefly for its huge engineering works which make automobiles, aero-engines, diesel motors, and so on, supplies of electricity having been made available from the hydro-electric plant built above the city where the new town of Zavolzhye is growing. Kazan (643,000 in 1959 as against 179,000 in 1926), the capital of the Tatar ASSR, already an old trading and administrative centre under the Tatars, became a fortified outpost of Russian culture and a gateway from Moscow to the Urals. It possesses a 'Kremlin' and claims to rival Moscow in magnificence and picturesqueness. Its noted university, founded in 1804, has a strong department of oriental studies, and among the industries of the city is the mass production of typewriters with *Latin* characters for the use of the various national groups of Turki speech. The manufacture of synthetic rubber, roiling-stock, and agricultural machinery are among the chief industries of the city which enjoys the advantage of the Volga as a means of transport and also that of the main railway line, which crosses the river *en route* between Moscow and Sverdlovsk, capital of the Ural industrial region. In particular, the Volga brings upstream to Kazan supplies of coal and petroleum. This is one of the few big towns situated on the left bank of the Volga – a natural position for a Tatar city. The Volga and Kama valleys, respectively to the south and east of the city, have been transformed as a result of the Great Volga Scheme into an elongated lake of some 120 miles in length which extends downstream almost to Saratov, and the Volga waters, thus controlled, now provide electric power, irrigation water, and better facilities for navigation. A new city on the Kama to serve a new oilfield – Niznekamsk – is now being built and is to become the second largest Tatar city with a population of 250,000.

Ulyanovsk, formerly Simbirsk (205,000 in 1959; 70,000 in 1926), is a railway junction situated on the Volga, where the railway from the Moscow region to Ufa and Chelyabinsk crosses this river. Between Simbirsk and Ufa this railway roughly marks the dividing line between the wooded steppe to the north and the true steppe to the south. Like Syzran farther south, Ulyanovsk works up various local agricultural commodities, such as leather and wool, as well as the timber coming down the Volga; now the manufacture of machine tools and the extraction of oil from shales are additional industries. Syzran (148,000) is overshadowed by its more powerful neighbour Kuibyshev (806,000 in 1959; 176,000 in 1926). Both towns lie on the main trunk line from Moscow which, in, fact, branches east of Kuibyshev, sending one line south-east to Orenburg and another north-east to Ufa. As already mentioned, Kuibyshev is picturesquely situated on the left bank of the Volga, where high land occurs as the result of faulting. The town has been a collecting point for the grain land east of the Volga since the establishment of steam navigation on the river (*c.* 1820), and is noted for grain elevators and flour mills. Other old industries work up agricultural produce (brewing, macaroni manufacture, etc.), but modern industries now dominate: oil refining and chemicals, shipbuilding and aircraft assembly, the manufacture of machines especially for the electrical and building industries. The removal of the administration from Moscow to Kuibyshev during the war of 1941–45 emphasises both its distance from central Europe and its excellent communications with the non-European parts of the USSR.

Saratov (581,000 in 1959; 220,000 in 1926), which was the largest city on the Volga before the 1930s, has sunk to fifth in size although it more than doubled its population. It remains an important distributing centre for grain, timber, salt (from the semi-desert), tobacco, fish, tallow, and skins, and retains flour milling, oil refining, and tobacco manufactures. Engineering, including the manufacture of agricultural machinery, aircraft, and ball-bearings, is a new development. Saratov is at the lowest bridging point of the Volga.

Opposite Saratov was the former capital of the Volga Germans, namely Engels (Pokrovsk; 90,000).

Volgograd (591,000 in 1959 as against 151,000 in 1926), was chosen for industrial development by the Soviet authorities, and has exploited its nodality at the convergence of the three railway lines which tap the Volga at this point, for the town numbered only 6,700 inhabitants in 1861. The railways link the river with (a) Moscow and central Russia, (b) the Donets coalfield, (c) the Black Sea at Novorossisk. Some of the oil from the Baku fields is transferred from the Volga steamers to the rail at this point, and oil refineries are established here; timber from the north is transhipped here for the Donets coalfield, and coal from the latter is transferred on to the river. The first Five-Year Plan brought about the great industrial development for which the city became noted, the huge tractor works, power stations, steel plant, new saw mills, and petroleum refineries. There is no bridge across the Volga here, no doubt because of the great width of the river, combined with the unproductive nature of the semi-desert on the eastern side. But irrigated cultivation now extends, thanks to the huge multi-purpose hydrological works which have been carried out. The completion of the Volga–Don canal in 1952 greatly improves the transport facilities of the city which has been rebuilt since its destruction during World War II.

Astrakhan (294,000) stands on an island in the delta on the left bank of the main distributary. It is the centre of the world-renowned sturgeon fisheries, and is a distributing centre for salt and petrol. A railway running through the semi-desert, via the salt lakes Elton and Baskunchak, gives the town communication with Saratov etc. at all seasons, while a new line provides a link with the Caucasus via Kizlyar. Astrakhan, however, is no longer the meeting place of maritime and river transport owing to the progressive shallowing of the Caspian Sea. This largest inland water body in the world has lost over 8 ft in depth since 1929 as a result of the Great Volga Scheme, which has markedly reduced the supply of water reaching the lower Volga, and of the excess of evaporation over inflow. Sea-going ships have now to load and unload a long way from the shore. The ultimate solution of this worsening situation is envisaged by diverting to the Volga one of the northern rivers which now flow into the Arctic.

## REFERENCES

See p. 619.

### CHAPTER 39

# THE PERIPHERAL MOUNTAINS OF EASTERN EUROPE: CRIMEA, URALS, CAUCASUS

**The Crimea.** Separated from the mainland by the narrow Perekop isthmus, the north of the Crimean peninsula continues the poor dry steppes characteristic of the south of the Ukraine to which Crimea administratively belongs. Three-quarters of the Crimea are occupied by this plain. Southwards, the land gradually rises to barren limestone mountains which drop towards the south-east coast by a series of steep scarps, separated by depressions which become more productive towards the south-east. The lower slopes of the mountains are clothed in trees, and productive agriculture, sometimes irrigated, is found in the depressions. The capital of the Crimean republic is Simferopol (189,000), with fruit-preserving and other alimentary industries. Sevastopol (148,000), on the south-west coast, is a naval base. The most productive and thickly populated part of the peninsula is the south-east coastal strip, which is so sheltered from the cold north winds that it enjoys exceptionally mild winters and a Mediterranean type of climate.

This 'Riviera' region is unique in the USSR, and its fame as a health and holiday resort is widespread. Yalta is perhaps the best known of its small, attractive, coastal towns. Eastwards the land falls to the low dry peninsula of Kerch, celebrated for its iron mines. The town of Kerch (99,000) has iron and steel plants.

**The Ural Region.** As already mentioned in Chapter 34, the northern Urals are largely undeveloped, but the central and southern sections are becoming increasingly important. In the low central section economic life is focused on Sverdlovsk (formerly Ekaterinburg), the old gateway to Siberia and starting point of the Trans-Siberian railway which is now electrified, at least between Kuibyshev and Novosibirsk. The town grew from 134,000 in 1926 to 777,000 in 1959, mainly owing to the great development of heavy industry and engineering. It draws on the iron, copper, gold, nickel, manganese, bauxite, and other ores which are mined both to north and south, mainly on the eastern side of the Urals, and derives some of its coal from the Kizel mines on the western side of the Urals near

Solikamsk.  As this hard coal is sulphurous and not of very good quality, Sverdlovsk is largely dependent on coal from Asiatic sources, particularly from the Kuzbas and Karaganda fields, respectively 1,200 miles and 700 miles away.  Local brown coal and peat are also utilised.  Besides being a large producer of pig-iron and steel, Sverdlovsk manufactures considerable quantities of machinery, machine tools, electric apparatus, and railway equipment.  In the north-west, below the mountains, chemical industries, especially the manufacture of potash fertilisers, operate on a large scale at Berezniki and Solikamsk.  Nizhni Tagil (338,000), some 75 miles farther north, is situated near famous platinum deposits and the great iron mountain of Mt Blagodat.  It also has heavy metallurgical works, railway wagon works, saw-mills, and cement works. Kamensk, south-east of Sverdlovsk, has a large aluminium plant.

Even greater industrial development has taken place in the southern part of the Urals.  The forested ranges and valleys round Zlatoust actually had important blast-furnaces in the eighteenth and early nineteenth centuries, but these charcoal-fired furnaces were unable to survive competition from the coke-fired furnaces of the developing Donets coalfield.  Zlatoust (161,000), a relatively old industrial centre in the inner Urals, has added the manufacture of high quality steels and ferro-alloys to its nineteenth century armaments industry, but has been far surpassed industrially since the 1930s by newer centres on the eastern and southern flanks of the Urals.  Previously, the rich ores of the latter areas were virtually unworked owing to the shortage of fuel, and also of man-power and communications.  Improved rail facilities and a large-scale inflow of labour from the older industrial areas have now overcome these difficulties.  The Ural Mountains, with all their diverse wealth of metallic and non-metallic minerals, are grossly deficient in sources of mechanical energy for the now far-flung Ural industrial region, which concentrates on metallurgy and machine-building and consumes no less than 15 per cent of the Union's current supplies of energy of all kinds.  However, the region includes part of the rich Volga–Ural oilfield and supplements its own small coal and larger brown coal resources by heavy shipments from the Asiatic fields which supply hard coal, including essential coking coal.  It is able to derive some of its electric power from stations fuelled with its own brown coal which forms about three-quarters of its coal production (see Table, p. 613).

Chelyabinsk (688,000), formerly a sleepy little provincial town, has great iron and steel works, rivalling those of Gary in USA, a large ferro-alloy plant, zinc foundries, and a great tractor works. The town of Magnitogorsk (311,000 in 1959) did not exist at the 1926 census, but has continued to grow enormously. Its *raison d'être* was the famous Magnet (Magnitnaya) Mountain, one of the world's greatest deposits of iron-ore, believed to contain 450 million tons of high grade magnetite ore. Planted in the once lonely valley of the upper Ural river, the town is now the most important single iron and steel centre, and cheapest steel producer, of the USSR, and one of the largest in the world. Industrialisation is also proceeding apace even farther south, and another great iron and steel centre has been created at Orsk (176,000), which in addition possesses chemical industries; a pipeline connects this centre with the Emba oilfield.

The extent and industrial weight of the Ural industrial region can be further indicated by reference to several other large towns which are now considered to lie within it. One is the old city of Perm (628,000), situated on the Kama river and known for a time as Molotov; this name originally applied to its new industrial suburb which has been incorporated into the city. Supplied with electric power from the Molotov hydro-electric plant above the city, it now manufactures aircraft, automobiles and ships, and exploits its nodal position on river and rail routes. Izhevsk (283,000), which lies half-way between Perm and Kazan, is the capital of Udmurt ASSR, having now many machine-building factories. Further south, Ufa (546,000), the Bashkir capital and chief industrial city, has absorbed the new town of Chernikovsk near by; it refines petroleum from the Volga–Ural field, on the eastern margin of which it stands. Mention should be made too of Orenburg (260,000), formerly Chkalov, situated on the right bank of the upper Ural river, which now has copper mines and heavy industries and good railway facilities, but was historically important as a Russian fortress town in the south Ural steppe and as a base from which Russian political power was extended into Kazakhstan and Central Asia. And at Sterlitamak (111,000) synthetic rubber is now being made from synthetic alcohol brought from Ufa on the oilfield.

With the overrunning of the Donets coalfield by the Germans in World War II, the newly industrialised Urals became the chief metallurgical armaments workshop of the USSR, and the region continues to play an increasingly important rôle in Russian industry.

**The Caucasus Mountains and Adjacent Regions.** This mountain range with its associated foreland to the north and the Trans-caucasian depression to the south, is separated from the populous Black Earth regions of the Ukraine, lower Don, and middle Volga by a thinly populated tract of poor soils, low rainfall, and scanty population. The Caucasus region may be regarded as a complex area comprising three main types of structure and landforms, (*a*) a relatively level but somewhat dissected foreland of young sediments at the northern foot of the Caucasus Mountains, similar in origin and build to the Alpine Foreland; (b) the great young folded mountains of the Caucasus proper; and (c) the tectonic depression to the south of that system.

Russian colonisation began comparatively late in this area, and is still chiefly confined to the northern foreland, and especially to its western section in the Kuban drainage area, which received large numbers of Russian colonists during the middle and latter part of the nineteenth century.[1]

*The Northern Foreland.* There are considerable differences between the western and eastern sections of this foreland. Although the natural vegetation is steppe in both sections, yet the Kuban region has a heavier precipitation, better distributed throughout the year than the eastern Kuma–Terek region, and has fertile Black Earth in contrast to sandy and salt impregnated soils. Agriculture, therefore, can flourish in the Kuban, while it is precarious farther east. The Kuban was one of the few areas of Russia which had large and prosperous peasant farms in pre-revolutionary days, and made considerable use of farm machinery. The present state and collective farms continue to grow large quantities of wheat, maize, and sugar-beet, while the soya bean appears to succeed well, and experiments have been made with kenaf, a new textile plant. In many ways the Kuban recalls the western Ukraine with its great variety of crops, its livestock, and its prosperous villages with their orchards and gardens, but the higher summer temperatures permit the cultivation of subtropical annuals, such as rice and cotton, where water is plentiful.

The eastern half of the foreland is still mainly the domain of the nomadic Nogaï Tatars, though there is some agriculture in the Kuma and Terek valleys, and more especially in the better watered foothills south of the Terek. The eastern part of the foreland is richer in mineral oil than the western part, and oil is piped from the large Grozny oilfields eastwards to the Caspian, north-west to Rostov-on-Don, and westward to Tuapse on the Black Sea. A pipeline also connects the last-named port with the western fields which lie between Krasnodar and Maikop.

Urban life is not greatly developed in either section. Krasnodar (312,000), in the west, is the chief administrative, commercial, and industrial centre; Novorossisk (93,000), a large manufacturer and exporter of cement, is the chief seaport. Farther east Ordzhonikidze (formerly Vladikavkaz, 'the gateway to the Caucasus'; 164,000) is the starting point for two of the most important roads which cross the Caucasus. Grozny (240,000) has large petroleum refineries.

[1] As many as 54,000 Russians immigrated in the single year of 1872.

*The Caucasus Mountains.* Physically, the Caucasus Mountains consist of a crystalline backbone, largely granitic, which runs as a single wall across the Caucasian isthmus. The flanking ranges are shorter, and though more or less parallel, they are generally arranged *en échelon* – that is to say, they tend to die out at one end and to be succeeded by another ridge which slightly overlaps.

On the north, the principal parallel range of Bokovoy (which simply means 'flanking' in Russian) is higher than the main chain, and gives rise to some of the most notable peaks – namely Mts Elbruz 18,481 ft, Koshtantau 16,877 ft, and Kazbek 16,558 ft. There are said to be some seventy passable foot-tracks across the Caucasus, most of which, however, are blocked by snow for eight or nine months of each year. Apart from the low north-western section of the Caucasus there is no railway and only one motor road, the so-called Georgian Military Road, which links Ordzhonikidze on the north with Tbilisi (formerly Tiflis) in Transcaucasia on the south. It has to climb about a thousand feet higher than Napoleon's famous Simplon military road in the Alps. The classical land route, now followed by a railway, by-passed the mountains by traversing the Caspian shore via Derbent, though a motor road and a railway have now been built with some difficulty along the Black Sea shore. The flanking seas continue to afford the best highways.

Like the Alps and Pyrenees, the Caucasus Mountains are not very rich in minerals, as far as is known, though molybdenum and tungsten ores are mined at Tyrny Auz, near Nalchik, and zinc near Ordzhonikidze. They possess great reserves of timber and water-power.

The Caucasus Mountains are scantily populated except in a few limited areas, but the diversity of languages, nationalities, customs, and traditions is very great. People of Turki, Armenian, Iranian, and Mongol origin are found, together with Georgians and Ossetians who are nearer to Europeans in language and probably in race. None of the people was Slavonic-speaking before the Russian conquest in the nineteenth century. The remoter valleys contain tribal communities which have lived in isolation for many centuries, but nevertheless, some of the highland people, such as the Georgians and Circassians, have long been in the habit of seeking their fortunes in the surrounding countries.

*Transcaucasia.* At the southern foot of the Caucasus Mountains lies the sheltered tectonic depression drained by the Rion to the Black Sea and by the Kura to the Caspian. It is not, however, a simple furrow, and lacks unity alike of climate, relief, and peoples. The western end of the depression drained by the Rion, together with the Black Sea coast south of the Caucasus range, is known as

Kolkhiz (Colchis of the Ancient Greeks).  The region receives a heavy annual rainfall, varying from 50 to 100 in, and has relatively high temperatures, averaging about 75° F (24° C) in July and August, and about 45° F (7° C) in January, the latter being exceptionally high for the USSR.  This humid subtropical climate permits the cultivation of tea and citrus fruits, as well as tobacco and rami, while the luxuriant forests of the mountain slopes provide another source of revenue.  Large-scale drainage works in the Kolkhiz depression are being carried out.

Farther east, between the alluvial valley of the Rion and the alluvial lower valley of the Kura, lies a belt of hilly, even mountainous, country, whose high broken relief, poor soils and only moderate rainfall provide a totally different environment.  Subsistence farming, with an emphasis on livestock, especially sheep, is the dominant note in this region which forms the heart of Georgia, though Tbilisi (Tiflis; 694,000), the capital, lies farther east in a fertile basin on the upper Kura.  South-east of Tbilisi, an iron and steel industry, to serve the needs of Transcaucasia, has been established at Rustavi (62,000) which uses ore brought from Dashkesan (in Azerbaidzhan) and coal from the Georgian fields at Tkibuli and Tkvarcheli.

The lower alluvial valley of the Kura lies in Azerbaidzhan.  The natural vegetation is steppe, as the plain is cut off from the rain-bearing winds by the surrounding mountains.  Winters are more liable to frost than those of Kolkhiz, but summers are even hotter, so that annual crops such as cotton and rice are grown on a large scale under irrigation.  The surrounding foothills are less arid than the valley, and maize, orchard trees, and the vine will grow without irrigation.

In addition to agriculture Transcaucasia is now developing considerable manufactures.  An area of relatively high population density and old handicrafts, it has the additional advantages of increasing supplies of hydro-electricity, considerable quantities of raw material, e.g. cotton, silk, and wool, and considerable mineral wealth, e.g. manganese near Chiatura in Georgia, copper in the Armenian SSR, and finally the petroleum resources of the Apsheron peninsula around and seawards of Baku.  The oil occurs at the junction of the plain with the Caucasus folds, in Oligocene grits and sandstones beneath a capping of younger limestones and clays. The oilfield was one of the richest in the world, although output had fallen to about 16 million tons in 1958 and now represents less than 14 per cent of the USSR's total production.  Baku (968,000), an ancient Persian foundation, was revivified by its new industries, especially oil refining, and its export of the 'black gold', but it also possesses engineering, timber and cotton-textile industries, and flour mills. It is also the intellectual and administrative capital of Azerbaidzhan.

South of the Rion–Kura depression rises the Armenian plateau, which averages 5,000–7,000 ft in height, with isolated volcanic massifs rising above it. From this plateau, historic and relatively easy passes lead to the Iranian and Anatolian plateaus. The Armenian SSR has shown greater industrial growth during the last twenty years than either Georgia or Azerbaidzhan, thanks above all to the generation of electricity from the falling waters of the River Razdan, the only outlet from the elevated Lake Sevan. This has fostered new industries at its capital Yerevan (509,000), above all the refining of aluminium and the manufacture of synthetic rubber. New railway construction keeps apace with these developments, notably that which will eventually link Yerevan with the Baku–Tbilisi line.

## REFERENCES

See p. 619.

### CHAPTER 40

# HISTORICO-ECONOMIC SUMMARY OF THE USSR

IN spite of the apparent great break with the past which took place in 1917, the clues to much of the present-day life of the USSR are to be found in history. For instance, the large number of autonomous republics stems from the fact that the Russians are recent intruders into the lands of other peoples, even into much of the European USSR section west of the Urals, their settlements until the seventeenth century being confined to the central wedge of mixed-forest and wooded steppe west of the Volga. Again, the dominance of the Moscow region dates from the historical fact that the conquering Tatars entrusted the princes of Muscovy with the collection of tribute from all the minor Russian rulers, and provided them with cavalry to enforce this collection. Many features of Russian life which seem curious to Western eyes date from contacts made long ago with the East rather than with the West; among these may be mentioned the Byzantine form of Christianity which, with its emphasis on asceticism and ritual rather than on ethics, its support of an oppressive autocracy, and its failure to be touched by the Renaissance, the Reformation, the Counter-Reformation, or the Humanitarian movements of the West, eventually alienated the Church from the people and brought it into contempt.

The effort to reach the sea, particularly an ice-free sea, has been a recurrent, though probably exaggerated, *motif* in Russian history, visible in some degree in the policies of the medieval princes and in those of the Tsars from Peter the Great onwards, as in the Stalinist policy of the USSR. Russia's long and historic remoteness from the sea may be adduced as a major cause of Russian aloofness from western Europe. On the south, Tatars and Turks barred the way to the Black Sea; on the west, Lithuanians, Swedes, and Finns barred the way to Moscow's nearest coast, the Baltic; the great northern forests rather than the few Finnic inhabitants barred the way to the White Sea, and it needed an Englishman to show the Russian landsmen their northern sea route from the White Sea.

Russian aloofness from the West was further strengthened by the early expansionist tendencies of her western neighbours, Lithuanians, Poles, and Swedes. Unlike the Tatars, who made no attempt to settle in the forest or to convert the Russians to their own ways of thought, the western peoples tended both to settle and to proselytise and thus were actually more feared and disliked than the Mongols. Pressure from the west had the effect of directing Russian expansionist movements eastward, and once the Tatars were conquered in mid-sixteenth century, there were only weak, primitive tribes to oppose the Russian advance right across the 3,000 miles of Siberia. The Pacific coast was actually reached as early as 1639, more than sixty years before a foothold was obtained on the Baltic coast, and nearly a hundred and fifty years before the Sea of Azov was attained. Small wonder, therefore, that the Russians looked eastwards and tended to turn their backs on the West; satisfied with their own achievements they failed to appreciate western Europe's persistent habit of regarding them as backward.

Nevertheless, Russia paid the penalty for this neglect of the West in a retarded economic and social evolution. Serfdom, which was widespread in Russia, was abolished only in 1861, and at the Revolution of 1917, the Russians, unlike the English, could look back on no long history of sturdy independent farmers, on no numerous, capable and hard-working middle class, and on no democratic Parliamentary traditions. Moreover, agriculture, industry, transport, and education were all greatly behind those of the countries of western Europe.

The present economic geography of the USSR presents a unique picture in that all agriculture, industry, transport, and commerce are in the hands of the state and all the land is State-owned. The state itself consists of a federation of republics, each nominally self-governing, which sends delegates to the Supreme Soviet in Moscow, but power is vested in the Præsidium of the Central Executive Committee, itself controlled by the Præsidium of the Communist Party.

It may be said that, in theory, Russia has undergone a process of 'rationalisation' similar to that recently adopted by some of the great manufacturing companies of western and central Europe and of North America, but among other differences, in Russia the process involves a whole country of 8·6 million square miles and 227 million people (including the Asiatic section), and no one is allowed to leave the firm. Such a process of rationalisation, known as state socialism when applied to a whole country, would tax the best brains of a land where the level of education stood high and whose leaders had already had long experience of organisation. There is no need for wonder, therefore, that the new system, introduced in 1917, resulted for many years in a great falling off in production, even though the pre-1914 level was already very low in comparison with those of the countries of central and western Europe.

This temporary decrease in productivity was due in particular to four causes: (a) the disturbances of war, including the civil war; (b) the large amount of time and energy consumed in establishing the new system and in experimenting with different methods of collectivism; (c) the loss of talent involved in the suppression and persecution of 'intellectuals'; and (d) the difficulty of obtaining foreign capital for a country which had repudiated its former debts. The production level of 1913 was practically re-attained in 1930, according to Soviet statistics, but in the interval the population suffered great miseries from the prevailing shortage of clothing, fuel, housing, and of the other necessities of life.

It must be remembered, however, that conditions of life in Russia at the end of the nineteenth century had changed very little since the Middle Ages, that the standard of living was very low, and that privations which would have been regarded as intolerable by people of western Europe were borne by the majority of Russians with docility. It may be said without exaggeration that the ideas of the French Revolution, of the Agricultural Revolution, and of the Industrial Revolution reached Russia at much the same time. In the twenty years or so before World War I the stirrings of new life were apparent and the country was being slowly reorganised on Western lines. Agriculture was then, as it still is, the staple industry of the USSR, but was in a very backward condition, except on the estates of the great landowners, which were situated mainly in the Black Earth belt. The old three-field system prevailed over most of the ploughed land. Even where enclosures had taken place the peasants were not in a much better position than before, owing to the smallness of their holdings, their primitive implements, and their ignorance of modern methods of tillage. As regards manufacturing industries, Russia had a good natural endowment of motive power (particularly of oil and coal) and of raw materials (particularly of timber and iron-ore), though such was the undeveloped state of the country that the full extent of these resources, even in the European part of Russia, was only just becoming known. Russia also possessed a vast home market, protected by an almost exclusive tariff wall, and large supplies of labour, but was handicapped by lack of capital and until the last years of the nineteenth century by the instability of her currency. The handicap of illiteracy was strongly felt both in agriculture and in the manufacturing industries. Great efforts were made to combat this in the country as a whole; illiteracy was reduced from 76 per cent in 1913 to 49 per cent in 1926, to 19 per cent in 1939, and is now virtually eliminated.

It may here be mentioned that one of the difficulties in describing the economic position of the European portion of the USSR lies in the fact that the organisation of the country largely ignores the intercontinental frontier. The Russian Soviet Socialist Federated Republic, which is the main unit of the USSR, includes the whole of Siberia.

The aim of the Five-Year Plans, the first of which was inaugurated in 1928, was no less than to catch up and overtake the great industrialised countries of the world. An industrial revolution on an unprecedented scale was envisaged, not only to expand old industries, but also to develop entirely new industrial regions, and both in the shortest possible time. Moreover, it was required to avoid calling on the outside world for capital to finance the new development. The great changes in agriculture which accompanied this industrial revolution were a necessary corollary, because only by an agricultural revolution could sufficient labour be obtained for the expanded mining and manufacturing industries. In 1927 at least 75 per cent of the population were engaged in agriculture and only 10 per cent in industry. In addition to the ideological motives involved, the 'collective' and 'state' farms were devised to take the place of individual peasant farming, because large mechanised farms would take less labour and would enable improved agricultural methods to be introduced more quickly than would have been possible by other means. It was eventually found necessary to obtain foreign equipment and to employ foreign technicians on a considerable scale, but the actual financing of the projects was an internal affair, which involved an enormous amount of compulsory saving and of sacrifices, especially by the collective farmers, and probably far greater than had been originally contemplated.

The first Five-Year Plan had a twofold aim: first, to expand heavy industry, which necessarily involved also a great increase in mining; secondly, to reduce the number of farm workers by the collectivisation of agriculture. The second Five-Year Plan also aimed at industrial expansion, but embraced a greater variety of goods; in fact, it aimed avowedly at producing more consumer goods, previous emphasis on heavy industry having brought about a veritable famine in clothing, household goods, etc., as well as a temporary setback in agricultural productivity, and the result had been a period of very severe rationing. The third Five-Year Plan was interrupted by war; the fourth Five-Year Plan (1946–50) more than made good the serious damage to the economy caused by World War II. The fifth (1959–65) Plan set out to overtake and outstrip the United States in production *per head*, alike in industrial and agricultural production, and thus to show the world the superiority of the Soviet system.  Blue-prints for the years 1971 and 1981 point to yet higher and higher production targets which, in so far as they are achieved, will greatly raise the living standards of the Soviet peoples.

The mineral wealth of the USSR is enormous, its scale ever increasing as geological prospecting proceeds.  The Union's mineable reserves of coal, of which one-third is brown coal, are put at 7,800 billion tons, of which only 7·6 per cent lie within European USSR, here taken to include the Urals and Caucasia.  Such reserves thus appear the greatest of any country.  In output of coal the USSR was reaching the highest figure in the world in 1963 (a rate of about 520 million tons), although it ranked only fourth in 1938. The distribution of its production, of which about 28 per cent is brown coal and 22 per cent coking coal, was as follows:

PRODUCTION OF COAL, INCLUDING BROWN COAL
(Million Metric Tons)

| Year | USSR | Donbas | Moscow | Pechora | Ural | Kuzbas | Karaganda | Eastern Siberia and Far East |
|------|------|--------|--------|---------|------|--------|-----------|------------------------------|
| 1938 | 132  | 80·7   | 7·4    | —       | 8·1  | 20·0   | 3·9       | 10·0                         |
| 1958 | 496  | 181·7  | 47·2   | 16·8    | 61·0 | 75·3   | 24·3      | 56·1                         |

Despite the fact that Asiatic USSR holds most of the reserves and despite the development of several fields there, it will be noted that the European fields, which are more expensive to work, contributed slightly above 60 per cent of the 1958 production.  Further, although eager to use more fully the growing abundance of petroleum and natural gas supplies and thus to reduce the dependence of the economy on coal – above all for the railways and for industry – the Soviet leaders recently announced a staggering programme for the doubling of coal output to 1,000 million tons by 1980, chiefly by the quarrying of brown coal in Western Siberia.  Indeed, despite the development of other power resources, coal remains king, although its share in the national energy consumption has decreased to barely 50 per cent.

Petroleum reserves similarly grow larger as knowledge of new sources is acquired.  They are now estimated at 9,200 million tons, enough it would seem to meet the country's needs for the rest of this century.  They make up only a minute fraction of the USSR's potential energy reserves from coal, but currently oil costs to produce only a quarter of the cost of its thermal equivalent in coal. An early starter in petroleum drilling (at Baku), the USSR has now displaced Venezuela from second world producer, with an output (in 1962) of 186 million tons.  No less than 80 per cent of the reserves lie in the immense Volga-Ural field, and 95 per cent lie in European USSR.

Water-power reserves are very considerable but they have been exploited so far mainly on the Volga and Dnieper, but also in South Caucasus and north European Russia. So far hydro-electricity contributes little over 20 per cent to the country's electricity supplies, which depend above all on coal, including brown coal, and to a much smaller extent on natural gas and peat, supplies of which are abundant. Of the potential reserves of water-power, now under vigorous exploitation, much the greater part lies in Asiatic USSR.

The wealth of metallic and non-metallic minerals is also large and varied. Industrial iron-ore reserves are estimated at 23,860 million tons, of which 69 per cent lie in European USSR, but recent discoveries, notably in Kazakhstan, will reduce this percentage. To the output of ore, Krivoi Rog contributes about half and the Ural mines more than a third. The USSR takes first place for the production of manganese (required in the making of steel), the ore coming almost wholly from two European sources – Nikopol in the Ukraine, and Chiatura in Georgia. The Union is also an outstanding producer of chrome ore (used for hardening steel) and of magnesite, now chiefly used as an alloy, e.g. in duralumin; both ores come mainly from the Urals. There are large reserves of nepheline and, to a lesser extent, of bauxite, from which aluminium is refined. European USSR contains a substantial part of the deposits from which copper, nickel, lead, and zinc are derived; production seems enough to meet domestic requirements, although their costs of production, unlike that of steel, appear high to the western world. Supplies of tin come chiefly from Asiatic USSR and appear insufficient. On the other hand, the Urals share with eastern areas the Union's wealth in gold, platinum and precious stones, although the principal source of industrial diamonds is the Vilui basin in Yakutia. Non-metallic minerals are widely available in large deposits, notably apatites, potassium salts, common salt, abrasives, mica and asbestos.

The manufacturing industries of the USSR are restricted, although less than in Tsarist times, to a few areas, mainly in the European sector. The location of industry still strongly reflects historical momentum, and in spite of the great devastation of the Ukraine during the war of 1941–45, and of the continuing development of industrial regions in Asia, it seems that industry is destined to remain predominantly in the west of the USSR for at least some decades. The five main manufacturing areas of the USSR are: 1. the Moscow–Ivanovo area; 2, the Ukraine; 3, the Urals; 4, the Leningrad area; 5, the Middle Volga. Far behind come the Asiatic centres of Kuzbas, Kazakhstan, Central Asia, Central Siberia and the Far East.

The greatest industrial advances since Revolutionary days have been made in the fields of heavy metallurgy and heavy engineering. The following table shows how the Russian world position has changed in regard to other large producing countries.

PRODUCTION OF PIG-IRON IN MILLION TONS[1]

| | 1900 | 1913 | 1937 | 1960 |
|---|---|---|---|---|
| Russia/USSR | 5·8 (1899) | 4·2 | 14·6 | 46·8 |
| United Kingdom | 8·9 | 10·3 | 8·5 | 16·0 |
| Germany | 8·3 | 16·4 | 15·9 | 25·9[2] |
| France | 2·6 | 5·1 | 7·9 | 14·4 |
| USA | 13·7 | 30·9 | 37·7 | 62·3 |
| World total | c. 46·0 | c. 78 | c. 103·0 | c. 260 |

[1] See also statistics — Appendix G (p. 629) [2] German Federal Republic

Heavy industry and engineering have undergone great expansion not only in output, but also in complexity of goods produced; moreover, entirely new areas have been developed, particularly in the Ural and Middle Volga regions, and to a less extent in the Kuzbas. Up to 1940, however, the Ukraine produced 65 per cent of the pig-iron as against 22 per cent for the Urals, and only 8 per cent for the Kuzbas. Comparable figures for 1958 show little change in the relative dominance of European USSR's production of pig-iron: Ukraine 51 per cent, Urals 34 per cent; Kuzbas 7·5 per cent. Fine metallurgy and engineering continue to be located in the Leningrad and Moscow areas, and in some towns of the Ukraine. The manufacture of machinery and locomotives is also chiefly situated west of Siberia, though with some scattered centres in Asia.

The heavy chemical industry is almost entirely a development of the last thirty or forty years, and it may be recalled that this industry has been revolutionised and vastly expanded in Great Britain, Germany, and the United States during this period. In the USSR this industry is associated closely with coal and salt (as in the Ukraine), with apatites (in Kola), copper and potash (Urals), and with by-products of the oilfields, used notably in synthesising rubber. The 1959–65 plans for the chemical industry included very large developments in the production of artificial and synthetic fibres, plastics, synthetic rubber and resins, and mineral fertilisers, but the plans were not going well as late as 1964 owing to shortfalls both in chemical engineering and in the provision of buildings for plant.

The progress of Soviet industrialisation has been revolutionary and rapid; it has been achieved too without the aid of a rapidly growing population and by large and enforced capital accumulation, to which the more numerous and less favoured peasantry necessarily made the major contribution. Only by 1928 was the 1913 level of industrial production exceeded, but by 1953 the 1928 level was in turn exceeded, if not by sixteen times as officially claimed, almost certainly by about ten times. As noted above, the enormous Soviet lands (8·6 million square miles) provide unparalleled resources; the Soviet labour force increased during the 1950s at the rate of 1·9 per cent per year, is becoming ever better educated and trained, and automation is being increasingly applied. Soviet industrial output has been growing during the last ten years or so at a very high rate – around 8 per cent per year, and the massive diversion of capital to the production of capital goods has meant restriction on housing and consumer goods which are now being steadily eased. In its competition with the United States in industrial production the USSR enjoys the advantages of greater natural resources and also of a greater labour supply. The official aim to 'overhaul the Americans by 1970' on the basis of production per head is probably too high an ambition, but it may well be that a later date will see this achievement.

The USSR's transport system appears still inadequate, even in European USSR. The railways carry an exceptionally heavy burden – 80 per cent of all the freight moved in 1960. The contribution of the rivers is only a little above 5 per cent, while pipelines for oil and natural gas, which are to carry as much as the rivers, are being built as fast as supplies of tubes allow. Tarred or macadamised roads are still rare outside the large cities and few compared with those available in western and central Europe; nor can aircraft, invaluable for moving passengers and goods of small bulk but high value, much lighten the work of the railways, where electric and diesel traction is being rapidly introduced.

Soviet agriculture has an enormous output – of grain, potatoes, sugar-beet, textile fibres, including cotton, as well as of meat, dairy, and other animal products. But this cannot be regarded as an efficient branch of the economy: the production costs of food, especially of meat and animal products, are very high (in terms of man-hours required) when compared with those in the United States. And, although Soviet citizens now enjoy higher living standards than ever before, the production of grain, including fodder grain, meat, milk, and butter continually falls below plan and results in greatly increased farm prices and shop prices in the towns. The area under crops within the present territory of the USSR in 1953 had increased by a third above the 1913 level of 295 million acres and in the early 1960s had virtually doubled: no less than 114 million acres were added to the sown area – mainly in Asiatic USSR but also in the Volga and Ural regions – as a result of the ploughing-up campaign launched in 1954. It should be noted that this staggering increase was slightly offset by reductions within European USSR, west of the Volga.[1] Large increases have been effected in the areas sown to wheat, maize, and other grains, potatoes, sugar-beet, sunflowers, and cotton, but the successful achievement of the high plans continually set for agriculture prove often elusive. The reasons for this relative failure are not easily established. Certainly, for example, the USSR has far to go to match the American degree of mechanisation and of the use of chemical fertilisers. But it should be recognised that the USSR's territory, for all its extent and range of climate, compares ill with that of the United States. Two comparable figures may be noted here: only 10 per cent of the Soviet lands are cultivated, as compared with 16 per cent of the United States; and whereas the USA enjoys 4 acres per head of its population, the comparable Soviet figure is 2. Further, the USSR's new lands recently brought into use are semi-arid with sharply varying yields from year to year, and further expansion can be made only at increasingly heavy reclamation costs. No less than three-quarters of the Soviet wheat supply now come from spring-sown lands where the yield is low and very uncertain, owing mainly to continual lack of precipitation. In short, although the USSR doubtless possesses a much richer estate in respect of energy, mineral and timber resources than does the United States, it is at a clear disadvantage in respect of agriculture. On economic ground, it could more profitably export steel, machine tools, and heavy equipment and import some of its food supplies. Owing to inadequate harvests, a very heavy import of wheat from North America was announced in the autumn of 1963.

Despite the vigorous and large-scale efforts which have been, and are being applied by the USSR to its Asiatic territories – alike in agriculture, mining, metallurgy and hydro-electrical construction – it still remains true that European USSR is the dominant part of the country. Although it has only a quarter of the total area, it has three-quarters of the population, with a density of over 75 per square mile as against 26 per square mile for the whole country. The great urban development, associated with the Five-Year Plans, which raised the urban population from 18 per cent of the total in 1926 to over 50 per cent in the 1960s, chiefly affected the European sector. Whereas in 1926 there were only twenty cities with over 100,000

---

[1] Thus there was a 10 per cent reduction in the area sown to grain in European USSR west of the Volga in 1958 as compared with 1953. Only the North Caucasus region and Azerbaidzhan registered increases there.

inhabitants, in 1959 there were 123, only 42 of which lie east of the
Urals. European USSR contains most of the Union's energy
reserves in the form of petroleum, natural gas, and oil shales, and
produces still over 60 per cent of the grain crop. It is a pointer to

Fig. 74. POLITICO–ADMINISTRATIVE DIVISIONS OF THE EUROPEAN
USSR
1. Udmurt ASSR; 2. Mari ASSR; 3. Chuvash ASSR; 4. Penza oblast;
5. Ulyanovsk oblast.

the decades ahead, however, that the population west of the Urals
increased during the years 1939–59 by only 200,000, when only the
Volga-Ural region and Transcaucasia made notable increases. In
other words, the displacement of population eastwards to the Volga,

the Urals, and into Asia, which began under the pressure of the war of 1941–45, ever continues, and Siberia, with its great reserves of coal, hydro-electricity, metals and timber, has only begun to develop its remarkable potential for industry and for settlement.

The external trade of the USSR does not reach high figures, when compared with those of the western world, if only because the government aims at economic self-sufficiency and is able largely to achieve this, thanks to the scale and variety of the domestic resources. Even so, the Union's increased participation in world trade is to be expected as part of the challenge it throws down to the capitalist world. Nor is the world left in doubt, given the high achievements of Soviet science, technology, and industry, that the USSR, with a population of some 227 million (1964), increasing yearly by between 2·5 and 3·0 millions, means to achieve a commensurate status in international affairs.

## REFERENCES TO SECTION VI

On the geography of the USSR: L. S. Berg, *Natural Regions of the U.S.S.R.*, trans. from Russian, London and New York, Macmillan, 1950; S. S. Balzak, V. F. Vasyutin, and Ya. G. Feigin, *Economic Geography of the U.S.S.R.*, New York, Macmillan, 1949; translated from the Russian, originally published in 1940; N. N. Baransky, *Economic Geography of the U.S.S.R.*, Moscow, Foreign Languages Publishing House, 1956; J. P. Cole and F. C. German, *A Geography of the U.S.S.R.: The Background to a Planned Economy*, London, Butterworths, 1961; Georges Jorré, *The Soviet Union: the Land and the People*, trans. from French and rev. by E. D. Laborde, 2nd ed., London, Longmans, 1961; W. G. East and O. H. K. Spate (Eds.), *The Changing Map of Asia*, London, Methuen and New York, Dutton, 4th ed., 1961: Chapter 6 deals with Asiatic USSR; N. Mikhailov, *Glimpses of the U.S.S.R.: its Economy and Geography*, trans. from Russian, Moscow, Foreign Languages Publishing House, 1960; N. T. Mirov, *Geography of Russia*, New York, John Wiley, 1951; Y. G. Saushkin, *Economic Geography of the Soviet Union* (8 lectures March–April 1956 delivered in the University of Oslo); Theodore Shabad, *Geography of the U.S.S.R.: a Regional Survey*, New York, Columbia University Press, 1951; G. W. Hoffman (Ed.), *A Geography of Europe*, New York, The Ronald Press and London, Methuen, 2nd ed., 1961: Chapter 9 on 'The Soviet Union', by Theodore Shabad; S. P. Turin, *The U.S.S.R., an Economic and Social Survey*, London, Methuen, 1944. On the USSRs neighbours in Europe, see N. J. G. Pounds (Ed.), *Geographical Essays on Eastern Europe*, Bloomington, Indiana University and the Hague, Mouton, 1961.

On the history of Russia: B. H. Sumner, *A Survey of Russian History*, London, Duckworth, 1944; M. T. Florinsky, *The End of the Russian Empire*, New York, Collier Books, 1961; G. H. N. Seton-Watson, *The Decline of Imperial Russia*, London, Methuen, 1952; Richard Pipes, *The Formation of the Soviet Union: Communism and Nationalism*, 1917–23, Cambridge, Mass., Harvard University Press, 1954.

Among the available atlases note: *Atlas Mira* (Atlas of the World), Moscow, 1954: this is a large library atlas invaluable for reference; useful student atlases are *Geographical Atlas of the U.S.S.R. for the 7th and 8th Classes of the Middle Schools*, Moscow, 1951, 75 pp., the *Oxford Regional Economic Atlas: The U.S.S.R. and Eastern Europe*, Oxford University Press, 1956, and G. Kish, *Economic Atlas of the Soviet Union*, The University of Michigan Press, 1960. Note also, for reference: *The Times Atlas of the World*, Vol. II, ed. J. Bartholomew, London, The Times Publishing Co., 1959.

On the progress of the USSR's planned economy: *Economic Survey of Europe in 1961*, Part I, Geneva, United Nations, 1962; Harry Schwarz, *Russia's Soviet Economy*, London, Jonathan Cape, 1951; *Forty Years of Soviet Power in Facts and Figures*, Moscow, Foreign Languages Publishing House, 1958; *Soviet Handbook 1959–1965*, Soviet Booklet No. 57, London, 1959: this gives an outline, with statistics, of the current plan.

On specific aspects of the USSR as a whole: W. Gordon East, *The U.S.S.R.*, Searchlight Book, Princeton, N.J. and London, Van Nostrand, 1963, (a politico-geographical introduction); W. G. East and A. E. Moodie (Eds.), *The Changing World: Studies in Political Geography*, London, Harrap and New York, The World Book Co., 1956; J. A. Hodgkins, *Soviet Power: Energy Resources, Production and Potentials*, London, Prentice Hall International, 1961; J. Beaujeu-Garnier, *Géographie de la Population*, Paris, Editions M. Th. Genin, 1958, Vol. II, pp. 405–448; S. Konovalov, *Russo-Polish Relations*, London, The Cresset Press, 1945.

For translations of selections from Soviet geographical research papers on the USSR and for information on current developments there, see *Soviet Geography: Review and Translation*, New York, American Geographical Society.

# POLITICO-ECONOMIC DEVELOPMENTS

EUROPE, with its population of over 600 million and covering an area equivalent to that of the United States of America, is, as noted above (pp. 46–49), sharply divided into a number of national units. This fragmentation is emphasised by the multiplicity of languages spoken and also by the completely separate economic structures of the various countries. In the present-day world, rising standards of living and strong economies are not compatible with a large number of separate entities each pursuing entirely its own course which may be opposed or even detrimental to those of its neighbours. Some form of cooperation has become necessary although how far this should move towards the establishment of supranational governments and the formulation of common policy is a matter of much heated debate. Under the Romans, Charlemagne, Napoleon, and the Habsburgs, varying areas of Europe have been coordinated temporarily for political, military, and economic purposes but it was not until after Hitler's unsuccessful attempt to dominate Europe by force that real progress towards cooperation and some degree of integration have been achieved.

After the end of World War II many people in Europe saw the need for closer ties between the countries if they were to rehabilitate their economies and to weather the economic and political storms of the future. An early step towards this closer association resulted from the Marshall Aid Plan in 1947 which was offered to all countries of Europe and rejected only by those now within the communist bloc. In order better to appraise the needs of Europe and to plan the use of aid the Organisation for European Economic Cooperation was established in 1948. Some six months earlier in October 1947 an important step towards cooperation was taken by the governments of Belgium, Luxembourg, and the Netherlands when they signed the Benelux treaty. This provided for the gradual formation of a customs and economic union (Belgium and Luxembourg had been in a customs union together since 1921). This project has slowly prospered but attempts to widen its scope by the inclusion of France and Italy were abortive owing to the reluctance of France.

In 1948 another important advance in international cooperation was taken by the establishment of the North Atlantic Treaty

Organisation which included not only European countries but also Canada and the United States. In 1952 the European Coal and Steel Community came into being. Under this treaty the coal, iron-ore, steel, and scrap resources and industries of the Benelux countries, France, Italy, and the German Federal Republic were grouped together for purposes of planning, and a common policy and marketing arrangements, etc., are being worked out. The ECSC has met with considerable success, the production of iron-ore and steel practically doubling during the first ten years of the Community's life. To a large extent the success was due to favourable world conditions of expanding demand. When coal surpluses built up and unrest at pit closure arose in Belgium the Community faced some difficult moments but the ECSC has survived.

The success of the ECSC and the desire for closer ties led the governments of the six countries to plan for closer unity. These ideas were finally embodied in the Treaty of Rome signed in March 1957 which launched the European Economic Community. Amongst the many aims of this Treaty were the intention to end the dissensions that had for so long bedevilled western Europe, to enable the economies to expand more rapidly, to raise the living standards, to help agriculture and industry by abolishing old trade hindrances, to help their former dependencies and ultimately to form a united states of Europe. The implications of this Treaty were many, alike at economic, social, and political levels. Owing to its political implications the United Kingdom felt that she could not join at that time.

The initial stages of the implementation of the Treaty of Rome were essentially economic with the gradual abolition of tariffs and trade restrictions in general between member countries and the gradual imposition of a common tariff on certain goods from outside. The gradual implementation of a common transport policy and the easing of the movement of capital and labour have gone hand in hand. With its population of over 170 million and its considerable output of coal, steel, chemicals, and manufactured goods, the Six has clearly become one of the chief industrial blocs in the world, being surpassed only by the USA and in some things by the USSR, and in population by India and China (see Table, p. 623). Former colonial dependencies of the Six are specially linked with the European members and have special access to the Market.

In 1957 too came into being Euratom, an organisation established to foster the peaceful use of nuclear power. It includes the same countries but the United Kingdom is also closely associated with it. When the Treaty of Rome came into effect, it included only a minority of the countries west of the Iron Curtain. Many of the others were unwilling or unable for various reasons to join the Common Market. Some, like Sweden, Switzerland and Austria, feared that the political implications would affect their neutral status. Others like Portugal, Greece, and Turkey had insufficiently developed economies to be able to participate fully in a customs union. The United Kingdom had the added problem of its Commonwealth responsibilities and, having failed to get the Six to agree to a wider customs union but without the political objectives, it helped to establish the European Free Trade Association (with Sweden, Norway, Denmark, Portugal, Austria, and Switzerland). This was formed in 1959 and involved the gradual elimination of trade barriers between members, but left each member free to establish its own external tariffs. Attempts have been unsuccessfully made to bring the two groups together but both have prospered, especially the Six. Greece and Turkey have been admitted as associated members of the Common Market and Portugal and Spain have applied for a similar status; Finland has become associated with the Seven and Denmark, Norway, the Republic of Ireland, and the United Kingdom applied for full membership of the Common Market. The application of the United Kingdom was rejected early in 1963, largely as a result of French policy. Another application had no more success in November 1967, when it was clear that, although the five Common Market members other than France firmly supported Britain's entry, France vigorously opposed it.

Such attempts to liberalise trade have been most successful in the industrial field. The table below indicates the industrial stature of EEC in comparison with those of the USSR, its satellites organised with it in CMEA, the United States, the United Kingdom, and Mainland China.

SOME COMPARATIVE INDUSTRIAL STATISTICS
all figures are for 1961 and in million metric tons, except for population and electricity

| | EEC (Common Market Countries) | CMEA[1] Members ex USSR | USSR | UK | USA | Mainland China | World |
|---|---|---|---|---|---|---|---|
| Population (millions) | 170·1 | 99·1 | 218·0 | 52·9 | 183·7 | c. 650·0 | 3,070 |
| Coal | 230·8 | 144·2 | 377·0 | 193·5 | 378·7 | 420·0[2] | 1,942·7 |
| Oil | 10·1 | 14·1 | 166·1 | 0·15 | 354·3 | 6·0 | 1,123·7 |
| Electricity 000 mkWh Prod. | 296·8 | 124·0 | 327·6 | 146·8 | 878·7 | 60·5 | 2,453·3 |
| Steel | 73·2 | 22·0 | 70·7 | 22·4 | 88·9 | 15·0 | 354·8 |
| Iron ore (iron equivalent) | 28·7 | 3·4 | 68·4 | 4·5 | 39·2 | ? | 230·3 |
| Paper | 7·3 | 1·2 | 2·5 | 2·9 | 15·6 | ? | 49·6 |
| Cement | 67·6 | 24·6 | 50·9 | 14·4 | 56·7 | 14·0 | 339·0 |

Source: United Nations *Statistical Yearbook*, 1962.
[1] The Council for Mutual Economic Aid alternatively known as COMECON.
[2] includes brown coal.

In agriculture progress has been very much slower and agreement much more difficult to get. In spite of the high degree of industrialisation in western Europe, a fair proportion of the population is employed on the land and therefore agricultural policies that might deprive them of their livelihood in certain areas cannot be lightly agreed; also there are the associated problems of a social and political nature.

Not only has western Europe been engaged in seeking closer integration but similar efforts have been made east of the Iron Curtain. In reaction to the Marshall Aid, which east European countries had to refuse, and the OEEC (OECD since 1962), the Russians established in 1949 the Council for Mutual Economic Aid (CMEA or alternatively COMECON), which includes Bulgaria, Czechoslovakia, East Germany, Hungary, Poland, Rumania, and USSR. This is essentially concerned with economic planning and the development of resources. Under Stalin attempts were made to industrialise all the satellites but under Khrushchev a rather more rational policy was introduced aimed at developing regional specialisation, for example of the chemical industry in East Germany, based on brown coal and salt deposits, in machine tools and engineering in Czechoslovakia, and in steel in Poland and Czechoslovakia. By a series of Five-Year Plans the production of industrial (both capital and consumer) goods and, to a lesser extent, of agriculture will be much increased in the east. The communists also reacted to NATO by the Warsaw Pact for mutual defence in 1955.

## REFERENCES

To date there are only a few articles on this subject in the geographical literature. Two which deal with Britain's role are: C. A. Fisher 'The Changing Significance of the Commonwealth in the Political Geography of Great Britain', and M. J. Wise, 'The Common Market and the Changing Geography of Europe', both in *Geography*, xlviii, April 1963, 113–128 and 129–138 respectively.

There is however a considerable literature available on the Common Market and other organisations of which a selection follows: Political and Economic Planning (P.E.P.), *European Organisations*, London, George Allen and Unwin, 1959, and *Regional Development in the European Economic Community*, London, George Allen and Unwin, 1962; *Britain and Europe*, London, Economic Intelligence Unit, 1957; *The Commonwealth and Europe*, London, Economic Intelligence Unit, 1960; L. Lister, *Europe's Coal and Steel Community*, New York, Twentieth Century Fund, 1960; W. Diebold, Jnr., *The Schuman Plan: A Study in Economic Cooperation 1950–1959*, New York, Frederick A Praeger, Inc., 1959; G. W. Hoffman (Ed.), *A Geography of Europe*, New York, Ronald Press, 2nd ed. 1961, Chapter 10.

European Community Information Service, *The European Community in Maps* Brussels, European Community Publications Dept., 1961, and many other booklets and periodicals put out by this organisation; see also J. W. Nystrom and P. Malof, *The Common Market: The European Community in Action*, London, Van Nostrand, 1962.

# APPENDIXES

# AREA AND POPULATION FIGURES

| | Area | | Popu-lation (000's)[a] | Population Density | |
|---|---|---|---|---|---|
| | Sq. miles | Sq. km | | Sq. mile[a] | Sq. km |
| Albania | 11,100 | 28,748 | 1,965 | 163 | 63 |
| Andorra | 175 | 453 | 14 | 63 | 25 |
| Austria | 32,374 | 83,849 | 7,323 | 223 | 86 |
| Belgium | 11,781 | 30,513 | 9,581 | 796 | 307 |
| Bulgaria | 42,729 | 110,669 | 8,309 | 190 | 74 |
| Cyprus | 3,572 | 9,251 | 614 | 164 | 63 |
| Czechoslovakia | 49,370 | 127,869 | 14,305 | 285 | 110 |
| Denmark | 16,619 | 43,043 | 4,839 | 284 | 110 |
| East Berlin | 156 | 403 | 1,081 | 6,930 | 2,682 |
| East Germany | 41,659 | 107,901 | 16,001 | 76 | 148 |
| Finland | 130,119 | 337,009 | 4,664 | 35 | 14 |
| France | 211,207 | 547,026 | 49,890 | 236 | 91 |
| Gibraltar | 2·5 | 6 | 25 | 10,000 | 4,167 |
| Greece | 50,944 | 131,944 | 8,716 | 171 | 66 |
| Holy See | 109 acres | 0·44 | 1 | | 2,273 |
| Hungary | 35,919 | 93,030 | 10,212 | 284 | 110 |
| Iceland | 39,768 | 103,000 | 200 | 5 | 2 |
| Ireland (Eire) | 27,135 | 70,280 | 2,899 | 107 | 41 |
| Italy | 116,303 | 301,225 | 52,334 | 449 | 174 |
| Liechtenstein | 61 | 157 | 20 | 328 | 127 |
| Luxembourg | 1,000 | 2,586 | 335 | 335 | 130 |
| Malta | 122 | 316 | 319 | 2,614 | 1,009 |
| Monaco | 0·5 | 1·49 | 24 | 48,000 | 16,107 |
| Netherlands | 12,978 | 33,612 | 12,597 | 971 | 375 |
| Norway | 125,181 | 324,219 | 3,784 | 30 | 12 |
| Poland | 120,664 | 312,520 | 31,944 | 264 | 102 |
| Portugal | 35,510 | 91,971 | 9,440 | 266 | 103 |
| Rumania | 91,699 | 237,500 | 19,287 | 210 | 81 |
| San Marino | 23 | 61 | 18 | 783 | 294 |
| Spain | 194,883 | 504,750 | 32,140 | 165 | 64 |
| Sweden | 173,665 | 449,793 | 7,869 | 45 | 17 |
| Switzerland | 15,941 | 41,288 | 6,050 | 379 | 147 |
| Turkey | 301,381 | 780,576 | 32,710 | 109 | 42 |
| in Europe | 9,121 | 23,623 | 27,902 | 306 | 118 |

[a] Estimated for 1967.

625

APPENDIX A *continued*

| | Area | | Popu-lation (000's)[a] | Population Density | |
|---|---|---|---|---|---|
| | *Sq. miles* | *Sq. km* | | *Sq. mile*[a] | *Sq. km* |
| United Kingdom | 94,220 | 244,030 | 55,068 | 582 | 226 |
| England and Wales | 58,347 | 151,120 | 48,391 | 829 | 320 |
| Northern Ireland | 5,462 | 14,146 | 1,491 | 273 | 105 |
| Scotland | 30,411 | 78,764 | 5,187 | 171 | 66 |
| USSR | 8,649,500 | 22,402,200 | 235,543 | 27 | 11 |
| in Europe | 2,150,967 | 5,571,000 | 178,424 | 82 | 32 |
| West Berlin | 186 | 481 | 2,173 | 11,682 | 4,518 |
| West Germany | 95,742 | 247,973 | 57,699 | 603 | 233 |
| Yugoslavia | 98,766 | 255,804 | 19,958 | 202 | 78 |

[a] Estimated for 1967.

Source: United Nations, *Demographic Yearbook, 1965* (New York, 1966); United Nations, *Demographic Yearbook, 1967* (New York, 1968).

APPENDIX B

# BITUMINOUS AND ANTHRACITE
# COAL PRODUCTION
(million metric tons)

| | 1928 | 1937 | 1954 | 1964 | 1966[a] |
|---|---|---|---|---|---|
| Austria | 0·2 | 0·2 | 0·2 | 0·1 | 0·02 |
| Belgium | 27·6 | 29·7 | 29·3 | 21·3 | 17·5 |
| Bulgaria | 0·07 | 0·1 | 0·3 | 0·6 | 0·5 |
| Czechoslovakia | 14·6 | 16·9 | 20·6 | 28·2 | 26·7 |
| France | 51·8 | 44·3 | 54·4 | 53·0 | 50·3 |
| Germany | 180·8 | 184·5 | | | |
| East | | | 2·6 | 2·3 | 2·0 |
| West | | | 145·7 | 143·0 | 126·3 |
| Hungary | 0·8 | 0·9 | 2·4 | 4·1 | 4·4 |
| Ireland | 0·01 | 0·1 | 0·2 | 0·2 | 0·2 |
| Italy | 0·1 | 1·0 | 1·0 | 0·5 | 0·4 |
| Netherlands | 10·9 | 14·3 | 12·1 | 11·5 | 10·1[b] |
| Norway | 0·2 | 0·8 | 0·3 | 0·4 | 0·4 |
| Poland | 40·6 | 36·2 | 91·6 | 117·3 | 122·0 |
| Portugal | 0·2 | 0·3 | 0·4 | 0·4 | 0·4 |
| Rumania | 0·3 | 0·3 | 3·2 | 5·9 | 4·8 |
| Spain | 6·4 | 5·3 | 12·4 | 12·2 | 13·0 |
| Sweden | 0·4 | 0·5 | 0·3 | 0·8 | 0·04 |
| Turkey | 1·4 | 2·3 | 3·7 | 4·4 | 4·9 |
| United Kingdom | 241·3 | 245·0 | 227·7 | 196·7 | 177·4[c] |
| USSR | 35·8 | 127·0 | 243·7 | 408·9 | 439·2 |
| Yugoslavia | 0·4 | 0·4 | 1·0 | 1·3 | 1·1 |

[a] Estimated.
[b] Low-grade coal has been included at its anthracite equivalent.
[c] Great Britain only.

Source: United Nations, *Statistical Yearbook, 1966* (New York, 1967);
United Nations, *Statistical Yearbook, 1967* (New York, 1968).

# BROWN COAL PRODUCTION
(million metric tons)

|  | 1929 | 1937 | 1954 | 1964 | 1966[a] |
|---|---|---|---|---|---|
| Albania | —[b] | — | 0·1 | 0·3 | 0·3 |
| Austria | 3·5 | 3·2 | 6·3 | 5·8 | 5·3 |
| Bulgaria | 1·6 | 1·7 | 8·6 | 23·7 | 24·7 |
| Czechoslovakia | 22·5 | 18·0 | 37·9 | 75·6 | 74·1 |
| Denmark | — | — | 0·7 | 2·2 | 2·0 |
| France | 1·2 | — | 1·9 | 2·2 | 2·6 |
| Germany | 174·4 | 184·7 |  |  |  |
| East |  |  | 181·9 | 256·9 | 249·0 |
| West |  |  | 87·9 | 110·9 | 98·1 |
| Greece | 0·1 | 0·1 | 0·7 | 3·8 | 4·8 |
| Hungary | 7·0 | — | 19·1 | 27·4 | 26·0 |
| Italy | 0·8 | 1·0 | 0·6 | 1·2 | 1·1 |
| Netherlands | 0·1 | 0·1 | 0·2 | — | — |
| Poland | 0·07 | 0·02 | 5·9 | 20·3 | 24·5 |
| Portugal | 0·03 | 0·02 | 0·06 | 0·1 | 0·05 |
| Rumania | 2·7 | 1·9 | 2·4 | 5·2 | 6·6 |
| Spain | 0·4 | 0·9 | 1·7 | 2·6 | 2·7 |
| Turkey | 0·01 | 0·1 | 1·1 | 3·0 | 3·6 |
| USSR | — | — | 103·4 | 145·1 | 146·4 |
| Yugoslavia | 5·2 | 4·6 | 12·7 | 28·2 | 28·2 |

[a] Estimated.
[b] A dash indicates data not available.

Source: United Nations, *Statistical Yearbook, 1966* (New York, 1967);
United Nations, *Statistical Yearbook 1967* (New York, 1968).

APPENDIX C

# PETROLEUM PRODUCTION AND REFINING CAPACITY

(million metric tons)

| | Crude Petroleum Production | | | Refining Capacity | | |
|---|---|---|---|---|---|---|
| | *1938* | *1954* | *1964* | *1938* | *1954* | *1964* |
| Austria | 0·05 | 3·0 | 2·7 | —[a] | — | 4·7 |
| Belgium | — | — | — | 0·6 | 4·8 | 14·8 |
| Bulgaria | — | 0·005 | 0·2 | — | 0·1 | 2·3 |
| Czechoslovakia | — | 0·1 | 0·2 | 0·2 | 1·0 | 5·0 |
| Denmark | — | — | — | — | — | 3·2 |
| Finland | — | — | — | — | — | 2·7 |
| France | 0·5 | 0·9 | 2·8 | 7·6 | 26·9 | 62·8 |
| Greece | — | — | — | — | — | 2·0 |
| Hungary | 0·05 | 1·0 | 1·8 | — | 1·5 | 4·5 |
| Ireland | — | — | — | — | — | 2·1 |
| Italy | — | 0·2 | 2·7 | 2·1 | 21·6 | 87·0 |
| Netherlands | — | 0·9 | 2·3 | 0·8 | 11·5 | 30·2 |
| Norway | — | — | — | — | 0·1 | 3·1 |
| Poland | 0·5 | 0·2 | 0·3 | — | 0·5 | 3·5 |
| Portugal | — | — | — | — | 0·5 | 1·7 |
| Rumania | 6·9 | 7·0 | 12·4 | 11·9 | 8·0 | 13·0 |
| Spain | — | — | — | 0·1 | 1·8 | 7·7 |
| Sweden | — | 0·08 | 0·08 | 0·2 | 1·8 | 3·8 |
| Switzerland | — | — | — | — | — | 2·2 |
| Turkey | — | 0·06 | 0·9 | — | 0·2 | 5·1 |
| United Kingdom | 0·05 | 0·1 | 0·1 | 1·9 | 29·2 | 69·6 |
| USSR | 28·1 | 58·0 | 223·6 | 31·5 | 69·0 | 225·0 |
| West Germany | 0·5 | 2·7 | 7·7 | 2·4 | 11·1 | 68·1 |
| Yugoslavia | — | 0·2 | 1·8 | — | — | 2·2 |

[a] A dash indicates data not available.

Source: United Nations, *Statistical Yearbook, 1966* (New York, 1967).

APPENDIX D

# ELECTRICITY PRODUCTION
(million kwh)

| | Total Electricity Production | | | Hydro-electric Production | | |
|---|---|---|---|---|---|---|
| | 1948 | 1965 | 1966[a] | 1948 | 1965 | 1966[a] |
| Austria | 5·3 | 22·2 | 23·8 | 4·4 | 16·0 | 17·3 |
| Belgium | 8·2 | 21·7 | 22·8 | 0·05 | 0·3 | · 0·3 |
| Bulgaria | 0·5 | 10·2 | 11·8 | 0·2 | 2·0 | 2·0 |
| Cyprus | 0·01 | 0·3 | 0·4 | —[b] | — | — |
| Czechoslovakia | 7·5 | 34·2 | 36·5 | 0·9 | 4·4 | 4·3 |
| Denmark | 1·8 | 7·9 | 9·3 | — | — | — |
| East Berlin[c] | — | 3·3 | — | — | — | — |
| East Germany | 14·6 | 53·6 | 56·9 | 0·0 | 0·8 | 1·1 |
| Finland | 2·9 | 14·6 | 15·9 | 1·9 | 9·5 | 10·4 |
| France | 28·4 | 101·4 | 106·1 | 14·7 | 46·4 | 51·7 |
| Greece | — | 4·4 | — | 0·08 | 0·7 | — |
| Hungary | 2·2 | 11·2 | 11·9 | 0·05 | 0·07 | 0·1 |
| Iceland | — | 0·7 | 0·7 | 0·1 | 0·6 | 0·6 |
| Ireland | 0·7 | 3·5 | 3·9 | 0·3 | 0·9 | — |
| Italy | 22·7 | 79·2 | 90·0 | 6·6 | 42·4 | 44·3 |
| Luxembourg | 0·5 | 2·3 | 2·3 | 0·001 | 0·9 | 1·0 |
| Malta[c] | 0·03 | 0·1 | 0·2 | — | — | — |
| Netherlands[c] | 5·6 | 25·0 | 27·9 | — | — | — |
| Norway | 12·8 | 48·9 | 48·3 | 12·7 | 48·8 | 48·2 |
| Poland | 7·5 | 43·8 | 47·4 | 0·4 | 0·9 | 0·9 |
| Portugal | 0·8 | 4·6 | 5·6 | 0·8 | 3·9 | 5·3 |
| Rumania | 1·5 | 17·2 | 20·8 | 0·1 | 1·0 | 0·9 |
| Spain[d] | 6·1 | 31·6 | 37·5 | 5·2 | 19·5 | 27·2 |
| Sweden | 14·0 | 49·1 | 50·6 | 12·6 | 46·4 | 45·5 |
| Switzerland | 10·4 | 24·5 | 28·0 | 10·3 | 24·0 | 27·4 |
| Turkey | 0·7 | 4·9 | 5·5 | 0·03 | 2·2 | 2·3 |
| United Kingdom | 48·00 | 196·0 | 202·6 | 1·3 | 4·6 | 4·6 |
| U.S.S.R. | 66·0 | 506·7 | 544·6 | 10·0 | 81·4 | 91·9 |
| West Berlin[c] | — | 3·6 | 3·8 | — | — | — |
| West Germany | 32·8 | 168·8 | 172·9 | 6·0 | 15·4 | 16·6 |
| Yugoslavia | 2·0 | 15·2 | 17·2 | 9·9 | 8·9 | 9·9 |

[a] Estimated.
[b] A dash indicates data not available.
[c] Thermal.
[d] Includes data for Canary Islands and possessions in North America.

Source: United Nations, *Statistical Yearbook, 1966* (New York, 1967); United Nations, *Statistical Yearbook 1967,* (New York, 1968).

APPENDIX E

# STEEL PRODUCTION
(million metric tons)

|  | 1938 | 1951 | 1964 | 1966[a] |
|---|---|---|---|---|
| Austria | 0·65 | 1·0 | 3·2 | 3·2 |
| Belgium | 3·0 | 5·0 | 8·7 | 8·9 |
| Bulgaria | —[b] | — | 0·5 | 0·7 |
| Czechoslovakia | 2·0 | 3·5 | 8·4 | 9·1 |
| Denmark | — | 0·2 | 0·4 | 0·4 |
| Finland | 0·03 | 0·1 | 0·4 | 0·3 |
| France | 7·0 | 9·7 | 19·8 | 19·6 |
| East Germany | — | 1·7 | 4·3 | 4·5 |
| Greece | — | — | 0·2 | 0·2 |
| Hungary | 0·6 | 1·2 | 2·4 | 2·6 |
| Ireland | — | — | 0·02 | 0·03 |
| Italy | 2·2 | 3·0 | 9·8 | 13·6 |
| Luxembourg | 1·9 | 3·0 | 4·5 | 4·4 |
| Netherlands | 0·05 | 0·5 | 2·6 | 3·3 |
| Norway | 0·004 | 0·08 | 0·6 | 0·7 |
| Poland | 1·5 | 2·7 | 8·6 | 9·9 |
| Portugal | — | — | 0·2 | 0·3 |
| Rumania | 0·25 | 0·6 | 3·0 | 3·7 |
| Spain | 0·4 | 0·8 | 3·1 | 3·8 |
| Sweden | 1·0 | 1·5 | 4·5 | 4·8 |
| Switzerland | — | 0·1 | 0·3 | 0·4 |
| Turkey | — | 0·1 | 0·4 | 0·8 |
| United Kingdom | 9·8 | 15·9 | 26·6 | 24·7 |
| USSR | 17·6 | 30·9 | 85·0 | 96·9 |
| West Germany | 18·5 | 13·3 | 37·3 | 35·3 |
| Yugoslavia | 0·1 | 0·4 | 1·8 | 1·9 |

[a] Estimated.
[b] A dash indicates data not available.

Source: *The Annual Statistics for the United Kingdom, 1966,* published by the Iron and Steel Board and the British Iron and Steel Federation; United Nations, *Statistical Yearbook, 1967* (New York, 1968).

## APPENDIX F

# IRON-ORE PRODUCTION
(million metric tons)

|  | 1928 | 1937 | 1954 | 1965 |
|---|---|---|---|---|
| Austria | 1·9 | 1·9 | 2·7 | 3·5 |
| Czechoslovakia | 1·8 | 1·8 | 2·5 | 2·6 |
| France | 49·2 | 37·8 | 43·8 | 59·5 |
| Germany | 6·3 | 9·6 | 13·0 | |
| East | | | | 1·6 |
| West | | | | 9·3 |
| Hungary | 0·2 | 0·3 | 0·4 | 0·8 |
| Italy | 0·6 | 1·0 | 1·1 | 0·8 |
| Luxembourg | 7·0 | 7·8 | 5·9 | 6·3 |
| Norway | 0·5 | 1·0 | 1·2 | 2·7 |
| Poland | 0·7 | 0·8 | 1·6 | 2·8 |
| Rumania | — | 0·1 | 0·7 | 2·5 |
| Spain | 5·8 | 1·0 | 4·0 | 5·8 |
| Sweden | 4·7 | 15·0 | 15·3 | 29·4 |
| United Kingdom | 11·4 | 14·4 | 15·5 | 15·4 |
| USSR[a] | 6·0 | 26·0 | 64·0 | 153·0 |
| Yugoslavia | 0·4 | 0·6 | 1·1 | 2·5 |

[a] In whole of USSR

Source: *The Annual Statistics for the United Kingdom, 1966,* published by the Iron and Steel Board and the British Iron and Steel Federation.

## APPENDIX G

# LEADING PRODUCERS OF PIG-IRON

(million metric tons)

|  | 1880 | 1900 | 1913 | 1937 | 1954 | 1966 |
|---|---|---|---|---|---|---|
| France | 1·7 | 2·6 | 5·1 | 7·9 | 8·9[a] | 15·4 |
| Germany | 3·6 | 8·3 | 16·4 | 15·9 | 12·6[b] |  |
| East |  |  |  |  |  | 2·1 |
| West |  |  |  |  |  | 25·0 |
| Russia/USSR | c | 5·8[d] | 4·2 | 14·6 | 30·0 | 69·2 |
| United Kingdom | 7·7 | 8·9 | 10·2 | 8·5 | 12·1 | 15·7 |
| USA | 3·9 | 13·7 | 30·9 | 37·7 | 54·2 | 82·3 |
| All others[e] | 1·1 | 6·5 | 11·0 | 18·4 | 36·3 | 96·4 |
| World total | 18·0 | 46·0 | 78·0 | 103·0 | 156·0 | 330·4 |

[a] Excludes the Saar production, which in 1954 was 2.5 million tons.
[b] West Germany only, since 1937.
[c] Data not available.
[d] Data are for 1899.
[e] Estimated.

Source: *The Annual Statistics for the United Kingdom, 1966,* published by the Iron and Steel Board and the British Iron and Steel Federation.

APPENDIX H

# VITAL STATISTICS

| | Birth Rate per Thousand | | Death Rate per Thousand | | Natural Increase per Thousand | |
|---|---|---|---|---|---|---|
| | 1931–35[a] | 1967 | 1931–35[a] | 1967 | 1931–35[a] | 1967 |
| Albania | 30·2 | 34·0[b] | —[c] | 8·6 | — | 25·4 |
| Austria | 14·4 | 17·4 | 13·5 | 13·0 | 0·9 | 4·4 |
| Belgium | 16·8 | 15·2 | 12·9 | 12·2 | 3·9 | 3·0 |
| Bulgaria | 29·3 | 15·0 | 15·5 | 9·0 | 13·8 | 6·0 |
| Cyprus | 29·7 | — | — | — | — | — |
| Czechoslovakia | 19·6 | 15·6[b] | 13·8 | 10·0[b] | 5·8 | 5·6[b] |
| Denmark | 17·7 | 18·4[b] | 10·9 | 10·3[b] | 6·8 | 8·1[b] |
| East Berlin | — | 16·4[d] | — | 16·4[d] | — | 0·0[d] |
| East Germany | — | 14·8 | — | 13·2 | — | 1·6 |
| Finland | 18·4 | 26·2 | 9·1 | 7·1 | 9·4 | 19·1 |
| France | 16·5 | 16·8 | 15·7 | 10·8 | 0·8 | 6·1 |
| Gibraltar | — | 23·8[b] | — | 8·2[b] | — | 15·6[b] |
| Greece | — | 18·5 | — | 8·3 | — | 10·2 |
| Hungary | 22·5 | 14·5 | 16·0 | 10·7 | 6·5 | 3·8 |
| Iceland | 23·5 | 23·9[b] | 11·1 | 7·1[b] | 12·4 | 16·8[b] |
| Ireland | 19·4 | 21·1 | 14·0 | 10·7 | 5·4 | 10·4 |
| Italy | 23·8 | 18·1 | 14·1 | 9·7 | 9·7 | 8·4 |
| Luxembourg | 16·9 | 14·8 | 12·4 | 12·3 | 4·5 | 2·5 |
| Malta | 33·2 | 16·5 | — | 16·5 | — | 7·1 |
| Netherlands | 21·2 | 18·9 | 8·9 | 18·9 | 12·3 | 11·0 |
| Norway | 15·2 | 18·0 | 10·4 | 9·2 | 4·8 | 8·8 |
| Poland | 27·6 | 16·3 | 14·6 | 7·7 | 13·0 | 8·6 |
| Portugal | 29·1 | 21·1 | 17·0 | 10·0 | 12·1 | 11·1 |
| Rumania | 32·8 | 27·1 | 20·6 | 9·3 | 12·2 | 17·8 |
| Spain | 26·9 | 21·1 | 16·2 | 8·7 | 10·7 | 12·4 |
| Sweden | 14·1 | 15·5 | 11·6 | 10·1 | 2·5 | 5·4 |
| Switzerland | 16·4 | 17·7 | 11·8 | 9·0 | 4·6 | 8·7 |
| United Kingdom | 15·5 | 17·5 | 12·2 | 11·2 | 3·3 | 6·3 |
| England and Wales | — | 17·2 | — | 11·2 | — | 6·0 |
| Northern Ireland | — | 22·4 | — | 9·8 | — | 12·6 |
| Scotland | — | 18·6 | — | 11·5 | — | 7·1 |
| USSR | 33·0 | 17·4 | 22·0 | 7·6 | 11·0 | 9·8 |
| West Berlin | — | 11·6 | — | 18·3 | — | −6·7 |
| West Germany | — | 17·3 | — | 11·2 | — | 6·1 |
| Yugoslavia | 31·9 | 19·5 | 17·9 | 8·7 | 13·9 | 10·8 |

[a] Average for period.
[b] Data are for 1966.
[c] A dash indicates data not available.
[d] Data are for 1965.

Source: United Nations, *Demographic Yearbook, 1965* (New York, 1966); United Nations, *Demographic Yearbook, 1967* (New York, 1968).

# TABLE OF GEOLOGICAL SEQUENCES

| *Era* | *Period or System* |
|---|---|
| Quaternary | $\left\{\begin{array}{l}\text{Recent}\\\text{Pleistocene}\end{array}\right.$ |
| Tertiary or Kainozoic | $\left\{\begin{array}{l}\text{Pliocene}\\\text{Miocene}\\\text{Oligocene}\\\text{Eocene}\end{array}\right.$ |
| Secondary or Mesozoic | $\left\{\begin{array}{l}\text{Cretaceous}\\\text{Jurassic}\\\text{(Liassic)}\\\text{Triassic}\end{array}\right.$ |
| Primary or Palæozoic | $\left\{\begin{array}{l}\text{Permian}\\\text{Carboniferous}\\\text{Devonian}\\\text{Silurian}\\\text{Ordovician}\\\text{Cambrian}\end{array}\right.$ |
| Archæan or Pre-Cambrian | . |

# INTERNATIONAL ORGANISATIONS IN EUROPE

*Organisation for Economic Co-operation and Development* (OECD) (1961 replacing OEEC formed in 1947).

Austria, Belgium, Canada, Denmark, France, German Federal Republic, Greece, Iceland, Irish Republic, Italy, Luxembourg, the Netherlands, Norway, Portugal, Spain, Sweden, Switzerland, Turkey, United Kingdom, USA, and Japan. *Special status:* Australia, Finland, Yugoslavia.

*North Atlantic Treaty Organisation* (NATO). Est. 1948.

Belgium, Canada, Denmark, France, Greece, German Federal Republic, Iceland, Italy, Luxembourg, the Netherlands, Norway, Portugal, Turkey, United Kingdom, and USA.

*Western European Union.* Est. 1948.

Belgium, Canada, France, German Federal Republic, Italy, Luxembourg, the Netherlands, United Kingdom and USA.

*Council for Mutual Economic Aid* (COMECON). Est. 1949.

Bulgaria, Czechoslovakia, German Democratic Republic, Hungary, Poland, Rumania, Mongolia, and USSR.

*Council of Europe.* Est. 1949.

Austria, Belgium, Cyprus, Denmark, France, German Federal Republic, Greece, Iceland, Irish Republic, Italy, Luxembourg, Malta, the Netherlands, Norway, Sweden, Switzerland, Turkey, and the United Kingdom.

*European Coal and Steel Community* (ECSC). Est. 1952.

German Federal Republic, France, Italy, Belgium, Luxembourg, the Netherlands. *Associate Members,* Switzerland and United Kingdom.

*Warsaw Pact.* Est. 1955.

Bulgaria, Czechoslovakia, German Democratic Republic, Hungary, Poland, Rumania, USSR.

*European Economic Community* (EEC). Est. 1958.

German Federal Republic, France, Italy, Belgium, Luxembourg, the Netherlands. *Associate Members,* in Europe, Greece and Turkey.

*European Atomic Energy Community* (EAEC or EURATOM). Est. 1958.

German Federal Republic, France, Italy, Belgium, Luxembourg, the Netherlands. *Associate Members,* United Kingdom, USA, and Canada.

*European Free Trade Association.* Est. 1960.

Austria, Denmark, Norway, Portugal, Sweden, Switzerland, United Kingdom. *Associate Member,* Finland.

# INDEX

*Where several references occur, the most important are in heavy type. Photographs are identified by the page they face. See the Appendixes for area, population, vital statistics, production of electricity, iron-ore and membership in international organisations of the countries of Europe.*